D1094484

Chemical Engineering Series

Absorption and Extraction

BUILDING THE LITERATURE OF A PROFESSION

Fifteen prominent chemical engineers first met in New York more than 30 years ago to plan a continuing literature for their rapidly growing profession. From industry came such pioneer practitioners as Leo H. Baekeland, Arthur D. Little, Charles L. Reese, John V. N. Door, M. C. Whitaker, and R. S. McBride. From the universities came such eminent educators as William H. Walker, Alfred H. White, D. D. Jackson, J. H. James, Warren K. Lewis, and Harry A. Curtis, H. C. Parmelee, then editor of *Chemical & Metallurgical Engineering*, served as chairman and was joined subsequently by S. D. Kirkpatrick as consulting editor.

After several meetings, this first Editorial Advisory Board submitted its report to the McGraw-Hill Book Company in September, 1925. In it were detailed specifications for a correlated series of more than a dozen texts and reference books which have since become the McGraw-Hill Series in Chemical Engineering.

Since its orgin the Editorial Advisory Board has been benefited by the guidance and continuing interest of such other distinguished chemical engineers as Manson Benedict, John R. Callaham, Arthur W. Hixson, H. Fraser Johnstone, Webster N. Jones, Paul D. V. Manning, Albert E. Marshall, Charles M. A. Stine, Edward R. Weidlein, and Walter G. Whitman. No small measure of credit is due not only to the pioneering members of the original board but also to those engineering educators and industrialists who have succeeded them in the task of building a permanent literature for the chemical engineering profession.

THE SERIES

ABSORPTION AND
EXTRACTION

Thomas K. Sherwood

Professor of Chemical Engineering and Dean of Engineering
Massachusetts Institute of Technology

AND

Robert L. Pigford

Professor of Chemical Engineering and Chairman
Department of Chemical Engineering
University of Delaware

New York   Toronto   London
McGRAW-HILL BOOK COMPANY, INC.
1952

ABSORPTION AND EXTRACTION

Library of Congress Catalog Card Number: 51-12644

VIII

56689

PREFACE

Simultaneously with the publication of the first edition in 1937, there occurred a great upsurge of interest in the subject of mass transfer between phases. This led to the publication of numerous research reports on the theory of diffusion in countercurrent equipment and on the performance of packed towers and other devices used in absorption and extraction. As a result, the literature on the subject is now very voluminous, so that the task of summarizing the available knowledge has proved time-consuming and difficult. One consequence is the greater length of the revised edition.

In spite of the large amount of work on many important aspects of mass transfer, the advances in fundamental theory have been disappointing. Methods of applying the Whitman "two-film" theory to various design problems have been extended and refined, but it is curious that after 28 years the theory itself has never been adequately checked experimentally. The many studies of packed towers have made it abundantly clear that gas and liquid flow through packings is complicated and irregular, but too little is known about the subject to do other than assume that true countercurrent flow obtains, and let the effects of mixing, uneven flow, and diffusion into laminar liquid films show up in empirical coefficients.

Perhaps the most important single development has been in the theory of mass transfer from a surface to a turbulent fluid stream, and in the relationships between fluid friction, heat transfer, and mass transfer. It now seems possible that the developing concepts of turbulence may make it possible to treat these three processes by a single theory. Much other new information and many refinements of design methods have appeared and are incorporated in the revised sections throughout the book.

The earlier edition has been very largely revised, so that little of the original material has been retained in its earlier form. The general sequence of subject matter of the first edition has been followed, although Chaps. II and III are new, and many new problems have been added, both as part of the text and at the end of each chapter. The new Chap. II describes the elementary concepts of fluid friction and turbulence, as a basis for an understanding of eddy diffusion and of the analogies between heat, mass, and momentum transfer. The new Chap. III summarizes the data on mass transfer to simple solid shapes, and is based largely on experiments in which liquids were allowed to evaporate into gas streams.

Solubility and equilibrium data on gas-liquid and liquid-liquid systems have been omitted, since the inclusion of the necessary tables would duplicate the recent excellent summaries by Markham and Kobe[297] and by Perry[359].

A very large number of friends and colleagues assisted in the preparation of the revised edition, and it is not possible to recognize their specific contributions. Among those to whom we are indebted are A. T. Ippen, H. C. Hottel, J. J. Goett, E. J. Honohan, J. E. Vivian, D. W. Peaceman, and A. P. Colburn.

T. K. SHERWOOD
R. L. PIGFORD

CAMBRIDGE, MASS.
NEWARK, DEL.
August, 1951

CONTENTS

packed towers—Absorption of carbon dioxide by alkaline solutions—Absorption of nitrogen oxides—Removal of sulfur dioxide from flue gas, absorption for production of bisulfite cooking liquor, and recovery from smelter gases.

CHAPTER X

CHAPTER I

DIFFUSION

Introduction. Absorption and extraction are but two of numerous industrial operations involving the transfer of a material from one phase to another. The air drying of a wet solid, for example, requires the transfer of water from the liquid to the gas phase under conditions such that the water does not boil but escapes into the air by a complicated diffusion process. In almost every case it is the *interphase* transfer that is of interest and importance, and the movement or diffusion of one substance through a single phase is usually a simple process compared with the transfer between phases. Before considering the latter, it is important to understand the principles of mass transfer by molecular and eddy diffusion within a single phase.

Molecular diffusion may be defined as the spontaneous intermingling of miscible fluids placed in mutual contact, accomplished without the aid of mechanical mixing. For example, a lump of sugar placed in the bottom of an unstirred cup of coffee will dissolve and diffuse slowly throughout the solution. If convection currents were entirely eliminated, the distribution of the sugar throughout the cup of coffee would require a very long time. Slight convection currents, due either to temperature differences within the solution or to residual or undamped mechanical motion, or to both, are invariably present to some slight extent in an apparently quiescent solution, so that even in the laboratory it is possible only to minimize these effects and so approach the conditions of molecular diffusion. The persistence of mechanical convection is greater in a gas than in a liquid, because of the greater viscosity of the latter. Because gases have large temperature coefficients of expansion and low viscosities, thermal convection currents are easily set up, especially at elevated pressures. For these reasons molecular diffusion in gases is even more difficult to approach than in liquids.

It is important to note that mixing by convection does not necessarily occur simply because the fluid is in motion. Viscous fluids at low velocities move in laminar or straight-line motion, with all particles moving along parallel paths. In such a moving fluid it is quite possible to have the process of molecular diffusion. At high velocities the motion of all fluids becomes turbulent, characterized by the development of

1

many tiny eddies, or swirls, causing mixing of parallel streams of the fluid. Molecular diffusion occurs in such a moving fluid, but mixing can and does take place, with considerably greater facility and speed. Thus, smoke leaving a tall chimney spreads conically with fair rapidity, owing to the eddy motion in the atmosphere, even at low wind velocities. The transference of material or the mixing of fluids by this mechanism has been termed eddy diffusion. It is much more rapid than molecular diffusion and is dependent principally upon the nature of the turbulent fluid and the conditions of flow. Molecular diffusion, on the other hand, is governed principally by the nature of the fluids involved.

Molecular Diffusion in Gases. According to the kinetic theory, a gas consists of a large number of individual molecules in rapid motion. The molecules move at random and so suffer frequent collisions with one another. The behavior of molecules at collision is not definitely known, but approximates that of hard elastic balls. Because of the frequent collisions, the molecular velocities are being continually changed in both direction and magnitude. The pressure of the gas on the walls of the containing vessel is due to the large number of impacts of impinging molecules. The temperature is determined by the mean kinetic energy of the individual molecules and hence by their weight and mean speed. For oxygen at 32°F. this mean speed corresponding to the mean kinetic energy of the molecule is approximately 1520 ft./sec., although there may be present molecules having speeds anywhere from zero to several thousand feet per second. The extremely high molecular speeds explain why pressure differences in a gas are equalized with such great rapidity.

At first thought it might seem that interdiffusion of gases must be very rapid if molecular speeds are in reality several hundred feet per second. Because of the large number of molecules of finite size present, however (7.9×10^{23} per cubic foot at 32°F. and 1 atm.) the collisions are extremely frequent, amounting to several billion per second, and the equalization of molecular distribution, or concentration, is relatively slow. Diffusion is more rapid at high temperatures because of the greater molecular velocities. It is similarly more rapid at low pressures because the average distance between the molecules is greater and because the collisions are less frequent. Small molecules diffuse rapidly, primarily because of their greater molecular speeds and also because the chance for collisions is not so great as for large molecules. The various experimental data on diffusion in gases are in remarkable agreement, both qualitatively and quantitatively, with the theoretical relations derived from the kinetic theory. Confirmation of the theory by the data on diffusion in gases is, in fact, one of the principal pieces of supporting evidence for the kinetic theory as a whole.

The theory of diffusion in gases was developed as a part of the kinetic theory* and is due principally to Maxwell[303] and to Stefan,[441,442] with later important contributions from O. E. Meyer, Sutherland, Langevin, Chapman, Enskog, and Jeans. The manner of application of the concepts of the kinetic theory to molecular diffusion is illustrated by the following simplified derivation due to Hottel.[203]

Referring to Fig. 1, consider the diffusion of the two components of a binary gas mixture across the plane PQ. Let λ represent the component in the z direction of the mean free path of the gas molecules, *i.e.*, the mean distance a molecule travels in the z direction before colliding with a second molecule. Then within the narrow regions $\pm\lambda$ on either side of the plane PQ, the gas molecules are free to cross the plane at their mean speed u (velocity component in the z direction). Half of the molecules in the narrow region to the left will cross PQ before colliding; the other half will pass to the left. The total moles of component A crossing PQ from left to right, therefore, will be $\frac{\lambda}{2} S \left(c - \frac{\lambda}{2} \frac{\partial c}{\partial z} \right)$, where c is the concentration of gas A at the plane PQ. Similarly, the total moles of A passing across PQ to the left from the narrow region to the right is $\frac{\lambda}{2} S \left(c + \frac{\lambda}{2} \frac{\partial c}{\partial z} \right)$. In each case the mean distance traveled is λ, requiring a total time λ/u. The net rate of transfer of A, therefore, is

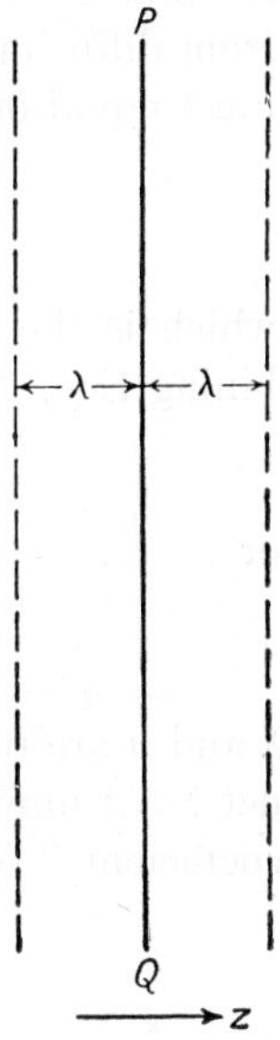

Fig. 1.

$$N_A S = - \frac{(\lambda S/2)(\lambda\, \partial c/\partial z)}{\lambda/u} = - \frac{\lambda u S}{2} \frac{\partial c}{\partial z} \tag{1}$$

where S is the area of the plane and N_A is the rate of diffusion of component A expressed as moles per unit time per unit area. Applying the gas laws, the molal concentration c is p_A/RT, where p_A is the partial pressure of the gas A. Thus

$$N_A = - \frac{\lambda u}{2RT} \frac{\partial p_A}{\partial z} \tag{2}$$

* For a readable outline of the kinetic theory, see "Kinetic Theory of Gases" by O. E. Meyer.[320] The book "Mathematical Theory of Non-Uniform Gases," by Chapman and Cowling,[73] gives an account of the most modern and complete developments of the classical kinetic theory. Perhaps the best general treatment of diffusion is Maxwell's article under the title "Diffusion" in the ninth edition of the Encyclopaedia Britannica, 1877.[305] The best discussion of diffusion, according to the kinetic theory, is believed to be found in Chap. XIII of Jeans's "Dynamical Theory of Gases."[218]

Restricting the treatment to the case of equal-molal diffusion of components A and B in opposite directions at constant T and λu, $N_A = -N_B$, and $p_A + p_B = P$, where P is the total pressure. In this case there is no bulk motion of the gas mixture, and the transfer rate N_A results only from diffusion. For any small element of volume of gas mixture, input must equal output plus accumulation, whence

$$\frac{\partial c_A}{\partial \theta} + \frac{\partial N_A}{\partial z} = 0 \qquad (3)$$

which is the "equation of continuity." Here θ represents time. Combining Eqs. (2) and (3),

$$\frac{\partial c_A}{\partial \theta} = \frac{\lambda u}{2RT} \frac{\partial^2 p_A}{\partial z^2}$$

or

$$\frac{\partial p_A}{\partial \theta} = \frac{\lambda u}{2} \frac{\partial^2 p_A}{\partial z^2} \qquad (4)$$

λ and u are functions of the properties of the gas mixture, and the product $\lambda u/2$ may be replaced by D_v, termed the "diffusivity," or "diffusion coefficient," for the pair of gases:

$$\frac{\partial p_A}{\partial \theta} = D_v \frac{\partial^2 p_A}{\partial z^2} \qquad (5)$$

The same result is obtained if the derivation is based on component B instead of component A, and since $dp_A = -dp_B$, it follows that the two results are compatible only if D_v for the diffusion of A through B and D_v for B through A are one and the same.

Equation (5) is the equation which is encountered most frequently in discussions of the theory of diffusion in gases. It must be remembered that it was derived for the equal-molal diffusion of two gases in opposite directions, and not for the diffusion of one gas through a second stagnant gas. The latter case will be discussed below. In differentiating Eq. (2) to obtain Eq. (4), λu was assumed to be independent of z and consequently of concentration. As brought out below, the experimental data indicate but slight variation of D_v with gas concentration, and so justify this step.

Unsteady-state Diffusion of Two Gases. If the partition separating two gas quantities is removed, the gases tend to diffuse into each other, and eventually the concentration becomes the same throughout the gas space. The rate at which the concentration equalizes is a function of the diffusivity, pressure, and dimensions of the container. Expressions relating concentration and time may be obtained by integration[420] of Eq. (5) and form the basis of the standard method of determining diffusivities experimentally for the permanent gases.

Equations and plots are given by A. S. Smith,[431] showing the time required for mixing of two gases by diffusion in a commercial gas cylinder 4 ft. high. If such a cylinder is originally half full of helium and half full of methane at a total pressure of 5 atm., nearly $2\frac{1}{2}$ hr. will be required for the average mole fraction of methane to fall to 0.7 in one half, and to rise to 0.3 in the other half of the cylinder. The calculation assumes mixing to be solely by molecular diffusion, with convection currents completely absent. Because of the low molecular weight of helium, the diffusivity for the system helium-methane is high, and other gases require much longer times to mix by diffusion. The case treated by Smith is of practical interest in the preparation of gas mixtures for experimental purposes by forcing a second gas into a cylinder of the first. Mixing by convection will be expedited if the heavier gas is placed on top of the lighter gas at the outset.

Steady-state Diffusion.[275] Most of the industrial operations to be discussed in later chapters involve steady-state operation, *i.e.*, continuous flow through an apparatus with steady conditions of temperature, pressure, concentrations, and flow rates at any one point. Diffusion under such conditions implies the continuous supply and removal of the diffusing material.

In the general case the total bulk flow of gas in the z direction is $N_A + N_B$; the net transfer of component A is the rate of diffusion plus the transfer of A due to the bulk flow:

$$N_A = -D_v \frac{dc_A}{dz} + (N_A + N_B) \frac{p_A}{P} \tag{6}$$

where P is the total pressure. Substituting $c = p/RT$ and integrating,

$$\frac{D_v P}{RTz} \ln \frac{1 - \left(1 + \dfrac{N_B}{N_A}\right) \dfrac{p_{A2}}{P}}{1 - \left(1 + \dfrac{N_B}{N_A}\right) \dfrac{p_{A1}}{P}} = N_A + N_B \tag{7}$$

For parallel diffusion N_A and N_B will have the same signs; for counterdiffusion N_A and N_B will have opposite signs. Equation (7) has various applications, but its use depends on knowledge of the relation between N_A and N_B. In adiabatic rectification, for example, the molal rates of condensation and vaporization are equal, and $N_A = -N_B$. If there is heat loss from the rectifying column, the estimated heat loss is a measure of the difference between N_A and N_B.

Steady-state Diffusion of One Gas through a Second Stagnant Gas. Here, $N_B = 0$, and from Eq. (6),

$$N_A = -\frac{D_v P}{p_B} \frac{dc_A}{dz} = -\frac{D_v P}{RT p_B} \frac{dp_A}{dz} = \frac{D_v P}{RT p_B} \frac{dp_B}{dz} \tag{8}$$

Integrating between the limits z_1 and z_2 in the direction of diffusion,

$$N_A = \frac{D_v P}{RT(z_2 - z_1)} \ln \frac{p_{B2}}{p_{B1}} \qquad (9)$$

where p_{B2} and p_{B1} are the partial pressures of the gas B at the planes z_2 and z_1, respectively. The logarithmic mean of the values p_{B2} and p_{B1} is defined as

$$p_{BM} = \frac{p_{B2} - p_{B1}}{\ln (p_{B2}/p_{B1})} \qquad (10)$$

Combining this with Eq. (9) and letting the length of path $z_2 - z_1 = z$, one obtains

$$N_A = \frac{D_v P}{RTz} \frac{p_{B2} - p_{B1}}{p_{BM}} = \frac{D_v P}{RTz} \frac{p_{A1} - p_{A2}}{p_{BM}} \qquad (11)$$

This states that the rate of diffusion is directly proportional to the decrease in partial pressure of the diffusing gas A and inversely proportional to the length of the path and to the logarithmic mean of the extreme values of the partial pressure of the interfering inert gas B. This equation is the relation found to be most generally applicable to diffusion in gas films, as encountered in commercial absorption equipment.

As an alternative form of the same relation, it is convenient to write

$$N_A = \frac{D_v P}{RTz} \frac{y_{A1} - y_{A2}}{(1 - y_A)_M} \qquad (12)$$

where y_A refers to the mole fraction of component A, and y_{BM} or $(1 - y_A)_M$ is the logarithmic mean of the two extreme values of the mole fraction of component B.

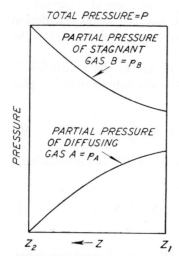

FIG. 2. Partial-pressure gradients in a layer of stagnant gas B through which a gas A is diffusing.

Equation (8) brings out the fact that for steady-state diffusion at constant total pressure, p_A is not linear in z, but the slope (dp_A/dz) is directly proportional to p_B, and therefore to $P - p_A$. A plot of p_A vs. z is consequently concave to the z axis, as shown in Fig. 2. This plot indicates the type of pressure gradients obtained in the steady-state diffusion of a gas A through a second, stagnant, gas B.

At first thought it seems impossible for A to diffuse without a simultaneous diffusion of B, since the gradients are similar for both gases.

The explanation lies in the fact that the pressure gradient of the gas B is maintained by the diffusion of A. It is the collisions with the moving molecules of A that increase the concentration of B molecules at the second boundary, and the result may be explained by stating that the number of molecules of B carried toward z_2 by these collisions is exactly equal to the number of molecules of B diffusing toward z_1 under the influence of the partial-pressure gradient so set up. The net diffusion of B is zero.

Steady-state, Equal-molal Counterdiffusion of Two Gases. Here, as in adiabatic rectification,

$$N_A = -D_v \frac{dc_A}{dz} = -\frac{D_v}{RT} \frac{dp_A}{dz} \tag{13}$$

Since N_A is constant, this may be integrated to give

$$N_A = \frac{D_v(p_{A1} - p_{A2})}{RTz} \tag{14}$$

which differs from Eq. (11) for one diffusing gas only by the substitution of P for p_{BM}.

Simultaneous Diffusion Involving More Than Two Gases. The cases presented have brought out the dependence of the diffusion rate of one gas on both the type and rate of diffusion of the second gas. Where more than two gases are involved, the basic relations are not complicated but lead to unwieldy integrated forms. Gilliland[160] has obtained an analytical solution for the case of two gases diffusing at a steady rate through a third stagnant gas. Curtiss and Hirschfelder[192] have recently developed a more general treatment of the multicomponent cases,

Illustration 1. Ammonia gas is diffusing at a constant rate through a layer of stagnant air 0.1 in. thick. Conditions are fixed so that the gas contains 50 per cent ammonia by volume at one boundary of the stagnant layer. The ammonia diffusing to the other boundary is quickly absorbed, and the concentration is negligible at that plane. The temperature is 68°F. and the pressure atmospheric, under which conditions the value of D_v for the ammonia-air system may be assumed to be 0.70 ft.²/hr. Calculate the rate of diffusion of ammonia through the air layer.

Solution. The conditions are those of steady-state diffusion of one gas through a second stagnant gas, and Eq. (11) applies. At one boundary of the gas layer the concentration is 50 per cent ammonia, and the partial pressure p_B of air and the partial pressure p_A of ammonia are each 0.5 atm. At the other boundary of the layer the concentration and consequently the partial pressure of ammonia are assumed to be zero, and the partial pressure of air is 1 atm. Hence

$$p_{A1} = 0.5, \quad p_{A2} = 0, \quad p_{B1} = 0.5, \quad p_{B2} = 1.0 \text{ atm.}$$

and

$$p_{BM} = \frac{p_{B2} - p_{B1}}{\ln(p_{B2}/p_{B1})} = \frac{1 - 0.5}{\ln(1/0.5)} = 0.72 \text{ atm}$$

Substituting in Eq. (11):

$$N_A = \frac{D_v P}{RTz} \frac{p_{A1} - p_{A2}}{p_{BM}} = \frac{(0.70)(1)(0.5 - 0)(12)}{(0.728)(528)(0.1)(0.72)} = 1.52 \times 10^{-1} \text{ lb. mole/(hr.)(ft.}^2)$$

Illustration 2. A simple rectifying column consists of a vertical tube supplied at the bottom with a mixture of benzene and toluene as vapor. At the top a reflux condenser condenses and returns some of the product as reflux which flows in a thin film down the inner wall of the tube. The tube is sufficiently insulated so that heat loss may be neglected. At one point in the column the vapor contains 70 mole per cent benzene, and the adjacent liquid reflux contains 59 mole per cent benzene. The temperature at this point is 194°F. Assuming the diffusional resistance to vapor transfer between vapor and liquid to be equivalent to the diffusional resistance of a stagnant vapor layer 0.1 in. thick, calculate the rate of interchange of benzene and toluene between vapor and liquid. The molal latent heats of vaporization of benzene and toluene may be assumed to be equal. The vapor pressure of toluene at 194°F. is 404.6 mm., and the diffusivity for toluene-benzene may be assumed to be 0.198 ft.^{2}/hr.

Solution. In a rectifying column operating without heat loss, the liquid will be at its boiling point. As a result, the toluene condensed liberates sufficient heat to vaporize an equal number of moles of benzene. At any point in the column, therefore, $N_A = -N_B$, and Eq. (14) applies.

Since the vapor composition at the point in question is 70 mole per cent benzene, the partial pressure of toluene in the vapor, p_{A1}, is 0.3 atm. The value of p_{A2} is obtained from Raoult's law as the vapor pressure of toluene in equilibrium with the liquid:

$$p_{A2} = (1.0 - 0.59) \frac{404.6}{760} = 0.218 \text{ atm.}$$

$$N_A = \frac{D_v(p_{A1} - p_{A2})}{RTz} = \frac{(0.198)(0.3 - 0.218)(12)}{(0.728)(654)(0.1)}$$

$$= 4.09 \times 10^{-3} \text{ lb. mole toluene/(hr.)(ft.}^2)$$

DIFFUSION COEFFICIENTS IN GASES

Because of its intimate association with the kinetic theory of gases, the development of a theory of diffusion has been a subject of great interest to physicists. The first theoretical expression connecting the diffusion coefficient with the molecular properties of the two diffusing gases was derived by Maxwell,[304] but similar forms have been proposed by Jeans,[218] Chapman,[72] and Sutherland.[446] These relate the diffusivity with the number of molecules per unit volume, the molecular speeds, the distance between the centers of molecules of the two types on collision, and the weights of the molecules of each type. If the distance between molecules in contact is replaced by the sum of the cube roots of the molecular volumes, the equations of Maxwell, Jeans, and Chapman take the form

$$D_v = b \frac{T^{3/2}}{P(V_A^{1/3} + V_B^{1/3})^2} \sqrt{\frac{1}{M_A} + \frac{1}{M_B}} \tag{15}$$

with b having various values depending on the derivation and on the method of evaluating molecular volumes. Noting that the several theories agree on the *form* of the equation for D_v, Gilliland[159] has evaluated b empirically by plotting the published results of some 400 experimental determinations, as shown in Fig. 3.

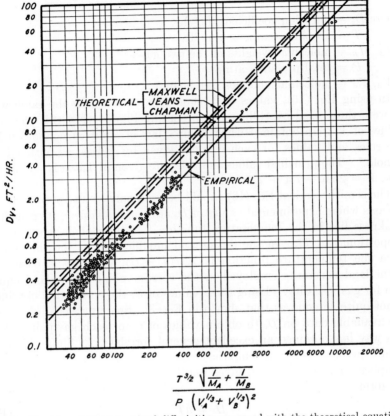

FIG. 3. Experimentally determined diffusivities compared with the theoretical equations based on the kinetic theory.

Figure 3 shows a wide band of points, with considerable deviation from the mean line. This is to be expected from the rather poor precision obtained by the experimental methods so far developed for obtaining diffusion coefficients. There is, however, no definite trend of deviation with molecular weight or with pressure, both of which were varied over quite wide ranges in the data plotted. The temperature range covered was narrow, being only from 32 to 212°F., except for a few points; therefore it is not advisable to employ the indicated temperature effect for extrapolation over wide ranges.

Inspection of Fig. 3 shows the empirical constant to be 0.0069, and the relation is, therefore,

$$D_v = 0.0069 \frac{T^{3/2}}{P(V_A^{1/3} + V_B^{1/3})^2} \sqrt{\frac{1}{M_A} + \frac{1}{M_B}} \qquad (16)$$

where D_v = diffusion coefficient, ft.²/hr.

T = absolute temperature, °R.

M_A, M_B = molecular weights of the two gases

P = total pressure, atm.

V_A, V_B = molecular volumes (see below)

In using Eq. (16), values of V should be obtained in the same way as were those used by Gilliland in preparing Fig. 3. For this plot, the values of V were obtained using Kopp's law of additive volumes, with the rules and values for each element given by LeBas, as outlined by Arnold.[7] The principal values and rules are given in Table I. Thus for SO_2, $V = 25.6 + 7.4 + 7.4 = 40.4$.

The semitheoretical Eq. (16) should be used only as an approximation in cases where experimental values of D_v are not available. Its principal weakness lies in the temperature function $T^{3/2}$, since D_v is more nearly proportional to T^2. In the Sutherland modification of the theoretical form the temperature function is $T^{5/2}/(T + C)$, where C is based on Sutherland constants employed in the corresponding Sutherland equation for gas viscosity. Using these values of C, the correlation obtained is not quite so good as that shown in Fig. 3. Spalding[438] has analyzed the available data on D_v to obtain values of C for each gas pair and in this way has obtained an excellent general correlation. Since this procedure involves separate empirical values of C for each system, it is complicated to employ and gives hardly better results than the use of the form

$$D_v = aT^2 \qquad (17)$$

in which a is an empirical constant, which, like C, is different for each system. Spalding[438] shows that the available data on water vapor in air, including the data of Klibanour, Pomerantsev, and Frank-Kamenetsky,[251] which go up to 2000°F., are well fitted by the equation

$$D_v = \frac{1.46 \times 10^{-4}}{P} \frac{T^{5/2}}{T + 441} \qquad (18)$$

Equation (16) is an empirical modification of an equation which results from the classical kinetic theory of gases, applied to hard, spherical molecules. If the molecules attract or repel each other, the $\frac{3}{2}$ power of the absolute temperature is not quite correct. If the potential energy of interaction is known, the simplest theory can be modified, with the

TABLE I. ATOMIC VOLUMES

For calculation of molal volumes at the normal boiling point, as used in Eq. (16).

Air	29.9
Antimony	24.2
Arsenic	30.5
Bismuth	48.0
Bromine	27.0
Carbon	14.8
Chlorine, terminal, as in R—Cl	21.6
Medial, as in R—CHCl—R'	24.6
Chromium	27.4
Fluorine	8.7
Germanium	34.5
Hydrogen, in compounds	3.7
In hydrogen molecule	7.15
Nitrogen, in primary amines	10.5
In secondary amines	12.0
In nitrogen molecule	15.6
Oxygen, doubly bound	7.4
Coupled to two other elements:	
In aldehydes and ketones	7.4
In methyl esters	9.1
In ethyl ethers	9.9
In higher esters and ethers	11.0
In acids	12.0
In union with S, P, N	8.3
Phosphorus	27.0
Silicon	32.0
Sulfur	25.6
Tin	42.3
Titanium	35.7
Vanadium	32.0
Zinc	20.4

Notes:

  For three-membered ring, as in ethylene oxide, deduct 6.0.

  For four-membered ring, as in cyclobutane, deduct 8.5.

  For five-membered ring, as in furan, deduct 11.5.

  For six-membered ring, as in benzene, pyridine, deduct 15.0.

  For naphthalene ring formation, deduct 30.0.

  For anthracene ring formation, deduct 47.5.

  The units of volume in the table are cc./g.-mole.

result that the temperature dependence of D_v is found to be different. Hirschfelder, Bird, and Spotz[192] have carried out such calculations for nonpolar gases, which have an energy of attraction which varies with the inverse sixth power of the distance between centers of adjacent molecules and a repulsive energy which varies with the inverse twelfth power. For pairs of nonpolar gases

$$D_v = 1.492 \times 10^{-3} \frac{T^{3/2}}{Pr_{AB}^2\phi} \sqrt{\frac{1}{M_A} + \frac{1}{M_B}} \qquad (18a)$$

where ϕ = collision function calculated by Hirschfelder *et al.*[192] and listed in Table II; function of k, T, and ϵ_{AB}

r_{AB} = arithmetic average of radii of the two molecules, A.

k = Boltzmann's gas constant per molecule

ϵ_{AB} = minimum energy of interaction between unlike molecules

In addition to the molecular properties included in Eq. (16), Eq. (18a) also involves the interaction energy ϵ_{AB}. Inasmuch as this same energy of interaction also affects other properties of the gas, such as gas density, critical temperature, and viscosity, it is possible to estimate ϵ_{AB} from other data. Hirschfelder *et al.* suggest the following empirical methods for pure gases:

either

$$\frac{\epsilon}{k} = 0.75T_c \qquad (18b)$$

or

$$\frac{\epsilon}{k} = 1.39T_b \qquad (18c)$$

$$r = 3.30V_c^{1/3} \qquad (18d)$$

where T_c = critical temperature, °R.

T_b = normal boiling point, °R.

V_c = critical volume, ft.³/lb. mole

For mixtures of two nonpolar gases

$$\epsilon_{AB} = \sqrt{\epsilon_1\epsilon_2} \qquad (18e)$$

In general, ϕ is a decreasing function of temperature, so that D_v increases faster than the ³⁄₂ power of T.

According to Eq. (18a), the diffusion coefficient is independent of the gas composition. This is true only to a first approximation, although the variation in the true value of D_v is not great, especially for pairs of molecules whose molecular weights are not too different. The true value of D_v does not differ from the first approximation by more than about 3 per cent.

Very few data are available as a basis for testing the indicated effect of total pressure on D_v. However, the data of Burnside[60] on ethyl ether, propylene, and ammonia in air indicate that D_vP is substantially constant up to 30 atm. total pressure [Burnside's values were actually some 30 per cent higher than predicted by Eq. (16)].

TABLE II. VALUES OF COLLISION FUNCTION
From Hirschfelder, Bird, and Spotz; used in Eq. (18a)

kT/ϵ_{AB}	ϕ	kT/ϵ_{AB}	ϕ
0.3	1.331	4.2	0.4370
0.4	1.159	4.4	0.4326
0.5	1.033	4.6	0.4284
0.6	0.9383	4.8	0.4246
0.7	0.8644	5.0	0.4211
0.8	0.8058		
0.9	0.7585	6	0.4062
1.0	0.7197	7	0.3948
		8	0.3856
1.1	0.6873	9	0.3778
1.2	0.6601	10	0.3712
1.3	0.6367		
1.4	0.6166	20	0.3320
1.5	0.5991	30	0.3116
		40	0.2980
1.6	0.5837	50	0.2878
1.7	0.5701		
1.8	0.5580	60	0.2798
1.9	0.5471	70	0.2732
2.0	0.5373	80	0.2676
		90	0.2628
2.2	0.5203	100	0.2585
2.4	0.5061		
2.6	0.4939	200	0.2322
2.8	0.4836	300	0.2180
3.0	0.4745	400	0.2085
3.2	0.4664		
3.4	0.4593		
3.6	0.4529		
3.8	0.4471		
4.0	0.4418		

Illustration 3. Estimate the diffusivity for ethyl alcohol in air at 32°F. and at atmospheric pressure.

Solution. The problem is simply that of substitution in Eq. (16). Using the values for atomic volumes given in Table I, for ethyl alcohol,

$$V_A = (2)(14.8) + (6)(3.7) + 7.4 = 59.2$$

for air,

$$V_B = 29.9$$

$$D_v = 0.0069 \frac{492^{3/2}}{(59.2^{1/3} + 29.9^{1/3})^2(1)} \sqrt{\frac{1}{46} + \frac{1}{29}} = 0.362 \text{ ft.}^2/\text{hr.}$$

The International Critical Tables give 0.395 ft.²/hr. for D_v at 32°F. and 1 atm. for ethyl alcohol in air. In this case the estimated value is approximately 8 per cent lower.

Illustration 4. Calculate the diffusivity of carbon dioxide through air at 1 atm. total pressure and at temperatures of 536, 900, 1800, and 2700°R., using the method of Hirschfelder *et al.*

Solution. From Eqs. (18b), (18c), and (18d), the following molecular properties are calculated:

Substance	T_c, °R.	V_c, ft.^{3}/lb. mole	r_0, A. Eq. (18d)	ϵ/k, °R. Eq. (18b)
Air.........	238.2	21	3.63	179
CO_2........	548	24.1	3.80	410

$$\frac{\epsilon_{AB}}{k} = \sqrt{(179)(410)} = 271$$
$$r_{AB} = (\tfrac{1}{2})(3.63 + 3.80) = 3.72 \ A.$$

At 536°R. the calculations are made as follows:

$$\frac{kT}{\epsilon_{AB}} = \frac{536}{271} = 1.98$$
$$\phi = 0.539 \qquad \text{from Table II}$$
$$D_v = \frac{(1.492 \times 10^{-3})(536)^{3/2}}{(3.72)^2(0.539)} \sqrt{\frac{1}{44} + \frac{1}{29}} = 0.597 \ \text{ft.}^2/\text{hr.}$$

An experimental value of D_v equal to 0.635 ft.^{2}/hr. is given by Perry[360] for this temperature.

At the other temperatures the results are as follows:

T, °R.	kT/ϵ_{AB}	ϕ	D_v, ft^2/hr. Eq. (18a)	Eq. (16)
536	1.98	0.539	0.597	0.536
900	3.31	0.462	1.50	1.16
1800	6.64	0.399	4.94	3.30
2700	9.98	0.371	10.0	6.06

Values of D_v calculated from Gilliland's equation [Eq. (16)] are included in the last column for comparison.

O. E. Meyer[320] has derived a theoretical equation which indicates a variation of the diffusion coefficient with the ratio of the quantities of the two gases present. Several investigators have carried out series of experiments to discover such an effect, if present, and their results show such a small variation of D_v with gas composition that it seems entirely allowable to neglect it in engineering computation.

According to the kinetic theory, the diffusion of a gas through itself, *i.e.*, for the case of molecules of a gas diffusing through identical molecules, is defined by

$$\frac{\mu}{\rho D_v} = \text{constant} \qquad (19)$$

where ρ and μ represent the density and viscosity of the gas. Perhaps the only possibility of measuring self-diffusion is by the use of radioactive gases, and there are probably no engineering applications. Equation (19) is important, however, in indicating the constancy of the group $\mu/\rho D_v$, which is found experimentally to be almost independent of temperature and pressure for one gas in dilute mixtures in a second gas. The dimensionless group $\mu/\rho D_v$, known as the "Schmidt group," will be shown to have important applications in later chapters.

No. 662,690.   Patented Nov. 27, 1900.

H. GEPPERT.
PROCESS OF PRODUCING COLD.
(Application filed Nov. 9, 1899.)

(No Model.)

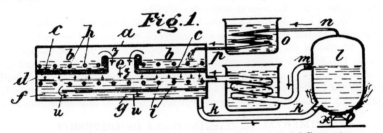

FIG. 4.   Illustration from a refrigeration patent of Geppert.

Illustration 5.   Figure 4 is reproduced from a United States patent issued to H. Geppert in 1900, describing a type of absorption refrigeration machine. Geppert proposed the use of ammonia as refrigerant and water as absorbent in a unit in which hydrogen was added to equalize the pressure between evaporator and absorber. The aqueous ammonia solution is boiled in l and the ammonia condensed in o. Liquid ammonia evaporates into hydrogen (does not boil) at b, thereby cooling any fluid circulated through the coil h. The ammonia gas is absorbed by the cooled, dilute aqueous solution in the lower section f, where the heat of solution is removed by cooling water in a submerged coil. The strong ammonia solution returns by gravity to the still l.

Since no circulation of the hydrogen is provided, the ammonia must pass from the upper evaporator section to the lower absorber section by molecular diffusion through the hydrogen. Assume reasonable apparatus dimensions and operating conditions, and calculate the cooling rate as equivalent pounds ice frozen per day.

Solution.   Assume the surface area of evaporating ammonia and absorbing solution to be 2 ft.² each. In order to simplify the calculation, assume that the diffusion path corresponds to diffusion between two parallel plane surfaces each 2 ft.² in area separated by a space of 6 in. filled with a stagnant mixture of ammonia and hydrogen.

Assume the total pressure to be 200 p.s.i.a. (condenser at 96°F.), with liquid ammonia evaporating at 17°F. (vapor pressure 45 p.s.i.a.).   Assume the surface of the solution in the absorber to be at 90°F. and to contain 20 mole per cent ammonia (partial vapor pressure of ammonia, 6.9 p.s.i.a.).

The case is one of steady-state diffusion of ammonia through stagnant hydrogen, and Eq. (11) may be employed, with the following substitutions:

$$T = 460 + \frac{90 + 17}{2} = 513.5; \qquad z = \frac{6}{12} = 0.5 \text{ ft.}$$

$$\frac{D_v P}{RT} = \frac{(0.0069)(513.5)^{1/2}}{(0.728)(26.7^{1/3} + 7.4^{1/3})^2} \sqrt{\frac{1}{2} + \frac{1}{17}} = 0.0066$$

$$p_{A1} = 45 \text{ p.s.i}; \qquad p_{A2} = 6.9 \text{ p.s.i}$$

$$p_{B1} = 200 - 45 = 155 \text{ p.s.i.}; \qquad p_{B2} = 200 - 6.9 = 193.1 \text{ p.s.i.}$$

$$p_{BM} = 174 \text{ p.s.i. (mean hydrogen partial pressure)}$$

$$N_A = \frac{0.0066}{0.5} \frac{45 - 6.9}{174} = 0.00289 \text{ lb. mole/(hr.)(ft.}^2)$$

Since the latent heat of vaporization of ammonia is about 556 B.t.u./lb. and the heat of fusion of water is 144 B.t.u./lb., the equivalent refrigerating effect for 2 ft.^{2} is

$$(0.00289)(2)(24)(17)(556/144) = 9.1 \text{ lb. ice/day}$$

This rate is obviously too low to be practical in view of the dimensions assumed; the poor result is due to the slowness of molecular diffusion.

Geppert's idea of introducing hydrogen into the standard ammonia-water absorption refrigeration system was actually a very good one, as witnessed by the later success of the Electrolux (Servel) unit. This was made possible by the modification suggested by two Swedish students, Platen and Munters, who provided a second conduit (in addition to e of Fig. 4) connecting the evaporator and absorber. This made it possible for the hydrogen to circulate by natural convection, and ammonia transfer from evaporator to absorber was no longer dependent solely on molecular diffusion.

EXPERIMENTAL DETERMINATIONS OF DIFFUSION COEFFICIENTS IN GASES

Several different methods have been devised for the measurement of diffusion coefficients in gases. The principal ones are described very briefly below.

1. Evaporation of Liquids in Narrow Tubes. One of the two components, in the liquid state, is placed in a small glass tube, filling the tube to within 0.2 to 1.0 in. of the top.   The tube and liquid are held at constant temperature and the second gas passed over the top of the tube.   The rate of diffusion is obtained by measuring the rate of fall of liquid in the tube.   This technique, devised and used by Stefan, is perhaps the best and most widely used of the experimental methods.   It is limited, however, to a fairly narrow range of temperature for any one system, since one component must be liquid, and the precision is poor at very low or very high vapor pressures.

Illustration 6. The diffusivity of toluene in air is determined experimentally by the method just described.   A vertical glass tube 0.118 in. in diameter is filled with liquid toluene to a depth 0.748 in. from the top open end. After 275 hr. at 102.9°F. and a total pressure of 1 atm., the level has dropped to 3.11 in. from the top. The density of liquid toluene is 53.1 lb./ft.^{3} and its vapor pressure at 102.9°F. is 57.3 mm. Hg. Neglecting counterdiffusion of air to replace the liquid, calculate the value of D_v, and compare with the value estimated by the use of Eq. (16).

Solution. The conditions are those of diffusion of one gas (toluene vapor) through a second stagnant gas (air), and Eq. (11) applies at any instant. If ρ_L represents the density of the liquid, M_L the molecular weight of toluene, and z the distance of the liquid level from the top of the tube, then

$$N_A = \frac{D_v P}{RTz} \frac{p_1 - p_2}{p_{BM}} = \frac{\rho_L}{M_L} \frac{dz}{d\theta}$$

whence

$$z_2{}^2 - z_1{}^2 = 2\theta \left(\frac{D_v P}{RT} \frac{p_1 - p_2}{p_{BM}} \frac{M_L}{\rho_L} \right)$$

At the open end of the tube there is no toluene, so $p_2 = 0$ and $p_{B2} = 1.0$ atm.; at the liquid surface $p_1 = 57.3/760 = 0.0754$ atm., and $p_{B1} = 1.0 - 0.0754 = 0.9246$ atm.; $p_{BM} = 0.962$ atm. Substitution gives

$$\frac{3.11^2 - 0.748^2}{144} = (2)(275) \frac{(D_v)(1.0)(0.0754)(92)}{(0.728)(562.9)(0.962)(53.1)}$$

from which $D_v = 0.35$ ft.^{2}/hr.

Following Illustration 3, substitution in Eq. (16) gives $D_v = 0.31$ ft.^{2}/hr.

2. Unsteady-state Interdiffusion of Two Gases.

The two gaseous components are placed in separate sections of a tube, and diffusion is allowed to take place by removing the partition separating the sections. After a definite time interval the gas from various portions of the tube is analyzed and the results compared with an integrated form of Eq. (5). This method has been widely used for systems of the permanent gases[488] but gives results somewhat less reliable than those obtained by the first method.

3. Miscellaneous Methods.

Diffusion coefficients for iodine in air have been obtained by measuring the rate of evaporation of a small sphere of iodine suspended in air. It seems probable that convection currents in the air make this method unreliable. Mullaly and Jacques[335] placed iodine and mercury, respectively, at the two ends of a tube filled with nitrogen at low pressure. The diffusion coefficients of both iodine and mercury were calculated from the measured amount, composition, and location of the deposit of mercurous and mercuric iodides formed. Special methods of this type are useful only for special types of systems.

Still another procedure is to measure the rate of evaporation of small liquid drops suspended in a quiescent gas at constant temperature. The integration of the basic equation for diffusion radially from a spherical surface results in[262]

$$N_A = 2 \frac{D_v}{D} (c_1 - c_2) \tag{20}$$

where D is the diameter in feet, c_1 is the vapor concentration corresponding to saturation, and c_2 is the vapor concentration at a distance in
pound moles per cubic foot. Substitution of experimental values of
N_A, D, c_1, and c_2 permits the calculation of D_v.[460,205]

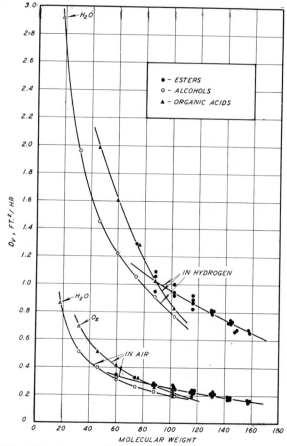

Fig. 5.   Diffusivities for various gases in air and in hydrogen at 32°F. and 1 atm.

Figure 5 illustrates the variation of diffusivity with molecular weights
of both components. The data are for several gases diffusing in air or
in hydrogen at 32°F. and 1 atm., plotted as D_v vs. molecular weight of
the diffusing gas. The plot shows a rather striking correlation of the
data for any one class of compounds, and a trend of decreasing values of
D_v with increased molecular weight in each case. The point for oxygen
falls, by chance perhaps, on a continuation of the line for organic acids.
Similarly, the point for water vapor falls on a continuation of the line
for normal alcohols.

Table III gives values of D_v and $\mu/\rho D_v$ in air for some of the more common gases. In most of the cases illustrated, Eq. (16) gives values of D_v somewhat lower than the experimental values, owing partly to coincidence in selecting the gases and partly to the fact that the constant in Eq. (16) is deliberately chosen to give somewhat low values, thereby allowing for the fact that many of the experimental values are high because of the difficulty in eliminating convection in making experimental measurements.

DIFFUSION IN LIQUIDS

Diffusion takes place very much more slowly in liquids than in gases. Because of the greater density of the liquid phase, the resistance to diffusion is much greater, and days are required for equalization of a concentration difference in a liquid, where a similar change in the gas phase would require but a few seconds. Because of the closer spacing of the molecules, molecular attraction plays an important part, and the kinetic theory of liquids has been but partially developed. There are consequently no theoretical equations for diffusion coefficients in liquids comparable with the Maxwell equation [Eq. (15)].*

Furthermore, the measured values of D_L are found to vary appreciably with the concentration of the solute, and no theory has been developed as a basis for predicting these variations. Consequently, it is customary to reason largely by analogy to the case of diffusion in gases, and to employ Eq. (5) for the unsteady-state case, and the simple form

$$N_A = \frac{D_L}{z}(c_{A1} - c_{A2}) \tag{21}$$

for the steady-state diffusion of the solute through the solvent.

DIFFUSION COEFFICIENTS FOR LIQUIDS

Diffusivities for most of the common organic and inorganic materials in the usual solvents, such as water, methyl and ethyl alcohols, and benzene at room temperature, lie in the range from 1.0 to 6.0×10^{-5} ft.²/hr. (Note that the values are of the order of one ten-thousandth those observed in gases.) Table IV gives a summary of experimental values for typical systems. More complete tables of such data are to be found in Vol. 5 of the International Critical Tables.

Where no experimental data are available, an estimate of the diffusion coefficient may be obtained by employing the empirical correlation pub-

* It may be noted, however, that Burnside[60] finds Eq. (16) to give values of D_v from 50 to 200 per cent of the experimental values for liquids, providing the internal pressure is substituted for P. The internal pressure is defined as the internal energy of vaporization divided by the specific volume of the liquid.

TABLE III. VALUES OF D_v AND $\mu/\rho D_v$ FOR VARIOUS GASES IN AIR AT 32°F. AND 1 ATM.

The value of μ/ρ is that for pure air, 0.512 ft.²/hr. The values of D_v used are those obtained from the International Critical Tables where available; otherwise the value from Eq. (16) as given in the first column is used. The experimental value for ammonia is directly from the data of Winkelman[516] corrected to 32°F.

Gas	D_v, ft.²/hr. Calc. from Eq. (16)	D_v, ft.²/hr. (I.C.T.)	$\mu/\rho D_v$
Acetic acid	....	0.413	1.24
Acetone	0.32	.....	1.60
Ammonia	0.62	0.836	0.61
Benzene	0.28	0.299	1.71
Bromobenzol	0.26	.....	1.97
Butane	0.29	.....	1.77
n-Butyl alcohol	....	0.273	1.88
Carbon dioxide	0.47	0.535	0.96
Carbon disulfide	....	0.346	1.48
Carbon tetrachloride	0.24	.....	2.13
Chlorine	0.36	.....	1.42
Chlorobenzene	0.24	.....	2.13
Chloropicrin	0.24	.....	2.13
2,2′-Dichloroethyl sulfide (mustard)	0.21	.....	2.44
Ethane	0.42	.....	1.22
Ethyl acetate	0.26	0.278	1.84
Ethyl alcohol	0.37	0.396	1.30
Ethyl ether	0.27	0.302	1.70
Ethylene bromide	0.26	.....	1.97
Hydrogen	2.17	2.37	0.22
Methane	0.61	.....	0.84
Methyl acetate	....	0.326	1.57
Methyl alcohol	0.47	0.515	1.00
Naphthalene	....	0.199	2.57
Nitrogen	0.52	.....	0.98
n-Octane	....	0.196	2.62
Oxygen	0.63	0.690	0.74
Pentane	0.26	.....	1.97
Phosgene	0.31	.....	1.65
Propane	0.34	.....	1.51
n-Propyl acetate	0.26	0.260	1.97
n-Propyl alcohol	0.31	0.330	1.55
Sulfur dioxide	0.40	.....	1.28
Toluene	0.25	0.275	1.86
Water	0.73	0.853	0.60

lished by Arnold[6] or the one by Wilke.[510] The latter bases his correlation on the Stokes-Einstein equation

$$D_L = \frac{T}{\mu F} \tag{22}$$

and proceeds to develop graphical correlations of F in terms of the
molecular volume of the solute. Three curves are given, for diffusion
in water, methyl alcohol, and benzene. These may be represented
approximately by the relation

$$D_L = \frac{4.0 \times 10^{-7} T}{\mu (V^{1/3} - k_1)} \tag{23}$$

where D_L is in square feet per hour, T is the absolute temperature of the
liquid in degrees Rankine, μ is the viscosity of the solution in lb./(hr.)(ft.),
and k_1 is 2.0, 2.46, and 2.84 for dilute solutions in water, methyl alcohol,
and benzene, respectively. Values of V are obtained from the values of
atomic volumes given in Table I, as when using Eq. (16). When V is
large compared with k_1, Eq. (23) indicates D_L to be inversely proportional to the molecular diameter, as called for by theory.

As an example, suppose it is desired to obtain D_L for acetic acid in
water at 54°F. and at low concentrations. Substituting $V = 63.8$,
$\mu = 2.98$ lb./(hr.)(ft.), and $T = 514$, D_L is found to be 3.4×10^{-5}
ft.^{2}/hr., as compared with the experimental value of 3.5×10^{-5} at this
temperature.

Equation (23) does not check the data well for small molecules and
some elemental gases, but experimental data are available for most such
cases. It is best used for organic solutes where data are not available.
It applies only in dilute solutions.

THERMAL DIFFUSION

The establishment of a steady thermal gradient in a mixture of two or
more gases may, and usually does, result in the setting up of a small but
definite concentration gradient. If a mixture of two gases is held in a
vessel with a flat top at a constant high temperature and a flat bottom
at a constant low temperature, the gas concentration in the region near
the hot upper surface reaches an equilibrium value which is definitely
different from that of the gas adjacent to the lower cold plate. This
effect is known as "thermal diffusion" and was first noted by Enskog[130]
as a logical corrollary of the kinetic theory.

The concentration gradient set up as a result of thermal diffusion is
very small, and the principle was not applied to the problem of separating two gases until Clusius and Dickel[80,81] found a simple way to

multiply the effect by employing the equivalent of multiple stages. Their apparatus, designed for the separation of gaseous isotopes, is illustrated diagrammatically in Fig. 6. The gases to be separated are contained in a hollow vertical cylinder, along the axis of which is stretched an electrically heated wire. The cylinder is cooled externally, and the

TABLE IV.   REPRESENTATIVE VALUES FOR DIFFUSION COEFFICIENTS IN THE LIQUID PHASE*

Solute	Solvent	Temp., °F.	Concentration, lb. moles/ft^3	$D_v \times 10^5$, ft.^{2}/hr. $\times 10^5$
H$_2$	Water	61	0†	18.2
N$_2$	Water	72	0†	7.9
CO$_2$	Water	68	0†	7.0
Cl$_2$	Water	54	0.0062	5.4
Br$_2$	Water	54	0.0062	3.5
NH$_3$	Water	54	0.062	6.2
HCl	Water	54	0.0062	8.9
H$_2$SO$_4$	Water	68	0.0062	6.7
HNO$_3$	Water	68	0.0062	10.1
NaCl	Water	64	0.0062	4.8
			0.025	4.6
			0.062	4.8
			0.187	5.3
KCl	Water	64	0.0062	5.9
			0.025	5.8
			0.062	6.2
			0.187	7.5
Acetic acid	Water	63	0.029	3.7
Ethyl alcohol	Water	59	0†	3.9
Glycerol	Water	59	0†	2.7
Saccharose	Water	59	0†	1.47
Urea	Water	68	0.062	4.3
CO$_2$	Ethyl alcohol	63	0†	12.4
Phenol	Ethyl alcohol	68	0.0062	3.1
Sodium acetate	Methyl alcohol	57	0.0062	3.5
Sodium iodide	Methyl alcohol	57	0.0062	3.9

* From the International Critical Tables.
† Indicates diffusion in very dilute solutions.

temperature gradient from wire to wall results in a radial concentration gradient. In most cases the lighter gas tends to concentrate near the hot wire. Natural convection currents result in a flow of gas upward around the wire and down along the inner surface of the containing cylinder. The gas at *C*, which is slightly richer in the light component than the gas at *G*, rises to *A*, where it is further enriched by thermal diffusion from the gas *F* descending from the still richer region *E*. The staging effect is analogous to the operation of a rectifying column in distillation, or to a countercurrent absorption column, as described in later chapters.

The performance of the Clusius and Dickel column has been described analytically by Furry, Jones, and Onsager[150–152] for the case of two parallel walls as well as for two concentric cylinders. The separation factor for a binary system in a tower with no throughput is found to be given by

$$\frac{(c_A/c_B)_{\text{top}}}{(c_A/c_B)_{\text{bottom}}} = e^{AAZ} \qquad (24)$$

where Z is the height of the column and A is a function of the clearance between wire and tube, gas velocity, gas density, the system diffusivity D_v, and the relative weights of the two molecules. Simon[428] has obtained data on a column 79 in. long of 0.865 in. i.d. used for the separation of the isotopes of argon (A^{36} and A^{40}), and gives a graph of the logarithm of the separation factor vs. the pressure. The curve passes through a maximum as predicted by the theory. Shrader[425] reports data on the separation of chlorine isotopes, using an inner heated glass cylinder instead of a wire. Bramley and Brewer[45] reported early results with a Clusius and Dickel column separating methane from ammonia and from other gas pairs.

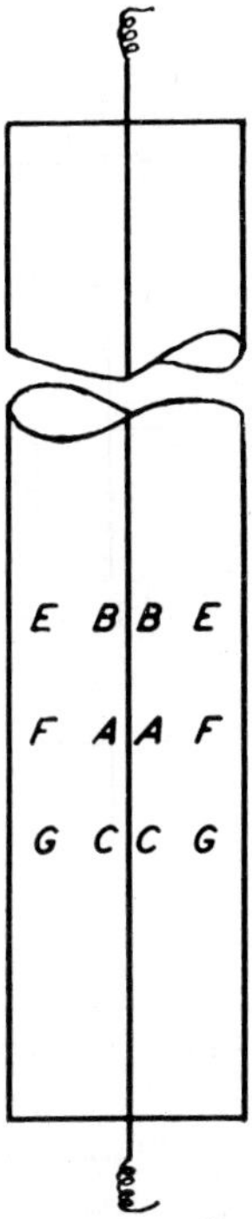

The possibility of separating isotopes of uranium by thermal diffusion techniques is known to have received intensive study during the war, but the results have not yet been published. In the case of isotope separation, the rates obtained were very small (of the order of 0.0002 lb./day in a fair-sized laboratory column), and the possible steady feed rates were very small indeed.

The theory of the thermal diffusion process and of cascades of columns is summarized well by Benedict.[29,30] The low capacity of the equipment and the large heat requirements are illustrated by a numerical example illustrating the design of a system for the separation of the isotope $C^{13}H_4$ from natural methane containing 1.06 per cent $C^{13}H_4$. To produce 0.22 lb./day at a concentration of 90 per cent with a yield of 50 per cent would require a total surface of 6.5 acres and a heat input of 7560 kw. This assumes a plate spacing of 0.3 in., a total pressure of 1 atm., and temperatures of 621 and 71°F.

It is evident that the process requires large equipment and operates at very low efficiency. It is perhaps useful only for the separation of

Fig. 6. Clusius and Dickel column employing thermal diffusion.

very valuable materials where the separation factor is more favorable than that attainable in other separation processes.

GASEOUS EFFUSION

The principles of separation by gaseous effusion are also summarized by Benedict.[30] Since the smaller, faster moving molecules of a gas

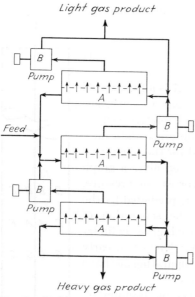

Light gas product

Heavy gas product

mixture tend to strike a given area of the container surface more frequently (in proportion to their number) than the larger, slower moving molecules, it follows that a gas mixture passing through a small hole will tend to be enriched in the lighter component. Since the velocities of the molecules are inversely proportional to their molecular weights, it follows that the ratio of concentrations in the enriched gas should be

$$\frac{y_A}{y_B} = \frac{x_A}{x_B} \sqrt{\frac{M_B}{M_A}} \qquad (25)$$

where y and x refer to mole fractions in the gas mixtures downstream and upstream from the hole, and M is the molecular weight. This applies only for holes in membranes with no thickness under conditions where

Fig. 7.   Multistage countercurrent separation of gases by effusion. (*After Benedict.*)

the mean free path is large compared with the diameter of the hole (low pressures, small holes). An adequate theory for actual porous barriers of finite thickness has apparently not been developed.

Hertz[182] has described a multistage countercurrent system for applying gaseous effusion to gas separation, which he used for the separation of the isotopes of neon. This is illustrated by Fig. 7. The separators shown at points A consist of passages separated by porous barriers. These are operated with an appreciable difference between the gas pressures on the two sides of the barriers and connected so that the gas enriched in the lighter component passes upward; the gas enriched in the heavier component passes downward. In the separator at the center, for example, the compressed gas enters at the left; the gas passing through the barrier passes to the stage above, while the gas not effusing goes to the stage below. Gas compressors are shown at points B.

Such a countercurrent system requires a gas compressor for each stage, and each separator corresponds to but one separation stage. By contrast, the thermal diffusion apparatus of Clusius and Dickel may give results corresponding to a number of separation stages in a single separator unit, and no compressor is needed. Multistage gaseous effusion is employed, therefore, only in large-scale processes where the attainable separation factor is good relative to alternative separation processes. It has been employed on a commercial scale only for the concentration of U^{235} by separation of uranium isotopes as uranium hexafloride. This is

Fig. 8. General view of the Oak Ridge plant for the separation of uranium isotopes. (*U.S. Army photograph.*)

done at the large K-25 plant of the Atomic Energy Commission at Oak Ridge, Tennessee.[434] The size of the plant is indicated by the fact that several thousand stages are employed, with a power requirement (mostly for gas compressors) of over 200,000 kw. (see Fig. 8).

The numerical example of the separation of $C^{13}H_4$ from natural methane has been extended by Benedict to cover the same production of 0.22 lb./day of the C^{13} isotope by gaseous effusion. The calculation indicates that under favorable conditions 345 stages and a total of 149 kw. of electric power would be needed. Even with appropriate allowance for inefficiencies of pumps and barriers, it appears that gaseous effusion is much more efficient than thermal diffusion for the purpose.

A variation of the gas-effusion process is the method described by Maier,[292] which employs a porous barrier operated with gas at the same pressure on both sides. The lighter gas diffuses through the holes more rapidly than the heavier gas, and the enriched mixture diffusing through is carried away by some condensable vapor such as steam. The barrier is simple, and the method is adaptable to countercurrent multistage operation, but the heat requirements are very large.

Nomenclature for Chapter I

a = constant in Eq. (17)
A = constant in Eq. (24)
b = constant in Eq. (15)
c = concentration or partial molal density, lb. moles/ft.^{3}
C = empirical constant
D = diameter, ft.
D_L = diffusion coefficient, or diffusivity, in liquid phase, ft.^{2}/hr.
D_v = diffusion coefficient, or diffusivity, in gas mixture, ft.^{2}/hr.
F = constant in Eq. (22).
k_1 = empirical constant in Eq. (23)
M = molecular weight
N = rate of diffusion, lb. moles/(hr.)(ft.^{2})
p = partial pressure of one component, atm.
p_{BM} = logarithmic mean of p_{B2} and p_{B1} [see Eq. (10)]
P = total pressure, atm.
R = gas-law constant = 0.728 (ft.^{3})(atm.)/(lb. mole)(°R.)
S = cross section normal to diffusion, ft.^{2}
T = absolute temperature, °R = 460 + °F.
u = mean velocity of molecules, ft./hr.
V = molecular volume (see Table I)
x, y = mole fraction
z = distance in the direction of diffusion, ft.
Z = height of thermal diffusion column, ft.
θ = time, hr.
λ = component of molecular mean free path in z direction, ft.
μ = absolute viscosity, lb./(hr.)(ft.)
ρ = density, lb/ft.^{3}

SUBSCRIPTS

A, B, referring to components A or B of a mixture of two substances
L, referring to a liquid
M, referring to logarithmic mean
1,2, referring to positions of planes at right angles to the direction of diffusion

Problems

1. A layer of water 0.04 in. thick is maintained at a constant temperature of 68°F. in contact with dry air at 86°F. and 1 atm. Assuming evaporation to take place by molecular diffusion through a gas film 0.20 in. thick, calculate the time (seconds) for the water to evaporate completely. The value of D_v for water vapor in air may be taken as 1.01 ft.^{2}/hr.

2. Hydrochloric acid is diffusing across an inert air film 0.08 in. thick at a temperature of 68°F. and 1 atm. total pressure. Estimate the effect on the rate of diffusion [lb. moles/(hr.)(ft.²)] of raising the pressure to 10 atm. if the concentration of HCl is (*a*) 0.1 atm., and (*b*) 10 per cent by volume on one boundary of the film, and zero on the other boundary in both cases. D_v for HCl and air at 68°F. and 1 atm. may be taken as 0.561 ft.²/hr.

3. The concentration of CO_2 at one boundary of a stagnant air film is 0.000625 lb. mole/ft.³ (0.01 g. mole/liter) at 68°F. and 1 atm. total pressure. Estimate the rate of diffusion across 1 ft.² if the effective film thickness is 0.118 in. and there is zero concentration of CO_2 at the other boundary of the film.

How much more time would be required for 1 g. mole of CO_2 under the same initial and final conditions of concentration (0.000625 lb. mole/ft.³, 0 lb. mole/ft.³) to diffuse across 1 ft.² of a film of liquid water of the same thickness?

4. Spheres of charcoal were burned in streams of air at atmospheric pressure during comprehensive tests of the mechanism of combustion of carbon. The following data were taken during one run:

Average sphere diameter...................... 0.98 in.
Surface temperature of sphere............... 3064°R.
Bulk temperature of gas..................... 3074°R.
Gas velocity at standard conditions.......... 0.12 ft./sec.
Specific combustion rate..................... 1.19 lb./(hr.)(ft.²)

Calculate the theoretical specific combustion rate on the basis that the controlling resistance is that represented by molecular diffusion of oxygen through a stagnant film of air 0.8 in. thick. It is agreed to assume that the partial pressure of oxygen is negligible at the carbon–gas–film surface and to neglect the effect of back diffusion of combustion products. The diffusivity of O_2 in N_2 may be computed from the equation

$$D_v = 0.702 \left(\frac{T}{492}\right)^{1.75} \quad \text{ft.}^2/\text{hr.}$$

5. A cooled metal tube 2 in. in diameter is used as a condenser to remove water from a water–vapor–air mixture. At one point in the tube the metal surface is at 95°F. and the gas mixture is at 212°F. and 1 atm. total pressure, with 80 mole per cent vapor. Based on the assumptions listed below, calculate the rate of condensation of water as pounds per hour per foot of tube length.

Assumptions: The conditions are essentially constant over the length of 1 ft. The thickness of the water film on the tube wall corresponds to a water-film coefficient of 2000 B.t.u./(hr.)(ft.²)(°F.). The transfer in the gas phase is by molecular diffusion only, the water diffusing through a path of 30 per cent of the tube radius. The molecular diffusivity for water in air at the mean temperature is 1.16 ft.²/hr. The gas and liquid phases are in equilibrium at the *surface* of the water film.

6. A solution (10 per cent by weight) of ammonia in water is stripped continuously at a rate of 36,800 lb./hr. by a current of initially ammonia-free steam in a counter-current, wetted-wall tower. The tower is 4 ft. in diameter and operates under a total pressure of 0.5 atm. The ammonia-rich vapor leaves the top of the column containing 20 per cent ammonia by volume, and the bottoms are essentially ammonia-free. The vapor velocity in the column is such that mass transfer may be considered to be accomplished by molecular diffusion through a stagnant gas film 0.0079 in. thick. At the point in the column where the liquid composition is 5 mole per cent ammonia and the temperature is 120°F., estimate the rate of mass transfer of ammonia as pounds per hour per square foot.

Data and notes:

Latent heats at 120°F.:

$$NH_3 = 500 \text{ B.t.u./lb.}$$
$$H_2O = 1026 \text{ B.t.u./lb.}$$

Vapor pressure over 5 mole per cent solution of NH_3 at 120°F $= 2.67$ p.s.i.a.
It is agreed to neglect the liquid-film resistance.

7. Odbert (S.M. thesis in Chemical Engineering, M.I.T., 1934) measured the diffusivities of N_2-CO_2 mixture at various temperatures, using the Loschmidt method. A vertical cylinder 8.0 in. long was divided in halves by a movable disk. The lower half was filled with CO_2 and the upper half with nitrogen, both at atmospheric pressure. The halves of the cylinder were connected for a measured length of time, then separated. The concentrations of CO_2 in the two sections were then determined by analysis.

A sample of the data obtained by Odbert is given below:

Mole fraction of CO_2 in lower section........... 0.848
Mole fraction of CO_2 in upper section.......... 0.152
Time for diffusion............................. 60 sec.
Temperature................................. 70°F.

a. Calculate the value of the diffusivity for CO_2-N_2 under the above conditions.

b. Compare this experimental value of diffusivity with that obtained from the Gilliland equation (16).

CHAPTER II

EDDY DIFFUSION

As was indicated at the outset, the diffusional operations of industrial importance generally involve the transfer of material from one phase to another. In the case of gas absorption, for example, the transfer of the solute gas is usually from gas phase to liquid phase. Molecular diffusion is one of the two mechanisms of transfer within a single phase, and it has been seen that this process is very slow in gases and extremely slow in liquids. If the fluid is agitated or mixed, transfer takes place by the relatively fast process of eddy diffusion. Conditions favorable to eddy diffusion may be maintained by special mixing devices or agitators,

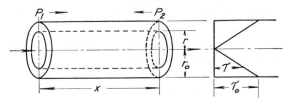

Fig. 9.   Shear stresses in flow through a round pipe.   (*After Bakhmeteff.*)

or by the establishment of turbulent flow. Eddy diffusion within a fluid stream moving in turbulent flow is a process of wide practical importance and will be discussed in some detail. Since the mechanism of eddy diffusion is tied closely to the nature of turbulent flow, it will first be necessary to review briefly the present general concepts of turbulence.

Turbulent Flow.[19]   Before attempting to describe the general nature of turbulence, it is desirable to review the basic concepts and relations defining turbulent flow, from a mass- or average-flow point of view. For this purpose it is convenient to consider the common and important case of flow of a fluid in a round pipe. Figure 9 illustrates a short section of such a conduit through which a fluid is flowing at a steady rate. The pressure P_1 is uniform across any plane normal to the axis, and the pressure at any point in a second plane a distance x downstream is P_2, where P_2 is less than P_1, owing to friction. A dynamic equilibrium exists, whereby the difference between the forces on the two planes is just balanced by the tangential friction forces acting on the surface of the pipe bounding the fluid element between the two planes. Considering a

29

differential length dx of a pipe of radius r_0, this force balance may be expressed by

$$-\pi r_0{}^2\, dP = 2\tau_0 \pi r_0\, dx$$

or

$$\tau_0 = -\frac{r_0}{2}\frac{dP}{dx} \tag{26}$$

where τ_0 represents the shear stress per unit area at the pipe wall. Considering any cylindrical surface of radius r, it is evident that

$$\tau = -\frac{r}{2}\frac{dP}{dx} = \tau_0 \frac{r}{r_0} \tag{27}$$

where τ is the internal shear stress at radius r. As indicated graphically in Fig. 9, the shear stress is linear in r, being zero at the axis. It is important to note that this relation does not depend on any assumption as to the nature of the flow.

Two quite different types of fluid motion have been observed experimentally in studies of flow in round pipes. At low flow rates the pressure gradient dP/dx is found to be directly proportional to the viscosity of the fluid, and to the average fluid velocity, U_{av}, defined as the volumetric flow rate divided by the conduit cross section. At higher velocities the pressure gradient is approximately proportional to $U_{av}{}^2$, and the viscosity has relatively minor importance. At low velocities the particles of fluid are observed to move parallel to the pipe wall, and the flow is termed "laminar" (or sometimes "viscous," or "streamline"), since thin annuli of fluid slide over each other like the concentric tubes of a telescope. At higher velocities the fluid is observed to be agitated, with rapid mixing of layers of fluid at different radii. The flow is then said to be "turbulent." The distinction between the two types of flow is best visualized by repeating Osborne Reynolds' famous experiment in which a colored liquid is introduced at the axis of a stream of water flowing in a glass pipe. When laminar flow exists, the colored fluid moves with the moving water as a thin undisturbed pencil along the axis of the pipe. In turbulent flow the colored stream moves in an irregular vibrating motion, rapidly mixing radially and diffusing throughout the whole of the water stream.

As the fluid velocity is increased from a low value, the flow remains laminar until a fairly definite critical velocity is reached, above which the flow is turbulent. It is found experimentally that the point of change-over from laminar to turbulent flow is dependent not only on the velocity, but also on the diameter of the pipe and the viscosity and density of the fluid, and that it is characterized by a fairly well defined value of the dimensionless group, $DU_{av}\rho/\mu$, in which D is the pipe diameter and ρ is the fluid density. This important ratio, known as the "Reynolds number," will be characterized by Re. Again experimentally, it is found that the flow in round pipes is laminar if Re is less than about 2000, and that the flow is usually turbulent if Re is greater than about 2000. For other shapes, as in the flow of a fluid past a sphere, the change-over from laminar to turbulent motion is not so sharp and well defined as for fluid flow in a pipe. It may be noted that the inertia forces tending to disrupt the smooth laminar flow are proportional to the square of the typical dimension D, to the density ρ, and to the square of the velocity, and that the internal forces tending to stabilize the flow are proportional to the viscosity, velocity, and D; the Reynolds number is a measure of the ratio of the inertia to the internal forces.

Fluid Friction. Dissipation of energy due to friction in fluid flow is evidenced by the decreasing pressure or head in the direction of flow, as in the case of steady flow in a round pipe. Quantitatively, the energy loss per unit time is the product of the volumetric rate of flow and the negative pressure change. This may be equated to the work done in overcoming the tangential resisting force at the wall:

$$-Q \, dP = 2U_{av}\tau_0 \, \pi r_0 \, dx \tag{28}$$

where Q represents the volumetric rate of flow. If Q is expressed in terms of U_{av}, this reduces to (26). The relation between Q or U_{av} and the pressure gradient requires knowledge of the shear stress at the wall, τ_0.

In laminar flow, the shear stress τ at any radius r is found to be proportional to the local velocity gradient across the pipe (at right angles to the direction of flow):

$$\tau = \frac{r}{r_0} \tau_0 = -\frac{\mu}{g_c} \frac{dU}{dr} \tag{29}$$

The proportionality constant μ is defined as the coefficient of viscosity, or absolute viscosity. It is found to be dependent on the nature of the fluid and not (except in the case of non-Newtonian fluids) on the conditions of flow. Equation (29) may be integrated, on the assumptions that μ is constant and that U is zero at the pipe wall, to give

$$\frac{U_m - U}{U_m} = \left(\frac{r}{r_0}\right)^2 \tag{30}$$

$$U_{av} = \frac{U_m}{2} \tag{31}$$

$$\tau_0 = \frac{4\mu U_{av}}{g_c r_0} \tag{32}$$

and

$$-\frac{dP}{dx} = \frac{8\mu U_{av}}{g_c r_0{}^2} \tag{33}$$

Equations (30) and (31) specify the velocity distribution across the diameter and the relation of average velocity to maximum or center-line velocity (U_m) for laminar flow in a round pipe. Equations (32) and (33) are forms of Poiseuille's law for pressure drop in laminar flow. For ordinary fluids the equations for velocity gradient and pressure loss in laminar flow have been confirmed by numerous experiments, indicating the soundness of the assumptions of constant μ and zero velocity at the pipe wall. The relations do not apply to fluids where μ depends on the rate of shear or to gases at very low pressure.

In the case of turbulent flow, τ is not related to the velocity gradient by a constant, and (29) does not apply. A great many experimental measurements have been correlated empirically, however, and the results for turbulent flow in round pipes expressed in the form

$$\tau_0 g_c = \tfrac{1}{2} f \rho U_{av}{}^2 \tag{34}$$

whence

$$-\frac{dP}{dx} = \frac{f \rho U_{av}{}^2}{g_c r_0} \tag{35}$$

These are forms of the familiar Fanning or Darcy equation for turbulent flow in pipes. Here f is an empirical "friction factor," which must be determined experimentally.

In one of the most remarkable correlations of physical data ever obtained, Stanton and Pannell[440] showed f for smooth pipes to be a function of Re only, obtaining a single curve of f vs. Re when plotting the results of experimental data on the flow of air, water, and oils in both laminar and turbulent flow. Figure 10 shows the line representing the results obtained. The break in the curve lies in the region of the critical value of Re, about 2000, with the branch to the left representing the data in laminar flow. The solid right branch represents the results for turbulent flow in smooth pipes, and the dotted branch to the right represents a typical curve for a rough pipe. The left branch is represented by the relation $f = 16/\text{Re}$, which may be substituted in Eq. (35) to give Poiseuille's law (33).

Drag Coefficients. In the case of flow in a pipe the force on the pipe wall is represented by the shear stress τ_0. In the case of a sphere or other solid object placed in a turbulent fluid stream, the force on the object is partly due to skin friction, as in the case of the pipe, and partly due to impact pressure. The latter may be measured by means of pressure taps and subtracted from the "total drag" to obtain the skin friction. In most cases only data on total drag are available. In the case of the pipe the total force is the product of τ_0 and the wall area. In the case of the sphere or cylinder it is common to employ the projected area normal to the flow rather than the actual surface of the solid, and to define a "drag coefficient" C_D by analogy to (34), by

$$\tau_0' g_c = \frac{C_D \rho U^2}{2} \tag{36}$$

where τ_0' is the total drag per unit projected area S. Since both skin friction and impact pressure are proportional to U^2, C_D represents the sum of two coefficients for the two effects. Only a limited amount of data is available on the division between the two, which, as might be

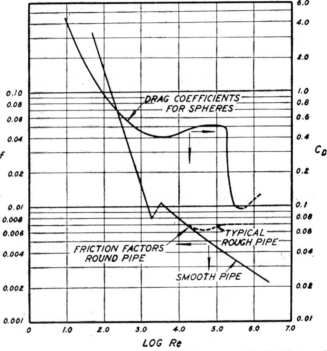

Fig. 10. Drag coefficients for spheres and friction factors for flow in round pipes.

expected, is a function of Re for each shape. Figure 10 shows values of C_D for spheres, as given by Goldstein.[325] In contrast with the curve representing f for round pipes, the curve of C_D vs. Re shows no sharp break in passing from laminar to turbulent flow but does exhibit a very sharp drop at a high value of Re.

Velocity Distribution for Flow in Pipes.[19] As will be shown later, the rate of mass transfer across a stream of fluid in turbulent flow is related to the velocity gradient, dU/dr, and for this reason information on velocity distribution is important. In laminar flow the relation between U and r is given by Eqs. (30) and (31). In turbulent flow the relation is more complicated and depends on both the Reynolds number and on the relative roughness of the pipe walls. For a constant total flow or U_{av} in a smooth pipe the curve of U vs. r is relatively flat across the central part of the diameter, and U_{av} is roughly 80 per cent of the axial or maximum velocity U_m. In the case of a rough wall and the same U_{av} the curvature of the velocity-distribution curve is greater, and U_{av} is a smaller fraction of U_m. This difference is due to the fact that τ_0 is greater with the rough pipe, and dU/dr must be greater at the wall to transfer the greater shear stress. If τ_0 is held constant by varying U_{av} in experiments with walls having various degrees of roughness, it is found that the velocity-distribution curves may all be represented by an equation of the form

$$U = U_w + f(r) \tag{37}$$

where $f(r)$ is the same in each case, but the constant U_w has a different value for each wall roughness. In other words, the *velocity deficiency*, defined as $U_m - U$, is the same function of r for all degrees of wall roughness, providing τ_0 is constant. The quantitative relation is found to be

$$\frac{U_m - U}{U_{av}} = 5.75 \sqrt{\frac{f}{2}} \log \frac{r_0}{r_0 - r} \tag{38}$$

This equation represents an excellent correlation of data on the flow of water in pipes where the degree of roughness of the pipe wall surface was varied over a wide range. It does not permit the calculation of the actual velocity distribution unless U_m is known but provides the general relation for the velocity gradient

$$\frac{dU}{dr} = -\frac{1}{0.40} \frac{U_{av} \sqrt{f/2}}{(r_0 - r)} \tag{39}$$

The velocity distribution across a pipe depends on the Reynolds number and, as suggested above, on the roughness of the wall. Consequently, the ratio of maximum velocity at the axis to average velocity is known to be a unique function of f, and by means of this relation U_m may be eliminated from Eq. (38) to give a general relation for the velocity gradient in round pipes:

$$\frac{U}{U_{av}} = 5.5 \sqrt{\frac{f}{2}} + 5.75 \sqrt{\frac{f}{2}} \log \frac{(r_0 - r) U_{av} \rho}{\mu} \sqrt{\frac{f}{2}} \tag{40}$$

or

$$u^+ = 5.5 + 5.75 \log y^+$$

where

$$u^+ = \frac{U}{U_{av}} \sqrt{\frac{2}{f}}, \quad \text{and} \quad y^+ = \frac{(r_0 - r) U_{av} \rho}{\mu} \sqrt{\frac{f}{2}} \tag{41}$$

Figure 11 shows the experimental data* of Nikuradse[342] covering a wide range of values of flow rate and pipe diameter for water in turbulent flow. Low values of y^+ correspond to points near the wall, where the velocity is measurable only by the use of very tiny pitot tubes. Adjacent to the wall the flow characteristics approach those of laminar flow, with

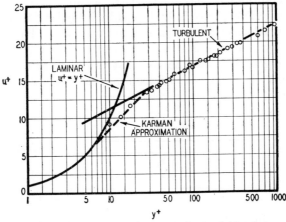

Fig. 11. Data of Nikuradse expressed as a generalized relation between velocity and distance from pipe wall.

the velocity being proportional to the distance from the wall. It may be shown easily that these conditions correspond to equality of u^+ and y^+, so the curved left branch of Fig. 11 may be assumed to represent the velocity pattern in this region where no data exist. It appears that the flow is laminar near the pipe wall, up to a value of y^+ of about 5, and that the flow is fully turbulent at values of y^+ greater than about 30. The region from $y^+ = 5$ to $y^+ = 30$ has been termed the "transition," or "buffer," layer. The generalized velocity distribution illustrated by Fig. 11 will be employed in the next chapter in the development of a theoretical equation for mass transfer between phases.

TURBULENCE[117,118,237]

Turbulence in a moving fluid is a condition of irregular motion evidenced by fluctuations in the fluid velocity measured at any point.

* As a result of an inquiry (1946) by Dr. Benjamin Miller of New York, Drs. Prandtl and Nikuradse explain a discrepancy between Tables II and III of the 1932 Nikuradse article[342] as being due to an arbitrary constant adjustment of y^+, applied to the data on velocity distribution in order to force the velocity gradient at the wall to become unity. Dr. Prandtl suggests that the newer data of Reichardt are more reliable than those of Nikuradse. Martinelli[299] gives a graph comparing the data of both Nikuradse and Reichardt; the latter fall 0 to 20 per cent below the three branches of the curve of Fig. 11.

Since the mean flow may vary rapidly, it is necessary to distinguish between changes in the mean conditions, which do not constitute turbulence, and irregular variations in relation to the mean. For example, the mean flow in a pipe may be represented by an average velocity U_{av} or by a time-average velocity U at a particular point. Owing to change in external conditions U may vary widely without necessarily developing turbulence. Turbulence is evidenced by irregular fluctuations of the instantaneous velocity about the time-mean value. Thus the instantaneous velocity at a point is $U + u$, where u is known as the "deviating velocity." In general it may be said that variations in U may be measured by ordinary instruments such as pitot tubes, orifices, etc., while the measurement of the deviating velocity u and its fluctuations require special instrumentation.

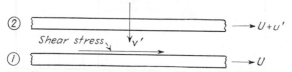

Fig. 12.   Shear stress due to velocity gradient in a turbulent stream.

At any point in a fluid stream the velocity components are U, V, and W, which are average values measured over some period of time. The instantaneous velocity components are $U + u$, $V + v$, and $W + w$, where u, v, and w are the components of the deviating velocity. The time average of each of the latter is zero. A small pitot tube may indicate the velocity U of air in the center of a pipe to be 3000 ft./hr.; actually the velocity may be 3035, 2990, 3070, 3018, 2945, etc., ft./hr. at intervals of a few milliseconds of time. Since the deviating velocities u, v, and w may be positive or negative, it is convenient to employ root-mean-square values $\sqrt{\overline{u^2}}$, $\sqrt{\overline{v^2}}$, and $\sqrt{\overline{w^2}}$, which for brevity will be represented by u', v', and w'. These are the components of the *intensity* of the fluctuations, or the "intensity of turbulence."

Consider the case of a fluid flowing at a steady rate in the sense that the time-average velocity U is constant at a point. Assume two adjacent layers or laminae of fluid, one moving at the velocity U and a second at a velocity $U + u'$, as illustrated in Fig. 12. Then there will be a sidewise motion carrying particles of the second at a velocity v', from the second into the first. On the basis of a unit area of the plane separating the two laminae the rate of mass transfer from the second to the first is $\rho v'$, and if the particles so transferred become part of the first stream traveling at the velocity U, then there will have been a transfer of momentum from the second to the first at the rate $\rho v'u'$ ft.-lb./hr.[2] per unit area of the plane separating the two. Because the first layer is moving slower than the second, it will exert a drag on the latter, and the resulting shear stress is equal to the rate of momentum transfer:

$$\tau g_c = -\rho u'v' \tag{42}$$

or more properly

$$\tau g_c = -\rho \overline{uv} \tag{43}$$

where the bar denotes a time average of the product uv. This is one of the several Reynolds or eddy stresses and is important for purposes of a later development of the theory of eddy diffusion.

Scale of Turbulence. If it is assumed that the distance L which a particle of fluid, or eddy, travels before losing its identity corresponds to the distance between two layers having velocities U and $U + dU$, then $u' = dU$, and

$$u' = L\frac{dU}{dy} \tag{44}$$

Here L is the Prandtl "mixing length," which for motion of eddies in a fluid in turbulent flow is analogous to the mean free path in the motion of molecules. It is a measure of the scale of the turbulence and is greater if the eddies are larger.

It is obviously necessary that in any small volume of the moving stream the fluid displaced in one direction must be replaced by fluid coming in from another direction. It is reasonable to suppose, therefore, that u', v', and w' will all be of the same order of magnitude. If u' is assumed equal to v', then

$$\tau g_c = -\rho L^2 \left(\frac{dU}{dy}\right)^2 \tag{45}$$

which is sometimes called the Prandtl equation. Experimental data on friction or pressure drop yield values of τ_0 and hence τ at any y or r, and these may be combined with data on the velocity distribution across a conduit to obtain values of L. It is found that in round pipes the curve of L vs. $r_0 - r$ is concave downward, passing through zero at the pipe wall and about $0.15r_0$ at the center line. For a distance of 10 per cent of the radius in from the pipe wall, the values of L are very nearly $0.4(r_0 - r)r_0$. The eddy size, if defined as the Prandtl mixing length, varies from zero at the wall to about one-seventh of the radius at the center line. At the higher Reynolds numbers the same results are obtained with smooth and with rough pipes.

If the velocity fluctuations were independently random, the product $\overline{uv}$ would be zero, and the shear stress τ would also be zero. Since τ is not zero in the ordinary case, it follows that there must be some correlation between u and v. The coefficient of correlation between two variables u and v is defined as

$$R_{u,v} = \frac{\overline{uv}}{u'v'} \tag{46}$$

in which, as will be recalled, u' and v' represent the square roots of the mean squares of u and v. Thus, from Eq. (43)

$$\tau g_c = \rho R_{u,v} u' v' \tag{47}$$

which reduces to Eq. (42) only if the correlation coefficient is unity.

In most cases of turbulent flow u', v', and w' are approximately equal, and the flow pattern is said to be one of isotropic turbulence. Isotropic turbulence is often assumed in order that the theory may be greatly amplified. Experimentally, the scale may be controlled by passing the fluid through a honeycomb or wire screen, which tends to set up turbulent flow of uniform eddy size in relation to the grid dimensions and isotropic in nature a short distance downstream. The intensity may be varied independently over a fairly wide range from about 0.1 to 20 or more "per cent turbulence." This latter is defined as $100u'/U$ and is usually measured by the use of a hot-wire anemometer of very small diameter (negligible thermal lag) and a special electrical circuit for following the rapid fluctuations in the electrical resistance of the wire.

THEORY OF EDDY DIFFUSION[117,118]

Since the velocity fluctuations or deviating velocities in a turbulent stream are relatively large, it is evident that diffusion within the stream may take place at a relatively rapid rate owing to the movement of the eddies in relation to the movement of the main mass of fluid. Although eddy diffusion occurs in all directions, the transverse diffusion normal to the direction of flow is of principal interest in connection with industrial diffusional processes, and the assumption of one-directional diffusion will be made in order to simplify the presentation.

At a point in a turbulent stream the velocity is U and the deviating velocity normal to the direction of flow is v'. The concentration of one component of the fluid mixture is c lb. moles/ft.^{3}. Then considering a plane of unit cross section parallel to the direction of flow, it may be supposed that the velocity of an eddy across this plane during one small time period $d\theta$ will be v', and during the second instant $d\theta$ will be $-v'$. In the first short time period the eddy will be assumed to travel a distance L, defined by Eq. (44), and lose its identity, so that the eddy returning during the second time instant will have a composition $c + dc$ characteristic of the fluid at the plane $y + dy$. The net flow of the component diffusing will be

$$v'c \, d\theta - v'(c + dc) \, d\theta = -v' \, dc \, d\theta$$

in time $2 \, d\theta$. If an "eddy diffusivity," E, is defined as the net rate of transfer divided by the concentration gradient, then

$$N_A = -E \frac{dc}{dy} = -\frac{v' \, dc \, d\theta}{2d\theta} \tag{48}$$

Since the distance dy is identified as the mixing length L, it follows that

$$E = \tfrac{1}{2}v'L \tag{49}$$

The eddy diffusivity E is proportional to the product of the mixing length and the deviating velocity and has the units square feet per hour. The result (49) may be compared with the equation for molecular diffusion of one gas through itself, in which case the diffusivity D_v is equal to one-third the product of the mean free path and the average speed of the molecules.

It may be noted that the general concept of diffusion by discontinuous movements, as outlined above, may be applied to the transport of other properties of the fluid, as for example, heat or momentum. The concentration c may be replaced by the momentum per unit volume, ρU, and since the rate of momentum transfer in the y direction is identical with the Reynolds stress $\rho \overline{uv}$, then

$$\tau g_c = -\rho \overline{uv} = -\rho \frac{Lv'}{2} \frac{dU}{dy} \tag{50}$$

In laminar flow, the proportionality constant between the shear stress and the velocity gradient is the absolute viscosity μ. By analogy, we may define an "eddy viscosity" $\epsilon = \rho Lv'/2$, and add the effects due to turbulence and viscosity, to get

$$\tau g_c = -(\mu + \epsilon) \frac{dU}{dy} \tag{51}$$

The viscosity may be assumed constant across the conduit; ϵ varies from a small value at the wall to a relatively large value in the middle of the stream. Referring to Fig. 11, the three regions correspond to conditions of μ large compared with ϵ (laminar layer); μ and ϵ of same order of magnitude (buffer layer); and ϵ large compared to μ (turbulent region). Values of ϵ for various locations across the diameter of a pipe may be obtained from experimental values of velocity gradient and shear stress τ_0, or may be obtained by combining Eqs. (51), (34), and (39):

$$\epsilon = 0.4 \sqrt{\frac{f}{2}} \, U_{av}(r_0 - r) \frac{r}{r_0} \rho \tag{52}$$

The shear stress τ may be set equal to $(r/r_0)\tau_0$ and Eq. (51) integrated, with ϵ assumed constant, to obtain a relation between U and r; the result is that the velocity deficiency $U_m - U$ is proportional to r^2. In so far as the velocity gradient may be fitted by a parabola of this type, therefore, ϵ is constant and not a function of the radius.

The difficulty with the use of the Prandtl mixing-length concept is that the eddies vary in size and speed and so cannot be considered as traveling a definite distance before losing their identity. A more satisfactory theory is based on the statistical theory of turbulence proposed by G. I. Taylor,[453] in which the variations in the properties defining turbulence are treated statistically.

Assume isotropic turbulence and a constant value of the deviating velocity v' at a point. Again consider the diffusion of one component of the fluid mixture in a direction normal to the direction of flow, *i.e.*, in the y direction. In time θ_1 the particles of the fluid will move a distance given by

$$y = \int_0^{\theta_1} v \, d\theta$$

and

$$\frac{1}{2} \frac{\overline{dy^2}}{d\theta} = \overline{y \frac{dy}{d\theta}} = \overline{yv_{\theta_1}} = \int_0^{\theta_1} \overline{v_{\theta_1} v_{\theta^1 - \theta}} \, d\theta \tag{53}$$

This may be simplified by defining a correlation factor R_θ, relating the velocity of a particle of fluid at time θ_1 to that at time $\theta_1 - \theta$:

$$R_\theta = \frac{\overline{v_{\theta_1} v_{\theta_1 - \theta}}}{\overline{v_{\theta_1}^2}} \tag{54}$$

whence

$$\frac{1}{2} \frac{\overline{dy^2}}{d\theta} = \overline{v^2} \int_0^{\theta_1} R_\theta \, d\theta \tag{55}$$

$$\overline{y^2} = 2\overline{v^2} \int_0^{\theta_1} \int_0^{\theta} R_\theta \, d\theta \, d\theta \tag{56}$$

If the times or distances are exceedingly small, then R_θ may be taken as unity, and

$$\sqrt{\overline{y^2}} = \sqrt{\overline{v^2}} \, \theta = v'\theta = v' \frac{x}{U} \tag{57}$$

or

$$\overline{y^2} = \left(\frac{v'}{U}\right)^2 x^2 \tag{58}$$

If the time or distance is relatively large, there will be no correlation between v_{θ_1} and $v_{\theta_1 - \theta}$, and R_θ will be zero, *i.e.*, R_θ may decrease from unity to zero as θ increases from zero to some value θ_2. Hence

$$\int_0^{\theta_1} R_\theta \, d\theta = \int_0^{\theta_2} R_\xi \, d\theta = \text{constant}$$

Here θ_2 is the average time for the particle to lose its velocity identity. Defining a new length L_θ as

$$L_\theta = v' \int_0^{\theta_2} R_\theta \, d\theta \tag{59}$$

then from (56),

$$\overline{y^2} = 2v'L_\theta\theta + \text{constant}$$

$$= 2\left(\frac{v'}{U}\right) L_\theta x + \text{constant} \tag{60}$$

For very short diffusion distances, therefore, the mean-square displacement of the particles is given by Eq. (58), while for longer distances Eq. (60) applies. Taylor[453] has shown that the displacement of the particle in time θ may be related to a diffusivity (rate of transfer divided by concentration gradient) by an equation[481] similar to that derived by Einstein[126] for Brownian motion:

$$E = \frac{1}{2} \frac{d\overline{y^2}}{d\theta} = \frac{U}{2} \frac{d\overline{y^2}}{dx} \tag{61}$$

For very short diffusion distances, this may be combined with Eq. (58) to give

$$E = v' \left(\frac{v'}{U}\right) x \tag{62}$$

while for diffusion distances sufficiently long so that θ is not only large compared with θ_2 but the constant is negligible compared with the first term in Eq. (60),

$$E = v'L_\theta \tag{63}$$

The eddy diffusivity is proportional to the root-mean-square deviating velocity and to a characteristic length, as was found in the simpler mixing-length theory, Eq. (49).

EXPERIMENTAL DATA ON EDDY DIFFUSION

Experimental studies of eddy diffusion are not numerous, as the technique is difficult, and the subject has received little attention until relatively recently. In some of the investigations which have been reported, numerous discrete particles have been fed continuously into a turbulent channel and their later location with respect to the direction of flow recorded photographically. Figure 13 illustrates data of this kind reported by Van Driest,[469] who injected small drops of a mixture of benzene and carbon tetrachloride into water in a flume $10\frac{1}{2}$ in. wide and 10 in. deep. Data on eddy diffusion in gases have been obtained by injecting a tracer gas into the center of an air stream and obtaining the concentration of the gas mixture at various points across the pipe diameter some distance downstream from the injector. Eddy-diffusion data over short distances in air have been obtained by measuring the air temperature across the stream a short distance downstream from a heated wire. Representative data obtained by these methods will be described briefly.

FIG. 13.   Eddy diffusion in a stream of water.

Towle[462,463] reports data on the diffusion of carbon dioxide and of hydrogen in a turbulent air stream in two round pipes 6 and 12 in. in diameter. The gas was introduced at the axis at a point 70 diameters downstream from an egg-crate baffle at the inlet end, and concentration traverses obtained over the middle third of the pipe diameter at several distances downstream from the point of introduction. For these conditions of a continuous point source in a fluid moving at uniform velocity U, Wilson[514] has integrated the differential diffusion equation (assuming diffusivity constant) to obtain

$$c = \frac{Q}{4\pi E R'}\, e^{-(U/2E)(R'-x)} \tag{64}$$

where Q is the volumetric feed rate, c is the volumetric concentration of the diffusing gas, E is the eddy diffusivity, x is the axial distance downstream, and R' is the direct distance from the injector tube to the sampling point. This may be written as

$$\ln cR' - \ln \frac{Q}{4\pi E} = -\frac{U}{2E}(R'-x) \tag{65}$$

which suggests that $\ln cR'$ should be linear in $R'-x$, and that the data should fall on straight lines of cR' vs. $R'-x$ on semilogarithmic coordinate paper. Figure 14 shows typical data from concentration traverses, and Fig. 15 some of the same data plotted as suggested by Eq. (65). Values of E obtained from the slopes check reasonably well with the values calculated from the intercepts. Although the analysis of the results was complicated by the variation of E with x (possibly due in part to the effect of the presence of the injector tube on the turbulence), the diffusivity corresponding to large values of x was found to be a function of Re, as given by Fig. 16, and not to depend on the nature of the diffusing gas. The values of the eddy diffusivity as large as 140 ft.^{2}/hr. may be compared with values of D_v of 0.3 to 2.4 ft.^{2}/hr. in air at 1 atm.

Woertz[423] has measured eddy diffusion of water vapor in turbulent streams of air, carbon dioxide, and helium. The gas was forced upward through a large vertical rectangular duct 2.1 by 24 in. in cross section, with water evaporating continuously from a water film on one of the two large, flat walls and being absorbed by a film of strong calcium chloride solution on the opposite wall. Thus the water vapor crossed the 2-in. passage through which the gas passed. The test section was preceded by a similar wetted-wall section to ensure a

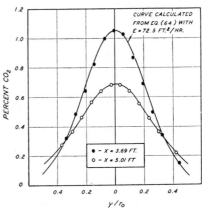

Fig. 14. Distribution of carbon dioxide across a turbulent air stream at two different distances downstream from the source.

steady state and minimize entrance effects. Hypodermic-needle pitot tube and sampling traverses were made to obtain the velocity pattern and the water-vapor concentration gradient, respectively. The latter values

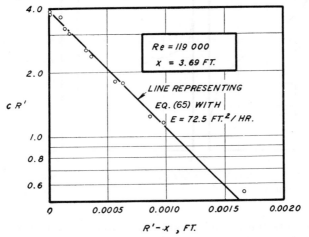

Fig. 15. Method of plotting data on eddy diffusion from a point source in an air stream.

were found to be linear over the main central portion of the duct, and values of E were obtained by dividing the measured rate of water-vapor transfer across the duct by the slope of the curve representing the concentration traverse. Hot-wire turbulence measurements were also made.

Figure 17 shows typical concentration traverses obtained in this way. In each graph the vertical axis at the left represents the wall where evaporation occurred, and the vertical axis at the right represents the wall where absorption in calcium chloride solution took place. The ordi-

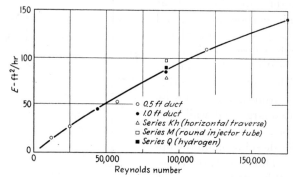

Fig. 16.   Relation between eddy diffusivity and Reynolds number in air.

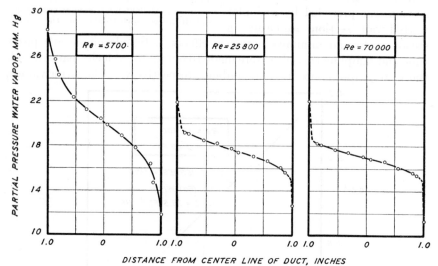

DISTANCE FROM CENTER LINE OF DUCT, INCHES

Fig. 17.   Concentration gradients for water-vapor transfer across a 2-in. turbulent air stream.

nate represents the partial pressure of water vapor in the gas stream, with the points at the extreme ends of each curve representing the vapor pressure of water at the water-film temperature, and the vapor pressure of water over the brine film, respectively. At low values of Re the curves were sigmoid in shape, but at intermediate and high values of Re the curves were nearly straight over the entire width where gas samples could be obtained. Values of E were calculated using the observed slopes of the central sections of these curves.

As observed by Towle, E was found to be roughly proportional to Re, but quite different relations were obtained when the main gas stream was air, carbon dioxide, or helium. Woertz found that the results could be correlated by plotting $E\rho$ vs. Re, as shown in Fig. 18, where ρ is the density of the gas. Furthermore, the solid line through the points is an excellent representation of Towle's data, as given in Fig. 16. Figure 18,

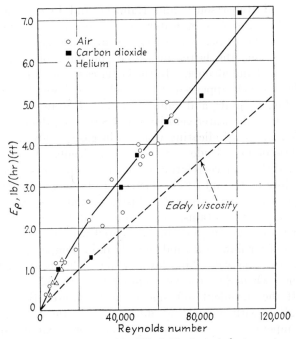

Fig. 18.   Correlation of eddy diffusivities in turbulent gas streams.

therefore, represents a correlation of E for eddy diffusion over a fairly wide range of conditions.

The velocity traverses obtained by Woertz indicated that in his experiments $U_m - U$ was very nearly proportional to the square of the distance from the center line of the duct. It has been pointed out that this condition corresponds to a constant value of the eddy viscosity, and the calculated values of ϵ were found to be related to Re by the dotted line shown on Fig. 18. Since $\epsilon = \rho L v'/2$ and since E was shown to be equal to $\frac{1}{2}v'L$, ϵ should be equal to E_e. It is evident from Fig. 18 that this is only approximately true, since ϵ is roughly $0.62E\rho$. Actually,

Woertz found that his results were well correlated by the relation

$$E = 0.08U_{\mathrm{av}}a_0 \sqrt{f} \qquad (66)$$

where a_0 represents one-half the width of the duct.

In general, both ϵ and E may be expected to vary across the diameter of the conduit, with ϵ varying as given by Eq. (52) and E changing approximately in proportion to ϵ. The simpler correlation obtained by Woertz was possible only by approximating the concentration traverses by straight lines and the velocity deficiency curves by parabolas.

Kalinske and Robertson[236] and Kalinske and Pien[235] have reported studies of eddy diffusion in water flowing in an open channel. The former studied the dispersion of discrete drops of carbon tetrachloride and benzene, while the latter measured the diffusion of a mixture of hydrochloric acid and alcohol. In the latter case concentration traverses were obtained which appeared very much like those shown in Fig. 14 for carbon dioxide in air, and values of $\overline{y^2}$ and E were obtained. In one experiment where the water velocity was 1.8 ft./sec., the calculated value of E was 5.3 ft.²/hr., indicating that, as in gases, eddy diffusivities are several orders of magnitude greater than molecular diffusivities. The data indicated that the correlation R_θ persisted up to distances of several inches. Values of $E\rho$ and ϵ were reported to be in good agreement.

The experiments of Schubauer[405] illustrate what happens in the region where correlation still obtains, *i.e.*, where the diffusion distance is small compared with the mixing length. A heated wire was placed normal to the direction of air flow in a wind tunnel, and a temperature exploration was made across the wake 2 in. downstream. Curves similar to Fig. 14 were obtained when the observed temperature was plotted vs. the distance y. If the turbulent diffusion of heat followed the ordinary diffusion equation with a constant diffusivity E, then the ratio of the observed temperature rise Δt at y to the axial or maximum temperature rise Δt_{max} should be given by

$$\ln \frac{\Delta t}{\Delta t_{\mathrm{max}}} = -\frac{y^2 U}{4Ex} \qquad (67)$$

and E (assumed to be independent of x) may be replaced by Eq. (61) to give

$$\ln \frac{\Delta t}{\Delta t_{\mathrm{max}}} = -\frac{y^2}{2\overline{y^2}} \qquad (68)$$

Note that E has the dimensions of thermal conductivity divided by specific heat and density.

Schubauer reported values of the angle α (in degrees) corresponding to the spread of the wake at which Δt was one-half of Δt_{max}. Since these angles were small, the tangent y/x was taken as equal to the angle, whence Eq. (58) may be combined with Eq. (68) to give

$$\alpha = 134.7 \frac{\sqrt{\overline{y^2}}}{x} = 134.7 \frac{v'}{U} \tag{69}$$

This relation suggests that the experimental method developed by Schubauer may be employed as a relatively simple method of measuring the intensity of turbulence. Schubauer showed that α was independent of air velocity from 8 to 54 ft./sec., and that a good correlation existed between α and the per cent turbulence $(100v'/U)$ measured simultaneously by the hot-wire technique mentioned previously.

Combining Eqs. (61), (62), and (69),

$$E = \frac{U\alpha^2 x}{36,400} = 0.5Ux \left(\frac{v'}{U}\right)^2 \tag{70}$$

Schubauer found the empirical constant in front of the last term to be 0.63 when v' is replaced by the value of u' obtained by the hot-wire turbulence measurement.

These results of Schubauer's emphasize the point that for short distances the material transfer in a turbulent stream does not take place by diffusion in the ordinary sense; *i.e.*, the rate of diffusion is not proportional to the concentration gradient. This shows up in the fact that E is proportional to x and so to the time, and that the mean displacement $\overline{y^2}$ is proportional to the square rather than the first power of x [Eq. (58)]. For long times or distances, Eq. (63) applies, and E depends only on the conditions of turbulence. For very short distances, E depends only on the intensity of turbulence; for long distances, E depends on both the intensity and the scale of turbulence.

In order to obtain a general relation which applies in both regions, it is necessary to know something about the variation of R_θ with time or distance. If it is assumed that R_θ decays exponentially with x, as given by

$$R_\theta = e^{-x/x_0} \tag{71}$$

then Eq. (56) may be integrated to give

$$\overline{y^2} = 2\left(\frac{v'}{U}\right)^2 x_0[x - x_0(1 - e^{-x/x_0})] \tag{72}$$

and by Eq. (61)

$$E = \left(\frac{v'}{U}\right)^2 Ux_0(1 - e^{-x/x_0}) \tag{73}$$

where $x_0 = L_\theta U/v'$. For large values of x Eq. (73) reduces to Eq. (63), while for small values of x it reduces to Eq. (62).   Van Driest[469] has shown that Eq. (73) (in an equivalent form, in which $\overline{y^2}/L_\theta^2$ is expressed as a function of x/x_0) can be employed to represent his data on eddy diffusion in water in an open channel.   Lacking values of L_θ, it was necessary to employ empirical values of x_0 (of the order of 7 in.), but these values were independent of x.

DIFFUSION IN THE ATMOSPHERE

The motion of the air over the surface of the earth is turbulent, and diffusion takes place at high speeds.   The scale of the turbulence is very great, with mixing lengths as large as several hundred feet.   Diffusion in the upper atmosphere has received some attention,[447,492] and the subject of diffusion at and near ground level became the object of serious study during the Second World War.

Large-scale field tests were carried out by several of the belligerents for the purpose of determining the rate of spread of gas and smoke clouds, and equations were developed from which it was possible to predict with reasonable accuracy the concentration of gas as a function of the source strength, the wind velocity, the distance downwind.   One of the main variables defining the turbulence was found to be the ratio of the mean wind speed at two points 3 and 6 ft. above the ground. During a lapse this ratio is generally greater than about 1.15, and the turbulence is relatively intense.   When an inversion occurs, the ratio of the two speeds is less than 1.15 and gas or smoke will spread slowly. The large amount of information obtained during the war has not yet been released for publication but will doubtless be made generally available.   A paper[79] covering wartime studies of dissipation of gas from tall chimneys has recently appeared.   The important studies of Sutton and the British group at Porton have been summarized in two recent papers by Sutton.   One[448] relates to the dispersion of gas clouds near the ground; the other[449] indicates the applicability of the new data to dispersion from tall stacks.   The application of Sutton's results to the dispersion of screening smoke clouds has been described by one of the authors.[413]

Nomenclature for Chapter II

a_0 = one-half width of rectangular duct, ft.
c = concentration, lb. moles/ft.^{3}
C = drag coefficient, dimensionless
C_D = total drag coefficient based on unit projected area, (force lb.)/(ft.^{2})$(\rho U^2/2)$
D = pipe diameter, ft.
E = eddy diffusivity, ft.^{2}/hr.
f = friction factor, dimensionless
g_c = 4.17×10^7 = conversion factor, (lb. mass)(ft.)/(lb. force)(hr.^{2})
L = Prandtl mixing length, ft.

L_θ = turbulence scale factor defined by Eq. (59), ft.

N_A = diffusion rate, lb. moles/(hr.)(ft.^{2})

P = total pressure, lb/ft.^{2}

Q = volumetric rate of flow, ft.^{3}/hr.

r = distance from axis to point in a round pipe, ft.

r_0 = radius of round pipe, ft.

R = coefficient of correlation

Re = Reynolds number, $DU_{av}\rho/\mu$

R' = direct distance from injector tube to sampling point = $\sqrt{x^2 + y^2}$, ft.

R_θ = correlation between the velocity of a particle at one instant and the velocity of the same particle at time θ later

S = cross-sectional area, ft.^{2}

u' = root-mean-square value of $u = \sqrt{\overline{u^2}}$, ft./hr.

u^+ = friction velocity = $(U/U_{av})\sqrt{2/f}$

u, v, w = components of fluctuating velocity in directions x, y, z, ft./hr.

U = time-average velocity at a point, ft./hr.

U_{av} = average velocity, volumetric flow rate divided by cross section of conduit, ft./hr.

U_m = maximum velocity, ft./hr.

U_w = velocity near the wall of a conduit, ft./hr.

v' = root-mean-square value of v; = $\sqrt{\overline{v^2}}$, ft./hr.

x = distance in direction of flow, ft.

x_0 = constant in Eq. (71) = $L_\theta U/v'$, ft.

y = distance from axis, normal to direction of flow, ft.

$y^+ = \dfrac{(r_0 - r)U_{av}\rho}{\mu}\sqrt{\dfrac{f}{2}} = \dfrac{y}{r_0}\,\mathrm{Re}\,\sqrt{\dfrac{f}{8}}$

Δt = temperature rise, °F.

Δt_{max} = temperature rise at axis, °F.

ϵ = eddy viscosity, lb./(hr.)(ft.)

α = angle of spread of wake, to point where $\Delta t/\Delta t_{max} = \frac{1}{2}$, deg.

θ = time, hr.

ρ = fluid density, lb./ft.^{3}

μ = viscosity, lb./(hr.)(ft.)

τ = shear stress, force lb./ft.^{2}

τ_0 = shear stress at pipe wall, force lb./ft.^{2}

Problems

1. The data on page 50 were obtained by B. B. Woertz on water-vapor concentrations in a turbulent stream of CO_2 flowing at a Reynolds number of 102,000 in a duct 2.0 in. wide. Water vapor was transferred at a constant rate from one vertical wall covered with water to the opposite wall covered by a film of strong $CaCl_2$ solution. The temperature of the experiment was 73°F. The rate of transfer of water vapor was 0.943 lb./hr. for a total cross section of 13.6 ft.^{2}.

a. Prepare a graph of partial pressure vs. position in the duct, and calculate the value of the eddy diffusivity for the main central portion, in which the gradient is essentially a straight line. Express the result as square feet per hour.

b. What fraction of the total resistance to water-vapor transfer is offered by the gas film at the water side, the main turbulent layer, and the gas film at the solution side?

Position, In. from Water Wall	Partial Pressure, H_2O, Atm.
0 (water wall)	0.0278
0.106	0.0226
0.169	0.0224
0.425	0.0216
0.677	0.0212
0.935	0.0207
1.06	0.0204
1.31	0.0199
1.82	0.0187
1.88	0.0183
2.00 (brine wall)	0.0125

2. *a.* At the same Reynolds number as in Prob. 1, what would be the distribution of resistances for water transfer in air instead of CO_2? Assume E to be inversely proportional to main-gas-stream density. Assume the resistance to transfer across the gas films to be inversely proportional to the molecular diffusivity, which is 1.60 times as great for water vapor in air as for water vapor in CO_2.

b. What would be the rate of transfer of water vapor as pounds per hour with the vapor pressures at the water film and at the brine film given in Prob. 1?

CHAPTER III

TRANSFER OF MATERIAL BETWEEN PHASES

The earlier chapters have discussed the transfer of material within a single phase by the processes of molecular and eddy diffusion. The important practical problems, however, have to do with the transfer of material from one phase to another. The air drying of solids, the recovery of valuable or nuisance gases by absorption, extraction of material dissolved in one solvent by use of a second solvent immiscible with the first, humidification of air in air conditioning, and the cooling of water in evaporative water coolers, are but a few of the important industrial operations involving transfer of material between two phases. The present chapter will be concerned with the mechanism of mass transfer near phase boundaries under steady-state conditions. The theory and methods of computation developed for handling transfer under steady-state conditions are applicable to differential interfacial areas in an apparatus such as a countercurrent gas absorber. The fifth chapter will develop the methods of applying these concepts to the various practical cases where conditions vary throughout the equipment.

The general problem has to do with transfer of material to or from a fluid flowing in turbulent motion, though diffusion across a stream in laminar flow is sometimes of importance and will be treated briefly. As was pointed out in Chap. II, the local velocity in a turbulent stream is a maximum at the center of the conduit and approaches zero at the conduit wall, or phase boundary. In the typical case of water in turbulent flow in a round pipe, the turbulence across the greater part of the diameter of the pipe is such that dissolved solute diffuses in a radial direction primarily by the process of eddy diffusion, since the relative rate of transfer by molecular diffusion is negligible. In this region the rate of transfer of solute is proportional to the eddy diffusivity E and to the solute concentration gradient dc/dr. In the region very near the pipe wall the turbulence approaches zero, and the rate of transfer by eddy diffusion may be considered negligible as compared with the rate of transfer of solute by molecular diffusion. As seen in Chap. I, the latter is proportional to the molecular diffusivity D_v and to the solute concentration gradient dc/dr. Transfer to the pipe wall from the main body of the fluid stream is partly by eddy diffusion and partly by molecular diffusion, but since both are proportional to the gradient dc/dr, it may be expected that the combined process is also proportional to dc/dr.

Assume that a pipe has an inner coating of a fused salt slightly soluble in water, in which case transfer will be radially from the wall into the turbulent water stream. Since the actual nature of the concentration gradients at various radii is not known, it is convenient to consider an over-all concentration difference or driving force $c_i - c$ as the potential causing transfer of salt. For this purpose c_i is taken to be the concentration of salt in water corresponding to equilibrium with the wall, *i.e.*, the concentration of a saturated solution of salt. Different molecules of salt travel different distances into the stream, and the salt concentration varies across the diameter; for convenience in engineering work c is taken as the average salt concentration in the water stream. Since the relative importance of eddy diffusion and molecular diffusion in the over-all process is not known, the unknown diffusivity and the average length of the diffusion path are lumped together in the form of a coefficient k_L, defined by the equation

$$N_A = k_L(c_i - c) \qquad (74)$$

Although of limited theoretical significance, this concept of a mass-transfer coefficient has proved to have great utility in engineering work.

Molecular diffusion in gases was shown in Chap. I to be proportional to the gradient of the partial pressure of the diffusing gas, and inversely proportional to the pressure of the inert, or nondiffusing, gas:

$$N_A = -\frac{D_v P}{R T p_B}\frac{dp_A}{dr} \qquad (75)$$

Since the concentration is proportional to the partial pressure and since eddy diffusion in a gas stream is also proportional to the partial-pressure gradient, the mixed process of eddy and molecular diffusion involved in mass transfer from a solid or a liquid to a turbulent gas stream may be expected also to be proportional to dp_A/dr. Following the same reasoning as for diffusion into a liquid stream, it is convenient to define a transfer coefficient k_G by the relation

$$N_A = k_G(p_i - p) \qquad (76)$$

where p_i is the partial pressure of diffusing gas in equilibrium with the conduit wall or phase boundary, and p is the average partial pressure of diffusing gas in the main gas stream.

Molecules disengaging from solid surfaces must overcome forces of attraction representing a considerable resistance to their movement.[260] This is evidenced by the fact that solids sublime at a finite rate even in an absolute vacuum. The important concentration or partial pressure at the pipe wall, therefore, is not that in the solid phase, but that in the fluid phase corresponding to equilibrium with the wall. Use of this value allows for the resistance to dislocation of molecules from the wall, since the equilibrium partial pressure or concentration is high or low depending on whether it is easy or difficult for the diffusing molecules to separate themselves from the phase represented by the wall.[261]

Equations (74) and (76) state simply that the rate of transfer into or out of a moving stream is proportional to a potential expressed in terms of concentrations in a liquid, or partial pressures in a gas. They have proved to be useful working rules, simplifying the collection and correlation of the empirical coefficients k_L and k_G very much as the concept of heat-transfer coefficients has aided the field of heat transfer.

Since eddy diffusivities in turbulent streams are usually very much greater than molecular diffusivities, the principal resistance to the overall transfer process lies in the region near the wall of the conduit, or other phase boundary. This fact led to the early "film concept," which pictured a stagnant fluid film at the wall representing the entire resistance to diffusion. It was assumed that solute passed through this film only by molecular diffusion. The film concept has had great educational value in supplying a simple picture of a complicated process. Actually, most of the resistance is in a region near the wall, but the resistance to transfer by eddy diffusion is not an insignificant fraction of the whole. The film concept has proved frequently misleading in suggesting that since the resistance was confined to a thin layer through which material passed by molecular diffusion, the over-all rate should be proportional to the molecular diffusivity.

If the simple film concept were correct, the rate of transfer of material into a fluid stream would be given by Eq. (11) for steady-state molecular diffusion:

$$N_A = \frac{D_L P}{RT z p_{BM}} (p_i - p) \tag{77}$$

or

$$N_A = \frac{D_L}{z} (c_i - c) \tag{78}$$

depending on whether the fluid is gas or liquid. Here z represents the thickness of the "film." Comparison of these relations with Eqs. (74) and (76) shows that

$$k_L = \frac{D_L}{z} \tag{79}$$

and

$$k_G = \frac{D_v P}{RT z p_{BM}} \tag{80}$$

It is evident that the results of experimental studies may be expressed in terms of the coefficients k_L and k_G, or, alternatively, in terms of the "film thicknesses" z. The latter is a fictitious length representing the thickness of a stationary fluid layer offering the same resistance to molecular diffusion as is encountered in the combined process of eddy and molecular diffusion in the turbulent stream.

It may be noted that the foregoing discussion applies to the physical diffusion of a solute through a fluid without the complicating effects of chemical reaction between solute and fluid or of simultaneous heat transfer and diffusion. These latter will be discussed in later sections.

TWO-FILM CONCEPT—OVER-ALL COEFFICIENTS

In the case of the solution of salt from the wall of a tube referred to above, or in the adiabatic evaporation of water into a stream of air, there is only one "film" and but one coefficient involved in each case. In the absorption of a gas by a liquid or in the extraction of a solute from a liquid by a second liquid immiscible with the first, the solute must diffuse out of one fluid and into a second fluid phase. In such cases the two fluids are in motion relative to the interface between them, and two films are visualized through which the solute must diffuse in series. This "two-film concept" was first suggested by W. G. Whitman[502] in 1923 and has proved to be a great aid in understanding the process of diffusion between two fluids.

There appears to be no evidence of an appreciable diffusional resistance at the actual interface, and it is assumed that the two phases are in equilibrium at all points on the surface of contact. In the case of transfer between a gas and a liquid the concentration c_i and the partial pressure p_i at the interface are related by the equilibrium conditions. In other words, p_i is the partial pressure of the solute over a solution of concentration c_i. In the case of liquid-liquid extraction, the values of c_i will be different in each phase, but the two will correspond to the concentration of two liquid phases in equilibrium.

Restricting the discussion to steady-state transfer of a solute from a gas stream to a liquid stream, as in gas absorption, it is evident that all solute diffusing from gas to interface must diffuse at the same rate from the interface to the main body of the liquid, whence

$$N_A = k_G(p - p_i) = k_L(c_i - c) \tag{81}$$

This equation has little practical utility, since it is necessary to know both k_G and k_L as well as the equilibrium relation between p_i and c_i in order to calculate N_A. It is convenient, therefore, to employ "over-all coefficients" K_L and K_G, which may be used to calculate N_A without knowledge of c_i or p_i. These are defined by the equations

$$N_A = K_G(p - p_e) = K_L(c_e - c) \tag{82}$$

where p_e is the partial pressure of solute over a solution having the composition of the main liquid stream c, and c_e is the concentration of a solution in equilibrium with the solute partial pressure p. Thus $p - p_e$ is the over-all driving force expressed in partial pressure units, and $c_e - c$ is the over-all driving force expressed in liquid concentration units. In the units here employed, N_A is the rate of interphase transfer as lb. moles/(hr.)(ft.²), p, p_e, and p_i are in atmospheres, and c_e, c_i, and c are concentrations expressed as lb. moles/ft.³.

The over-all coefficients K_G and K_L have great utility, and most experimental studies of mass transfer between phases give information as to K_G or K_L, but not k_G or k_L. The latter are difficult to obtain experimentally, and most of the data on absorption and extraction for various systems pertain to over-all coefficients.

The significance and relative magnitudes of the driving forces in gas and liquid phases are best visualized with the aid of a graph relating partial pressure and liquid composition. Figure 19 shows the typical curved line representing the gas-solubility, or partial-pressure–liquid-concentration, equilibrium. Point A represents the conditions at any differential surface across which diffusion from gas to liquid phase is taking place.

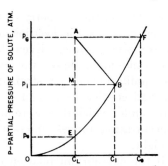

Fig. 19. Illustration of partial-pressure and concentration driving forces for gas absorption.

The ordinate p is the average partial pressure of the diffusing gas in the main gas stream, and the abscissa c is the average concentration of solute in the liquid stream. The equilibrium curve indicates the liquid concentration c_e corresponding to the partial pressure p, and the pressure p_e corresponding to the concentration c. Referring to Eq. (82) and Fig. 19, the driving force in terms of pressures, $p - p_e$, is represented by the vertical distance AE, and the driving force in terms of concentrations, $c_e - c$, is represented by the horizontal distance FA.

The conditions at the gas-liquid interface are represented by some point B on the equilibrium curve. Referring to Eq. (81), the driving force $p - p_i$ is represented by the vertical distance AM, and the driving force $c_i - c$ by the horizontal distance BM. It follows from Eq. (81) that

$$\frac{p - p_i}{c_i - c} = \frac{k_L}{k_G} \tag{83}$$

from which it is evident that AB has a negative slope k_L/k_G, and that point B may be located as the intersection of the equilibrium curve and of a straight line through A having a slope $-k_L/k_G$. If values of k_L and k_G are known, therefore, the driving forces corresponding to any gas-liquid compositions may be obtained graphically in this way. Alternatively, over-all coefficients and over-all driving forces may be employed.

The coefficients k_L and k_G are expected to depend on the nature of solute and solvent and on the turbulence conditions but should not vary with the concentration of solute in gas or liquid phases. From (76) and (82),

$$\frac{K_G}{k_G} = \frac{p - p_i}{p - p_e} = \frac{\text{distance } AM}{\text{distance } AE}$$

Inspection of the geometry of Fig. 19 will show this ratio to be constant (independent of the location of point A) only if the equilibrium curve OF is a straight line. Even though k_G is independent of concentrations in gas and liquid phases, the over-all coefficient K_G will vary with c unless the equilibrium curve is straight. Similar reasoning applies to k_L and K_L. Over-all coefficients should be employed only for conditions similar to those under which they were measured and cannot be employed for other concentration ranges unless the equilibrium curve for the system is straight.

If the equilibrium relation can be represented by Henry's law, then the equilibrium curve is a straight line representing the proportionality

$$p_e = Hc \tag{84}$$

where H is the Henry's law constant for the system. It is evident from the geometry of Fig. 19 that, for this case, $(p - p_i)/(p - p_e)$ and hence K_G/k_G are constant as the location of A varies. Similarly, K_L/k_L and K_L/K_G are constant ratios if k_L and k_G are constant.

The following relations between individual and film coefficients are obtained by eliminating c_i and p_i from Eqs. (81), (82), and (84):

$$\frac{1}{K_G} = \frac{1}{k_G} + \frac{H}{k_L} \tag{85}$$

and

$$\frac{1}{K_L} = \frac{1}{k_L} + \frac{1}{Hk_G} \tag{86}$$

The reciprocal of the over-all coefficient may be looked upon as the over-all resistance to mass transfer by diffusion from gas to liquid phase. It is the sum of the individual film resistances, represented by the terms on the right-hand side of the above equations. In terms of pressures, $1/K_G$ represents the over-all or total resistance, $1/k_G$ the gas-film resistance, and H/k_L the liquid-film resistance. In terms of liquid concentrations, $1/K_L$ is the over-all resistance, $1/k_L$ the liquid-film resistance, and $1/Hk_G$ the gas-film resistance. The numerical values of the resistance will depend on the units in which the driving force is expressed.

It is evident from Eqs. (85) and (86) that the liquid-film resistance may be negligible in comparison with the gas-film resistance if H is sufficiently small. The coefficient H is a measure of the solubility of the solute gas in the liquid, and it follows that the gas-film resistance becomes controlling in the case of a very soluble gas. The converse is also true: for a relatively insoluble gas the liquid-film resistance is large in comparison with the gas-film resistance, and the liquid film is said to be controlling. It is customary to report experimental data in terms of K_L in the case of relatively insoluble gases, where the liquid film is believed to be controlling, and vice versa. If Henry's law holds, however, the data may be expressed equally well in terms of K_L or K_G, since the two coefficients bear a constant relation one to the other. In the contacting of one liquid with a second liquid immiscible with the first, as in solvent extraction, the same general principles apply, with H replaced by the distribution coefficients, and p replaced by the solute concentration in the second liquid phase.

The two-film theory and the addition of film resistances was proposed by Lewis and Whitman[281] more than 20 years ago. The experimental difficulty of measuring the individual film coefficients is such that they are not known for very many systems, and the validity of the concept of additivity of resistance has not been adequately tested. In some instances this appears to have proved successful; in other cases discrepancies have appeared which may possibly be due to a fault in the basic concept or in its interpretation. Until further data on the point become available, the validity of the theory must be accepted, and Eqs. (85) and (86) will be employed in estimating over-all coefficients from film coefficients.

Illustration 7. In an experimental study of the absorption of SO_2 by water in a wetted-wall column the value of K_G is found to be 0.0714 lb. mole/(hr.) (ft.^{2})(atm.). The barometer is normal, and the temperature is 68°F.

Estimate the value of K_G for the absorption of NH_3 by water at 50°F. in the same equipment at the same gas and water mass velocities.

Assume the resistances of gas and liquid films to be equal for SO_2 absorption. In both cases the physical properties of the gas may be taken as the same as for air. As will appear from Eq. (110) in the latter portion of this chapter, k_G is proportional to $D_v^{0.56}$.

Solution. From Eq. (85)

$$\frac{1}{K_G} = \frac{1}{0.0714} = 14.0 = \frac{1}{k_G} + \frac{H}{k_L}$$

Since the resistances of the two films are equal, $1/k_G = H/k_L$, whence

$$k_G = k_L/H = 2K_G = (2)(0.0714) = 0.143$$

At 68°, D_v for SO_2 is $(0.40)(^{528}\!/_{492})^{3\!/_2} = 0.44$, and at 50°, D_v for NH_3 is

$$(0.84)(^{510}\!/_{492})^{3\!/_2} = 0.89$$

(for values of D_v at 32°, see Table III). For NH_3, therefore,

$$k_G = 0.143 \left(\frac{0.89}{0.44}\right)^{0.56} = 0.212$$

Since data are not available on D_L for NH_3 and SO_2 in liquid water, it will be assumed that k_L is the same in each system. The values of H for NH_3 and SO_2 at 68° are approximately in the ratio 1:0.018. For NH_3, therefore

$$\frac{1}{K_G} = \frac{1}{0.212} + \frac{0.018}{0.143} = 4.85$$

whence

$$K_G = 0.206 \text{ lb. mole}/(\text{hr.})(\text{ft.}^2)(\text{atm.})$$

Note: The conditions described were those of tests reported by Haslam, Hershey, and Kean,[173] who obtained experimental values for K_G of 0.0714 for SO_2 and 0.205 for NH_3. Neither NH_3 or SO_2 solutions follow Henry's law closely, and Eq. (85) is consequently not rigorous.

THEORY OF MASS TRANSFER TO A FLUID IN TURBULENT MOTION

The kinetic theory of gases provides a statistical picture of the behavior of the gas molecules, on the basis of which many properties of gases have been predicted with considerable accuracy. As shown in Chap. I, for example, the theoretical equations for D_v agree within 25 to 50 per cent with the experimental values. Similar knowledge of the motion of molecules or eddies in a turbulent fluid is not available, and it has not been possible to develop wholly theoretical relations from which values of k_G and k_L may be calculated. Many attempts have been made to do this, and recent advances in our understanding of turbulence have made it possible to develop theoretical relations which fit the mass-transfer data remarkably well.[415] Although these theories are incomplete and will doubtless be developed further, it will be of interest to review them briefly, since they shed considerable light on the mechanism of the mass-transfer process.

From the discussion of turbulence in Chap. II it should be evident that both eddy diffusion and heat transmission in a turbulent stream depend on velocity gradients, and that friction (momentum transfer), mass transfer, and heat transfer must be intimately related. Certainly the theoretical developments in the three fields are closely analogous. Most of the theoretical and experimental work has been on the study of turbulence and the connection between wall friction and the properties of the turbulent stream. A number of authors have employed this background to derive theoretical expressions for heat transfer, and in a few cases the corresponding theoretical equations for mass transfer have been developed. With further advances in the theory of turbulence it may be expected that the separate fields of friction, heat transfer, and mass transfer in turbulent flow may gradually merge to become a single branch of science.

The earliest theoretical equation for heat transfer was the Reynolds "analogy"[388] relating heat transfer and friction. Assuming that the heat lost due to friction, divided by the momentum of the stream, is equal to the ratio of the actual heat transferred in a pipe section to the heat which would be transferred were the fluid to come to thermal equilibrium with the pipe wall, the following relation is obtained:

$$h = \frac{fC_p\rho U_{av}}{2} \qquad (87)$$

In the first edition of this book, the corresponding equation for mass transfer was derived

$$k_c = \frac{fU_{av}}{2} \qquad (88)$$

For gases, in which $c = p/RT$, this becomes

$$k_G = \frac{k_c}{RT} = \frac{fU_{av}}{2RT} = \frac{f\rho U_{av}}{2PM_M} \qquad (89)$$

where k_c = mass-transfer coefficient, lb. moles/(hr.)(ft.^{2})(lb. mole/ft.^{3})
  k_G = mass-transfer coefficient, lb. moles/(hr.)(ft.^{2})(atm.)
  f = friction factor in Eq. (34)
  C_p = specific heat at constant pressure, B.t.u./(lb. fluid)(°F.)
  U_{av} = average stream velocity, ft./hr.
  ρ = fluid density, lb./ft.^{3}
  R = gas constant, (ft.^{3})(atm.)/(lb. mole)(°R.) = 0.728
  T = temperature, °R.
  P = total pressure, atm.
  M_M = average molecular weight of fluid stream

Equations (87) and (89) have been found to check the data on heat transfer and mass transfer within about 35 per cent for gases inside pipes, where $C_p\mu/k$ and $\mu/\rho D_v$ are fairly close to unity, but to show poor agreement with the data in all other cases. Here μ is the viscosity of the fluid, and k is its thermal conductivity.

Von Kármán[482] suggests an alternative derivation of (88) based on the relation between the eddy diffusivity E and the eddy viscosity ϵ. If

Eq. (48) is modified to allow for the contribution of molecular diffusion, it becomes

$$N_A = -(D_v + E)\frac{dc}{dy} \tag{90}$$

which may be compared with Eq. (51):

$$\tau = -\frac{\mu + \epsilon}{g_c}\frac{dU}{dy} \tag{91}$$

If the variation of N_A and the shear stress τ across the stream are taken to be similar to the extent that τ/N_A is constant, and if μ and D_v are assumed negligible in comparison with ϵ and E, then (90) and (91) may be integrated to give

$$k_c = \frac{N_A}{c - c_i} = \frac{\alpha\tau_0 g_c}{U_{av}\rho} = \frac{\alpha f U_{av}}{2} \tag{92}$$

where $\alpha = E\rho/\epsilon$. As shown in Chap. II, α is between 1.0 and 2.0 in the turbulent core of the stream.

If E and ϵ are assumed negligible in comparison with D_v and μ, the result is

$$k_c = \frac{\rho D_v}{\mu}\frac{f U_{av}}{2} \tag{93}$$

indicating the possible importance of the Schmidt group $\mu/\rho D_v$.

It is evident from this derivation that the Reynolds analogy (89) is based on the similarity of momentum and mass transfer in the turbulent core of the fluid stream and does not allow properly for the gradual change in the relative importance of D_v and E in going from the wall to the center of the stream.

The first important modification of the Reynolds analogy was made by Prandtl[379] and by Taylor,[452] who considered heat transfer to take place through two resistances in series: a laminar layer at the tube wall and a turbulent layer to which the Reynolds analogy applied. The corresponding analogy for mass transfer has been derived by Colburn,[84] who obtained the equation for gases:

$$k_c = k_G RT = \frac{\frac{1}{2}f U_{av}(P/p_{BM})}{1 - a_1 + a_1(\mu/\rho D_v)} \tag{94}$$

This is similar to the Prandtl-Taylor equation for the heat-transfer coefficient, with the Schmidt group $\mu/\rho D_v$ replacing the Prandtl group $c\mu/k$. Here a_1 represents the ratio of the fluid velocity at the boundary of the laminar film to the average velocity of the stream. If this "boundary" is taken as the intersection of the two solid curves of Fig. 11, *i.e.*, at $y^+ = 11.6$, then a_1 is given by the simple relation

$$a_1 = 8.2\sqrt{f} \tag{95}$$

Equation (94) compares well with experimental data on k_G for the evaporation of water but gives poor results for the evaporation of organic liquids. The corresponding equation for heat transfer gives poor results for oils and other fluids for which the Prandtl group is large. Chilton and Colburn[75] found that the correlation of the data on heat transfer could be improved greatly by substituting the empirical function $(C_p\mu/k)^{2/3}$ for the denominator of the Prandtl-Taylor form, and suggested that by analogy it should be possible to represent mass-transfer data by a form of Eq. (94), in which the denominator is replaced by the empirical function $(\mu/\rho D_v)^{2/3}$. Using these new equations, they defined two new functions j_H and j_D:

$$j_H = \frac{h}{C_p\rho U_{av}}\left(\frac{C_p\mu}{k}\right)^{2/3} = \frac{1}{2}f \tag{96}$$

$$j_D = \frac{k_c p_{BM}}{U_{av}P}\left(\frac{\mu}{\rho D_v}\right)^{2/3} = \frac{k_G p_{BM}}{G_M}\left(\frac{\mu}{\rho D_v}\right)^{2/3} = \frac{1}{2}f \tag{97}$$

The first equality defines j_H and j_D. These are found experimentally to approximate $\frac{1}{2}f$ for certain simple streamline shapes, but to be much smaller than $\frac{1}{2}f$ for flow past bluff objects, including spheres and cylinders. The deviation of j_H from $\frac{1}{2}f$ tends to parallel that of j_D, so that heat transfer and mass transfer are related in a useful way by equating j_H and j_D. This holds true in some cases where neither j_H nor j_D agrees with $\frac{1}{2}f$. The explanation appears to be that friction factors are commonly calculated from measurements of total drag, including both skin friction and the normal pressure drag, whereas the analogy holds only when skin friction alone is considered. Data on this point will be presented in a later section.

Illustration 8. It is desired to estimate the value of k_G for the absorption of NH_3 by the wet surface of a streamlined shape placed in a turbulent air stream flowing 15 ft./sec. The rod has an airfoil cross section, and no data on mass transfer to such a section exist. However, heat-transfer tests with the proposed setup at an air velocity of 15 ft./sec. indicate the heat-transfer coefficient h to be 9.2 B.t.u./(hr.) (°F.)(ft.²).

Solution. Assume $j_D = j_H$, whence, from Eqs. (96) and (97),

$$k_G = h\frac{G_M}{C_p\rho U_{av}p_{BM}}\left(\frac{C_p\mu}{k}\right)^{2/3}\left(\frac{\mu}{\rho D_v}\right)^{-2/3}$$

For air $C_p\mu/k$ is 0.74 and from Table III (page 20) $\mu/\rho D_v$ for NH_3-air is 0.61. For dilute NH_3-air mixtures, p_{BM} may be taken as 1.0 atm., and M_M as 29, whence

$$G_M/U_{av}\rho = \frac{1}{29}.$$

$$k_G = \frac{h}{C_p M_M p_{BM}}\left(\frac{C_p}{k}\right)^{2/3}\left(\frac{\mu}{\rho D_v}\right)^{-2/3} = \frac{9.2}{(0.24)(29)}\left(\frac{0.74}{0.61}\right)^{2/3}$$

$$= 1.50 \text{ lb. moles/(hr.)(ft.²)(atm.)}$$

In 1932 Murphree[337] attempted to allow for the gradual transition from laminar flow at the pipe wall to turbulent flow in the core by assuming the eddy viscosity ϵ in the region near the wall to be proportional to the cube of the distance from the wall. The resulting equation agreed well with the data existing at that time for heat transfer to air and to water and approximated the data on heating oils (high values of $C_p\mu/k$). As suggested by Murphree, a similar equation for mass transfer has been developed.[415] Later data on velocity gradients in the boundary have made obsolete his assumption regarding the variation of ϵ, but his contribution was an important step in the development of the theory.

With the development of generalized relations for the velocity gradient across the turbulent stream and in the region near the wall, based primarily on the experimental data of Nikuradse[342] for water, further developments of the theory have been made possible. Theoretical equations for heat transfer have been developed by von Kármán,[482] by Boelter, Martinelli, and Johassen,[40] by Hoffman,[197] by Mattioli,[301] Reichardt,[386] and Martinelli.[299]

The application of the von Kármán theory to mass transfer has been outlined in detail by one of the present authors.[415] It is assumed that the eddy diffusivity E is equal to $\alpha\epsilon/\rho$, where α is the proportionality constant, indicated by Woertz's data in Chap. II to be 1.6. Values of the eddy viscosity ϵ are obtained from the generalized velocity-distribution data of Nikuradse given in Fig. 11. The relation between u^+ and y^+ is represented by a curve having three branches; these are represented by three separate equations. In this way the variation of ϵ and E through the laminar, buffer, and turbulent layers is calculated. The Reynolds analogy is applied in the turbulent core, with a constant value of E. The result is

$$k_c = k_G RT = \frac{(f/2)\alpha U_{\mathrm{av}}}{1 + 5\sqrt{f/2}\,\{\psi - 1 + \ln\left[(1 + 5\psi)/6\right]\}} \qquad (98)$$

where ψ represents the modified dimensionless Schmidt group $\alpha\mu/\rho D_v$. The constants 5 and 6 originate in the empirical equations used to represent the relation between u^+ and y^+ given by Fig. 11. Although several assumptions are made in the course of its derivation, including the application of the Reynolds analogy to the core and the assumption that μ and $\rho D_v/\alpha\mu$ are small compared with ϵ, the resulting Eq. (98) is in remarkable agreement with experimental data on vaporization of liquids in wetted-wall towers. This comparison will be presented in a later section.

Several of the theoretical equations have the common form

$$k_c = k_G RT = \frac{fU_{\mathrm{av}}}{2\phi_D} \qquad (99)$$

where ϕ_D is the variable denominator, 1.0 in Eq. (88), $\mu/\rho D_v$ in Eq. (93), $1 - a_1 + a_1(\mu/\rho D_v)$ in Eq. (94), $(\mu/\rho D_v)^{2/3}$ in Eq. (97), and $1 + 5\sqrt{f/2}\{\psi - 1 + \ln[(1 + 5\psi)/6]\}$ in Eq. (98). Equations (92) and (98) have the α correction, and Eqs. (94) and (97) include the ratio P/p_{BM}, both of which should perhaps appear in every equation for k_c.

The heat-transfer equations of Reichardt[386] and of Boelter, Martinelli, and Johassen[40] have been transformed[362] into mass-transfer equations with the following results:

Reichardt:

$$\phi_D = \frac{R_c}{R_u}\left\{1 + a_2 + R_u\sqrt{\frac{f}{2}}\left[2(\psi - 1) + 13.5\left(\frac{\psi \ln \psi}{\psi - 1} - 1\right)\right]\right\} \quad (100)$$

Boelter *et al.*:

$$\phi_D = 5R_c\sqrt{\frac{f}{2}}\left[\psi + \ln(1 + 5\psi) + \frac{1}{2}\ln\left(\frac{Re}{60}\sqrt{\frac{f}{2}}\right)\right] \quad (101)$$

Here R_c is the ratio of the mean concentration difference to the maximum concentration difference, wall to center line; R_u is the ratio of average velocity to maximum velocity, U_{av}/U_M; and a_2 is a small correction for the variation in the ratio N_A/τ from wall to center line. These will be compared with each other and with certain suitable experimental data in a later section.

MASS TRANSFER TO PLANE SURFACES

Before considering the performance of plant equipment employed for absorption and extraction, it is of interest to review the existing information on transfer between a moving fluid and certain standard shapes, such as flat plates, spheres, and cylinders. Almost all the experimental data for these cases have been obtained by studying the vaporization of water or other liquids into air, and it must be assumed for the present that the methods of correlation employed provide an adequate basis for other situations, as for the solution of a solid by a liquid. Three flow conditions may be encountered: forced convection with turbulent flow, forced convection with laminar flow, and no flow ("still air") with motion of the fluid resulting only from convection currents caused by temperature or concentration gradients.

The evaporation of liquids from a free liquid surface or from a wet solid has been studied in wind tunnels by a number of investigators. Others have measured the evaporation of water from pans or ponds in the open in order to obtain data of interest to meteorologists. Although the literature on atmospheric evaporation is extensive, the data to be discussed were obtained mostly in wind tunnels.

Hinchley and Himus[189] measured the rate of evaporation of water from heated rectangular pans placed flush with the floor of a small wind tunnel 18 in. wide and 9 in. high. They confirmed the proportionality between rate of vaporization per unit area and the vapor-pressure difference up to values of $p_e - p$ of 400 mm. Hg and recommended an empirical equation expressing k_G as a linear function of the air velocity over the surface. Himus[188] later proposed a modified empirical equation based on the same data. Thiesenhusen[456] describes measurements of the rate of evaporation in a very small laboratory tunnel at air speeds up to about 5 ft./sec. Lurie and Michailoff[290] report data on the vaporization of water from a circular pan 8 in. in diameter placed flush with the floor of a small wind tunnel 1 ft. square. The air was warmer than the surface, varying from 100 to 430°F., and the highest air speed was 25 ft./sec., above which water was entrained from the free liquid surface. Powell and Griffiths[377] employed a wind tunnel 18 in. square, flared at the inlet, and a heated, wet, flat, horizontal plate placed near the center of the air stream. The rate of evaporation was measured from the upper surface of this plate, which had a rounded or streamlined leading edge. The surface was covered with stretched linen, kept wet by water supply from below. Their data show that the rate is the same for wet linen and for wet blotting paper as for a free liquid surface. Various surfaces were employed with downwind lengths from 1 to 10 in. Powell[376] later reported similar data with the surface in the vertical position. Millar[323] experimented with rectangular pans up to 2 ft. in downwind length set flush with the floor in one of two wind tunnels. Shepherd, Hadlock, and Brewer[412] measured the rate of vaporization of water from wet sand of two sizes and from a free water surface using a foot-square pan having a blunt vertical leading edge set in the middle of the air stream in a laboratory tunnel. Their work included a study of the effect of insulating the bottom of the pan on heat transfer to the wet material. Kamei, Mizuni, and Shiomi[238] report somewhat similar data on the effect of air speed on the drying of wet clay.

The vaporization of organic liquids is of interest in chemical warfare and also in connection with the behavior of lacquers as the solvents evaporate. Hine[190] measured the rates of vaporization of toluene, chlorobenzene, m-xylene, and nitrobenzene from a pan 23 in. in diameter set in the floor of a large wind tunnel 6 ft. square. Hoffman[198] reports the relative rates of vaporization of a number of solvents from aluminum dishes standing in the laboratory. Wade,[485] using a heated 3.5-in.-square pan flush with the floor of a small wind tunnel 4.7 in. wide by 2.37 in. high, studied the rates of vaporization of water, acetone, benzene, ethyl acetate, toluene, trichloroethylene, and carbon tetrachloride in air at velocities up to 12 ft./sec. With the volatile liquids employed, values of $p_e - p$ of over 400 mm. Hg were obtained. Pasquill[354] made similar tests with rectangular and square glass plates covered with wet filter paper and set flush with the floor of a wind tunnel 2 ft. 6 in. square in cross section. The data, which are not given in detail, cover water, aniline, methyl salicylate, and bromobenzene.

A number of articles describe the results of studies of evaporation of water from pans and reservoirs in the open air. These have usually been made with less care in measuring wind speed and liquid-surface temperature than the tests in wind tunnels and will not be summarized. Reference may be made to Rowher,[395] Fitzgerald,[140] Banerji and Wadia,[23] Carpenter,[67] Sleight,[430] Bigelow,[33] and O'Brien and Stutzman.[342a]

The generalized theoretical equation (99) suggests a basis for correlation of the wind-tunnel tests on evaporation. With the P/p_{BM} correction, this may be written

$$\frac{k_G p_{BM}}{G_M} \phi_D = \frac{f}{2} \tag{102}$$

where G_M is the molal mass velocity of the stream in lb. moles air per hr. per ft.², and ϕ_D is some function of f and the modified Schmidt group. Since the data do not warrant complicating refinements, ϕ_D will be taken as a simple power function of $\mu/\rho D_v$. On the basis of an analysis of his own and Wade's data, Pasquill finds k_G to be proportional to the $\frac{2}{9}$ power of D_v, but correlations using this exponent are definitely inferior to the use of $(\mu/\rho D_v)^{\frac{2}{3}}$, as suggested by Eq. (97). Actually, the data are inadequate to determine the proper function of $\mu/\rho D_v$, since the range covered is only from 0.60 for water to 1.6–2.7 for the several organic liquids investigated. Tests should be made with helium or hydrogen in order to extend the range. Assuming the friction factor to be a function of Re alone, and substituting $(\mu/\rho D_v)^{\frac{2}{3}}$ for ϕ_D, as in Eq. (97), $k_G p_{BM}(\mu/\rho D_v)^{\frac{2}{3}}/G_M$ will be plotted vs. Re and compared with $f/2$.

Powell and Griffiths[377] and Powell[376] found the average rate of vaporization per unit area of wet surface to decrease with increase in the downwind length of the wet surface. Using lengths from less than an inch up to 10 in., k_G was found to be inversely proportional to the 0.23 power of the length. This is similar to the variation of f with Re and suggests that a "length Reynolds number" Re_x be employed in plotting the data. This suggestion is strengthened by the fact that Pasquill with a 30- by 30-in. tunnel obtained rates of evaporation similar to those of Wade and Powell with small ducts, indicating that the diameter of the duct is not an important factor.

In line with this reasoning, the principal data have been plotted on Fig. 20 as $k_G p_{BM}(\mu/\rho D_v)^{\frac{2}{3}}/G_M$ vs. Re_x. In most cases the original data were reported only in the form of graphs, so most of the points shown are taken from the various authors' smoothed curves. The lower section of the solid line represents $f/2$ for smooth plates, as given by Goldstein[162] for turbulent flow, and the upper section (to the left) represents Blasius' theoretical equation for $f/2$ in the region of streamline flow. The data are reasonably well represented by the solid lines, and it may be concluded that Eq. (97) is valid for plane surfaces placed parallel to the direction of flow. Of the other data not shown, Hine's results fall roughly on a line approximately parallel to the right-hand branch of the

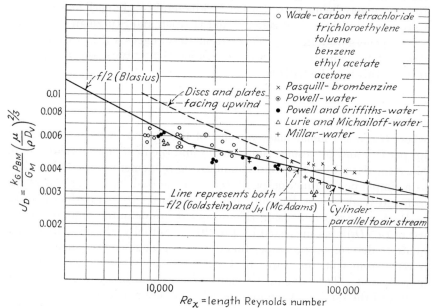

FIG. 20. Summary of data on evaporation from flat plates.

solid line at ordinates about 2.5 times as great. The data of Shepherd, Hadlock, and Brewer are more consistent but lie at about twice the ordinates of the solid line. The explanation of this discrepancy is not clear, although Powell and Griffiths suggest that it is due to blunt edges or perpendicular ridges at the upwind edge of the wet surfaces. By deliberately placing such ridges in front of flat wet surfaces, Powell and Griffiths found the rate of vaporization to be increased only 30 per cent in the case of a 3-in. ridge, not enough to explain the variation of 2- to 2.5-fold.

Pohlhausen[371] has derived a theoretical equation for heat transfer from a flat plate to a fluid in streamline flow, which Colburn[87] expresses in the approximate form

$$j_H = 0.66 \, Re_x^{-\frac{1}{2}} \tag{103}$$

Drew[113] summarizes other theoretical equations for the same case. Equation (103) agrees exactly with Blasius' equation for $f/2$ in this region, confirming Eq. (96). In view of this it seems reasonable to assume that j_H and j_D are equal and to employ the Blasius line for mass transfer from a smooth plate to a fluid in streamline flow. McAdams[311] uses the same solid lines shown in Fig. 20 to represent the data on heat transfer to plates, in a graph of j_H vs. Re_x. The recent heat-transfer data of Jakob and Dow[217] also agree well with the branch of the line for turbulent flow. Furthermore, the theoretical equation for heat transfer in turbulent flow due to Latzko[265] for $C_p\mu/k$ of unity is essentially identical with the Blasius equation for $f/2$ in the turbulent range. Summarizing, the theoretical values of j_H and $f/2$ agree with each other and with the heat-transfer data in the laminar-flow region; the experimental values of j_H, j_D, and $f/2$ agree with each other and with the Latzko theory in the turbulent region.

The boundary layer immediately downstream from the leading edge of a flat plate is laminar, breaking into turbulent motion further downstream as determined by the critical value of Re_x. It may be expected, therefore, that the rate of mass transfer to or from a flat plate will be a function of the position as well as the length of the wetted surface. For heat transfer, Jakob and Dow found h to be proportional to the group $1 + 0.4(x_0/x)^{2.75}$, where x_0 and x are the distances from leading edge to upstream and downstream edges of the heated surface. Devins[108] measured the rate of vaporization of flat surfaces of water into air, using values of x from 7.1 to 26.1 in. and values of x_0 from 5.1 to 40.1 in. The wetted length $x - x_0$ was found to be a more important factor than the approach length x_0, but the data were well correlated by the group suggested by Jakob and Dow for heat transfer. A somewhat better correlation of Devin's data was obtained by Maisel,[293] using $[1 - (x_0/x)^{0.8}]^{0.11}$, *i.e.*, by plotting $\dfrac{k_c x}{D_v[1 - (x_0/x)^{0.8}]^{0.11}}$ vs. Re_x, where Re_x is based on x.

The recent work of Linton[284] on rate of solution of solid plates in water provides data at large values (1000 to 3000) of the Schmidt group. For water in turbulent flow over small cast plates the data fall 1.5- to 2-fold above the solid line of Fig. 20. Since the plates extended across the full diameter of a 2-in. tube, they are not entirely representative of plates in an open stream. The agreement obtained, however, is excellent support for the $\frac{2}{3}$ exponent on the Schmidt group in j_D.

It may be noted that the correlation represented by Fig. 20 indicates k_G to be inversely proportional to p_{BM}, which is the logarithmic mean of $P - p_e$ and $P - p$. Where the liquids are of low vapor pressure, p and p_e are small compared to P, and p_{BM} is essentially equal to P, which was 1 atm. in all the tests reported. In the case of some of the data plotted,

$p_e - p$ was as large as 400 mm.; yet the rate of vaporization was found to be linear over the entire range from 0 to 400 mm. This suggests that p_{BM} is not involved, since the curves of rate vs. $p_e - p$ should have been concave upward. The importance of p_{BM} in this case is not established but it is retained in the correlation presented because Gilliland, as will be seen later, found it necessary in the correlation of forced-convection data on the vaporization of liquids inside tubes.

Powell reports data on evaporation of water from plane surfaces facing the wind and has shown that his data agree well with those of Molstad, Farevaag, and Farrell,[327] who made similar tests with watch glasses 3 to 8.25 in. in diameter filled with water and placed in a jet of air leaving a 6-in. duct. Powell used disks 2.1, 4.3, 6.2, and 8.7 in. in diameter and rectangular plates 7.6 in. on one side by 1.5, 3.5, 7.6, and 10.5 in. on the other side. These data are well represented by the dashed line on Fig. 20. This has a negative slope of about 0.5, indicating that the rate of vaporization of water from the entire wet surface of a disk facing upwind is proportional to the 1.5 power and not to the square of the diameter. For similar surfaces facing downstream the rates are 15 to 20 per cent less than when facing upstream. For rectangular plates the angle of inclination to the stream was found to affect the rate much more for wide plates than for narrow strips. In the case of the plate 10.5 in. wide the rate of vaporization of water from the downwind face of the plate with air moving 15.8 ft./sec. passed through a maximum at 40 deg. as the angle of inclination was varied from 0 to 90 deg. This maximum was twice that for parallel flow (0 deg.) or for a 90-deg. inclination; the latter were approximately equal. With the narrower plates the maximum was less marked, and for the strip 1.5 in. wide it was hardly noticeable. These results were with the flat surface facing downwind; with the wet surface facing upwind the angle of inclination was of little importance.

Although various authors[38,189,376,411,485] have reported data on evaporation into "still air," it seems doubtful whether many of these results have wide application in design. Without forced convection the water or other vapor formed is carried away from the wet surface by natural convection implemented by density differences set up by the existing concentration and temperature gradients. The air currents vary widely depending on the geometry of the system, the pressure, the temperatures of wet surface, and the fluid viscosity. The situation is even more complicated than for heat transfer without mass transfer, for which case the data are few and the correlations poor.

Sharpley and Boelter[411] report data on evaporation of water from a pan 1 ft. in diameter under such closely controlled conditions that reproducible data were obtained. The pan was placed at the bottom of a quieting chamber 5 by 5 by 7 ft. high, open at the top, and with air ports at the bottom. It was found that the natural air movement reversed direction at a critical water-surface temperature, and this critical point was related to a modified Grashof group containing the principal variables expected to influence natural convection. Boelter, Gordon, and Griffin[38] extended the earlier tests to much higher water temperatures and obtained a good correlation of both sets of data by the simple empirical equation

$$18N_A = 2.5 \frac{p_e - p}{p_{BM}}, \qquad \text{lb./(hr.)(ft.}^2) \qquad (104)$$

where p_e is the vapor pressure of the water and p is the partial pressure of water in the air "far away." Since the ratio $(p_e - p)/p_{BM}$ was varied from 0 to 1.7, the data provide a good confirmation of the importance of p_{BM} in the relation between rate and partial-pressure difference. Equation (104) is in approximate agreement with the empirical equations of Hinchley and Himus[189] and of Rowher[395] for "still air."

CYLINDER WITH AXIS PARALLEL TO DIRECTION OF FLOW

Powell[376] reports data on evaporation of water from the wet outer surface of a 1.72-in. cylinder placed with its axis parallel to the direction of air flow in a small wind tunnel. Both ends were streamlined with wooden nosepieces, and the wetted length was varied from 3 to 43 in. by covering downstream sections with aluminum foil. As in the case of disks and plates, the average rate of evaporation per unit area was found to decrease as the wetted length increased, and the same general type of correlation based on a length Reynolds number was used. The result is shown as the lower dotted line of Fig. 20, which is seen to agree fairly well with the data on flat surfaces.

EFFECT OF SMALL AMOUNTS OF ADDITIVES ON THE RATE OF VAPORIZATION OF WATER

Various authors[321] have reported the marked effect of certain additives on the rate of evaporation of water. With large amounts of oil on the surface, Powell[375] reports a minimum evaporation rate at a layer thickness of about $\frac{1}{4}$ in., with greater rates for thicker or thinner oil layers. Other materials affect the rate of evaporation appreciably when present in minute quantities.[263] Thus essentially monomolecular films of myristyl alcohol, stearic acid, arachidic acid, octadecyl alcohol, cetyl alcohol, and *n*-docosanol are noticeably effective. Traces of cetyl alcohol or *n*-docosanol are reported to be especially active, reducing the rate of vaporization from a quiet water surface to as little as 1 to 4 per cent of the rate with pure water.

CYLINDER TRANSVERSE TO AIR STREAM

Powell[376,377] included cylinders of several sizes in his study of the evaporation of water into air. Representative results are shown on Fig. 21, where the coordinates are similar to those of Fig. 20 except that Re is based entirely on tube diameter. Powell used eight cylinders ranging in diameter from 0.063 to 14.6 in., and air speeds up to about

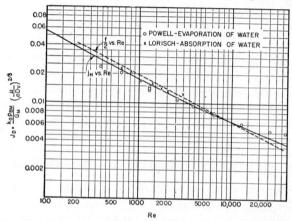

FIG. 21.   Data on mass transfer to cylinders placed normal to air flow.

32 ft./sec. The graph also shows the data of Lohrisch[287] for the absorption of water vapor by solid cylinders of caustic. Lohrisch obtained similar results when absorbing ammonia on cylinders wet with phosphoric acid. Vint's data[478] on evaporation of water, toluene, and n-butyl alcohol from the outside of a vertical tube 1.75 in. in diameter at air speeds from 3 to 12 ft./sec. are not shown but check reasonably well, though the points are more scattered. Similarly, the data of London, Nottage, and Boelter[288] on evaporation of water from 0.5- and 1.0-in. cylinders are also in substantial agreement with the solid line.

Linton[284] measured the rate of solution of cast cylinders of benzoic and cinnamic acid placed in water in turbulent flow. The cinnamic acid data fall very close to the solid line of Fig. 21; the benzoic acid data some 15 per cent higher. These results lend excellent support to the $\frac{2}{3}$ exponent on the Schmidt group, which was in the range 1000 to 3000 in these tests.

The effect of air turbulence on vaporization from wet cylinders has been studied by Comings, Clapp, and Taylor,[94] and by Maisel.[293] The former investigators studied both mass and heat transfer, obtaining an increase in j_H of about 25 per cent as the intensity of turbulence (see page 36) was increased from 2 to 20 per cent by the introduction of grid-type turbulence generators upstream from the test object. Maisel, using both cylinders and spheres, found the mass-transfer coefficient to increase as much as 50 per cent as the intensity of turbulence was increased from 3.5 to 24 per cent. Over a twofold range, scale of turbulence had no effect on mass transfer.

Although the solid line on Fig. 21 represents the data well, it is actually taken from McAdams[311] as representative of a large collection of data on heat transfer to single cylinders placed transverse to air streams. It is evident that j_D and j_H are in excellent agreement.

Using a nonagonal prism approximating a cylinder 3.15 in. in diameter, Powell and Griffiths[377] obtained data on the relative rates of evaporation of water from surfaces at different positions around the perimeter. High rates were observed at the front (0 deg. to the wind direction), somewhat lower rates at the back (180 deg.), and sharp minima just behind the middle, at about 100 and 250 deg. Their polar diagram of rate vs. position is similar to that shown by McAdams[310] for the distribution of heat transfer around a single cylinder placed transverse to an air stream.

Winding and Cheney[515] have recently reported data on vaporization from single cylinders, obtained by measuring the rate of sublimation of cast naphthalene tubes placed transverse to a turbulent air stream in a small wind tunnel. By observing the loss of naphthalene from a number of points around the periphery of the tubes, they were able to obtain additional data similar to those of Powell and Griffiths. Their data on whole cylinders fall some 10 to 35 per cent above the solid line of Fig. 21, at Reynolds numbers from 5000 to 33,000.

In order to compare these data with friction, it is necessary to distinguish between total drag and skin friction. Values of drag coefficients for cylinders, which are well established, are usually plotted as C_D vs. Re, where C_D is the total drag per unit length of cylinder divided by $\frac{1}{2}U_{av}{}^2\rho d$. This is made up of the skin friction and the normal pressure drag, and it is possible to estimate skin-friction coefficients by subtracting measured pressure drag from measured total drag. This has been shown by Thom, as quoted by Goldstein,[162] and the results are shown as $f/2$ by the dotted line of Fig. 21. Here $f/2$ is that part of C_D due to skin friction, divided by 2π. The per cent of the total drag due to skin friction is 12.6 at Re = 1000 and only 1.9 at Re = 31,600, so the values of $f/2$ at high Reynolds numbers, obtained by difference, are subject to considerable error. The agreement between j_D, j_H, and $f/2$ is quite remarkable.

Except for the limited data of Powell[373] there is little information on mass transfer to or from a cylinder under conditions of still air or natural convection. In this case the data on heat transfer, which are plentiful, cannot be used directly as a basis for mass-transfer calculations, since the magnitudes of the convection currents are not the same in the two cases. Jacob[217] suggests that the conversion may be accomplished by the use of a modified Grashof group involving both concentration and temperature differences to define the magnitude of convection currents.

SINGLE SPHERES

Mass transfer to or from a sphere placed in a stagnant fluid, as, for example, the evaporation of a liquid drop in absolutely still air, follows the laws of molecular diffusion developed in Chap. I. Langmuir[262] has shown that the radial diffusion into a quiet medium of infinite size may be expressed by

$$N_A = \frac{2D_v(p_i - p)}{DRT} \tag{105}$$

or

$$\frac{k_cD}{D_v} = \frac{k_GRTD}{D_v} = 2 \tag{106}$$

Here D is the diameter of the sphere, p_i is the vapor pressure at the surface, and p is the partial pressure of the diffusing material at a remote point (theoretically at infinity). The validity of Eq. (106) has been confirmed by a number of investigators, including Topley and Whytlaw-Gray[460] for iodine spheres in air, Whytlaw-Gray and Patterson[507] for benzophenone in air, Houghton,[205] Froessling,[145] and Whytlaw-Gray and Patterson[507] for water in air, Froessling[145] for aniline in air, and Houghton and Radford[206] for the absorption of water from air by drops of an aqueous solution of calcium chloride. In most instances these data for small drops checked Eq. (106) within 5 per cent, and it may be taken as definitely established that k_cD/D_v approaches 2.0 as an asymptote as the velocity of the fluid medium approaches zero. There appear to be no data on mass transfer to or from spheres under conditions of natural convection, and the remarks of the preceding section on cylinders apply to the use of heat-transfer data as a basis for the calculation of mass transfer in this region.

A large number of investigators have studied mass transfer to and from spheres under conditions of forced convection, and good correlations of the data have been obtained.[145,362,415,512] Most of the data are for evaporation of liquids into air streams, though some studies of absorption by drops have been reported. The spheres ranged in diameter from 0.04 to 6 in.. and the data were obtained by a variety of techniques.

Froessling[145] reports extensive data on the evaporation of small drops of nitrobenzene, aniline, and water and small solid spheres of naphthalene. Powell[376] measured the evaporation of water from wet surfaces of solid spheres up to 6 in. in diameter. Powell[374] also measured the rate of sublimation of ice from a 3.5-in. sphere. Houghton and Radford[206] absorbed water vapor from air by drops of a strong aqueous solution of calcium chloride. Vyrubov[484] absorbed ammonia from air using spheres coated with phosphoric acid. Johnstone and Williams[233] absorbed ammonia, sulfur dioxide, hydrogen sulfide, and carbon dioxide by single falling drops of water (see Fig. 109). Whitman, Long, and Wang,[504] Takahasi,[457] and Majima and Togino[294] also report studies of the evaporation of water into air.

The relatively new data of Maisel[293] and of Linton[284] supply information on the effect of air turbulence on evaporation from spheres and on the effect of the Schmidt group. As indicated in the section on cylinders (page 70), the effect of intensity of turbulence at a constant Reynolds number is appreciable but not large. Linton's data are for the rate of solution of benzoic acid cylinders in water, where the Schmidt group is 2000 to 2500. The results correlate well with the vaporization data on the basis of a $\frac{2}{3}$ exponent on $(\mu/\rho D_L)$ in j_D.

Froessling found that his extensive data could be well correlated by the semitheoretical equation

$$\frac{k_c D}{D_v} = 2.0 \left[1 + 0.276 \ \text{Re}^{1/2} \left(\frac{\mu}{\rho D_v} \right)^{1/3} \right] \tag{107}$$

and this has been found to fit the other data quite well. Williams[512] and Sherwood[415] employed a graph of j_D vs. Re, similar to Fig. 21 for cylinders. Pigford,[362] however, noted that the effect of $\mu/\rho D_v$ was a function of Re and developed a correlation based on a graph of $k_c D/D_v$ vs. Re $(\mu/\rho D_v)^{2/3}$, as suggested by the form of Eq. (107).* This graph is reproduced as Fig. 22, with a solid line best representing the points, and a dashed line representing Froessling's equation. The asymptote representing Eq. (106) for conditions of stagnant fluid surrounding the sphere is indicated at the lower left-hand corner of the graph. Data on absorption of carbon dioxide, hydrogen sulfide, etc., are omitted since appreciable liquid-film resistance is anticipated for such cases. The dotted line represents the corresponding correlation for heat transfer to spheres, based on the line recommended by McAdams.[313]

The data indicate no effect of pressure, but since Gilliland's results for the analogous case of evaporation of liquids in wetted-wall towers indicate

* See also the recent data and correlation of Ranz and Marshall,[383a] who evaporated not only pure liquids but water containing dissolved salts and suspended solids.

k_c and k_G to be inversely proportional to p_{BM}, it seems logical to introduce this correction in cases where p_{BM} differs appreciably from the total pressure P. Thus the ordinate of Fig. 22 would be $k_c D p_{BM}/D_v P$, or, what amounts to the same thing, the value of k_c or k_G obtained from Fig. 22 as shown should be multiplied by P/p_{BM}. Note that the product $D_v P$ is independent of pressure, and the uncorrected correlation indicates k_c or k_G to be inversely proportional to the total pressure P; the suggested correction makes the coefficient inversely proportional to p_{BM} instead of to P.

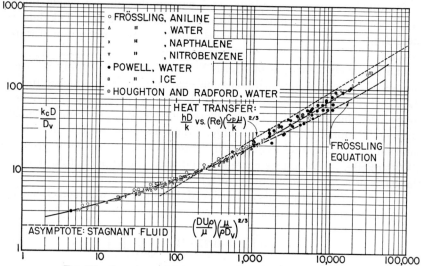

Fig. 22.   Summary of data on mass transfer to single spheres.

The data on mass transfer and heat transfer for spheres are in fair agreement, as indicated by Fig. 22. It is not possible to compare these results with friction or momentum transfer, since the breakdown of total drag into skin friction and normal pressure drag has not been made. The total drag for spheres has been measured by a number of investigators, and Goldstein[162] summarizes the information available on the relation between the coefficient of total drag, C_D, and Re. These data may be used to calculate the terminal velocities of falling drops preliminary to the estimation of rates of mass transfer for such conditions. Approximate values of terminal velocities of water drops[285,512] are given in Table V. The last column gives Lenard's[266] values for the limiting velocity, which is the air speed at which the drop is shattered. Since the limiting and terminal velocities approach each other as the drop size is increased, it is evident that large drops falling freely are shattered before they reach their terminal velocities, and drops larger than about 0.25 in. in diameter (Re = 4000) cannot exist in free fall. Drops in the diameter range 0.2

to 0.25 in. are distorted by the normal pressure drag and tend to assume the shape of chocolate drops with a flat or concave leading surface. Williams[512] obtained some good high-speed pictures of such drops in free fall. Drops in this range show somewhat higher mass-transfer rates than spheres of the same volume.

TABLE V. TERMINAL AND LIMITING VELOCITIES OF WATER DROPS IN AIR AT 1 ATM.

Drop diameter		Terminal velocity, ft./sec.	Limiting velocity, ft./sec.
In.	Mm.		
0.00196	0.05	0.18	
0.0079	0.2	2.3	735
0.0196	0.5	7.0	295
0.0394	1.0	12.7	152
0.079	2.0	19.2	81
0.118	3.0	23.8	59
0.157	4.0	26.0	47
0.196	5.0	26.8	40
0.236	6.0	27.0	33.4

Information regarding mass transfer, heat transfer, and drag for spheres has application in various branches of technology. For example, Boelter[37] has shown the application of such data to air-water contacting and the performance of spray towers. Houghton's work was based on an interest in the use of large-scale spraying of calcium chloride solutions to eliminate fog over aircraft landing fields. During the Second World War there was considerable interest in the possibility that the Germans might spray the vesicant mustard from aircraft at high altitudes. In this connection Williams[512] made an interesting study of the evaporation of drops of liquid mustard during free fall, with allowances for the variation of pressure with altitude and decrease in terminal velocity as evaporation proceeds. He finds that the initial drop size is critical; in air at 68°F. the evaporation of a pure mustard spray released at 20,000 ft. is approximately as follows: drops initially 0.24 in. (6 mm.) in diameter evaporate to the extent of only 2 per cent; 0.079 in. (2 mm.), 15 per cent; 0.0394 in. (1.0 mm.), 56 per cent; drops initially 0.028 in. (0.72 mm.) or smaller evaporate completely before reaching the ground.

MASS TRANSFER INSIDE PIPES—WETTED-WALL TOWERS

Mass transfer from the inner wall of a tube to a moving fluid is of importance not only because of its practical applications but because data for this case provide the best test of the various theories. Here again most of the data are for vaporization of liquids into air, and few data are available on transfer to a moving liquid.   The principal data are those of Gilliland[161] and Barnet and Kobe[24] on vaporization of liquids in wetted-wall towers, although Chilton and Colburn,[75] Uchida and Maeda,[468] Krebs,[256] Greenewalt,[164] Hollings and Silver,[200] Cogan and Cogan,[82] and Kirschbaum and Keinzle[248] also report data on vaporization of liquids or absorption of soluble gases in wetted-wall columns.   Johnstone and Pigford[227] and Surowiec and Furnas[445a] have obtained data on the mass-transfer process of rectification in wetted-wall columns.

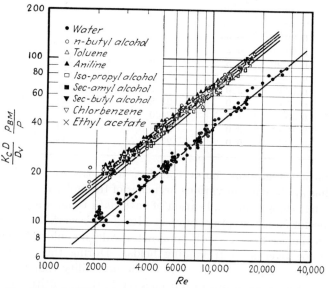

FIG. 23.   Data of Gilliland on vaporization of liquids in a wetted-wall tower.

Gilliland studied the vaporization of nine different liquids into air, using a 1-in. wetted-wall column 46 in. long with calming sections both above and below the wetted-wall section.   This was operated at pressures from 0.145 to 3.06 atm., with air and liquid at approximately the same temperature.   Partial-pressure driving forces at top and bottom of the wetted-wall section were calculated from the liquid temperatures, measured vaporization rate, and measured air humidities, and the logarithmic-mean driving force was used in calculating k_c and k_G.   Gilliland elected to plot the data as $(k_c D/D_v)(p_{BM}/P)$ vs. Re, with the result shown in Fig. 23.   Separate parallel lines are shown for each liquid, indicating that k_c is not proportional to D_v, as for molecular diffusion.   The intercepts were plotted vs. the Schmidt group $\mu/\rho D_v$, giving a slope of 0.44 on logarithmic coordinates.   The final correlation is indicated by Fig. 24, where the line is represented by the empirical equation

$$\frac{k_c D}{D_v}\frac{p_{BM}}{P} = 0.023\ \mathrm{Re}^{0.83}\left(\frac{\mu}{\rho D_v}\right)^{0.44} \tag{108}$$

This equation has been found generally reliable over the range of Reynolds numbers from 2000 to 35,000, $\mu/\rho D_v$ from 0.60 to 2.5, and pressures from 0.1 to 3 atm. The Reynolds number is based on the velocity of the gas relative to the pipe, since data on parallel and countercurrent flow of liquid and gas gave a poorer correlation when velocity of gas relative to liquid surface was employed in calculating Re.

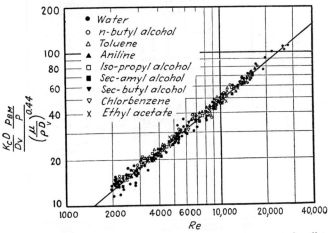

Fig. 24. Correlation of data on vaporization of liquids in a wetted-wall tower.

It may be noted that $\mu/\rho D_v$ was varied only over a fourfold range, with the liquids falling into two groups: water and organic liquids. The exponent 0.44 is not established with great assurance, therefore, though these data are possibly the best indication available as to what it should be. The exponent of $\frac{2}{3}$ on the Schmidt group in j_D was taken by Chilton and Colburn by analogy from the known effect of $C_p\mu/k$ on heat transfer and has been used in previous correlations. This indicates k_c to be proportional to $D_v^{\frac{2}{3}}$, whereas Gilliland's data, as represented by Eq. (108), indicate k_c to be proportional to $D_v^{0.56}$. This discrepancy cannot be settled on the basis of data covering such a narrow range of values of D_v, and graphs of j_D vs. Re may be employed as a basis of correlation of wetted-wall-tower data, in place of Fig. 24.

Although Gilliland varied p_{BM} over a wide range, the ratio p_{BM}/P was varied little and could have been omitted from the left-hand side of Eq. (108). It is retained primarily because it applies in molecular diffusion, and theory indicates that molecular diffusion is important in the over-all process.

Gilliland took special pains to provide calming sections preceding the test section. Greenewalt[164] found the coefficient for absorption of water vapor by sulfuric acid to be some eight times as great as predicted by Eq.

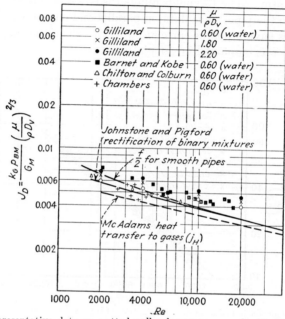

FIG. 25. Representative data on wetted-wall columns compared with friction and heat transfer.

(108), if the gas was allowed to enter through a small pierced header, and twice as great when a venturi diffuser approach tube was employed (see Fig. 106).

Figure 25 illustrates typical data on vaporization in wetted-wall columns plotted as j_D vs. Re. Representative smoothed results of Gilliland's work are shown, along with data from other sources. The spread of the points with variation in $\mu/\rho D_v$ is due to the fact that Gilliland got an exponent of 0.56, not $\frac{2}{3}$, as representing the effect of D_v. This is evidenced by the fact that Gilliland's equation (108) may be written

$$j_D = 0.023 \text{ Re}^{-0.17} \left(\frac{\mu}{\rho D_v}\right)^{0.11} \qquad (109)$$

or

$$\frac{k_G p_{BM}}{G_M} = 0.023 \text{ Re}^{-0.17} \left(\frac{\mu}{\rho D_v}\right)^{-0.56} \tag{110}$$

Similarly, the McAdams equation for heat transfer in pipes may be expressed as

$$j_H = 0.023 \text{ Re}^{-0.20} \left(\frac{C_p \mu}{k}\right)^{0.07} \tag{111}$$

This is represented by the dashed curve shown, which falls considerably below the mass-transfer data. The curve for $f/2$, representing friction in smooth tubes, is the upper solid curve.

Johnstone and Pigford[228] report data on the rectification of several binary mixtures in a wetted-wall column, under conditions such that the gas-film resistance was some 90 per cent or more of the total. The mixtures used were ethanol-water, acetone-chloroform, benzene-toluene, ethylene dichloride–toluene, and ethylene dichloride–benzene. For these mixtures $\mu/\rho D_v$ varied from 0.54 to 0.72. They obtained an excellent representation of their data by an equation which may be written

$$j_D = 0.033 \text{ Re}^{-0.23} \tag{112}$$

This is represented by the lower solid line on Fig. 25, showing excellent agreement with the other data, especially when a small allowance is made for the liquid-film resistance in the rectification tests.

Additional data on rectification in a wetted-wall column have been obtained by Jackson and Ceagelske,[215] who obtained data on short sections of the column as well as on the column as a whole. The system studied was 2-pentanol–water at both total and partial reflux. The results check well with those of Johnstone and Pigford, showing good agreement between j_D and $f/2$ over a range of Re from 3500 to 70,000.

Illustration 9. The following data were obtained by F. S. Chambers on the absorption of ammonia from an ammonia-air stream by acid in a wetted-wall column of 0.575 in. i.d., 32.5 in. long:

Inlet acid ($2N$ H_2SO_4) temperature, °F	76
Outlet acid temperature, °F	81
Inlet air temperature, °F	77
Outlet air temperature, °F	84
Total pressure, atm	1.00
Partial pressure NH_3 in inlet gas, atm	0.0807
Partial pressure NH_3 in outlet gas, atm	0.0205
Air rate, lb. moles/hr	0.260

The operation was countercurrent, the gas entering at the bottom of the vertical tower and the acid passing down in a thin film on the inner wall. The change in acid strength was inappreciable, and the vapor pressure of ammonia over the liquid may be assumed to have been negligible.

a. Calculate the absorption coefficient k_G.

b. Compare with the value obtained from Eq. (110).

c. Obtain a value for the heat-transfer coefficient h for this case from the literature, and estimate k_G from h by equating j_D and j_H.

d. Obtain a value of the friction factor f and estimate k_G from Eq. (97).

Solution. The average molecular weight of the inlet gas is

$$(0.0807)(17) + (0.9193)(29) = 28.0;$$

at outlet, 28.8; $M_M = 28.4$.

Taking the mean temperature as 80°, μ is 0.45 lb./(hr.)(ft.), whence

$$G_M = \frac{(0.260)(144)(4)}{(3.14)(0.575)^2} \frac{29}{28.4} = 147 \text{ lb. moles/(hr.)(ft.}^2)$$

and

$$\text{Re} = \frac{(0.575)(147)(28.4)}{(12)(0.45)} = 4450$$

For NH_3 in air, $\dfrac{\mu}{\rho D_v} = 0.61; \left(\dfrac{\mu}{\rho D_v}\right)^{\frac{2}{3}} = 0.72$

Mean Δp or driving force $= \dfrac{0.0807 - 0.0205}{\ln (0.0807/0.0205)} = 0.044 \text{ atm.}$

Mean p_B at bottom $= \dfrac{1.0 + 0.92}{2} = 0.96$; at top, 0.99; $p_{BM} = 0.975 \text{ atm.}$

Wetted surface $= \dfrac{(3.14)(0.575)(32.5)}{144} = 0.407 \text{ ft.}^2$

NH_3 absorbed $= 0.260 \left(\dfrac{0.807}{0.9163} - \dfrac{0.0205}{0.9795}\right) = 0.0174 \text{ lb. mole/hr.}$

a. NH_3 absorbed $= 0.260 \left(\dfrac{0.0807}{0.9163} - \dfrac{0.0205}{0.9795}\right)$

$$= k_G = \frac{0.0174}{(0.407 \times 0.044)} = 0.97 \text{ lb. mole/(hr.)(ft.}^2)(\text{atm.})$$

b. $k_G = 0.023 \dfrac{147}{0.975} (4450)^{-0.17}(0.61)^{-0.56} = 1.09 \text{ lb. moles/(hr.)(ft.}^2)(\text{atm.})$

c. From McAdams's, Eq. (4k) ("Heat Transmission," 2d ed., p. 174),

$$h = 0.0144 \frac{C_p(G_M M_M)^{0.8}}{D^{0.2}} = \frac{(0.0144)(0.24)(790)}{0.545} = 5.0 \text{ B.t.u./(hr.)(ft.}^2)(\text{°F.})$$

Equating j_D and j_H as defined by Eqs. (96) and (97):

$$k_G = \frac{h}{C_p M_M p_{BM}} \left(\frac{C_p\mu}{k}\right)^{\frac{2}{3}} \left(\frac{\mu}{\rho D_v}\right)^{-\frac{2}{3}} = \frac{5.0}{(0.24)(28.4)(0.975)} \frac{0.818}{0.72}$$
$$= 0.86 \text{ lb. mole/(hr.)(ft.}^2)(\text{atm.})$$

Note: k_G calculated from h is 78 per cent of the value obtained from Eq. (110), as would be indicated by the comparison of the heat-transfer line and the data points on Fig. 25.

d. From McAdams, or from Fig. 25, f is 0.0102 at Re = 4450. From Eq. (97):

$$k_G = \frac{(0.0102)(147)}{(2)(0.975)(0.72)} = 1.07 \text{ lb. moles/(hr.)(ft.}^2)(\text{atm.})$$

EVAPORATION OF LIQUIDS IN WETTED-WALL COLUMNS WITH AIR IN STREAMLINE FLOW

At values of the Reynolds number less than about 2000, the flow in a round pipe is streamline in character, and the central turbulent core disappears. Since there is no mixing of successive layers of fluid moving parallel to the wall, the laws of molecular diffusion may be expected to apply, providing proper allowance is made for the velocity gradient across the stream. The basic differential equation has been integrated for the case of heat conduction[113] by Levêque on the assumption of rodlike flow (no velocity gradient), and by Graetz for the parabolic velocity distribution found for streamline flow where the density is constant throughout the fluid. Boelter[37] has modified Graetz's derivation to allow for natural convection currents due to density changes where evaporation occurs from the wall of a vertical pipe.

The Levêque equation as applied to mass transfer is

$$\frac{p_2 - p_1}{p_i - p_1} = 1 - 4 \sum_{n=1}^{\infty} \frac{1}{\alpha_n{}^2} e^{-\alpha_n{}^2 \pi D_v \rho N / w} \tag{113}$$

where p_1 and p_2 are the average partial pressures of the diffusing gas in the entering and leaving streams, p_i is the vapor pressure of the liquid at the wall, D_v is the molecular diffusivity, ρ is the gas density, w is the mass flow rate (lb./hr.), N is the length of wetted wall, and α_n is the nth root of the Bessel equation $J_0(x) = 0$.

Similarly, the Graetz equation for a parabolic velocity distribution is

$$\frac{p_2 - p_1}{p_i - p_1} = 1 - 8 \, [0.10238 e^{-14.6272(\pi/4)(D_v \rho N / w)}$$

$$+ \, 0.0122 e^{-89.22 \, (\pi/4)(D_v \rho N / w)} + \cdots] \tag{114}$$

Both of the equations may be conveniently represented by a graph of $(p_2 - p_1)/(p_i - p_1)$ vs. $w/D_v \rho N$, and are indicated by solid and dotted lines on Fig. 26. This also shows the data of Gilliland for vaporization of liquids and of Haslam, Hershey, and Kean[173] for absorption of ammonia and of sulfur dioxide, obtained in the region of streamline flow. The asymptote of 1.0 at the left is approached at such low flow rates that the gas leaves the tube saturated or in equilibrium with the liquid on the wall (complete removal of the solute for absorption with solute-free solvent). Although the points scatter, the data appear to fit the Levêque equation better than the Graetz equation, though it would be expected that the velocity distribution across the pipe would be parabolic.

Linton[284] has recently studied the rate of solution of solids in water moving in streamline flow through round tubes formed by casting the solid material to be dissolved. Because of the small values of D_L, the range of values of $w/\rho D_L N$ was from 60,000 to 4,000,000. The data agree well with the theoretical Levêque equation:

$$\frac{c - c_0}{c_s - c_0} = 5.5 \left(\frac{w}{\rho D_L N} \right)^{-\frac{2}{3}} \tag{115}$$

This was derived for flow over a flat plate with linear velocity gradient in the fluid near the surface. It applies for tubes only at high values of $w/\rho D_L N$, for which condition the solute diffuses only a very short distance

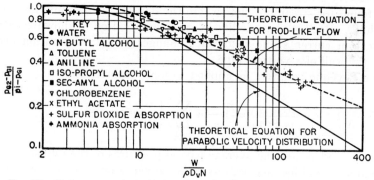

FIG. 26. Data on mass transfer in a wetted-wall tower with streamline flow.

from the surface (within the region of linear velocity gradient) in the time of fluid passage through the tube. In Eq. (115) c and c_0 are the outlet and inlet average concentrations, and c_s is the saturation concentration at the surface. Linton's experimental values of $(c - c_0)/(c_s - c_0)$ were from 2 to 50 $\times$ 10^{-4}.

Boelter[37] introduces the modified Grashof group $\dfrac{D^3 \rho g_c}{\mu^2} \left(\dfrac{M_0 T_w}{M_w T_0} - 1 \right)$, the Schmidt group $\mu/\rho D_v$, and the ratio N/D and obtains a family of curves on Fig. 26 to allow for the distortion of the parabolic velocity distribution due to density gradients. Each curve represents a different value of the product of dimensionless groups:

$$\frac{D^3 \rho g_c}{\mu^2} \left(\frac{M_0 T_w}{M_w T_0} - 1 \right) \frac{\mu}{\rho D_v} \frac{D}{N}$$

Here M_0 and T_0 are the molecular weight and absolute temperature of the entering gas, and M_w and T_w are the average molecular weight and temperature of the gas saturated with the diffusing gas at the temperature of the liquid surface.

Boelter shows that Gilliland's vaporization data agree with this theory and so explains why Gilliland's data fail to check the Graetz equation. Although the agreement of the data with the Levêque equation (113) must be taken as purely fortuitous, the Levêque line of Fig. 26 may be considered as an empirical representation of the data over the range covered.

WETTED-WALL COLUMNS—DIFFUSION IN THE LIQUID FILM

In cases where the diffusing material is relatively insoluble in the liquid, the resistance to transfer between the liquid surface and the gas may be small compared with the resistance to diffusion into or out of the moving liquid layer on the wall (see Chap. VI). In such cases the concentration of solute on the surface of the moving liquid is that in equilibrium with the gas phase. An example is the desorption of oxygen from solution in water, with air passing through the column.

In the common case of a liquid film in streamline flow the velocity gradient is parabolic, and the analytical treatment of the unsteady-state diffusion process proves to be quite complicated. A solution has been obtained by Pigford, however, and is given in the appendix to an article by Johnstone and Pigford.[227] For most applications very nearly the same result is given by a simpler equation based on the assumption that the velocity is uniform at all points in the liquid film and equal to the actual velocity at the surface of the film. The solution to the differential equation in this case leads to the same equation as for heat conduction or moisture movement in a solid slab. If c_0 is the uniform concentration of the liquid fed, and c_z is the average concentration of the solution leaving the column, then[340,421]

$$E' = \frac{c_i - c_z}{c_i - c_0} = \frac{8}{\pi^2} \left(e^{-p} + \frac{1}{9} e^{-9p} + \frac{1}{25} e^{-25p} + \cdots \right) \qquad (116)$$

where $p = (\pi^2/4)(D_L\theta/x_1^2)$
$\quad D_L$ = diffusion coefficient, solute in liquid, ft.^{2}/hr
$\quad \theta$ = time of contact, hr.
$\quad x_1$ = thickness of liquid layer, ft.

Wetted-wall columns are usually operated at liquid rates such that streamline flow prevails, and x_1 is given by

$$x_1 = \sqrt[3]{\frac{3\mu\Gamma}{\rho^2 g}} \qquad (117)$$

where μ is the liquid viscosity, Γ the liquid-flow rate per unit width of wetted wall [lb./(hr.)(ft.)], g is the acceleration due to gravity, and ρ is the liquid density. Furthermore, the time of contact is short, so that E' is near 1.0, and the concentration is affected only in a region near the surface of contact with the gas. For this last condition, Eq. (116) reduces to[178]

$$E' = 1 - 6\sqrt{\frac{p}{\pi^3}} \tag{118}$$

The time of contact is determined by the column height Z and by the velocity of the liquid surface, which is $\frac{3}{2}$ times the average velocity; whence

$$\frac{4}{\pi^2} p = \frac{D_L\theta}{x_1^2} = \frac{D_L Z}{v_m x_1^2} = \frac{2 D_L Z \rho}{3 \Gamma x_1} \tag{119}$$

Now by definition, using a logarithmic-mean driving force,

$$k_L = \frac{\Gamma(c_z - c_0)}{\rho Z \left[\dfrac{(c_i - c_0) - (c_i - c_z)}{\ln \dfrac{c_i - c_0}{c_i - c_z}} \right]} = \frac{\Gamma}{\rho Z} \ln \frac{c_i - c_0}{c_i - c_z} = \frac{\Gamma}{\rho Z} \ln \frac{1}{E'} \tag{120}$$

and since E' is usually near 1.0,

$$k_L = \frac{\Gamma}{\rho Z} (1 - E')$$

$$= \frac{6\Gamma}{\rho Z} \sqrt{\frac{p}{\pi^3}} = \left(\frac{72}{\pi^3} \frac{g \mu^2 \Gamma^2}{Z^3 \rho^4} \right)^{\frac{1}{6}} \left(\frac{\rho D_L}{\mu} \right)^{\frac{1}{2}} \tag{121}$$

Experiments on the desorption of oxygen from water in a wetted-wall column indicate that the observed values of k_L are appreciably greater than given by Eq. (121) (see Fig. 107). The discrepancy is presumably due to the ripples which tend to develop in the water film (see Grimley[166]).

COMPARISON OF WETTED-WALL DATA AND THEORY

The theoretical equations of von Kármán, Reichardt, and others outlined in an earlier section of this chapter were developed partly on the basis of experimental isothermal velocity distributions in round pipes and can be best tested by data on mass transfer in wetted-wall columns. As pointed out previously, the more important theoretical equations are of the form

$$k_c = k_G RT = \frac{fU_{\text{av}}}{2\phi_D} \tag{122}$$

and may be compared with the data by plotting $2k_c/fU_{\text{av}}$ vs. $\mu/\rho D_v$, since ϕ_D is some function of the Schmidt group. This comparison is made on Fig. 27, in which α is taken as 1.6, as suggested by Woertz. The points represent Gilliland's data on vaporization of nine different liquids in a 1-in. tube at Re = 10,000, with f taken as 0.0081, as measured by Gilliland in his apparatus.

Linton[284] has recently extended the experimental range of the Schmidt group by measuring the rate of solution of three organic solutes by passing water in turbulent flow through tubes formed by melting and casting the material to be dissolved. The diffusing solutes, benzoic acid, cinnamic acid, and β-naphthol, were relatively insoluble in water, so the tube diameter did not change appreciably during a test. For these solutes in water $\mu/\rho D_L$ ranged from 1000 to 3000. It is evident from Fig. 25 that these results represent a very great extension of the range of previous data.

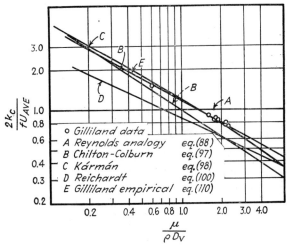

FIG. 27. Comparison of theoretical equations for mass transfer with data for wetted-wall columns (Re = 10,000).

Linton's values of $2k_c/fU_{av}$ fall within a few per cent of the extension of line B, representing the Chilton-Colburn relation. At these high values of the Schmidt group this is midway between Gilliland (line E) and von Kármán (line C). In view of the enormous extension of the experimental range, this agreement is quite remarkable.

The data of Johnstone and Pigford[227] on the rectification of binary mixtures in a wetted-wall column may also be compared with the theoretical lines of Fig. 27, although only some 90 per cent of the observed diffusional resistance was in the gas film. The five points representing these data (one for each binary pair) fall almost exactly on line B (Chilton-Colburn) in the range of $\mu/\rho D_v$ from 0.54 to 0.72. With a small correction for the liquid-film resistance they would bunch closely on either side of the single point for water shown on Fig. 27 at a value of $\mu/\rho D_v$ of 0.60.

In the range of Gilliland's data on vaporization the agreement with the von Kármán theory is considered excellent in view of fact that the latter employs experimental data only to the extent of Nikuradse's velocity traverses for water in a pipe and the known friction factor, yet predicts Gilliland's data within 6 per cent. The empirical equation of Gilliland fits the data well, as it was designed to do.

EVAPORATION FROM BEDS OF WET GRANULAR SOLIDS

Mass transfer in beds of granular solids is of importance in drying by through air circulation, adsorption of gases by solid desiccants or other absorbents, and gas absorption in packed towers. In some types of catalyst-bed operations, mass-transfer rates may control the speed of the over-all process.

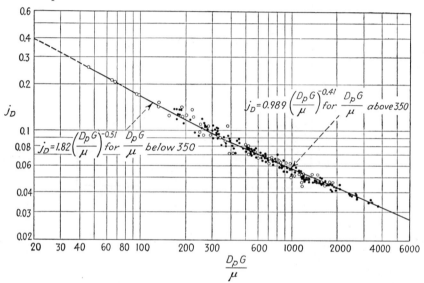

FIG. 28.   Mass transfer in beds of granular solids with through air circulation.

Gamson, Thodos, and Hougen[154] and Wilke and Hougen[511] have reported data on the drying of small, wet cylinders and spheres placed in a random packing with through air circulation at 80 to 160°F. Evaporation of water was studied during the constant-drying-rate period, using spheres 0.09 to 0.456 in. in diameter and cylinders 0.161 to 0.74 in. in diameter, the latter having lengths approximately the same as the diameters. Per cent voids ranged from 37 to 43. The wet-surface temperature was assumed equal to the wet-bulb temperature of the entering air, and calculated values of j_D were found to correlate well when plotted vs. a modified Reynolds number (see Fig. 28). Here D_p represents diameter for the spheres; for the cylinders D_p represents the diameter of a sphere having the same surface:

$$D_p = \sqrt{D_c x_c + \frac{D_c^2}{2}} \qquad (123)$$

where D_c and x_c are the diameter and height, respectively, of the cylinder. In using these results, it is necessary to have values of a, the surface in square feet per cubic foot, for which the authors give the values quoted in Table VI.

TABLE VI. SURFACE OF GRANULAR BEDS OF CYLINDERS AND SPHERES

D_p		Mesh size (Tyler)	Per cent void space			
			26	30	40	50
In.	Ft.		Values of a, ft.^{2}/ft.^{3}			
0.50	0.0417	. . . . .	107	101	86	72
0.40	0.0333	2	133	126	108	90
0.30	0.0250	2–5	178	168	144	120
0.20	0.0167	3–5	266	252	216	180
0.10	0.0083	7–8	533	504	432	360
0.05	0.00417	12–14	1066	1008	864	720

The authors also report values of j_H, but since the surface temperature was not measured, these values are not based on independent measurements and can be calculated from j_D. Calculated values of j_H were about 8 per cent greater than j_D. Data on pressure drop for air flow through the several beds studied are given in the two articles cited.

These data are supported by the results of Hurt,[209] who measured mass transfer in beds of granular solids for adsorption of water from air and for evaporation of naphthalene into air and into hydrogen. Hobson and Thodos[195] have extended the earlier work of Hougen *et al.* to the transfer from a packed bed to liquid streams, as have Gaffney and Drew.[153]

Illustration 10. Estimate the value of k_G for the mass transfer of water in a turbulent air stream moving 10 ft./sec. at 1 atm. and at 100°F. for (*a*) a horizontal flat plate 1 ft. long, (*b*) a wetted-wall tube 1 in. i.d., (*c*) a 1-in. cylinder placed normal to the air stream, (*d*) a single sphere 1 in. in diameter, and (*e*) a bed of 1-in. spheres. Assume the driving force to be about 0.1 atm., so that p_{BM} may be taken as 0.95 atm.

Solution. For air at 1 atm. and 100°F., $\rho = 0.071$ lb./ft.^{3};

$$\mu = 0.0183 \text{ centipoise} = (0.0183)(2.42) = 0.0444 \text{ lb./(hr.)(ft.)};$$

$D_v = (0.853)(560/492)^{3/2} = 1.04$ ft.^{2}/hr. [using $D_v = 0.853$ from Table III (page 20) corrected in proportion to the $\frac{3}{2}$ power of the absolute temperature]. From these values [or from Table III (page 20)],

$$\frac{\mu}{\rho D_v} = \frac{0.0444}{(0.071)(1.04)} = 0.60; \qquad \left(\frac{\mu}{\rho D_v}\right)^{2/3} = 0.712$$

For the flat plate. Referring to the solid line of Fig. 20:

$$\text{Re}_x = \frac{(1)(10)(3600)(0.071)}{0.0444} = 57,700$$

and from the graph,

$$j_D = \frac{k_G p_{BM}}{G_M} \left(\frac{\mu}{\rho D_v}\right)^{\frac{2}{3}} = 0.0041$$

$$k_G = 0.0041 \frac{(10)(3600)(0.071)}{(29)(0.95)(0.712)} = 0.534 \text{ lb. mole/(hr.)(ft.}^2)(\text{atm.})$$

For the wetted-wall tube. Substitution in Eq. (108) gives

$$k_c = 0.023 \left(\frac{(10)(3600)(0.071)}{(12)(0.0444)}\right)^{0.83} (0.60)^{0.44} \frac{1.04}{0.95} \times 12 = 272$$

$$k_G = \frac{k_c}{RT} = \frac{272}{(0.728)(560)} = 0.668 \text{ lb. mole/(hr.)(ft.}^2)(\text{atm.})$$

Alternatively, from Eq. (109)

$$j_D = (0.023)(4800)^{-0.17}(0.60)^{0.11} = 0.00515$$

Whence,

$$k_G = 0.00515 \frac{(10)(3600)(0.071)}{(29)(0.95)(0.712)} = 0.670 \text{ lb. mole/(hr.)(ft.}^2)(\text{atm.})$$

For the transverse cylinder. Referring to the solid line of Fig. 21:

$$\text{Re} = \frac{(10)(3600)(0.071)}{(12)(0.0444)} = 4800; \qquad j_D = 0.0086$$

Whence, by the same substitution as for the tube,

$$k_G = 1.12 \text{ lb. moles/(hr.)(ft.}^2)(\text{atm.})$$

For the single 1-in. sphere. For this case the solid line of Fig. 22 will be used:

$$\text{Re} \left(\frac{\mu}{\rho D_v}\right)^{\frac{2}{3}} = (4800)(0.712) = 3420; \qquad \frac{k_c D}{D_v} = 38$$

$$k_G = \frac{k_c}{RT} = \frac{(38)(1.04)(12)}{(0.728)(560)} = 1.16 \text{ lb. moles/(hr.)(ft.}^2)(\text{atm.})$$

For the bed of 1-in. spheres. Using Fig. 28:

$$\frac{D_p G}{\mu} = 4800; \qquad j_D = 0.0305$$

$$k_G = 0.0305 \frac{(10)(3600)(0.071)}{(29)(0.95)(0.712)} = 3.97 \text{ lb. moles/(hr.)(ft.}^2)(\text{atm.})$$

Calculation of Rate of Evaporation. For the estimation of the rate of evaporation of water from a wet surface which may be assumed to be at the wet-bulb temperature, it is convenient to convert k_G to k' (see Chap. IV) and use absolute humidity as the driving force. For example, if the dry-bulb temperature is 100°F. and the wet-bulb temperature is 65°F., then from a standard humidity chart the humidity of the main air stream is 0.0053 and the saturated humidity at 65° is 0.0133; the driving force in humidity units is $0.0133 - 0.0053 = 0.0080$ lb./lb. From Eq. (135) of Chap. IV,

$$k' = k_G M_{MP} p_{BM} = (0.95)(29)k_G = 27.5 k_G$$

Consequently, the rate of vaporization of water is

$$(27.5k_G)(0.0080) = 0.22k_G \qquad \text{lb./(hr.)(ft.}^2)$$

WORKING CHART FOR EVAPORATION PROBLEMS

Illustration 10 indicates the methods of calculation employed in using the various general correlations presented in the preceding sections and

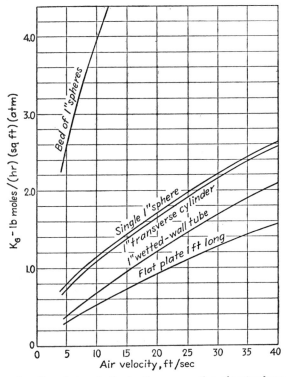

FIG. 29. k_G as a function of air velocity for the evaporation of water from various shapes (air at 100°F.; $p_{BM} = 0.95$ atm.).

may serve to clarify the usage in the matter of units. Extending this illustration, Fig. 29 has been prepared to indicate the magnitude of values of k_G for common applications. The graph represents values of k_G for mass transfer of water vapor in air at 1 atm. and 100°F., with p_{BM} of 0.95 atm., but may be used to obtain k_G for other conditions by proportion. For example, k_G varies inversely as p_{BM} and, as a first approximation, may be assumed to be proportional to D_v.

EVAPORATION OF CONSTANT-BOILING MIXTURES

When a liquid mixture is boiled, the composition of the vapor formed is determined by the vapor-liquid equilibrium for the system. When the same mixture is allowed to evaporate into air or other inert gas at a temperature below the boiling point, the composition of the vapor leaving is dictated by the relative rates of diffusion of the components through the gas film on the surface. Although the diffusion of each vapor is affected by the simultaneous diffusion of the others present, the simple relation for the diffusion of a single vapor through an inert gas may be used as an approximation. Thus the rate of transfer may be assumed to be proportional to the diffusivity and the driving force and inversely proportional to the effective film thickness. If the liquid is exposed to a turbulent current of vapor-free air, the molal rate of diffusion is proportional to the partial pressure over the solution and to approximately the square root of the diffusivity. In the evaporation of a binary mixture under these conditions the relative rates of removal of the two components A and C having partial vapor pressures p_A and p_C will be

$$\frac{N_A}{N_C} = \frac{p_A}{p_C} \sqrt{\frac{D_A}{D_C}} \qquad (124)$$

and the liquid composition will change accordingly as evaporation proceeds.

The effect of the relative diffusivities on the evaporation of constant-boiling mixtures has been pointed out by Lewis, Squires, and Sanders.[280] When the relative rates of removal of the two vapors are equal to the ratio of the amounts of the two components present in the liquid, evaporation produces no change in the composition of the liquid left behind. The composition at which this occurs is termed the "constant-evaporating composition," as distinguished from the composition at the constant boiling point. At the constant boiling point the equilibrium vapor and liquid compositions are identical and the ratio p_A/p_C is equal to the ratio of A to C in the liquid. Lewis and Squires[279] find toluene-ethanol to have a constant-evaporating mixture of 19 per cent toluene, whereas the constant-boiling mixture at the same temperature (77°F.) contains approximately 32 per cent toluene.

If A and C form a constant-boiling mixture having a minimum boiling point, the boiling of any mixture of A and C results in a progressive change of liquid composition away from the constant-boiling composition. If the same mixture is allowed to evaporate into air, however, the liquid composition may change in the opposite direction, and actually cross the constant-boiling composition, owing to the influence of the relative diffusivities. Lewis and Squires studied this effect by allowing mixtures of methanol and benzene to evaporate in a small vessel covered with a wire gauze and placed in an air current. The vaporization of a mixture initially 56 mole per cent methanol gave a liquid composition of 46 mole per cent methanol after 63 per cent by weight of the original mixture had vaporized, crossing the constant-boiling composition of 51 mole per cent methanol.   The application of the diffusion equations to the problem of relating liquid composition to fraction vaporized is dealt with by Lewis and Squires.

If the evaporation is carried on in an efficient bubbler or other saturating device, so that the air-vapor mixture leaving the apparatus is at all times in equilibrium with the liquid left behind, then no time element is involved, and the relative diffusivities obviously have no bearing on the result.   Such a process is essentially the same as boiling at the same temperature, and the Rayleigh equations for batch distillation apply.

Nomenclature for Chapter III

a_1 = ratio of fluid velocities at boundary of laminar film and in main fluid stream

a_2 = constant in Eq. (100)

c = concentration, lb. moles/ft.^{3}

c_e = concentration of solute in liquid in equilibrium with p, lb. moles/ft.^{3}

c_0 = inlet concentration, lb. moles/ft.^{3}

c_i = concentration at phase boundary, lb. moles/ft.^{3}

c_s = saturation concentration, lb. moles/ft.^{3}

C_D = drag coefficient, force lb./ft.^{2} projected area

C_p = specific heat at constant pressure, B.t.u./(lb.)(°F.)

D = diameter, ft.

D_c = diameter of cylinder in packed bed, ft.

D_L = molecular diffusivity in liquid, ft.^{2}/hr.

D_p = diameter or principal dimension of particle in packed bed, ft.

D_v = molecular diffusivity in gas, ft.^{2}/hr.

E = eddy diffusivity, ft.^{2}/hr.

E' = ratio defined by Eq. (116).

f = friction factor, dimensionless

g_c = 4.17 $\times$ 10^8 = conversion factor, (lb. mass)(ft.)/(lb. force)(hr.^{2})

G_M = molal mass velocity of stream, lb. moles/(hr.)(ft.^{2}).

h = individual or film coefficient of heat transfer, B.t.u./(hr.) (ft.^{2})(°F.).

H = Henry's law constant = p_e/c, lb. moles/(ft.^{3})(atm.)

$$j_D = \frac{k_c p_{BM}}{U_{av}P}\left(\frac{\mu}{\rho D_v}\right)^{2/3} = \frac{k_G p_{BM}}{G_M}\left(\frac{\mu}{\rho D_v}\right)^{2/3}$$

$$j_H = \frac{h}{C_p \rho U_{av}}\left(\frac{C_p \mu}{k}\right)^{2/3}$$

k = thermal conductivity, B.t.u./(hr.)(ft.^{2})(°F./ft.)

k_c = $k_G RT$ = mass-transfer coefficient, lb. moles/(hr.)(ft.^{2})(lb. mole/ft.^{3})

k_G = individual or gas-film coefficient, lb. moles/(hr.)(ft.^{2})(atm.)

k_L = individual or liquid-film coefficient, lb. moles/(hr.)(ft.^{2})(lb. mole/ft.^{3})

K_G = over-all mass-transfer coefficient, lb. moles/(hr.)(ft.^{2})(atm.)

K_L = over-all mass-transfer coefficient, lb. moles/(hr.)(ft.^{2})(lb. mole/ft.^{3})

M_0 = mean molecular weight of entering stream

M_M = average molecular weight of fluid stream

M_w = mean molecular weight of stream saturated at T_w.

N = length of wetted-wall section, ft.

N_A = rate of mass transfer, lb. moles/(hr.)(ft.^{2})

p = partial pressure of diffusing gas in main stream, atm.

p_A = partial pressure of diffusing gas A, atm.

p_B = partial pressure of nondiffusing gas B, atm.

p_{BM} = logarithmic mean of p_B at phase boundary and p_B in bulk of fluid

p_e = partial pressure of solute gas in equilibrium with c, atm.

p_1 = mean partial pressure of diffusing gas in inlet stream, atm.

p_2 = mean partial pressure of diffusing gas in outlet stream, atm.

p_i = partial pressure of diffusing gas at phase boundary, atm.

P = total pressure, atm.

r = radial distance from axis of tube, ft.

R = gas constant, (ft³)(atm.)/(lb. mole)(°R.) = 0.728

R_c = ratio of mean to maximum concentration difference

Re = Reynolds number, $DU_{av}\rho/\mu$

Re_x = length Reynolds number, based on the distance from the leading edge to the downwind boundary as the characteristic dimension

R_u = ratio of average to maximum velocity = U_{av}/U_m

T = absolute temperature, °R.

T_0 = temperature of entering stream, °R.

T_w = temperature of gas at liquid surface, °R.

u^+ = friction   velocity = $(U/U_{av}) \sqrt{2/f}$

U = fluid velocity, ft./hr.

U_{av} = mean velocity in conduit, volumetric flow rate divided by cross section, ft./hr.

U_M = maximum velocity (at center line of pipe), ft./hr.

v_m = surface velocity of liquid layer, ft./hr.

w = mass flow rate, lb./hr.

x = distance from the leading edge of a plate to the downstream edge of a heated or wet surface, ft.

x_c = length of cylinder in packed bed, ft.

x_0 = distance from the leading edge of a plate to the upstream edge of a heated or wet surface, ft.

x_1 = thickness of liquid layer, ft.

y = distance from wall or interface, ft.

$$y^+ = \frac{(r_0 - r)U_{av}\rho}{\mu} \sqrt{\frac{f}{2}} = \frac{y}{r_0} \text{ Re } \sqrt{\frac{f}{8}}$$

z = thickness of stagnant film, ft.

Z = column height, ft.

Γ = liquid-flow rate per unit width wetted wall, lb./(hr.)(ft.)

ϵ = eddy viscosity, lb./(hr.)(ft.)

ϕ_D = denominator of Eq. (99) = $fU_{av}/2k_c$

Θ = time, hr.

α = $E\rho/\epsilon$

α_n = nth root of Bessel equation $J_0(x) = 0$

ρ = density, lb./ft.³

τ = shear stress at radius r, force lb./ft.²

τ_0 = shear stress at wall, force lb./ft.²

μ = viscosity, lb./(hr.)(ft.)

ψ = $\alpha\mu/\rho D_v = E\mu/D_v\epsilon$

Problems

1. Estimate the coefficient k_G for the sublimation of naphthalene from a cast cylinder 0.5 in. in diameter, placed normal to an air stream at 20 ft./sec. at 100°F.

2. Referring to Illustration 9, what fraction of the inlet ammonia would be absorbed if the absorbent were water, supplied at the rate of 3.30 lb./hr.? The gas rate and inlet gas composition are the same as in the test described. The water temperature is constant at 68°F. It may be assumed that the gas film is controlling and that k_G is the same as in the test with acid.

3. Air at 149°F. is blown through a grid-packed tower at the rate of 555 lb./hr. The tower is supplied with water, which is found to pass through at a constant temperature of 77°F. The total wetted surface in the tower is 129 ft.^{2}. The air leaves the tower at 91°F.

Estimate the absorption coefficient k_G obtainable with this apparatus for the absorption of methanol by water from a dilute methanol-air mixture entering at the same gas rate of 555 lb./hr.

4. Hollings and Silver[200] report data on the absorption of ammonia from air by water in a small wetted-wall tower. At a mass velocity of 52.5 lb. gas per min. per ft.^{2}, they obtained a transfer coefficient K_G of 340 lb. absorbed per hr. per ft.^{2} per unit driving force, where the driving force was expressed as pounds of NH_3 per cubic foot of gas mixture. Compare this result with k_G as predicted from Eq. (110).

Data: Tower diameter, 0.394 in.; temperature, 75°F.; total pressure, 1.00 atm. The gas supplied contains less than 2.0 per cent NH_3, and properties of the gas mixture may be taken to be the same as for air.

What would you estimate k_G to be for operation under similar conditions but a total pressure of 3.4 atm.? Assume temperature, mole per cent NH_3 in inlet gas, tower length and diameter, and entering linear velocity of gas to remain unchanged.

5. Benzene-toluene mixtures having a constant boiling point at 1 atm. do not occur.

a. Is there a constant-evaporating composition for benzene-toluene mixtures evaporating at 68°F. into pure dry air? If so, what is its composition as mole per cent benzene? The vapor pressures at 68°F. are 0.0986 atm. for benzene and 0.0297 atm. for toluene. Assume that the diffusional resistance to evaporation can be represented by a stagnant air layer and that its thickness is the same for both benzene and toluene.

b. Would there be a constant-evaporating mixture if the air contained benzene corresponding to a partial pressure of 0.0263 atm.? If so, what would be the composition of the liquid, as mole per cent benzene?

6. In an experimental study of the evaporation of lacquer solvents a small amount of the solvent mixture was placed in a 2-in. evaporating dish, and the dish covered with a wire screen. The covered dish was placed in a very large desiccator, and the liquid in the dish maintained at 72°F. The dish was weighed at frequent intervals, and the following data obtained on the relation between per cent by weight evaporated and liquid composition:

Per cent evaporated	0	20	40	60	80
Mole per cent methanol	59.1	57	54	43	24

The initial liquid contained 59.1 mole per cent methanol in benzene. Prepare a plot comparing the experimental data with the relation predicted using the theoretical diffusion equations for the range from 0 to 80 per cent evaporation.

Data: The constant-boiling mixture of benzene and methanol at 72°F. contains 50 mole per cent methanol. Over the range of liquid compositions from 25 to 60 mole per cent methanol, the composition of the vapor in equilibrium with the liquid is essentially constant at 50 mole per cent methanol. Assume the resistance to diffusion to be entirely that of the stagnant gas layer between the liquid surface and the wire screen. Make any other reasonable assumptions.

Note: For a qualitative treatment of the problem, see Lewis, Squires, and Sanders.[280]

CHAPTER IV

SIMULTANEOUS HEAT AND MASS TRANSFER

In nearly all cases of mass transfer between two phases there occurs a simultaneous transfer of heat either in the same direction as that of diffusion or opposite to it. Gas-absorption equipment, cooling towers, dryers, condensers, dehumidifying equipment, and many special types of apparatus are designed for mass transfer under conditions in which the heat transfer may be negligible or may dominate design considerations. It is important to distinguish between heat transfer and heat effects: in the drying of humid air by contact with strong sulfuric acid, for example, the heat effects may be large, as evidenced by the temperature rise of the acid, yet the heat transfer between gas and liquid phases may be negligible if the two are at essentially the same temperature.

Theoretically, the transfer of heat through a fluid near a phase boundary will be expedited or retarded by the superimposed parallel diffusion or counterdiffusion of components of the fluid mixture. In the condensation of water from a hot-air–steam mixture, for example, the hot water molecules diffusing toward the cold surface carry heat in addition to that normally transported across the boundary as a result of the prevailing temperature difference. Furthermore, the conduction of heat in a gas where there is mass motion of some of the gas molecules (diffusion) in the direction of heat flow is greater than if the gas were stagnant. This last effect appears to be negligible in most practical cases; in any case, the applicable theory has not been developed. Consequently, it is usual to apply ordinary diffusion and heat-transfer equations as though each process were occurring independently of the other.

For the case of condensation of water from an air-steam mixture, the total heat effect may be written

$$q_T = h(t_G - t_i) + k_G M_A \lambda (p - p_i) \tag{125}$$

where the first term on the right represents the rate of sensible-heat transfer, and the second is the rate of liberation of latent heat of condensation of the water vapor arriving at the cold surface. Here h is the coefficient of sensible-heat transfer, k_G is the gas-film coefficient for mass transfer, M_A is the molecular weight of the diffusing vapor (water), λ is the latent heat of condensation of the water, p and p_i are the partial pres-

94

sures of the diffusing vapor in the steam-air mixture and at the cold surface, and t and t_i are the corresponding temperatures. Colburn and Hougen[91] show how this relation may be employed in the design of a condenser, giving details of a numerical example involving the cooling of air saturated with water at 203°F. by contact with the outer surface of tubes cooled internally with water. Values of q_T are calculated for a series of points along the cooling path and the required area obtained by a graphical integration of

$$A = \int \frac{dq}{q_T} \tag{126}$$

where A is the total surface and q_T is the total rate of heat transfer for the whole apparatus.

The gas mixture is assumed to be cooled to saturation at 104°F. In this example the over-all coefficient of heat transfer from gas to cooling water is estimated to vary from 294 B.t.u./(hr.)(ft.²)(°F.) at the hot end to 60 at the cold end. Logarithmic-mean driving forces are shown to give erroneous results and the graphical integration to be clearly necessary. This example, published in detail, may be referred to in connection with the application of Eq. (125) for similar cases.

CONDENSATION OF MIXED VAPORS

For the more general case of condensation of mixed vapors with no inert gas present, the movement of mixed vapor toward the cold surface carries each component more rapidly than if transfer were solely by diffusion. Similarly, diffusion of each component carries heat more rapidly than by simple heat transfer through a noncondensing film.[2] The general equations for a binary system have been given by Colburn and Drew[89] and are well worth summarizing. Let N_A and N_B represent the molal rates of condensation [lb. moles/(hr.)(ft.²)] of components A and B from a binary mixture containing y_{AG} mole fraction A at total pressure P. Let y_{Ai} be the mole fraction A in equilibrium with the surface of the condensate at t_i, and z the distance in the direction of diffusion. Then [see Eqs. (75) and (80) of Chap. III]

$$N_A = -k_{GZG}\frac{dp_A}{dz} + (N_A + N_B)y_A \tag{127}$$

The first term on the right represents the rate of diffusion and the second the rate of bodily transport of A due to condensation. The former is an approximation only, since thermal diffusion is neglected, and k_G for component A doubtless depends on the partial pressure and rate of diffusion of component B. Equation (127) may be integrated between the limits of $z = 0$ and $z = z_G$, $p_A = p_{AG}$ and $p_A = p_{Ai}$, to give

$$N_A + N_B = k_G P \ln \frac{\dfrac{N_A}{N_A + N_B} - y_{Ai}}{\dfrac{N_A}{N_A + N_B} - y_{AG}} \tag{128}$$

Similarly, the total heat-transfer rate is given by

$$q_s = h z_G \frac{dt}{dz} + (N_A M_A C_{pA} + N_B M_B C_{pB})(t - t_i)$$

which may be integrated to give

$$q_s = \frac{C_0}{1 - e^{-c_0}} h(t_G - t_i) \tag{129}$$

where $C_0 = (1/h)(N_A M_A C_{pA} + N_B M_B C_{pB})$, and $M_A C_{Ap}$ and $M_B C_{pB}$ are the molal heat capacities of the vapors A and B. From (128) and (129) the total heat effect (at the cold surface) is

$$q_T = \frac{C_0}{1 - e^{-c_0}} h(t_G - t_i) + (M\lambda)k_G P \ln \frac{\dfrac{N_A}{N_A + N_B} - y_{Ai}}{\dfrac{N_A}{N_A + N_B} - y_{AG}} \tag{130}$$

where a single value $(M\lambda)$ of the molal latent heat of condensation is used for both components.

Equation (129) shows that diffusion affects the rate of sensible-heat transfer to the extent that the multiplying factor $C_0/(1 - e^{-c_0})$ may differ from unity. If C_0 is in the vicinity of zero, the factor is approximately $1 + (C_0/2)$; if C_0 is 4.0 or greater, the factor is C_0; if C_0 is less than -2.0 the factor is $-C_0 e^{-c_0}$. If N_A and N_B are equal and opposite in sign, as in adiabatic rectification of a binary mixture, there is no net diffusion, and the sensible-heat transfer will be approximately $q_s = h(t_G - t_i)$. In applying Eqs. (128) to (130) it is often reasonable to assume t_i to be the same as the temperature of the main body of the mixed liquid, and to take y_i as the equilibrium vapor composition corresponding to the mixed-liquid composition. In the case of condensation on vertical surfaces the coefficient of heat transfer through the condensate layer may be estimated by standard heat-transfer correlations in order to relate t_i to the metal-surface temperature.

Colburn and Drew give an interesting numerical example of the application of these equations to the cooling of a mixture of methanol and water vapor. At low cooling rates the condensate is essentially in equilibrium with the vapor; for a vapor containing 70 mole per cent methanol this static dew is 34 mole per cent methanol. At large cooling rates the condensate is much richer in methanol, approaching the main-vapor composition. This "dynamic dew" is much richer in methanol because the lower surface temperature greatly increases the rate of condensation of water; methanol is carried along with this water vapor in spite of the fact that the equilibrium methanol composition y_i at the cold surface is greater than the main-vapor composition y_G.

THEORY OF THE WET-BULB THERMOMETER

Although well over a century old, the ordinary wet-bulb thermometer continues in common use as the simplest instrument for the measurement of humidity, or water-vapor content, of air. The history of this device, and especially of the theory underlying its use, is a fascinating story worth reviewing briefly.

A wet surface exposed to an air current tends to assume an equilibrium temperature t_i below that of the air, t_G, such that the rate of heat input by convection due to the temperature difference $t_G - t_i$ is just sufficient to evaporate water at a rate corresponding to diffusion with a driving force $p_i - p_G$. Here p_i is the vapor pressure of water at t_i, and p_G is the partial pressure of water vapor in the air. Maxwell's theory given in the 1877 edition of the Encyclopaedia Britannica[302] assumes heat transfer by conduction and evaporation by molecular diffusion through an air layer of thickness z_G:

$$\frac{k}{z_G} A (t_G - t_i) = \frac{\lambda D_v P A}{R T z_G P_{BM}} (p_i - p_G) \tag{131}$$

This relation fits the facts remarkably well but is at fault in making no allowance for the effects of eddy diffusion. It does not hold for vapors other than water.

In 1908 Grosvenor[167] published the familiar humidity chart with absolute humidity H defined as weight of water vapor per unit weight of dry air, and with "adiabatic-saturation" lines intersecting the saturation curve at temperatures of adiabatic saturation, t_s. These were defined by the heat balance

$$C_s(t_G - t_s) = \lambda(H_s - H_G) \tag{132}$$

where C_s is the "humid heat," or heat capacity of 1 lb. of dry air plus the water content H_G. On the basis of a large collection of simultaneous dew-point and wet-bulb temperatures reported by the U.S. Weather Bureau, W. H. Carrier[68] concluded that the temperatures of adiabatic saturation and the wet-bulb temperatures were the same. Carrier and later W. K. Lewis[274] proposed theories as to why this should be so.

Lewis first rewrote Maxwell's heat balance [Eq. (131)] using transfer coefficients and a humidity driving force for evaporation of water:

$$hA(t_G - t_i) = \lambda k' A(H_i - H_G) \tag{133}*$$

Here k' is defined by the expression

$$N_A M_A = k'(H_i - H_G) \tag{134}$$

By definition

$$H_i - H_G = \left(\frac{p_i}{P - p_i} - \frac{p_G}{P - p_G}\right) \frac{M_A}{M_B}$$

and since p_i and p_G are normally small compared to P, $P - p_i$ is approximately equal to $P - p_G$ and each is approximately equal to p_{BM}. Consequently,

$$H_i - H_G = \frac{M_A}{M_B} \frac{(p_i - p_G)}{p_{BM}}$$

and

$$k' = \frac{N_A M_A}{(H_i - H_G)} = \frac{DPM_B}{RTz_G} = k_G p_{BM} M_B \tag{135}$$

Thus the use of k' with absolute humidity as a potential is sounder than the use of k_G with partial pressure as a driving force, since the former makes allowance for variations in p_{BM}.

Lewis concluded that Eqs. (132) and (133) were identical and that t_i and t_s were the same: the wet-bulb temperature is identical with the temperature of adiabatic saturation. Furthermore, the coefficients must be the same, whence

$$\frac{h}{k'} = C_s \tag{136}$$

Although Lewis later showed his own derivation to be in error, the "Lewis equation" (136) has proved to be of great importance. If t_i and t_s are known or assumed to be the same, as noted by Carrier, then comparison of Eqs. (132) and (133) leads to (136). Thus *the Lewis equation is true if,* as is the case for water vapor in air, *the wet-bulb and adiabatic-saturation temperatures are identical.* Equation (136) does not apply except for water vapor in air, which is, of course, the most important combination in practice.

In Chap. III it was shown that the various theoretical equations for

---

* The latent heat of evaporation must traverse the air film surrounding the bulb; the smaller heat quantity required to raise the temperature of the vapor formed need traverse only part way across the gas film, since the temperature of the vapor rises as it diffuses away from the liquid surface. Equation (133) neglects this sensible-heat effect, which may be allowed for in an approximate way by adding $(t_G - t_i)/4$ to λ.

mass transfer in turbulent flow had the common form

$$k_c = k_G RT = \frac{k'RT}{p_{BM}M_B} = \frac{fU_{av}}{2\phi_D}$$

The corresponding equations for heat transfer are of the form

$$h = \frac{fC_p\rho U_{av}}{2\phi_H}$$

whence from Eq. (135)

$$\frac{h}{k'} = C_p\rho \frac{RT}{p_{BM}M_B} \frac{\phi_D}{\phi_H} \approx C_s \frac{\phi_D}{\phi_H} \tag{137}$$

It will be recalled that the various theoretical forms of ϕ_D involve the Schmidt group $\mu/\rho D_v$, and ϕ_H is similarly dependent on $C_p\mu/k$. The simplest theory is the Reynolds analogy, in which both ϕ_D and ϕ_H are unity, and (137) reduces to the Lewis equation (136). The Chilton-Colburn analogy, with p_{BM}/P taken as 1.0, gives

$$\frac{h}{k'} = C_s \left(\frac{\mu/\rho D_v}{C_p\mu/k} \right)^{2/3} \tag{138}$$

For relatively dry air the parenthesis is $(0.60/0.74)^{2/3}$ or 0.87. Arnold[8] employs the Prandtl-Taylor analogy in a similar way.

It is a remarkable coincidence that the erroneous derivations of Carrier and of Lewis led to a valid generalization for water and air, and to the important Eq. (136), which is good to within a few per cent for water vapor and air. The later theories are still inadequate, since the best theoretical values of ϕ_D and ϕ_H are based partially on friction data or velocity gradients *inside pipes*. Lacking data on the effects of $\mu/\rho D_v$ and $C_p\mu/k$ for flow normal to a cylinder, as for a wet-bulb thermometer, the simple form (138) may be taken as the most useful expression of present theory of the wet-bulb hygrometer. This may be employed for any vapor-gas pair, obtaining $\mu/\rho D_v$ from Table III (page 20) and substituting h/k' in Eq. (133) to obtain the relation between t_i and H_G. Wet-bulb thermometers are normally operated at gas velocities and at temperature levels such that radiation to the wet wick is negligible in comparison with heat transfer by convection. An allowance for radiation from surroundings at the dry-bulb temperature may be made by multiplying the left-hand side of Eq. (133) by $1 + (h_r/h)$, where h_r is the effective coefficient of heat transfer by radiation. Both h and h_r may be estimated by methods given by McAdams.[309] One of the unique features of the wet-bulb thermometer is the relatively small effect of air velocity on the observed reading. Since h and k' vary similarly with gas velocity, the only effect is on the ratio h_r/h.

Experimental determinations of the ratio h/k' are difficult, since radiation and sensible heat in the liquid feed must be avoided, and small errors in measuring t_i have opposite effects on numerator and denominator when Eq. (133) is solved for h/k'. Table VII summarizes some of the best measurements on glass thermometer bulbs fitted with cloth wicks, using various liquids in air. The last column represents values calculated by the use of Eq. (138), showing good agreement in most cases. Measurements of h/k' for water in air in wetted-wall columns give values in the range $0.95C_s$ to $1.12C_s$.

TABLE VII. SUMMARY OF VALUES OF h/k' CALCULATED FROM WET-BULB MEASUREMENTS IN AIR*

Vapor	Arnold[8]	Hilpert[187]	Mark[296]	Calculated from Eq. (138)
Benzene	....	0.49	0.41	0.44
Bromobenzene	....	0.46	....	0.47
Carbon tetrachloride	....	0.50	0.44	0.49
Chorobenzene	....	0.51	0.44	0.48
Ethyloacetate	....	....	0.42	0.46
Ethylene bromide	....	0.53	....	0.47
Ethylene tetrachloride	....	....	0.50	0.51
Ethyl propionate	0.50	....	....	0.46
Methyl alcohol	0.35	....	....	0.31
Propyl alcohol	0.43	....	....	0.41
Toluene	0.50	0.46	0.44	0.47
Water	0.27	....	0.26	0.21

* The values tabulated have not been corrected for radiation from the surroundings. Mark's data were obtained with high air velocities, and the correction is negligible; the radiation correction would reduce Arnold's values by 12 to 16 per cent.

Bedingfield and Drew[28] have recently measured "wet-bulb" temperatures with cylinders of solid naphthalene and three other solids, which were allowed to sublime into air flowing normal to the test cylinder. The Schmidt group differed by less than 10 per cent for the four solids, but an empirical correlation was suggested on the basis of these results and the data of Arnold, Mark, and Dropkin:

$$\frac{h}{k'} = 0.294 \left(\frac{\mu}{\rho D_v}\right)^{0.56} \tag{139}$$

For wet-bulb thermometers in air this is better than Eq. (138), since the smaller exponent makes it possible to fit both water and the organic compounds.

The common practice of employing the adiabatic cooling lines on the standard humidity chart to obtain the humidity H_G from measured wet-

and dry-bulb readings is acceptable only for water in air, because the wet-bulb temperature is essentially the same as the temperature of adiabatic saturation, *i.e.*, because h/k' happens to be numerically close to C_s. Humidity charts have been prepared with lines of constant wet-bulb temperature, based on Eq. (133), but this is hardly worth doing for water and air. For the organic vapors in air such lines have slopes up to twice those of the adiabatic cooling lines, and the wet-bulb temperatures are very considerably higher than the temperatures of adiabatic saturation.

For various discussions of wet-bulb theory and data see Awberry and Griffiths,[12] Dropkin,[116] Van Mieghem,[474] Arnold,[8] Carrier and Mackey,[69] and Lewis.[272]

Illustration 11. A thermometer covered with a clean, porous wick wet with benzene is placed in a current of a gas mixture containing air and benzene vapor. Care is used to maintain the wick adequately wet with benzene supplied at a temperature as near as practicable to the observed wet-bulb temperature. The gas velocity is sufficiently great so that radiation to the wick may be assumed to be small as compared with heat transfer by convection. Under these conditions the observed wet-bulb temperature is 67.5°F. at a dry-bulb temperature of 197.6°F. and under a barometric pressure of 768.4 mm. Estimate the benzene content of the gas.

Data and assumptions: The latent heat of vaporization of benzene at 67.5°F. is 14,600 B.t.u./lb. mole; the vapor pressure of benzene at this temperature is 74.5 mm. Hg.

Solution. The wetted wick may be assumed to be in dynamic equilibrium with its surroundings, as expressed by Eq. (133). Using the value of 0.44 for h/k', as given by Eq. (138), and Table VII, this becomes

$$(0.44)(197.6 - 67.5) = \frac{14,600}{78}\left(\frac{74.5}{768.4 - 74.5}\frac{78}{29} - H_G\right)$$

whence $H_G = -0.017$ lb. benzene/lb. air. (The temperatures quoted were observed by Mark[296] for a benzene wet-bulb thermometer in air containing no benzene. The correct value of $H_G = 0$ would have been obtained in the calculation by employing $h/k' = 0.415$.)

Illustration 12. Air at atmospheric pressure has a dry-bulb temperature of 86.0°F. and a wet-bulb temperature of 68.0°F. To what degree does the wet-bulb temperature differ from the temperature of adiabatic saturation? Assume the best experimental value of h/k' to be 0.265.

Solution. At 68°F. the vapor pressure of water is 17.5 mm. Hg, and the latent heat of vaporization is 1054 B.t.u./lb. Substituting in Eq. (133)

$$(0.265)(86 - 68) = 1054\left(\frac{17.5}{760 - 17.5}\frac{18}{29} - H_G\right)$$

whence $H_G = 0.0101$.

At this condition $C_s = 0.24 + (0.48)(0.0101) = 0.245$, and by Eq. (132)

$$(0.245)(86 - t_s) = (1054)(H_s - 0.0101)$$

H_s and t_s are related by the saturation curve of the humidity chart, whence, by trial and error, $t_s = 67.6$°F.; *i.e.*, the wet-bulb temperature and the temperature of adiabatic saturation differ by 0.4°F., the wet-bulb temperature being higher.

THEORY OF COOLING-TOWER OPERATION

Many industrial operations require that large quantities of heat be discarded to the atmosphere. In most cases water is employed as the cooling medium, and in areas where it is expensive or not plentiful, it is economical to cool and recirculate the water. This is done in so-called "cooling towers" or "evaporative water coolers," in which the principal cooling effect is the evaporation of a part of the water being cooled. Although the water is normally warmer than the air, cooling by evaporation can be effective even though the air is somewhat warmer than the water. The water is brought into intimate contact with large quantities of air in large crosscurrent or countercurrent towers usually made of wood or other inexpensive water-resistant materials. The total installed volume of existing cooling towers is probably several times greater than that of all other industrial mass-transfer equipment, single units being as large as 40 ft. wide, 26 ft. high, and several hundred feet long.

The theory of mass and heat transfer under conditions of usual cooling-tower operations will be presented in two parts. In this section the basic theory will be outlined, leaving the application to countercurrent equipment to a later chapter. At any point in a cooling tower water in the form of small drops or a thin flowing film is in contact with a moving air stream, and the conditions are not dissimilar to those of a wet-bulb thermometer. The basic differential equations defining the mass- and heat-transfer phenomena were given by C. S. Robinson[392] and by Walker, Lewis, and McAdams[486] in 1923, but it was Merkel[319] or Hirsch[191] in 1925 who showed how the problems of using these equations might be greatly simplified by employing total heat or enthalpy as the useful driving force.[316,429]

Let G represent the flow rate of dry air expressed as lb./(hr.)(ft.^{2} horizontal cross section). Let a represent the surface of contact between air and water in 1 ft.^{3} of tower. Then the contact surface in a tower height dx is $a\,dx$ ft.^{2} per ft.^{2} of tower cross section. The rate of sensible-heat transfer across this surface is

$$GC_s\,dt_G = ha(t_i - t_G)\,dx \qquad (140)$$

where t_G is the air temperature and t_i is the temperature of the water surface. Following Eq. (134) the corresponding mass-transfer equation is

$$G\,dH_G = k'a(H_i - H_G)\,dx \qquad (141)$$

where H_i is the humidity of saturated air at the water surface temperature t_i. The products ha and $k'a$ may be considered as heat- and mass-transfer coefficients on a *volume* basis: ha as B.t.u./(hr.)(ft.^{3})(°F.) and

$k'a$ as lb./(hr.)(ft.^{3})(unit ΔH). The rate at which heat is given up by the water is the sum of the sensible-heat transfer and the latent heat of vaporization:

$$G(C_s \, dt_G + \lambda_i \, dH_G) = G \, di_G = [ha(t_i - t_G) + \lambda_i k'a(H_i - H_G)] \, dx \quad (142)$$

where i_G is the enthalpy of the air system, B.t.u./lb. dry air content. As noted in the preceding section, the ratio h/k' is approximately equal to C_s for the case of water in air, whence

$$G \, di_G = k'a[C_s(t_i - t_G) + \lambda_i(H_i - H_G)] \, dx \quad (143)$$

Since the enthalpy of moist air per pound of dry-air content at temperature t_G and humidity H_G is $C_s(t_G - t_0) + \lambda_0 H_G$, it follows that Eq. (143) may be approximated closely by

$$G \, di_G = k'a(i_i - i_G) \, dx \quad (144)$$

where i_i is the enthalpy of saturated air at the water surface temperature t_i. Note that $k'a$ represents either the mass-transfer rate as lb./(hr.)(ft.^{3})(unit ΔH) or the heat-transfer rate as B.t.u./(hr.)(ft.^{3})(°F.); the same numerical value applies. This expression indicates that the simultaneous evaporation and sensible-heat transfer may be allowed for quite simply by employing air enthalpy as the driving force in calculating total heat transfer.

By analogy to Eq. (144), an over-all coefficient may be defined by the equation

$$G \, di_G = K'a(i_L - i_G) \, dx \quad (145)$$

where i_L is the enthalpy of air saturated at the temperature of the main water stream. Combining Eqs. (144) and (145),

$$\frac{i_L - i_G}{i_i - i_G} = \frac{k'a}{K'a} \quad (146)$$

from which it follows that $K'a$ bears a constant relation to $k'a$ (independent of t_L) providing $(i_L - i_G)/(i_i - i_G)$ is constant. Equation (144) is not generally useful since the surface temperature t_i and hence i_i are not known, and it is convenient to employ Eq. (145) involving a driving force based on enthalpies at the main-stream temperatures. The use of an over-all coefficient is justified if the left side of Eq. (146) can be assumed to be constant. This does not necessarily mean that the liquid-film resistance is neglected; it would be true in any case in a narrow temperature range over which i_L can be taken as linear in t_L.

The enthalpies of saturated air (per pound of dry air content) are tabulated as a function of temperature in the 1945 A.S.H.V.E. "Guide" and in later references. Figure 30 shows these values plotted for the ordinary cooling-tower temperature range of 70 to 130°F. Point O represents the condition of the air at any point in the cooling tower, located by plotting its enthalpy i_G, not against air temperature but against the water temperature at the same point in the tower. Thus point P represents the enthalpy i_L of air saturated at the water temperature, and the vertical distance PO represents the over-all enthalpy driving force $i_L - i_G$ used in Eq. (145) with the over-all coefficient $K'a$. If the

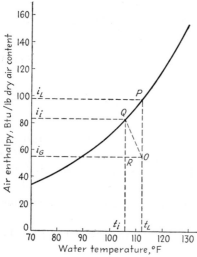

water "film" represents an appreciable thermal resistance, the conditions at the water surface will be represented by a point Q at a lower temperature than the main water stream. The vertical distance QR represents the driving force $i_i - i_G$ as used in Eq. (144) with the coefficient $k'a$. Since the ratio of the length OP to the length RQ is given by Eq. (146) as $k'a/K'a$, it follows that, if the ratio of the two coefficients (or the relative resistances of gas and liquid films) is known, then point Q and the conditions at the water surface may be defined. This would permit the use of the more rigorous Eq. (144). In ordinary

FIG. 30.   Enthalpy-temperature diagram.

cooling-tower calculations, however, the use of an over-all coefficient $K'a$ with the simpler Eq. (145) has proved to be quite satisfactory.

The use of enthalpy as a driving force in cooling-tower calculations not only provides a valuable simplification but aids in understanding cooling-tower operation. Adiabatic cooling lines on the humidity chart are lines of constant enthalpy, and since the temperature of adiabatic saturation and the wet-bulb temperature are the same for air-water mixtures, it follows that the enthalpy of humid air is dependent only on its wet-bulb temperature. Consequently, the performance of a given cooling tower should be dependent on the inlet air wet-bulb temperature but independent of the dry-bulb temperature. This explains a well-known empirical observation.

Values of $K'a$ have been obtained[429] experimentally for cooling towers of various designs. The use of these coefficients and the graphical integration of Eq. (145) for design purposes will be described in a later chapter.

Where values of the film coefficients are known, the driving forces for both air and water films may be derived by a simple graphical construction on Fig. 30, as explained by McAdams.[312]

H. S. Mickley[322] has shown how data on the individual film coefficients may be employed to follow the changes in dry-bulb temperature through cooling-tower or dehumidification equipment.

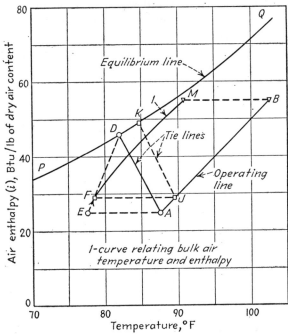

FIG. 31.   Determination of air conditions through air-water contacting equipment.   (*After Mickley.*)

From Eqs. (140) and (145) and the assumption $h/k' = C_s$,

$$\frac{di_G}{dt_G} = \frac{i_i - i_G}{t_i - t_G} \tag{147}$$

which gives the slope of a curve of i_G vs. t_G.   If h_L represents the individual coefficient of heat transfer through the water film, then

$$\frac{i_i - i_G}{t_i - t_L} = -\frac{h_L}{k'} \tag{148}$$

Referring to Fig. 31, PQ is the equilibrium graph of enthalpy of saturated air vs. temperature. AB is the "operating line" (see Chap. V) based on the enthalpy balance

$$G \, di_G = L C_L \, dt_L \tag{149}$$

Points A and B represent the conditions at the air inlet and outlet, respectively. The "tie line" AD is drawn through A with a slope $-h_L/k'$; the intersection at D fixes the interface conditions. Thus the potential $i_i - i_G$ at the air inlet is represented by the difference in ordinates of D and A.

Point A and the line AB represent air enthalpy as a function of *water* temperature. Curve EFM is the desired curve of air enthalpy vs. air temperature. This is obtained by starting at E (inlet air enthalpy; inlet air temperature) and constructing the straight line ED, which from Eq. (147) will have the slope di_G/dt_G. Point F, a short distance along ED, is taken as a new starting point and the tie line JK drawn. In this way the dry-bulb curve EFM is approximated by a series of short segments, and the outlet dry-bulb temperature found as the abscissa of point M.

DEHUMIDIFICATION OF AIR

The partial removal of water vapor from a gas is accomplished in many industrial operations by bringing the mixture into contact with a cold surface. Sensible heat and moisture are transferred in the same direction, from gas to surface. The two may be assumed to move independently, and the Colburn-Hougen method of calculation employed. The principal interest in dehumidification, however, is in air conditioning, where air is cooled and dehumidified by being passed through a refrigerated extended-surface coil. Because of the interest in this special application, it will be worth while to consider a design method which is both simple and elegant and which is particularly applicable to air-conditioning coils.

Although the analysis is not restricted to any particular type of apparatus, it is helpful to have a particular design in mind in order to follow the derivation more readily. A typical coil is illustrated in Fig. 32. This shows the horizontal tubes carrying boiling Freon or other refrigerant, the vertical gang fins providing a large extended surface, and the narrow passages between the fins for horizontal air flow. For data on heat transfer without condensation in coils of this type, see McAdams.

Let G represent the air flow rate as pounds of dry air content per hour per square foot of superficial or face area of the coil. Then the sensible-heat transfer and the moisture transfer may be expressed separately by

$$-GC_s \, dt_G = h(t_G - t_i) \, dA \tag{150}$$

and

$$-G \, dH_G = k'(H_G - H_i) \, dA \tag{151}$$

Taking h/k' as equal to C_s for water vapor in air [Eq. (136)], the following is obtained by division:

$$\frac{dH_G}{dt_G} = \frac{H_G - H_i}{t_G - t_i} \tag{152}$$

This expression, due to Lewis and Keevil,[277] makes it possible to follow the change of humidity with air temperature through the coil. In most

Fig. 32.   Dehumidifying coil with gang fins.   (*Courtesy of Fedders-Quigan Corp.*)

refrigerated coils the metal-surface temperature is very nearly constant, for which case Eq. (152) may be integrated to give

$$\frac{H_{G2} - H_i}{H_{G1} - H_i} = \frac{t_{G2} - t_i}{t_{G1} - t_i} \tag{153}$$

The air enters at H_{G1} and t_{G1} and leaves with humidity H_{G2} and temperature t_{G2}. This is the equation of a straight line and is the basis of the "straight-line rule" used in following the course of air cooling with the help of a humidity chart.

Referring to Fig. 33, OPQ is the saturation curve of the familiar graph of humidity vs. temperature.   Point B represents the inlet air conditions H_{G1} and t_{G1}, and point P represents the coil-surface conditions H_i and t_i.

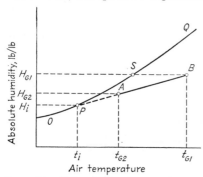

Equation (153) states that point A, representing the outlet air conditions H_{G2} and t_{G2}, must lie on the straight line connecting B and P. If the surface is warmer than the dew point S, no condensation will occur and the path will be along the horizontal line BS.   Some years ago it was commonly believed that all the air would have to be cooled to the dew point before any condensation would occur and that the cooling path was along BSP; it should have been obvious, perhaps, that condensation would occur when the humid air first contacts the surface below the dew point, since condensation of water on cold windowpanes is a common observation.

Fɪɢ. 33. Dehumidification path on humidity chart.

Applying Eqs. (150) and (151) to the removal of sensible heat and moisture from the air passing through the refrigerated coil, the total heat effect may be obtained as

$$dq_T = -G(C_s\,dt_G + \lambda_i\,dH_G) = G\,di_G$$
$$= h(t_G - t_i)\,dA + k'\lambda_i(H_G - H_i)\,dA \qquad (154)$$

Again using the relation $h = k'C_s$ [Eq. (136)], and noting that i_G is $C_s(t_G - t_0) + \lambda_0 H_G$, it follows that Eq. (154) may be rewritten, approximately but not rigorously,

$$dq_T = -G\,di_G = k'(i_G - i_i)\,dA \qquad (155)$$

whence, assuming i_i constant,

$$\ln\frac{i_{G1} - i_i}{i_{G2} - i_i} = \frac{k'A}{G} = N_t \qquad (156)$$

where A is the total surface per square foot of superficial or face area.

From Eq. (156)

$$i_{G1} - i_{G2} = (1 - e^{-N_t})(i_{G1} - i_i) = C_1(i_{G1} - i_i) \qquad (157)$$

and

$$q_T = G(i_{G1} - i_{G2}) = C_1 G(i_{G1} - i_i) \qquad (158)$$

As in the case of a cooling tower, the total heat effect is given by a rate equation involving enthalpy as the driving force; the enthalpy change of the air stream is proportional to the initial enthalpy potential. The proportionality constant C_1 is a simple function of k', the air rate G, and the total surface A. Since air enthalpy is determined only by the wet-bulb temperature, it follows that for a fixed air rate over a specified coil the total cooling load is determined by the inlet wet-bulb and the surface temperatures and is independent of the inlet dry-bulb temperature.* This also confirms a common empirical observation.

In most refrigerated coils for air-conditioning use, the thermal resistance of the boiling refrigerant, the metal tube, and the fins is relatively small compared to that on the air side, and the surface is only some 5°F. warmer than the refrigerant. Under these conditions the method of calculation may be simplified by the use of over-all coefficients, thus avoiding the trial-and-error determination of surface conditions. Thus

$$dq_T = k'(i_G - i_i)\, dA = U_m(t_i - t_R)\, dA = K'(i_G - i_R)\, dA \quad (159)$$

where U_m is the over-all coefficient of heat transfer from metal surface to refrigerant, per square foot of total surface in contact with the air stream; t_R is the refrigerant temperature; K' is the over-all coefficient defined by the equation, and i_R is the enthalpy of air saturated at t_R. From Eq. (159), it follows that

$$\frac{1}{K'} = \frac{1}{k'} + \frac{C_2}{U_m} \quad (160)$$

where

$$C_2 = \frac{i_i - i_R}{t_i - t_R}$$

which is the slope of a chord on the enthalpy saturation curve. This ratio C_2 is fixed by the properties of air and water but varies with temperature. Over the important temperature range of 45 to 55°F., C_2 varies from about 0.48 to 0.58; since the term involving C_2 is smaller than $1/k'$, it is satisfactory to employ an average value of 0.53 in calculating the relative resistances.

Illustration 13. A manufacturer's bulletin gives the following performance data on a six-row finned cooling coil: inlet air, 80° dry-bulb, 67° wet-bulb; refrigerant boiling at 45°; air rate, 500 ft./min. or 2165 lb. dry air content per hr. per ft.² face area; total cooling load, 9.70 B.t.u. per lb. dry air; sensible-heat removal, 6.50 B.t.u. per lb. dry air.

Derive the characteristic coefficients $K'A$, $U_m A$, and C_1.

Solution. From the A.S.H.V.E. Table, the enthalpy of the inlet air is 31.51 B.t.u./lb.:

$$i_{G1} = 31.51; \qquad i_{G2} = 31.51 - 9.70 = 21.81$$

---

* This is true if there is condensation, but not if the surface temperature t_i is above the inlet air dew point.

Wet-bulb temperature of outlet air = 52.8° (obtained from enthalpy table corresponding to $i = 21.81$). Temperature drop of air = $6.50/C_s = 6.50/0.246 = 26.4°$. Outlet dry-bulb temperature = $80 - 26.4 = 53.6°$. Since inlet and outlet dry-bulb and wet-bulb temperatures are known, points A and B of Fig. 33 are fixed; extension of this straight line shows the surface temperature t_i to be 51.3°. The temperature difference $t_i - t_R$ is $51.3 - 45 = 6.3°$, and $U_m A = (2165)(9.70)/6.3 = 3340$. From the enthalpy table, $i_R = 17.61$ at 45°, whence $i_{G1} - i_R = 31.51 - 17.61 = 13.90$, and $i_{G2} - i_R = 21.81 - 17.61 = 4.20$. Consequently [Eq. (156)]

$$K'A = 2165 \ln \frac{13.90}{4.20} = 2600 \text{ B.t.u./(hr.)(ft.}^2 \text{ face area)} \text{ (unit } \Delta i \text{ driving force)}$$

N_t is $2600/2165$ or 1.2, and $C_1 = 0.70$. This means that the air passing through the coil is cooled 70 per cent of the distance toward saturation at the refrigerant temperature.

From Eq. (160),

$$\frac{1}{2600} = \frac{1}{k'A} + \frac{0.53}{3340}$$

whence $k'A = 4430$, and the air side is found to present 59 per cent of the total resistance.

Inspection of performance data on commercial coils indicates that results obtainable with coils from different manufacturers differ quite widely. This is indicated by the representative data given in Table VIII for four commercial air-conditioning coils.

TABLE VIII. PERFORMANCE OF EXTENDED-SURFACE COOLING COILS IN DEHUMIDIFYING AIR FOR AIR CONDITIONING
(Face velocity 500 ft./min.)

Characteristics	Coil A	Coil B	Coil C	Coil D
Number of rows tubes.............	4	6	3	5
Coil depth, in. (front to back)..........	9	9		
Number of fins per inch..............	7	8	8	8
Fin thickness, in.....................	0.013	0.006		
Surface per ft.^{2} face, ft.^{2}..............	105	143		
Pressure drop, in H$_2$O.................	0.25	0.24	0.31	0.50
$K'A$ (per ft.^{2} face)...................	1750	2500	1220	1990
$U_m A$ (per ft.^{2} face).................	3780	4100	1210	2000
K'.................................	16.7	17.5		
U_m.................................	36.0	28.6		
Per cent of total resistance represented by metal and refrigerant..............	24	32	53	53
C_1, fractional approach to saturation at refrigerant temperature.............	0.632	0.686	0.423	0.608
Per cent latent-heat removal with refrigerant at 45° and 67° inlet air wet-bulb...	33	33	27	30

The design method presented in the foregoing is remarkably versatile and simple, in view of the complexity of the physical process of dehumidification. If values of U_m and K' are established as a function of air rate, then it is relatively easy to calculate total cooling load, per cent latent-heat removal, and outlet air conditions for a specified coil. The method is particularly useful in simplifying the program of tests performed as a basis for the preparation of the detailed and complex performance tables provided by the manufacturers to users of such equipment.

Use of the separate coefficients U_m and k' to allow for the varying coil-surface temperature is explained by Mickley.[322] Referring to Fig. 34, PQ is the equilibrium line or saturation curve of enthalpy vs. air temperature. From Eq. (159),

$$\frac{i_G - i_i}{t_i - t_R} = \frac{U_m}{k'} \qquad (161)$$

which is the negative slope of the tie line AD. Points A and B represent the inlet and outlet air enthalpies plotted against the refrigerant temperature t_R; AB is the "operating line." The construction AD with slope $-U_m/k'$ locates the point D,

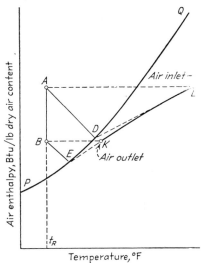

Fig. 34. Allowance for varying coil-surface temperature in dehumidification.

representing the conditions at the metal surface at the air inlet. From Eqs. (150) and (155),

$$\frac{di_G}{dt_G} = \frac{i_G - i_i}{t_G - t_i} \qquad (162)$$

from which it follows that the path LK representing air enthalpy vs. air temperature must start at L with a slope equal to that of LD, *i.e.*, tangent to LD. The path curve can be constructed in short segments in this way, since the starting point and the slopes are known. The end point K is fixed by the design conditions of cold-air temperature or enthalpy decrease. The enthalpy potentials to use with k' are obtained from the graph: at the air inlet Δi is the vertical distance from D to A or L; at the air outlet it is the vertical distance from E to B or K.

FOG FORMATION IN CONDENSERS

Fog is frequently formed in gas coolers where condensation occurs and is usually a nuisance because it is difficult to collect. In order for fog to form, it is necessary that the gas mixture be cooled below its dew point, ordinarily by admixture with still colder air. Fog may occur in the gas film near the cold surface, though no detailed study of this complicated phenomenon has been made.

Figure 35 indicates the application of the straight-line rule to determine the cooling path in a case where the initial air is nearly saturated. The straight line connecting the initial point B with the point P representing the surface conditions passes across the saturation curve, suggesting that the mixture would be supersaturated when cooled to t_{G2}. Actually, the path is along BP to the saturation curve and then down the saturation line. In such a case fog forms in the main body of the gas.

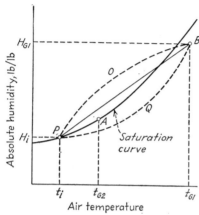

Fig. 35. Illustration of conditions determining fog formation in gas coolers.

The straight-line rule expressed by Eqs. (152) and (153) applies only to water vapor in air, since Eq. (136) was used in combining Eqs. (150) and (151). For the more general case, let C_3 represent $h/C_s K'$, whence Eq. (152) becomes

$$\frac{dH_G}{dt_G} = \frac{1}{C_3}\frac{H_G - H_i}{t_G - t_i} \quad (163)$$

For organic vapors in air C_3 is 1.3 to 2.1, as is evident from the values of h/k' given in Table VII. It follows from Eq. (163) that in such cases the slope of the cooling-path curve is always less than that of a chord to point P, and the path is of the type BOP. Such a path would clearly be conducive to fog formation. For the rarer case of a very small C_3 the curvature is reversed, and the path can be of the type BQP, with no fog formation.

As a means of preventing fog formation in condensers, Colburn and Edison[90] suggest the simultaneous addition of sensible heat along the cooling path. In a vertical tubular condenser cooled externally, for example, they suggest locating a heated rod in the vertical axis of the condenser. Addition of heat to the gas does not affect the condensation process, since the pressure or humidity driving forces causing mass transfer are not affected, but the temperature of the main gas stream is kept above the dew point all along the path, which is of the type BQP. The same end result would be obtained by letting the fog form and then reheating the gas leaving the condenser.

Nomenclature for Chapter IV

a = surface of contact between phases, ft.^{2}/ft.^{3} of apparatus

A = surface of contact between phases, ft.^{2}

$C_1 = 1 - e^{-Nt}$

$C_2 = (i_i - i_R)/(t_i - t_R)$

$C_3 = h/C_s k'$

C_L = specific heat of liquid, B.t.u./(lb.)(°F.)

$C_0 = (1/h)(N_A M_A C_{pA} + N_B M_B C_{pB})$

C_p = heat capacity at constant pressure, B.t.u./(lb.)(°F.)

C_s = "humid heat," or heat capacity of 1 lb. dry gas plus its vapor content, B.t.u./ (lb. dry gas content)(°F.)

D = diameter, ft.

D_v = diffusion coefficient, ft.²/hr.

f = friction factor, dimensionless

G = mass velocity of fluid, lb./(hr.)(ft.² cross section)

h = surface coefficient of heat transfer, B.t.u./(hr.) (ft.²)(°F.)

h_L = individual coefficient of heat transfer through water film, B.t.u./(hr.)(ft.²)(°F.)

h_r = coefficient of heat transfer by radiation, B.t.u./(hr.)(ft.²)(°F.)

H = absolute humidity, lb. vapor/lb. dry gas

H_s = humidity of gas saturated with vapor at t_s

i = enthalpy, B.t.u./lb. dry gas content

k = thermal conductivity, B.t.u./(hr.)(ft.²)(°F./ft.)

k_G = mass-transfer coefficient for gas film, lb. moles/(hr.)(ft.²)(atm.)

K' = over-all coefficient of mass transfer, defined by Eq. (145), B.t.u./(hr.)(ft.²) (unit Δi)

k' = mass-transfer coefficient defined by Eq. (134), lb./(hr.)(ft.²)(unit ΔH), or B.t.u./(hr.)(ft.²)(unit Δi)

M = molecular weight

N = rate of mass transfer, lb. moles/(hr.)(ft.²)

$N_t = k'A/G$

p = partial pressure of one component in a gas mixture, atm.

P = total pressure, atm.

p_{BM} = logarithmic-mean partial pressure of nondiffusing component in gas "film," atm.

q = rate of heat transfer, B.t.u./(hr.)(ft.²)

q_s = rate of sensible-heat transfer, B.t.u./(hr.)(ft.²)

q_T = total heat effect, B.t.u./hr.

R = gas constant = 0.728 (ft.³)(atm.)/(lb. mole)(°R.)

t = temperature, °F.

t_s = temperature of adiabatic saturation, °F.

T = absolute temperature, °R.

U_{av} = average velocity of main gas stream, ft./hr.

U_m = over-all coefficient from external metal surface to cooling fluid, B.t.u./(hr.) (ft.²)(°F.)

x = distance, or height of equipment, ft.

y = mole fraction of one component

z = distance in the direction of diffusion, ft.

z_G = equivalent thickness of gas "film," ft.

λ = latent heat of vaporization, B.t.u./lb.

ϕ_D = function appearing in Eq. (99)

ϕ_H = corresponding function for heat transfer

ρ = density, lb./ft.³

μ = viscosity, lb./(hr.)(ft.)

1   refers to initial or inlet condition.
2   refers to final or outlet condition.
A refers to component A.
B refers to component B.
G refers to main gas stream.
i refers to conditions at surface or phase boundary.
L refers to main liquid stream.
0   refers to datum or reference state.
R refers to cooling fluid.

Problems

1. In a solvent-cleaning plant a waste air stream carries an unknown amount of carbon tetrachloride vapor. In order to estimate the loss, a thermometer having a cloth wick wet with carbon tetrachloride is placed in the air stream. At a dry-bulb temperature of 158°F. the observed wet-bulb temperature is 68°F. with the barometer at 767 mm. Hg. The duct is 2 ft. square, and the gas velocity is 5.0 ft./sec.

Estimate the loss of carbon tetrachloride in this air stream, as pounds per hour.

Data: At 68°F. the latent heat of vaporization of carbon tetrachloride is 97 B.t.u./lb., and the vapor pressure is 91 mm. Hg. Assume the emissivity of the wet-bulb thermometer to be 0.8 and the heat-transfer coefficient, gas to wet-bulb, as 8.5 B.t.u./(hr.) (ft.²)(°F.). Allow for radiation to duct wall at 68°F.

2. Tests on a small forced-draft countercurrent cooling tower give the following results:

Inlet air dry-bulb temperature . . . .   80°F.
Inlet air wet-bulb temperature . . . .   70°F.
Outlet air wet-bulb temperature . . . .   90°F.
Inlet water temperature . . . . 110°F.
Outlet water temperature . . . .   80°F.

Assuming air and water rates to be unchanged, what is the maximum temperature of the water delivered by this tower in the summer? It is anticipated that the worst condition will be an air supply at 90°F. with a wet-bulb temperature of 78°F. The cooling load is constant; *i.e.,* the heat removed by the water stream and delivered to the tower is maintained the same as in the test.

CHAPTER V

PRINCIPLES OF THE DESIGN OF ABSORPTION EQUIPMENT

PRINCIPAL TYPES OF ABSORPTION EQUIPMENT

Industrial apparatus for gas absorption or stripping may usually be classified as one of four quite different types, each having as a principal objective the promotion of interphase contact between gas and liquid. Many varieties and combinations of these types exist or are possible, but only the major classifications will be described briefly. A fuller description of various commercial absorption towers will be found in Chap. VII.

Spray towers consist of large empty chambers through which the gas circulates and into which the liquid is introduced in the form of droplets by means of spray nozzles or other atomizing devices. The sprays may be introduced at the top of a cylindrical tower and the gas passed in at the bottom. The contact is not truly countercurrent, however, as the momentum of the injected spray is usually sufficient to stir the gas thoroughly in a tower only a few diameters high. As a result, the composition of the gas is nearly uniform throughout the chamber. The spray nozzles break the liquid into a large number of small drops, providing the interfacial surface across which diffusional transfer takes place. Within the smallest drops the liquid is stationary, and movement of the solute takes place by molecular diffusion. The larger drops of the spray may be mixed internally, however, on account of liquid circulation caused by frictional drag at the drop surface.

Although diffusion is slow inside the smaller drops, the continuous formation of fresh liquid surface at the spray nozzles allows absorption to take place rapidly. The spray is formed by the collapse of high-velocity liquid jets at the nozzles, and the gas-film resistance around the drops is relatively small because of the high velocities with which the drops are propelled into the gas. The interfacial area present in a spray chamber is surprisingly small, so that the rate of absorption per unit volume of chamber may be smaller than for other types of equipment.

The principal problem met in the design of a spray absorber is the difficulty of keeping fine droplets suspended in a rising stream of gas, which tends to carry the spray upward and out of the chamber. This entrainment of spray is reduced in the wet-cyclone gas washer, in which the gas spirals upward and the spray is thrown from the axis toward the walls by centrifugal force. Spray apparatus is suitable for applications which require small changes in the composition of the liquid or gas being treated and where countercurrent action is not necessary. Typical applications are humidification and dehumidification of air by water, desorption of insoluble gases from water, and absorption of ammonia by water. Low pressure drop across the spray chamber and simple construction are advantages of this type of apparatus.

Quite opposite in principle to the spray tower are the units in which the gas is dispersed in pools of the liquid in the form of fine bubbles. The subdivision of the gas stream may be accomplished by forcing the gas through a porous plate or cylinder placed at the bottom of the liquid-filled vessel, or by introducing the gas from a tube which opens underneath an agitator. The small bubbles present a very large surface of contact between the phases; interphase diffusion takes place as the bubbles are formed and as they rise through the liquid. The liquid-phase resistance is reduced by the motion of the bubbles upward or by the action of the agitator, but the gas-phase resistance may be relatively great because of the lack of turbulent mixing within the bubbles. For this reason, equipment of this sort is most useful for the absorption of relatively insoluble gases, where the liquid-phase resistance controls the rate of mass transfer. The aeration of sewage is a typical application of a porous-plate device. Other types of equipment may be more economical when expensive power must be supplied to overcome the large liquid head in introducing the gas below the surface.

Bubble-plate and sieve-plate absorbers are commonly used in industry. They represent a case intermediate between simple spray chambers and aerated-tank absorbers. In them, bubbles are formed at the bottom of a shallow pool of liquid by forcing the gas either through a metal plate drilled or punched with many small holes or under a number of slotted, bell-shaped metal caps immersed in the liquid. A large share of the interphase transfer occurs as the gas bubbles are formed and as they rise through the agitated liquid. Additional transfer takes place above the liquid surface, owing to the spray and foam which are thrown up by the violent mixing of liquid and vapor on the plate. Such plates or trays are arranged one above another in a cylindrical shell. The liquid flows downward, crossing first one plate and then the next below. The vapor rises through the plates. This type of equipment has the practical advantage that the gas stream is dispersed nearly uniformly through all the liquid. There are no stagnant zones which are by-passed by one of the fluid streams, and channeling is avoided. Plate-type absorbers and strippers are used frequently in the petroleum and chemical industries, especially for absorbing soluble gases. A more complete description of such equipment will be given in Chap. VII.

The fourth general type of equipment is the packed tower, in which the liquid stream is subdivided to provide a large interfacial area as it flows by gravity over the surface of a packing material. A large number of different types of "packing" are in use, ranging from crushed stone through specially fabricated hollow ceramic cylinders to wood or ceramic slats formed into grids. The liquid flows down the packing surface in thin films or individual streams, without filling the void space within the packing. The gas may flow downward, parallel to the liquid, or upward. Both the liquid and the gas phases are well agitated, and the equipment of this type may be used for absorbing either soluble or relatively insoluble gases. Some difficulty is experienced in maintaining uniform liquid and gas flow throughout a cross section of a packed tower, so that the operation may not be truly countercurrent. Nevertheless, equipment of this type is used frequently, especially where low pressure drop is required or where corrosive fluids are encountered. The wetted-wall column may be considered to be a special form of packed tower. A more complete description of packed towers is given in Chap. VII.

PACKED COLUMNS–MASS-TRANSFER COEFFICIENT ON A VOLUME BASIS

The mass-transfer coefficient K_G was defined by Eq. (82) as the rate of interphase diffusion expressed as moles per unit time per unit area per unit of driving force in terms of pressures. Although the wetted-wall column described in Chap. III has a definite interfacial surface area, the corresponding area in the case of most absorption equipment is difficult, if not impossible, to evaluate. It is usually possible to calculate the total surface of the dry packing, but this is somewhat greater than the interfacial area because the solvent circulated tends to collect at the points of contact of the lumps of packing and all the surface may not be wet. For this reason it is convenient to introduce a new variable a, which represents the interfacial area per unit of volume. Since both a and K_G depend on the nature of the packing and on the flow rates of the liquid and vapor streams, they may be combined as a product $K_G a$, which represents the over-all capacity coefficient, on a volume basis, for any particular packing. Thus $K_G a$ represents the rate of interphase diffusion as moles per unit time per unit volume per unit of driving force in terms of pressures. It is defined by the equation

$$N_A a \, dV = K_G a (p - p_e) \, dV \qquad (164)$$

where $N_A a$ is the rate of transfer as moles per unit volume of equipment, and V represents the volume of packing. $K_L a$ is similarly defined by the equation

$$N_A a\, dV = K_L a(c_e - c)\, dV \qquad (165)$$

as the rate of diffusion expressed as moles per unit time per unit volume per unit of driving force in terms of concentrations.

The capacity coefficients $K_G a$ and $K_L a$ are of fundamental importance in engineering-design calculations. $K_G a$ will be expressed as lb. moles/ (hr.)(ft.³)(atm.). $K_L a$ will be expressed as lb. moles/(hr.)(ft.³)(unit Δc), where Δc represents the over-all driving force as pound moles solute per cubic foot of solution. The net units of $K_L a$ are hr.$^{-1}$ The same units will be employed in connection with the individual film coefficients on a volume basis, $k_G a$ and $k_L a$.

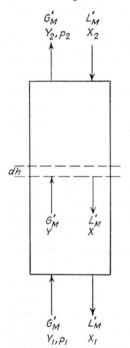

Fig. 36. Countercurrent contacting of gas and liquid.

GRAPHICAL DESIGN METHOD

In the application of the various rate equations to the conditions of a commercial absorption tower, it is necessary to allow for the fact that both gas and liquid concentrations may vary throughout the apparatus. Allowance for these variables is best made by the graphical method developed and described by Walker, Lewis, and McAdams.[487] The present treatment will follow these authors closely in method and nomenclature but will employ partial pressures or mole fractions instead of stoichiometric units for gas concentrations, in an attempt to make the method somewhat less restricted in application, and less confusing for use with coefficients based on a driving force in partial pressures.

Consider any countercurrent absorption equipment, such as a packed tower, illustrated diagrammatically in Fig. 36. The absorbent enters at the top, containing L_M' lb. moles/hr. of solute-free, nonvolatile liquid per square foot of tower cross section with X_2 lb. moles solute per lb. mole solvent. On the volume basis, the concentration may be expressed as c_2 lb. moles solute per ft.³ solution. In passing through the apparatus the solute concentration increases to X_1 or c_1. The gas to be treated enters at the bottom, containing G_M' lb. moles/(hr.)(ft.²) of solute-free, or "inert," gas, and with a partial pressure of the solute gas of p_1 atm. At the top the partial pressure of the solute in the gas leaving has been reduced to p_2. If the pressure drop through the apparatus is assumed to be negligible in comparison with the total pressure P, we may write the over-all material balance

$$L_M'(X_1 - X_2) = G_M'\left(\frac{p_1}{P - p_1} - \frac{p_2}{P - p_2}\right) \tag{166}$$

Similarly, if the concentrations at any point in the apparatus are X and p, respectively, then

$$L_M'(X_1 - X) = G_M'\left(\frac{p_1}{P - p_1} - \frac{p}{P - p}\right) \tag{167}$$

If the concentrations X_1 and p_1 are fixed, and the ratio L_M'/G_M' known, then Eq. (167) specifies the relation between the variable X and p. If the relation between the concentration and density of the solution is known, the relation between X and c can be obtained readily. Equation (167) is based on a material balance only and involves no assumptions other than steady flow and constant conditions of the streams fed to the tower. Consequently it may be relied upon as an expression for the relation between gas and

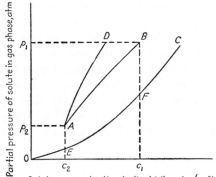

Fig. 37. Operating lines and equilibrium line for countercurrent column.

liquid concentrations at any point in the apparatus.

Figure 37, curve AB, represents a typical relation between p and c. The point B represents the conditions at the gas inlet, where both gas and liquid concentrations are high. The point A represents the conditions at the gas outlet, the partial pressure of solute in the gas having been reduced from p_1 to p_2. The curve AB expresses graphically the relation between p and c and is termed the "operating line." On the same figure is shown a representative equilibrium curve OC, indicating the relation between the concentration of solute in the liquid and the partial pressure of the solute in the gas phase in equilibrium with it. The location of this line depends on the nature of the solute and the solvent and on the temperature of the liquid absorbent. Although the equilibrium curve may be any one of a number of shapes, the curve shown slightly concave upward is typical of the equilibrium relation for various common systems. For absorption to take place, the solute concentration in the gas must be greater than in the liquid, *i.e.*, the operating line must lie above the equilibrium curve. For the reverse operation of "desorption" or "stripping," the operating line will lie below the equilibrium curve.

Gas–film Resistance Controlling. In some cases the gas absorbed is highly soluble in the absorbent, and the liquid-film resistance may be assumed to be negligible in comparison with the resistance of the gas film. Under such conditions the concentration drop across the liquid film may be neglected. The partial pressure p_i of the solute at the gas-liquid interface may thus be taken as the equilibrium pressure p_e corresponding to the main body of the solution. The driving force across the gas film is obtained, therefore, as the difference between the pressures read from the operating and equilibrium curves, respectively, at any concentration c in the main body of the liquid. Similarly, the mean inert-gas pressure p_{BM} at any point becomes the logarithmic mean of $P - p$ and $P - p_e$, where p is the partial pressure of solute in the gas phase and p_e is the equilibrium pressure over the solution.

The material balance leading to Eq. (167) and to the "operating line" provides the relation between p and c necessary for the integration of the diffusion equations. For the case of gas-film resistance controlling, the rate of absorption, obtained by differentiating Eq. (167), is equated to the rate of diffusion as given by Eq. (164):

$$L_M' \, dX = \frac{G_M'P}{(P - p)^2} \, dp = k_G a(p - p_e) \, dh = k_G' a P \frac{p - p_e}{p_{BM}} \, dh \quad (168)$$

In this equation dh is the differential tower height (volume per square foot of tower cross section), and a is the interphase surface per unit volume. The mass-transfer coefficient k_G' has the same units as k_G but is independent of the gas composition. The two are related by the equation

$$k_G' = k_G \frac{p_{BM}}{P} \quad (169)$$

The partial pressure of inert or nondiffusing gas is easily obtained from the known total pressure P and the curves EF and AB. In this way p_{BM} is obtained as a function of X and the tower height found by integration:

$$h = \int_0^h dh = L_M' \int_{X_2}^{X_1} \frac{p_{BM} \, dX}{k_G' a P (p - p_e)} = G_M' \int_{p_2}^{p_1} \frac{p_{BM} \, dp}{k_G' a (P - p)^2 (p - p_e)} \quad (170)$$

Although it is often possible to use simplified forms of this relation, as explained below, the general relation given above must be used in any case where the inert-gas pressure varies appreciably from one end of the apparatus to the other. In some cases a large fraction of the total inlet gas is absorbed, and the gas-film coefficient k_G' may vary considerably because of the reduced gas velocity. If the relation between $k_G'a$ and G_M' can be expressed in terms of p, its variation can be allowed for in the integration of Eq. (170). In the analysis of test data on absorption towers, $k_G'a$ should be obtained by graphical integration. An approximate value may be obtained, however, by using the mean of the values of p_{BM} for the two ends of the apparatus.

Illustration 14. Using a 4-in.-diameter column filled to a depth of 1 ft. with 1-in. Raschig rings, Vivian[479] obtained the following data for the absorption of chlorine from air by means of an aqueous solution of sodium hydroxide:

$L_2 = 12,300$ lb. caustic solution/(hr.)(ft.^{2})
$G_1 = 396$ lb. total gas/(hr.)(ft.^{2})
$p_1 = 0.503$ atm., $p_2 = 0.0403$ atm., $P = 1$ atm. (total pressure)
Normality of caustic at top of tower $= 3.68$
Normality of caustic at bottom of tower $= 2.82$
Average gas temperature $= 75°F.$
Average liquid temperature $= 83°F.$

Calculate the value of the gas-film absorption coefficient at the bottom of the tower.

Solution. Owing to the high concentration of sodium hydroxide, there was negligible vapor pressure of chlorine over the liquid at the interface, and all the resistance to mass transfer was in the gas phase. Since the gas velocity decreased sharply as chlorine was removed from the gas, the absorption coefficient decreased toward the top of the tower. This variation must be allowed for in calculating the value of the integral on the right of Eq. (170). If we assume that the gas-film coefficient $k_G a$ varies as the 0.8 power of the mass velocity of the gas, we may write

$$k_G'a = k_G a \frac{p_{BM}}{P} = \left(\frac{k_G a p_{BM}}{P}\right)_1 \left(\frac{G}{G_1}\right)^{0.8} \tag{171}$$

where $(k_G a p_{BM}/P)_1$ represents the value of this group at the bottom of the packing. The mass velocity ratio is related to the gas composition by the equation

$$\frac{G}{G_1} = \frac{M}{M_1} \frac{P - p_1}{P - p} = \frac{71p + 29(P - p)}{71p_1 + 29(P - p_1)} \frac{P - p_1}{P - p} \tag{172}$$

Since $p_e = 0$, and $p_{BM}/p = 1/\ln[P/(P - p)]$, Eq. (170), used for calculating

$$(k_G a p_{BM}/P)_1$$

now becomes

$$\left(\frac{k_G a p_{BM}}{P}\right)_1 = \frac{G_M'}{h} \left(\frac{M_1}{P - p_1}\right)^{0.8} \int_{p_2}^{p_1} \frac{dp}{\left(\frac{M}{P - p}\right)^{0.8} (P - p)^2 \ln\left(\frac{P}{P - p}\right)} \tag{173}$$

For the above data,

$$M_1 = (71)(0.503) + (29)(0.497) = 50.0 \text{ lb./lb.mole}$$

$$G_M' = \frac{(396)(0.497)}{50} = 3.94 \text{ lb. moles air/(hr.)(ft.}^2)$$

$$\left(\frac{k_G a p_{BM}}{P}\right)_1 = \frac{(3.94)(50/0.497)^{0.8}}{1} \int_{0.0403}^{0.503} \frac{dp}{\left(71\frac{p}{P - p} + 29\right)^{0.8} (P - p)^2 \ln\left(\frac{P}{P - p}\right)}$$

The integral is easily evaluated numerically, after dividing the total interval of p into eight parts, each 0.0578 atm. in width.

p, atm.	$\dfrac{1}{\left(71\dfrac{p}{P-p}+29\right)^{0.8}(P-p)^2\ln\dfrac{P}{(P-p)}}$	
0.0403	1.65	$\times 1 = 1.65$
0.0981	0.662	$\times 4 = 2.648$
0.1559	0.413	$\times 2 = 0.826$
0.2137	0.302	$\times 4 = 1.208$
0.2715	0.240	$\times 2 = 0.480$
0.3293	0.200	$\times 4 = 0.800$
0.3871	0.174	$\times 2 = 0.348$
0.4449	0.158	$\times 4 = 0.632$
0.5030	0.139	$\times 1 = 0.139$
		8.731

The value of the definite integral is, by Simpson's rule,

$$\frac{(0.0578)(8.731)}{3} = 0.168$$

and

$$\left(\frac{k_G a p_{BM}}{P}\right)_1 = \frac{(3.94)(50)^{0.8}(0.168)}{(1)(0.497)^{0.8}} = 26.4 \text{ lb. moles/(hr.)(ft.}^2)$$

An alternative, approximate method of solution,* based on the assumption that $k_G a$ is proportional to G_M, leads to the equation

$$\left(\frac{k_G a p_{BM}}{P}\right)_1 = \frac{G_{M1}}{\ln\dfrac{\ln (P-p_1)}{\ln (P-p_2)}} = \frac{396\frac{4}{50}}{\ln\dfrac{\ln (1-0.503)}{\ln (1-0.0403)}} \qquad (174)$$
$$= 27.9 \text{ moles/(hr.)(ft.}^2)$$

Liquid-film Resistance Controlling. Under conditions such that the liquid film offers the principal resistance to diffusion, the liquid at the interface may be assumed to be in equilibrium with the main body of the gas. The driving force, therefore, is the difference between the concentrations c_e and c, obtained from the equilibrium and operating lines, respectively, at any partial pressure p in the main body of the gas.

Combining the material balance with the diffusion relation [Eq. (165)], there results

$$L_M' \, dX = k_L a(c_e - c) \, dh \qquad (175)$$

whence

$$h = L_M' \int_{X_2}^{X_1} \frac{dX}{k_L a(c_e - c)} \qquad (176)$$

After constructing the operating and equilibrium curves, it is not difficult

* This method is discussed on pages 137 to 138.

to evaluate the terms under the integral sign and carry out the integration graphically.

Where the liquid density ρ_L may be taken as constant,

$$L_M' \, dX = \frac{L}{\rho_L} \, dc; \qquad h = \frac{L}{\rho_L} \int_{c_2}^{c_1} \frac{dc}{k_L a(c_e - c)} \qquad (177)$$

where L is the liquid rate expressed as lb./(hr.)(ft.^{2}).

Allowance for Resistance of Both Gas and Liquid Phases. As shown in Chap. III, the rate of interphase transfer is proportional to the difference in the bulk composition of the phases, expressed in the same units, provided there is a linear relation between the compositions of the phases at equilibrium. Thus,

$$N_A a \, dV = K_G a(p - p_e) \, dV = k_G a(p - p_i) \, dV = k_G a P(y - y_i) \, dV$$
$$= K_L a(c_e - c) \, dV = k_L a(c_i - c) \, dV = k_L a \rho_M(x_i - x) \, dV \qquad (178)$$

where p_e is the equilibrium vapor pressure over a solution having a concentration c, and where p_i and p are similarly related to c_i and c_e. Here x and y are mole fractions of solute in liquid and gas, respectively, and ρ_M is the molal density of the liquid, *i.e.*, ρ_L divided by the average molecular weight of the liquid stream. The equalities involving c_i and p_i are true only if a plot of p_i vs. c_i is linear over the range of concentrations of interest. Under this condition

$$\frac{1}{K_G a} = \frac{1}{k_G a} + \frac{H}{k_L a} \qquad (179)$$

$$\frac{1}{K_L a} = \frac{1}{k_L a} + \frac{1}{H k_G a} \qquad (180)$$

where the constant H is equal to $(p_i - p_e)/(c_i - c_e)$. Where Henry's law applies, H is the Henry's law constant defined by $p_i = H c_i$.

When the use of the over-all transfer coefficients is justified, the equations used for calculating the tower height are similar to Eq. (170), with $K_G' a$ replacing $k_G' a$. Since experimental data are usually reported as over-all coefficients, the resulting equations are used most frequently for design calculations. Such calculations often involve dilute solutions, with the result that Eqs. (196) and (198) below are the ones used for most practical work.

Strictly speaking, over-all coefficients cannot be used except when the equilibrium line is straight over the region which includes the interfacial and bulk compositions. Otherwise it is unsafe to use over-all coefficients for conditions other than those for which the coefficients were determined experimentally.

In the absorption of most gases which are moderately soluble, such as, for example, sulfur dioxide in water, the resistance to diffusion is appreciable in both phases.   In Chap. III it was shown that, if the equilibrium and operating lines are straight, the combined resistance can be expressed by an over-all coefficient which is independent of liquid or gas concentrations.   Curved equilibrium lines are encountered in some cases, however, and in these instances the calculation should be based on one or the other individual resistance, if these are known.

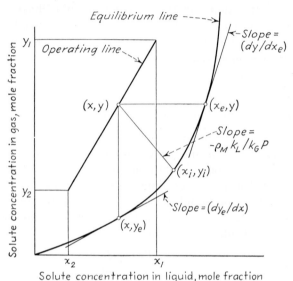

FIG. 38.   Determination of interfacial compositions in countercurrent absorber.

As outlined in Chap. III, the interfacial compositions y_i and x_i may be found for each pair of values of y and x, *i.e.*, for each level in the apparatus, by drawing a line from the point (x,y) on the operating line toward the equilibrium line with a slope equal to $-(\rho_M k_L / k_G P)$.   This procedure is illustrated in Fig. 38.   The values of y_i and x_i determined at the intersections with the equilibrium line are then used in the integrals in either of the equations

$$ h = \frac{G_M}{k_G a P} \int_{y_2}^{y_1} \frac{dy}{y - y_i} \tag{181} $$

$$ h = \frac{L_M}{\rho_M k_L a} \int_{x_2}^{x_1} \frac{dx}{x_i - x} \tag{182} $$

An alternative procedure gives an approximately correct result when the curvature of the equilibrium line is slight and when the resistance in one phase is small but not zero.   When most of the resistance is in the gas phase, for example, the interfacial compositions are nearly but not exactly equal to x and y_e. Actually, y_i is slightly greater than y_e, and x_i is slightly greater than x. To a first approximation, x_i and y_i are located on a straight line which is tangent to the equilibrium curve at the point (x,y_e) and has a slope dy_e/dx. The equation of this line is

$$\frac{y_i - y_e}{x_i - x} = \frac{dy_e}{dx} \tag{183}$$

The over-all driving force is made up of two parts, one across each film, i.e.,

$$y - y_e = (y - y_i) + (y_i - y_e) \tag{184}$$

Eliminating $y_i - y_e$ by using Eq. (183),

$$y - y_e = (y - y_i) + (x_i - x)\frac{dy_e}{dx} \tag{185}$$

Since

$$N_A = K_G aP(y - y_e) = k_G aP(y - y_i) = k_L a\rho_M(x_i - x) \tag{186}$$

Eq. (185) shows that

$$\frac{1}{K_G aP} = \frac{1}{k_G aP} + \frac{1}{k_L a\rho_M}\frac{dy_e}{dx} \tag{187}$$

According to this equation, $K_G a$ is not constant throughout the tower even though $k_G a$ and $k_L a$ may be constant, since dy_e/dx varies. When $K_G a$ varies, it must be placed under the integral sign in Eq. (181), giving for the tower height

$$h = G_M \int_{y_2}^{y_1} \frac{dy}{K_G aP(y - y_e)} = \frac{G_M}{k_G aP} \int_{y_2}^{y_1} \frac{dy}{y - y_e}$$
$$+ \frac{G_M}{k_L a\rho_M} \int_{y_2}^{y_1} \frac{dy_e}{dx}\frac{dy}{y - y_e} \tag{188}$$

This equation avoids the graphical solution for the interfacial compositions but does not eliminate the need for both individual coefficients.

According to Eq. (188) the average slope of the equilibrium line m_{av}, is given by

$$m_{av} = \frac{\displaystyle\int_{y_2}^{y_1} m\, dy/(y - y_e)}{\displaystyle\int_{y_2}^{y_1} dy/(y - y_e)} \tag{189}$$

This may be seen by comparing Eq. (188) with the equation for column height obtained by assuming that the value of $K_G aP$ is independent of composition,

$$h = \frac{G_M}{k_G aP} \int_{y_2}^{y_1} \frac{dy}{y - y_e} + \frac{G_M}{k_L a\rho_M} m_{av} \int_{y_2}^{y_1} \frac{dy}{y - y_e} \tag{190}$$

When most of the resistance is in the liquid phase and the equilibrium line is only slightly curved, a similar derivation gives

$$h = \frac{L_M}{k_L a \rho_M} \int_{x_2}^{x_1} \frac{dx}{x_e - x} + \frac{G_M}{k_G a P} \int_{x_{e2}}^{x_{e1}} \frac{dx_e}{x_e - x} \tag{191}$$

By comparing Eq. (191) with a similar equation for the column height based on the assumption that $K_L a$ is independent of composition, we find the following equation for the average slope of the equilibrium line:

$$\frac{1}{m_{\text{av}}} = \frac{\int_{x_2}^{x_1} dx/m(x_e - x)}{\int_{x_2}^{x_1} dx/(x_e - x)} \tag{192}$$

Equations (189) and (192) give two different expressions for the average slope m_{av}. It is therefore apparent that the use of an average value of m for calculating the over-all coefficient from the individual film coefficient is generally unjustified; the correct average is different depending on whether the resistance is mainly in the liquid or in the vapor phase. If the resistance is known to be principally in the vapor or in the liquid phase, average values of m calculated from Eqs. (189) and (192), respectively, are more accurate than other arbitrarily selected methods[121,149] of calculating m_{av}.

Simplified Procedure for Lean Gas Mixtures. The general procedure described above may be simplified considerably for cases where the following conditions hold:

1. The mean partial pressure of the inert carrier gas remains essentially constant or equal to the total pressure throughout the apparatus.

2. The capacity coefficients $k_G a$ and $k_L a$ remain constant throughout the apparatus.

3. The solute content of the gas and liquid phases is sufficiently low so that the partial pressure p may be assumed proportional to the concentration Y expressed in stoichiometric units (moles of solute per mole of inert carrier gas) and the concentration may be taken as proportional to the concentration X in stoichiometric units, i.e., $Y \doteq y = p/P$, and $X \doteq x = c/\rho_M$, where ρ_M is the density of the liquid expressed in pound moles per cubic foot. Under these conditions $G_M' \doteq G_M$ and $L_M' \doteq L_M$.

In stoichiometric units the material balance may be written exactly as

$$L_M'(X_1 - X) = G_M'(Y_1 - Y) \tag{193}$$

or approximately as

$$L_M(x_1 - x) = G_M(y_1 - y) \tag{194}$$

Since this relation assumes only steady flow and constant feed strength of gas and liquid, it must hold whatever the mechanism of the diffusion may be for any tower construction or type of steady operation. Figure 39 shows the "operating line" AB representing this relation between x and y as given by this equation. Point B represents the conditions at the gas inlet and liquid outlet, where the concentrations are y_1 and x_1; point A represents the corresponding conditions at the gas outlet, where the concentrations are y_2 and x_2. Since Eq. (194) is linear, only inlet and outlet concentrations are necessary to place this "operating line," representing the relation between gas and liquid concentrations throughout the apparatus.

Equilibrium data for the system may be plotted on the same diagram as the operating line, as indicated by the curve OC of Fig. 39. As explained above, the operating line must be above the equilibrium curve if absorption is to take place, but for the reverse operation of stripping the operating line will be below the equilibrium curve.

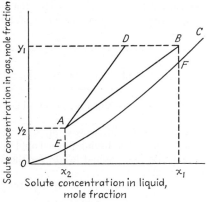

Fig. 39. Operating lines and equilibrium line for countercurrent column.

Where the gas-film resistance controls, the difference in concentration between gas and liquid phase, and consequently the driving force causing diffusion, is represented by the vertical distance between the curves AE and BF. The rate equation may be written

$$L_M \, dx = G_M \, dy = K_G a P(y - y_e) \, dh = \frac{K_L a}{\rho_M}(x_e - x) \, dh \qquad (195)$$

in which y and y_e are the mole fractions in the gas phase and in equilibrium with the liquid, respectively, and x and x_e are the mole fractions in the liquid phase and in equilibrium with the gas. The tower height may be calculated either in terms of gas-phase compositions, by using the equation

$$h = \frac{G_M}{K_G a P} \int_{y_2}^{y_1} \frac{dy}{y - y_e} \qquad (196)$$

or in terms of liquid-phase compositions, by using

$$h = \frac{L_M}{\rho_M K_L a} \int_{x_2}^{x_1} \frac{dx}{x_e - x} \qquad (197)$$

Equations (196) and (197) are obtained from Eq. (195), assuming the mass-transfer coefficients to be constant.   Alternatively, since the liquid is a dilute solution,

$$h = \frac{L}{\rho_L K_{La}} \int_{x_2}^{x_1} \frac{dx}{x_e - x} = \frac{L}{\rho_L K_{La}} \int_{X_2}^{X_1} \frac{dX}{X_e - X} \qquad (198)$$

Illustration 15.   An NH_3-air mixture containing 2.0 per cent NH_3 at 68°F. and 1 atm. is to be scrubbed with water in a tower packed with 1-in. stoneware Raschig rings.   The water rate will be 240 lb./(hr.)(ft.²) and the gas rate 240 lb./(hr.)(ft.²) at the gas inlet.   Assume the tower temperature remains constant at 68°F.   At this temperature the partial pressures of NH_3 over aqueous ammonia solutions are as follows:

p_e, mm. Hg	12.0	18.2	31.7	50.0	69.6	166
Concentration, lb. NH_3/100 lb. water	2.0	3.0	5.0	7.5	10	20

For the above packing, K_{Ga} is obtained from Chap. VIII as 3.9 lb. moles/(hr.)(ft.³) (atm.).

Note that for absorption of dilute gases in systems obeying Henry's law, the logarithmic-mean driving force should be used (see below).

Estimate the required height for the absorption of 98 per cent of the NH_3 in the entering gas.

Solution.   Basis: 1 ft.² of cross-sectional area of the tower.

$$y_1 = 0.02 \text{ mole fraction } NH_3$$

$$Y_1 = \frac{0.02}{0.98} = 0.02041 \text{ lb. mole } NH_3/\text{lb. mole air}$$

$$NH_3 \text{ absorbed} = (0.02041)(0.98) = 0.0200 \text{ lb. mole } NH_3/\text{lb. mole air}$$

$$Y_2 = 0.00041 \text{ lb. mole } NH_3/\text{lb. mole air}$$

$$y_2 = 0.00041 \text{ mole fraction } NH_3$$

$$G_{M'} = \frac{240}{\{1 + [(0.02041)(17)/29]\}(29)} = 8.18 \text{ lb. moles air/(hr.)(ft.²)}$$

$$L_{M'} = {}^{240}\!/_{18} = 13.33 \text{ lb. moles/(hr.)(ft.²)}$$

$$X_2 = x_2 = 0$$

$$X_1 = \frac{8.18}{13.33} \times 0.0200 = 0.01227 \text{ lb. mole } NH_3/\text{lb. mole } H_2O$$

$$x_1 = \frac{0.01227}{1.012} = 0.01210 \text{ mole fraction } NH_3$$

From the equilibrium data it is seen that Henry's law holds approximately through the range of concentrations encountered in this problem.   Therefore

$$y_e = \frac{p_e}{P} = \frac{Hc}{P} = \frac{H\rho_M x}{P}$$

$$H\rho_M = \frac{p_e}{x} = \frac{(12)(100)(17)}{(760)(2)(18)} = 0.746 \text{ atm./mole fraction}$$

and

$$y_e = 0.746x$$

K_{Ga} is given as 3.9 lb. moles/(hr.)(ft.³)(atm.).   Substituting in Eq. (196),

$$h = \frac{8.18}{3.9} \int_{0.00041}^{0.02} \frac{dy}{y - 0.746x}$$

Since the equation of the operating line is approximately

$$(8.18)(y - 0.00041) = (13.33)(x - 0)$$

the equation for the tower height becomes

$$h = \frac{8.18}{3.9} \int_{0.00041}^{0.02} \frac{dy}{y - \dfrac{(0.746)(8.18)}{13.33} (y - 0.00041)}$$

$$= \frac{8.18}{3.9} \int_{0.00041}^{0.02} \frac{dy}{0.542y + 0.000188}$$

$$= \frac{8.18}{(3.9)(0.542)} \ln \frac{(0.542)(0.02) + 0.000188}{(0.542)(0.00041) + 0.000188}$$

$$= 12.7 \text{ ft.}$$

As shown in the text, use of the logarithmic-mean driving force leads to the same result:

$$y_{e1} = \frac{H_\rho M x_1}{P} = (0.746)(0.012) = 0.00895$$

$$y_1 - y_{e1} = 0.02 - 0.02 - 0.00895 = 0.01105$$
$$y_2 - y_{e2} = 0.00041 - 0 = 0.00041$$

$$(y - y_e)_{\text{l.m.}} = \frac{0.01105 - 0.00041}{\ln \frac{1105}{41}} = 0.00320$$

$$h = \frac{G_M(y_1 - y_2)}{K_G a P (y - y_e)_{\text{l.m.}}} = \frac{(8.18)(0.02 - 0.00041)}{(3.9)(0.00320)} = 12.7 \text{ ft.}$$

Logarithmic-mean Driving Force. Although the graphical or analytical procedure outlined above must be employed in many practical design problems, it is frequently possible to use a simple mean driving force or potential and so to obviate the integration. Where it is possible to assume that the equilibrium curve and the operating line are linear over the range in which they are to be used, it can be shown that the logarithmic mean of the terminal potentials is theoretically correct. When the over-all gas-film coefficient is used to express the rate of interphase transfer, the calculation then reduces to the solution of the equation

$$L_M(x_1 - x_2) = G_M(y_1 - y_2) = K_G a P h (y - y_e)_{\text{av}} \tag{199}$$

$$(y - y_e)_{\text{av}} = \frac{(y - y_e)_1 - (y - y_e)_2}{\ln [(y - y_e)_1 / (y - y_e)_2]} \tag{200}$$

Assume the equilibrium curve to be linear in the range x_1 to x_2. Then, since the operating line is also linear, the difference in ordinates of the two lines must also be linear in x or y; *i.e.*, $y - y_e$, designated by Δ, is linear in y, and

$$\frac{d\Delta}{dy} = \frac{\Delta_1 - \Delta_2}{y_1 - y_2} \tag{201}$$

Substituting this in Eq. (196),

$$\frac{hK_G a P}{G_M} = \int_{y_2}^{y_1} \frac{dy}{\Delta} = \frac{y_1 - y_2}{\Delta_1 - \Delta_2} \int_{\Delta_2}^{\Delta_1} \frac{d\Delta}{\Delta} = \frac{y_1 - y_2}{\Delta_1 - \Delta_2} \ln \frac{\Delta_1}{\Delta_2} \tag{202}$$

whence, from Eq. (199),

$$(y - y_e)_{av} = \Delta_{av} = \frac{\Delta_1 - \Delta_2}{\ln (\Delta_1/\Delta_2)} \tag{203}$$

In general, the logarithmic mean applies wherever the potential is linear in the variable defining the amount transferred ($y - y_e$ linear in y; Δt linear in t; etc.).

A similar procedure may be followed to show that, when the over-all liquid-film coefficient is used,

$$G_M(y_1 - y_2) = L_M(x_1 - x_2) = \rho_M K_L a h(x_e - x)_{av} \tag{204}$$

where

$$(x_e - x)_{av} = \frac{(x_e - x)_1 - (x_e - x)_2}{\ln [(x_e - x)_1/(x_e - x)_2]} \tag{205}$$

It may be noted that with gas film controlling it is necessary that the equilibrium curve be linear between x_2 and x_1 if the logarithmic mean is to be used. With liquid film controlling, the logarithmic mean applies if the equilibrium curve is linear over the range y_2 to y_1.

Limiting Gas and Liquid Rates. It is evident from Eq. (195) that the slope of the operating line of Fig. 39 is L_M/G_M. It is also apparent from the figure that large values of L_M/G_M correspond to steep operating lines and to large values of the driving force, $x_e - x$ or $y - y_e$. The gas- and liquid-flow rates consequently have a profound effect on the required size of the apparatus, quite apart from their effect on the capacity coefficients $K_G a$ and $K_L a$. The lines AD and AB of Figs. 37 and 39 represent the conditions in two absorbers operating over the same range of gas compositions, but with different ratios of liquid to gas rates. AD is farther from the equilibrium curve, and the apparatus need not be so large to absorb the same weight of solute. As the ratio L_M/G_M is decreased, the operating line approaches the equilibrium curve, and the driving force causing diffusion decreases. Actual touching of operating and equilibrium curves would represent equilibrium at that point in the apparatus; this would be impossible in an actual apparatus of finite length. There is consequently a minimum value of the ratio L_M/G_M below which the absorber could not operate, no matter how large it might be. For a fixed gas capacity, the liquid rate corresponding to this minimum value of L_M/G_M is termed the minimum liquid rate and may be used as a basis for choosing a practical liquid rate to be used. The operating liquid rate should be chosen by balancing the cost of additional absorber volume against the cost of recovering the solute from its dilute solution in the solvent. These economic factors will be discussed more completely in a later section. Good practice usually requires that the operating and equilibrium lines have roughly the same slope.

The maximum gas and liquid rates are fixed by the tendency toward flooding, entrainment, or carry-over. These phenomena will be discussed in a later section.

Illustration 16. Two hundred cubic feet per minute of an air-SO_2 mixture containing 10 per cent SO_2 by volume at 68°F. and 1 atm. are to be scrubbed with water in a countercurrent packed tower for the purpose of recovering 95 per cent of the SO_2. Cooling coils will be installed in the tower to maintain the liquid temperature constant at 68°F. Determine the minimum water rate at which the tower would operate as planned, assuming that there is no limitation on the height of packing available. Vapor pressure of SO_2 over aqueous SO_2 solution at 68°F.:

Concentration, lb. SO_2/100 lb. water..	0.5	1.0	2.0	3.0	5.0	10.0
Partial pressure SO_2, mm. Hg........	26	59	123	191	336	698

Solution

$$p_1 = (0.10)(760) = 76 \text{ mm.}$$

$$SO_2 \text{ absorbed} = \frac{200}{359} \frac{492}{528} (64)(60)(0.10)(0.95) = 190 \text{ lb./hr.}$$

At the minimum water rate the gas and solution will be in equilibrium at the bottom of the tower where the gas is 10 mole per cent SO_2, corresponding to a partial pressure of 76 mm. Hg. By interpolation, the concentration of an aqueous SO_2 solution which has a partial pressure of SO_2 of 76 mm. is 1.27 lb. SO_2/100 lb. water. Therefore,

$$\text{Minimum water rate} = \frac{190}{1.27} \times 100 = 15,000 \text{ lb./hr.}$$

THE HEIGHT OF A TRANSFER UNIT

A convenient method for estimating the height of a countercurrent absorption column is based on the concept of the "height of a transfer unit," which was introduced originally by Chilton and Colburn.[76] This method is used frequently in practical design work for the following reasons:

1. The procedure is simple, direct, and rapid, especially for rough estimates.

2. The mass-transfer resistance of the packing is expressed in terms of an experimentally determined number which has the dimensions of length only.

3. The procedure closely parallels that used in the design of plate columns.

The basic concept is that the estimation of the height of a tower always depends upon the evaluation of a definite integral, such as

$$N_{OG} = \int_{y_2}^{y_1} \frac{dy}{y - y_e} \tag{206}$$

The value of this integral, which is dimensionless, expresses the difficulty of absorbing the solute from the gas; it is greater the smaller the mean driving force and the larger the required change in gas composition. Chilton and Colburn have called it the "number of transfer units" based on an over-all gas-phase driving force. The equation used for calculating the packed height for the case of a dilute gas stream becomes, instead of Eq. (196),

$$h = \frac{G_M}{K_G a P} N_{OG} \tag{207}$$

or

$$h = H_{OG} N_{OG} \tag{208}$$

where the "height of a transfer unit," or H.T.U., is

$$H_{OG} = \frac{G_M}{K_G a P} \tag{209}$$

with the dimensions of length. For fully developed turbulent flow H_{OG} varies less with G than does $K_G a$, since $K_G a$ itself increases as the value of G is increased.

When the depth of the packing is equal to the H.T.U., and when one transfer unit is available to cause interphase transfer, the change in gas composition is equal to the average driving force. If there is no "back pressure," *i.e.*, no vapor pressure of the solute over the liquid ($p_e = 0$), one transfer unit is sufficient to cause y to fall to 36.8 per cent ($1/e = 1/2.718$) of its initial value. In this simple case the percentage of the initial solute which is absorbed varies with the packing depth as follows:

N_{OG}	Per Cent Solute Absorbed, $(y_1 - y_2)/y_1$
0.5	39
1	63
2	86.5
3	95.0
4	98.2
5	99.3

Addition of Diffusional Resistances in Terms of H.T.U.'s. The value of H_{OG} is proportional to the over-all resistance to mass transfer, expressed in terms of gas-phase concentrations. Just as the over-all transfer coefficient is related to the individual coefficients when the equilibrium line is straight, so also is the over-all H.T.U. related to H.T.U. values for the individual phases. Multiplying Eq. (179) by the molar mass velocity G_M,

$$\frac{G_M}{K_G a P} = \frac{G_M}{k_G a P} + \frac{H \rho_M G_M}{P L_M} \frac{L_M}{\rho_M k_L a} \tag{210}$$

$$\frac{G_M}{K_G a P} = \frac{G_M}{k_G a P} + \frac{m G_M}{L_M} \frac{L_M}{\rho_M k_L a} \tag{211}$$

where $m = dy_e/dx = H\rho_M/P$, to the degree of approximation necessary for dilute solutions. By analogy with Eq. (209), two new characteristic heights may be defined:

$$H_G = \frac{G_M}{k_G a P} \quad \text{and} \quad H_L = \frac{L_M}{\rho_M k_L a} \quad (212)$$

These are called the "height of a gas-film transfer unit" and the "height of a liquid-film transfer unit," respectively. From Eq. (211) they are related to H_{OG} by

$$H_{OG} = H_G + \frac{mG_M}{L_M} H_L \quad (213)$$

Similarly,

$$H_{OL} = \frac{L_M}{\rho_M K_L a} \quad (214)$$

$$= H_L + \frac{L_M}{mG_M} H_G \quad (215)$$

In terms of the individual H.T.U.'s, the tower height becomes

$$h = H_G N_G = H_L N_L \quad (216)$$

where

$$N_G = \int_{y_2}^{y_1} \frac{dy}{y - y_i}; \quad N_L = \int_{x_2}^{x_1} \frac{dx}{x_i - x} \quad (217)$$

As shown above, the true mean driving force is the logarithmic mean when both equilibrium and operating lines are straight. For this case, therefore,

$$N_{OG} = \frac{y_1 - y_2}{(y - y_e)_{\text{lm}}} \quad (218)$$

In order to use Eq. (218), two values of y and two values of y_e must be calculated. An equivalent equation which involves only two gas compositions and one liquid composition, and which shows the effect of the group mG_M/L_M has been suggested by Colburn.[88]

$$N_{OG} = \frac{\ln\left[\left(1 - \frac{mG_M}{L_M}\right)\left(\frac{y_1 - mx_2}{y_2 - mx_2}\right) + \frac{mG_M}{L_M}\right]}{1 - (mG_M/L_M)} \quad (219)$$

Figure 40 is based on this equation and may be used conveniently for design calculations.

Illustration 17. Repeat the calculation required in Illustration 15, in terms of transfer units.

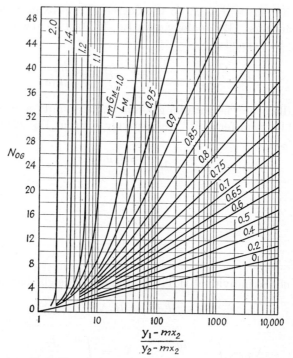

Fig. 40. Number of transfer units in an absorption column, condition of constant mG_M/L_M.

Solution

$$m = \frac{y_e}{x} = 0.746$$

$$G_M = (8.18)\left(1 + \frac{0.0204}{2}\right) = 8.26$$

$$L_M = (13.33)\left(1 + \frac{0.012}{2}\right) = 13.4$$

$$\frac{mG_M}{L_M} = \frac{(0.746)(8.26)}{13.4} = 0.46$$

$$\frac{y_1 - mx_2}{y_2 - mx_2} = \frac{y_1}{y_2} = \frac{0.02}{0.00041} = 48.9$$

From Eq. (219),

$$N_{OG} = \frac{\ln\left[(0.540)(48.9) + 0.460\right]}{0.540} = 6.10$$

The same result is obtained from Fig. 40. From Eq. (209) $H_{OG} = 2.13$ ft., and

$$h = (6.10)(2.13) = 12.9 \text{ ft.}$$

Problems involving stripping or desorption operations are handled most conveniently by calculating N_{OL} rather than N_{OG}. The equation for the number of over-all liquid-phase transfer units, similar to Eq. (219), may be derived from Eq. (219) by interchanging the symbols for the liquid and vapor streams. Thus

$$N_{OL} = \frac{\ln\left[\left(1 - \frac{L_M}{mG_M}\right)\left(\frac{x_1 - x_{e2}}{x_2 - x_{e2}}\right) + \frac{L_M}{mG_M}\right]}{1 - (L_M/mG_M)} \tag{220}$$

Figure 40 may be used for solving this equation if the abscissa and ordinate are considered to represent $(x_1 - x_{e2})/(x_2 - x_{e2})$ and N_{OL}, respectively, and the parameter is considered to be L_M/mG_M.

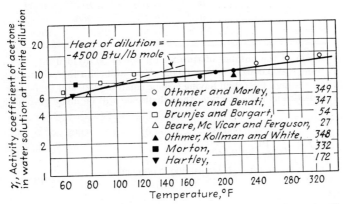

FIG. 41. Effect of temperature on the activity coefficient of acetone in dilute water solution.

Illustration 18. An aqueous solution containing 5 per cent by weight of acetone is to be fed at its boiling point to the top of a packed column supplied at the bottom with open steam. The composition of the bottoms is to be 0.00025 mole fraction acetone, and the reflux ratio L_M/G_M will be 19. Calculate the number of over-all liquid-phase transfer units required. The vapor pressure of acetone at the feed temperature is 2797 mm. Hg.

Solution. The activity coefficient of acetone in dilute aqueous solution at $212°F$ is shown by Fig. 41 to be 10, which gives for the value of m at the origin

$$m = \frac{y}{x_e} = \frac{p}{Px_e} = \gamma_1 \frac{P_1}{P} = (10)(2797)/(760) = 36.9$$

The equilibrium curve may be constructed accurately enough for the present problem by assuming that the activity varies with concentration according to the equation[65]

$$\log_{10} \gamma_1 = A(1 - x)^2$$

On this basis the following values of y and x_e may be calculated:

x_e	0	0.005	0.01	0.02
γ_1	10	9.773	9.552	9.129
y	0	0.152	0.262	0.405
$m = y/x_e$	36.9	30.5	26.2	20.2

The initial value of x, using a fictitious molecular weight of 62.2 to make the operating line straight,* is

$$x_1 = \frac{0.05/62.2}{(0.05/62.2) + (0.95/18)} = 0.0150$$

The corresponding value in the stripped aqueous effluent is

$$x_2 = \frac{(0.00025)(58/62.2)}{(0.00025)(58/62.2) + 0.99975} = 0.000233$$

In terms of mole fractions based on the fictitious molecular weight of acetone, the equilibrium data become:

x_e.................	0	0.005	0.01	0.02
y....................	0	0.152	0.260	0.396
$m = y/x_e$..........	36.9	30.3	26.0	19.8

The calculation of the number of transfer units will be divided into two parts, as follows: (a) from $x = 0.000233$ to $x = 0.002$, the equilibrium line will be assumed to be straight line through the origin having a slope equal to 36.9, and (b) from $x = 0.002$ to $x = 0.0150$ fictitious mole fraction, the calculation will be made graphically.

Part (a):

$$x_2 = 0.000233; \qquad x_{e2} = 0; \qquad x_1 = 0.002$$

$$\frac{L_M}{mG_M} = \frac{19}{36.9} = 0.515$$

$$N_{OL} = \frac{\ln\left[(1 - 0.515)(0.002/0.000233) + 0.515\right]}{1 - 0.515} = 3.18$$

Part (b):

x	y	x_e	$x - x_e$	$\dfrac{1}{x - x_e}$
0.002	0.0336	0.00097	0.00103	$972 \times 1 = 972$
0.005	0.0905	0.00297	0.00203	$493 \times 4 = 1972$
0.008	0.1475	0.00532	0.00268	$373 \times 2 = 746$
0.011	0.204	0.00800	0.00300	$333 \times 4 = 1332$
0.014	0.261	0.01125	0.00275	$364 \times 1 = \underline{364}$
				5386
0.015	0.280	0.01243	0.00257	389

By Simpson's rule for integration,

$$\int_{0.002}^{0.0150} \frac{dx}{x - x_e} = \frac{0.003}{3}(5386) + 0.0010\frac{364 + 389}{2}$$

$$= 5.39 + 0.38 = 5.77$$

Therefore,

$$N_{OL} = 3.18 + 5.77 = 8.95$$

* Based on this fictitious molecular weight the molar latent heat of vaporization of acetone, including the heat of dilution in dilute solution is 19,300 B.t.u./lb. mole, which is equal to the latent heat of water. When the molal latent heats are equal, a heat balance shows that the molal flow rates of total liquid and total vapor will be constant.

Calculation of the Number of Transfer Units for Concentrated Mixtures. When the resistance is concentrated in the gas phase, which contains appreciable concentrations of the solute, the height of the packing must be calculated by using Eq. (170), which allows for the decrease in gas rate and the change in mean partial pressure of inerts as the solute gas is removed from the gas stream. Chilton and Colburn[75] suggest that the variation of $k_G'a$ with gas velocity may be allowed for approximately by assuming $k_G'a$ to be proportional to the total molar gas velocity, $G_M'/(1 - y)$, i.e., that H_G is independent of gas velocity. Equation (170) then becomes

$$h = \int_{y_2}^{y_1} \frac{G_M'(1 - y)p_{BM}\, dp}{k_G'a(P - p)^2(p - p_e)} = H_G \int_{y_2}^{y_1} \frac{(1 - y)_{\text{l.m.}}\, dy}{(1 - y)(y - y_i)} \quad (221)$$

where $(1 - y)_{\text{l.m.}}$ represents the logarithmic mean of $1 - y$ and $1 - y_i$. When $k_G'a$ is not precisely proportional to the total molar gas velocity, Eq. (221) and the similar equations which follow should contain values of H_G, etc., which apply in the part of the column where the driving force is smallest. Colburn suggests,[88] by analogy with Eq. (221), that

$$h = H_{OG} \int_{y_2}^{y_1} \frac{(1 - y)_{\text{l.m.}}\, dy}{(1 - y)(y - y_e)} \quad (222)$$

in which $(1 - y)_{\text{l.m.}}$ is the logarithmic mean of $1 - y$ and $1 - y_e$, and also that

$$h = H_L \int_{x_2}^{x_1} \frac{(1 - x)_{\text{l.m.}}\, dx}{(1 - x)(x_i - x)} \quad (223)$$

$$= H_{OL} \int_{x_2}^{x_1} \frac{(1 - x)_{\text{l.m.}}\, dx}{(1 - x)(x_e - x)} \quad (224)$$

For most practical cases not involving extremely rapid absorption it is permissible to assume that the logarithmic mean is equal to the arithmetic mean, as suggested by Wiegand.[508] The integral in Eq. (222) then becomes

$$N_{OG} = \int_{y_2}^{y_1} \frac{[(1 - y) + (1 - y_e)]\, dy}{2(1 - y)(y - y_e)}$$

$$= \frac{1}{2} \int_{y_2}^{y_1} \frac{dy}{1 - y} + \int_{y_2}^{y_1} \frac{dy}{y - y_e}$$

$$= \frac{1}{2} \ln \frac{1 - y_2}{1 - y_1} + \int_{y_2}^{y_1} \frac{dy}{y - y_e} \quad (225)$$

Thus, the value of N_{OG} may be calculated as though the vapor stream were dilute, the first term of Eq. (225) being added to the previous result.

In the special case where there is no equilibrium vapor pressure of the solute over the solution, so that y_i becomes zero, the integral in Eq. (221) may be evaluated exactly. For this case[114]

$$h = H_G \int_{y_2}^{y_1} \frac{dy}{(1-y)\ln(1-y)}$$

$$= H_G \ln \left[\frac{\ln(1-y_2)}{\ln(1-y_1)} \right] \tag{226}$$

Solution of the problem in Illustration 14 gave a value of $(k_G'a)_1$ of 26.4 lb. moles/(hr.)(ft.²)(atm.) when the calculation was made by a tedious numerical procedure, compared with 27.9 lb. moles/(hr.)(ft.²)(atm.) when Eq. (226) was used. Equation (225) gives very nearly the same results as Eq. (226) in this case, indicating the accuracy of the approximations made. Equation (181), based on the assumption of a dilute gas stream, gives $(k_G'a)_1 = 31.6$ lb. moles/(hr.)(ft.²)(atm.).

Rapid Calculation of Transfer Units When Equilibrium or Operating Lines Are Curved Slightly. Colburn[86] has shown that, when the equilibrium line is straight at the origin but is curved slightly at its upper end, the value of N_{OG} is given by

$$N_{OG} = \int_{y_2}^{y_1} \frac{dy}{y - y_e}$$

$$= \frac{1}{1 - (mG_M/L_M)_2} \ln \left\{ \frac{[1 - (mG_M/L_M)_2]^2}{1 - (y_{e1}/y_1)} \frac{y_1 - y_{e2}}{y_2 - y_{e2}} + \left(\frac{mG_M}{L_M} \right)_2 \right\} \tag{227}$$

Othmer and Scheibel[351] have derived an equation for the same case which is somewhat less convenient in application. It should be apparent that Fig. 40 may be used instead of Eq. (227) if the abscissa is chosen as

$$\frac{y_1 - y_{e2}}{y_2 - y_{e2}} \frac{1 - (mG_M/L_M)_2}{1 - (y_{e1}/y_1)}$$

and the parameter is taken to be $(mG_M/L_M)_2$.

The application of Eqs. (219), (220), and (227) to a variety of diffusional unit operations, through the use of Fig. 40, is indicated by Table IX.

Illustration 19. Repeat the calculation of Illustration 18, using Eq. (227) to allow for the curvature of the equilibrium line.
Solution

$$x_1 = 0.0150 \text{ fictitious mole fraction}$$
$$x_2 = 0.000233 \text{ fictitious mole fraction}$$
$$y_{e2} = 0$$

$$m_2 = 36.9; \qquad \left(\frac{L_M}{mG_M} \right)_2 = \frac{19}{36.9} = 0.515$$

$$x_{e1} = 0.01243$$

$$N_{OL} = \frac{1}{0.485} \ln \left[\frac{0.485^2}{1 - (0.01243/0.0150)} \frac{0.0150}{0.000233} + 0.515 \right] = 9.26$$

This same result is obtained by using Fig. 40, as indicated by Table IX. The result is 3.4 per cent higher than that obtained by the more accurate calculation on page 135.

Graphical Construction of Transfer Units. A graphical construction on the x-y diagram may be substituted for the analytical or numerical calculations required to evaluate the integrals occurring in Eqs. (207) and (227), if a rapid approximate result is acceptable. Two methods have been proposed.[17,500] Each brings out the similarity, discussed more completely below, between theoretical plates and transfer units. Whereas one theoretical plate produces a change in vapor composition, $y_1 - y_2$, equal to the driving force at the point where the liquid *leaves* the section, $y - y_{e1}$, one transfer unit gives a change in composition equal to the *average* driving force $(y - y_e)_{av}$.

TABLE IX. SUMMARY OF EQUATIONS FOR TRANSFER UNITS

$$N_T = \frac{2.3 \log [(1-Q)S + Q]}{1-Q}; \qquad R = \frac{L_M}{G_M}$$

Case	N_T	Q	S
Absorption			
Case I, constant $\dfrac{m}{R}$	N_{OG}	$\dfrac{m}{R}$	$\dfrac{y_1 - mx_2}{y_2 - mx_2}$
Case II, varying $\dfrac{m}{R}$	$N_{OG} - 1.15 \log \dfrac{1 - y_2}{1 - y_1}$	$\dfrac{m_2}{R_2}$	$\dfrac{y_1 - m_2 x_2}{y_2 - m_2 x_2} \dfrac{1 - m_2/R_2}{1 - y_{e1}/y_1}$
	$N_{OG} + 1.15 \log \dfrac{1 + Y_1}{1 + Y_2}$	$\dfrac{m_2}{R_2}$	$\dfrac{Y_1 - m_2 X_2}{Y_2 - m_2 X_2} \dfrac{1 - m_2 R_2}{1 - Y_{e1}/Y_1}$
Desorption			
Case I, constant $\dfrac{R}{m}$	N_{OL}	$\dfrac{R}{m}$	$\dfrac{x_1 - y_2/m}{x_2 - y_2/m}$
Case II, varying $\dfrac{R}{m}$	$N_{OL} - 1.15 \log \dfrac{1 - x_2}{1 - x_1}$	$\dfrac{R_2}{m_2}$	$\dfrac{x_1 - y_2/m_2}{x_2 - y_2/m_2} \dfrac{1 - R_2/m_2}{1 - x_{e1}/x_1}$
	$N_{OL} + 1.15 \log \dfrac{1 + X_1}{1 + X_2}$	$\dfrac{R_2}{m_2}$	$\dfrac{X_1 - Y_2/m_2}{X_2 - Y_2/m_2} \dfrac{1 - R_2/m_2}{1 - X_{e1}/X_1}$
Distillation, enriching *			
Case I, constant $\dfrac{m}{R}$	N_{OG}	$\dfrac{m}{R}$	$\dfrac{y_1 - mx_2}{y_2 - mx_2}$
Case II, varying $\dfrac{m}{R}$	N_{OG}	$\dfrac{m_2}{R_2}$	$\dfrac{y_1 - m_2 x_2}{y_2 - m_2 x_2} \dfrac{1 - m_2/R_2}{1 - y_{e1}/y_1}$

ABSORPTION AND EXTRACTION

TABLE IX. SUMMARY OF EQUATIONS FOR TRANSFER UNITS. (*Continued*)

Case	N_T	Q	S
Distillation, stripping, closed steam †			
Case I, constant $\dfrac{R}{m}$	$N_{OL} + \dfrac{2.3 \log m/R}{1 - R/m}$	$\dfrac{R}{m}$	$\dfrac{x_1 - x_2/m}{x_2 - x_2/m}$
Case II, varying $\dfrac{R}{m}$	$N_{OL} + \dfrac{2.3 \log m_2/R_2}{1 - R_2/m_2}$	$\dfrac{R_2}{m_2}$	$\dfrac{x_1 - x_2/m_2}{x_2 - x_2/m_2} \dfrac{1 - R_2/m_2}{1 - x_{e1}/x_1}$
Distillation, stripping, open steam †			
Case I, constant $\dfrac{R}{m}$	N_{OL}	$\dfrac{R}{m}$	$\dfrac{x_1}{x_2}$
Case II, varying $\dfrac{R}{m}$	N_{OL}	$\dfrac{R_2}{m_2}$	$\dfrac{x_1}{x_2} \dfrac{1 - R_2/m_2}{1 - x_{e1}/x_1}$
Extraction, stripping			
Case I, constant $\dfrac{R}{m}$	N_{OL}	$\dfrac{R}{m}$	$\dfrac{w_1 - (v_2/m)}{w_2 - (v_2/m)}$
Case II, varying $\dfrac{R}{m}$	$N_{OL} - \theta$	$\dfrac{R_2}{m_2}$	$\dfrac{w_1 - v_2/m_2}{w_2 - v_2/m_2} \dfrac{1 - R_2/m_2}{1 - w_{e1}/w_1}$
Extraction, enriching			
Case I, constant $\dfrac{m}{R}$	N_{OG}	$\dfrac{m}{R}$	$\dfrac{v_1 - mw_2}{v_2 - mw_2}$
Case II, varying $\dfrac{m}{R}$	$N_{OG} - \theta'$	$\dfrac{m_2}{R_2}$	$\dfrac{v_1 - m_2w_2}{v_2 - m_2w_2} \dfrac{1 - m_2/R_2}{1 - v_{e1}/v_1}$

Notes:

Equations for varying m/R or R/m are approximate and hold best for large values of S (say, 20 or larger).

For each case the number of theoretical plates may be computed from

$$N_P = \frac{\log [(1 - Q)S + Q]}{\log (1/Q)}$$

$$\theta = 1.15 \log_{10} \left(\frac{1 - w_2}{1 - w_1}\right) - 1.15(1 - r) \log_{10} \frac{1 - (1 - r)w_2}{1 - (1 - r)w_1}$$

$$\theta' = 1.15 \log_{10} \left(\frac{1 - v_2}{1 - v_1}\right) - 1.15(1 - r) \log_{10} \frac{1 - (1 - r)v_2}{1 - (1 - r)v_1}$$

r = ratio of molecular weight of solute-free stream to that of solute

* Concentrations and m are based on high boiler or "heavy key."
† Concentrations and m are based on low boiler or "light key."

Probably the most useful procedure for calculating transfer units in practical design work is that in which the simplified analytical equations, such as Eq. (207), are used for the ranges of composition corresponding to the "pinches," and the graphical procedure is used for the intermediate composition ranges. Thus, calculations for concentrated solutions are made graphically, while simple equations suitable for dilute solutions are

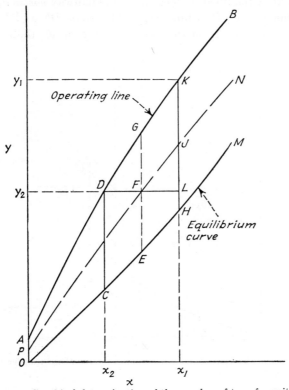

FIG. 42. Graphical determination of the number of transfer units.

used rather than enlarged portions of the x-y diagram. This procedure was followed in Illustration 18.

The simplest graphical procedure is that described by T. C. Baker,[16] illustrated in Fig. 42. For calculating the number of over-all gas-phase transfer units, a line PN is located midway vertically between the operating line and the equilibrium curve. Starting at any point D (coordinates x_2,y_2) on the operating line, the horizontal line DF is drawn to PN and is continued an equal distance to L, such that $DF = FL$. The vertical line KH through L intersects the operating line at K, corresponding to (x_1,y_1). The change in gas composition $y_1 - y_2$, corresponds to one transfer unit, because the mean driving force GE is twice GF, which in turn is one-half of KL and one-half of $y_1 - y_2$.

A study of Fig. 42 will show that a theoretical plate is more effective than a transfer unit in an absorber for which mG_M/L_M is less than unity; the reverse is true if mG_M/L_M is greater than unity.

When the liquid-phase resistance predominates, the graphical procedure should be modified by locating a line halfway *horizontally* between the operating and equilibrium lines. The steps DF and FL should be taken vertically away from the operating line rather than horizontally.

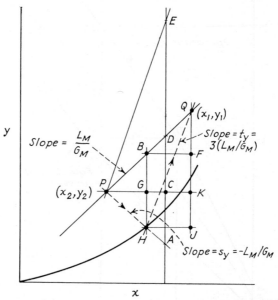

Fig. 43. Graphical determination of the number of gas-phase transfer units (N_{OG}) by method of White.

A second interesting graphical construction, suggested by White,[500] allows intermediate cases to be handled, in which the resistance is divided between the phases. This procedure will be illustrated first by applying it to the case of pure gas-phase resistance, as shown in Fig. 43. A step equivalent to one gas-phase transfer unit is taken in the following manner: Starting at point P (coordinates y_2, x_2) on the operating line, a horizontal line is drawn. Then any vertical line is drawn intersecting the horizontal line at C, to the right of P. Points A and E are located so that $CE = 3CD$ and $CA = CD$. The line from (y_2, x_2) to A intersects the equilibrium curve at H, and the step to (y_1, x_1) is completed by drawing a line through H parallel to PE. The validity of the construction is proved if BH can be shown to equal both the mean driving force and the change in y. That $BG = GH$ follows from similar triangles. Since HQ has three times the slope of BQ, $QJ = 3QF$, and $QF = BG$. Thus $QK = BH$, and the construction is proved.

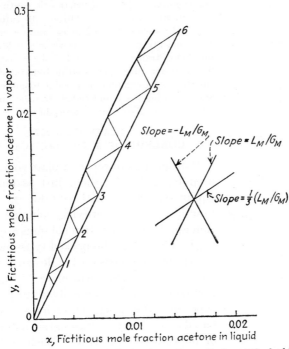

Fig. 44. Graphical determination of transfer units by method of White.

White's method of construction has two advantages over the somewhat simpler method of Baker.[16] It can be used for stepping off transfer units in either direction, while Baker's method requires a cut-and-try construction in the direction of decreasing x or y. Adjustable triangles can be set to correspond to the two slopes, and a series of steps can be taken quickly in either direction by placing the triangles successively against a horizontal T square. Moreover, White's method is more general, since it includes all variations between pure liquid-phase and pure gas-phase resistance. For the intermediate cases,

$$s_y = \frac{-L_M/G_M}{1 + 2H_L/H_G} \qquad (228)$$

$$t_y = \frac{3L_M/G_M}{1 - 2H_L/H_G} \qquad (229)$$

Illustration 20. Repeat the calculation of transfer units required in Illustration 18, using the graphical method of White in the concentrated range.

Solution. An x-y diagram for this problem is shown in Fig. 44. Beginning at $x = 0.002$ on the operating line, a line is drawn toward the equilibrium curve having a negative slope equal to L_M/G_M. This is followed by a second line drawn toward the operating line with a slope equal to $\frac{1}{3}(L_M/G_M)$. The intersection with the operating line at $x = 0.0030$ completes one over-all liquid-phase transfer unit. The construction is continued until the seventh step crosses $x_1 = 0.0150$. By interpolation, the required number of liquid-phase transfer units is 6.07 for the concentrated region above $x = 0.002$. The total number of transfer units is $6.1 + 3.2 = 9.3$, compared to 9.26 transfer units calculated in Illustrated 19, using an equation approximately applicable to curved equilibrium and operating lines, and to 8.95 transfer units calculated by a numerical integration procedure.

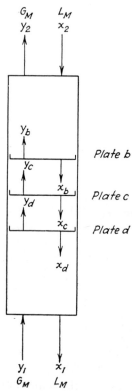

FIG. 45. Symbols used in plate-column design.

PLATE COLUMNS
CONCEPT OF A THEORETICAL PLATE

Both packed towers and plate columns may be used for gas absorption, just as both types of equipment are found suitable in distillation practice. Large rectifying columns for distillation and large absorption columns are more often of the plate than the packed type, however, and the traditional basis for the design of such equipment is the "theoretical plate." Small absorption equipment is commonly of the packed-tower type, and the design of such towers is usually based on capacity coefficients such as K_Ga or K_La, or on values of the H.T.U. such as H_{OG} or H_{OL}. The two types of equipment are compared in Chap. VII. Just as the equipment is interchangeable in practice, so also the design methods for the two processes may be interchanged and the "theoretical plate" used as the basis for absorption-tower design, or capacity coefficients and H.T.U.'s used in rectifying-column design. As pointed out on page 131, the design procedures involving transfer units and theoretical plates are closely similar.

The design procedure based on the theoretical-plate concept may be followed by referring to Fig. 45. The use of mole fraction units will be continued, although the method may be modified for rich gases, as explained above for use with capacity coefficients.

The horizontal lines at b, c, d, etc., represent bubble-cap or other plates or trays, the solvent overflowing from one plate to the next down through the column. The gas to be treated, containing G_M' lb. moles/hr. of inert carrier gas, passes up through the column, countercurrent to the flow of solvent, being brought into intimate contact with the solvent by bubble caps or other devices on each plate. On a theoretically perfect plate the contact between phases will be sufficiently good to bring the two streams into equilibrium. The gas leaving plate c will be in equilibrium with the liquid leaving the same plate. For a column of theoretical plates, therefore, it is possible to represent the relationship between gas and liquid compositions leaving any plate by the equilibrium curve for the system.

The relation between the gas and liquid compositions between any two plates, *i.e.*, the relation between the composition y_c of the gas leaving plate c and the composition x_b of the liquid leaving plate b, is given by the material balance

$$G_M(y_1 - y_c) = L_M(x_1 - x_b) \tag{230}$$

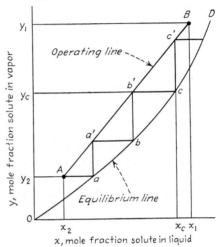

Figure 46 shows a diagram for this case, with the operating line designated as AB and the equilibrium curve as OD. It should be noted that the operating line now gives the relation between the composition of gas leaving a plate and the composition of liquid from the plate next above. The vapor leaving any plate c will be in equilibrium with the concentration x_c

Fig. 46. Graphical representation of concentration changes for theoretical plates.

of the liquid on the plate, and the vapor composition y_c will be determined by referring to the point c on the equilibrium curve. The liquid leaving the plate b, next above, will have a composition determined by the abscissa of the point b' on the operating line, corresponding to the gas composition y_c. The composition of the gas leaving plate b may then be determined, and the equilibrium curves and operating line used alternately until point A is reached, corresponding to conditions at the top of the column. With any fixed operating line this stepwise calculation may be employed to determine the compositions of liquid and gas on the successive plates and, what is more important, the number of theoretical plates required.

It is obvious that, when the operating line lies close to the equilibrium curve, a large number of plates will be required. If the two curves touch, the staircase construction will indicate an infinite number of plates, because equilibrium cannot be reached in any finite flow apparatus.

Comparison of this stepwise procedure with that described on page 141 for transfer units indicates that the change in the composition of the gas which flows through a theoretical plate is equal to the driving force at the liquid overflow from the plate, while the change for a column packed to a depth equivalent to one transfer unit is equal to the average driving force throughout the packing.

Analytical Calculation of Theoretical Plates Required.   Although the graphical procedure just described is of general applicability, an algebraic or analytical procedure may be more convenient in those cases where solute concentrations in the gas and liquid phases are low and where the equilibrium relation is straight.

The material balance, as applied at a section below the cth plate of a plate column, may be written

$$L_M(x_1 - x_c) = G_M(y_1 - y_d) \tag{231}$$

If the plates are theoretical plates and the equilibrium relation is linear, *i.e.*, if

$$y_{en} = mx_n + B \tag{232}$$

an expression for the terminal compositions may be derived in terms of the total number of plates, N_P, as shown by Kremser.[257]   The derivation may be made to depend on the solution of a linear difference equation, as shown by Tiller and Tour.[458]   The result* may be expressed in the form

$$\frac{y_1 - y_2}{y_1 - y_{e2}} = \frac{(L_M/mG_M)^{N_P+1} - (L_M/mG_M)}{(L_M/mG_M)^{N_P+1} - 1} \tag{233}$$

as shown by Souders and Brown,[435] or in the alternative form

$$N_P = \frac{\ln\left[\left(1 - \frac{mG_M}{L_M}\right)\left(\frac{y_1 - mx_2}{y_2 - mx_2}\right) + \frac{mG_M}{L_M}\right]}{\ln\left(L_M/mG_M\right)} \tag{234}$$

as suggested by Colburn.[88]   The left-hand side of Eq. (233) represents the actual change in composition of the gas flowing through a column having N_P theoretical plates, divided by the change which would occur if the gas came to equilibrium with the liquid entering, *i.e.*, in an infinite column.   A high degree of recovery may be obtained either by the use of a large number of plates or by employing a large liquid-gas ratio.

Equation (234) is the preferred form when the number of plates is the

---

* In some problems it may be desirable to express the concentrations in mole-ratio units Y and X, and the flow rates as G_M' and L_M', with units of pound moles of inert gas and of nonvolatile liquid per hour per square foot.   In this case the consistent units for m are mole ratio in the gas divided by mole ratio in the liquid.   For dilute solutions the results are identical with Eqs. (233) and (234).

unknown quantity in the problem. The similarity to Eq. (219), which was derived previously for transfer units instead of plates, is evident. Figure 47, showing the relation between the number of plates, the concentration change, and the parameter mG_M/L_M, is similar to Fig. 40 for transfer units. Figure 47 may also be used for diffusional operations other than absorption, as indicated by Table IX.

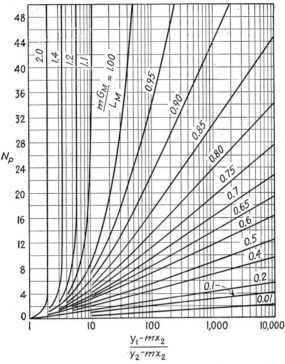

Fig. 47. Number of theoretical plates in an absorption column, condition of constant mG_M/L_M.

When mG_M/L_M is greater than unity, complete removal of the solute from the gas in an absorber is impossible, no matter how many plates or transfer units are available and even if there is no solute in the entering liquid ($y_{e2} = 0$). This is indicated by the fact that Eq. (233) reduces to

$$\frac{y_1 - y_2}{y_1 - y_{e2}} = \frac{L_M}{mG_M}$$

when N_P is infinite and L_M/mG_M is a fraction.* For an absorption column the operating line lies above the equilibrium line; if the slope of the former

* When $L_M/mG_M = 1.0$, the right-hand side of Eq. (233) is indeterminate but may be shown to be equal to $N_P/(N_P + 1)$ for any value of N_P.

(L_M/G_M) is smaller than m, the liquid absorbent becomes saturated with the solute soon after it has entered the absorber. Similarly, the amount of stripping is limited to a maximum value in a stripping column for which L_M/mG_M is greater than unity.

Illustration 21. How many theoretical plates are required for the conditions of Illustration 15?

Solution. Substituting $y_1 = 0.02$, $y_2 = 0.00041$, $y_{e2} = 0$, $mG_M/L_M = 0.46$ into Eq. (234).

$$N_P = \frac{\ln\,[(0.54)(0.02/0.00041) + 0.46]}{\ln\,(1/0.46)}$$

$$= 4.2$$

The same result is obtained from Fig. 47.

If the over-all plate efficiency were 75 per cent, 4.3/0.75, or 5.7, actual trays would be required. Actually, six trays would be installed, and the column height between the top and bottom trays would be 7.5 ft. if the plate spacing were 18 in.

Illustration 22. How many theoretical plates are required for the conditions of Illustration 18?

Solution. We may divide the problem into two parts, as before: (a) the number of theoretical plates required to change the composition of the liquid from 0.000233 to 0.002 fictitious mole fraction will be calculated analytically, using the equation for N_P for open-steam stripping given in Table IX; and (b) the number of theoretical plates required to change x from 0.002 to 0.0150 fictitious mole fraction will be calculated graphically.

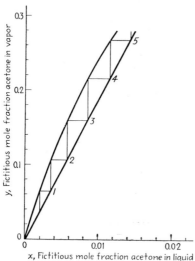

FIG. 48. Graphical determination of theoretical plates (Illustration 22).

Part (a):

$$x_2 = 0.000233, \qquad x_{e2} = 0, \qquad x_1 = 0.002, \qquad \frac{L_M}{mG_M} = 0.515$$

$$N_P = \frac{\ln\,[(0.485)(0.002/0.000233) + 0.515]}{\ln\,0.515} = 2.32$$

Part (b). An x-y diagram is constructed, as shown in Fig. 48, and the stepwise construction is begun at $x = 0.002$. After laying out five steps, the fictitious mole fraction of the liquid flowing onto the fifth plate is 0.0155. The number of equilibrium stages is estimated to be 5.2.

The total number of theoretical plates is 2.3 + 5.2, or 7.5.

As indicated by Table IX, approximate equations are available[86] for calculating the number of plates when either the equilibrium line or the operating line is curved slightly. These are not derived rigorously but are written by analogy with the similar equations for transfer units and plates. Nevertheless, the approximations are likely to be quite satisfactory for rapid, routine calculations. They should not be used, however, for computing numbers of theoretical plates from test data when accuracy is required.

Relation between Actual and Theoretical Plates. Plate Efficiency. The calculation of the number of theoretically perfect plates required for an absorber or stripper closely parallels the calculation of transfer units as already discussed. The actual height of a packed column is not known until some knowledge of the specific rate of interphase transfer is available, expressed in terms of an absorption coefficient or H.T.U. Similarly, the number of actual plates or trays cannot be estimated until the rate of interphase transfer on each actual plate is known. This information is usually expressed in terms of a "plate efficiency."

The simplest definition of plate efficiency from the point of view of application to column design is that of the *over-all plate efficiency E.* This is equal to the ratio of the number of theoretical plates required for a given separation to the number of actual plates required. Once the number of theoretical plates has been calculated, the number of actual plates is found by dividing by E (compare Illustration 21). The over-all plate efficiency is usually less than 100 per cent but may exceed 100 per cent under special circumstances.

The Murphree plate efficiency[336] is related more closely to the resistance to interphase diffusion on the plates. The *Murphree vapor efficiency* of the cth plate is defined by the equation

$$E_{MV} = \frac{y_c - y_d}{y_{ec} - y_d} \tag{235}$$

where y_c = average mole fraction of solute in gas leaving the cth plate
y_d = average mole fraction of solute leaving the plate below and entering the cth plate
y_{ec} = mole fraction of solute in gas in equilibrium with the liquid *leaving* the cth plate

If E_{MV} is the same for each plate in a column and if both operating and equilibrium lines are straight, the number of actual plates N_P' may be calculated from the equation[298]

$$N_P' = \frac{\ln\left[\left(1 - \frac{mG_M}{L_M}\right)\left(\frac{y_1 - y_{e2}}{y_2 - y_{e2}}\right) + \frac{mG_M}{L_M}\right]}{-\ln\{1 + E_{MV}[(mG_M/L_M) - 1]\}} \tag{236}$$

Under these conditions, therefore, the relation between the over-all and Murphree vapor efficiencies is

$$\frac{N_P}{N_P'} = E = \frac{\ln\{1 - E_{MV}[(mG_M/L_M) - 1]\}}{\ln(mG_M/L_M)} \tag{237}$$

Figure 49 shows this relationship graphically. When operating and equilibrium lines are parallel, the two efficiencies are equal; if E_{MV} is not equal to 1, E may be greater or less than E_{MV} as mG_M/L_M is greater or less than unity. No exact relationship has been developed between the two efficiencies for cases where either the operating line or the equilibrium line is curved, though the efficiencies may be expected to be nearly equal if the two lines are parallel on the average.

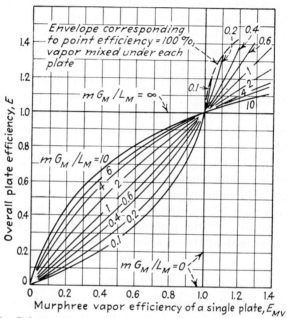

FIG. 49.   Relation of average plate efficiency to Murphree vapor efficiency.

Illustration 23. Carbon dioxide is being absorbed from hydrogen gas under pressure in a plate tower using an aqueous solution of diethanolamine as absorbent. The temperature, pressure, and degree of conversion of the amine solution are such that there is no appreciable vapor pressure of CO_2 over the liquid at equilibrium. Determine the number of actual plates required to reduce the carbon dioxide of the hydrogen from 10 to 1 per cent by volume. The Murphree vapor efficiency of each plate is assumed to be 25 per cent. Solve the problem both graphically and analytically.

Solution. The conditions are such that the equilibrium curve coincides with the x axis. The liquid-gas ratio need not be specified, as shown by Eq. (236), since L_M/G_M enters only in combination with m and its effect therefore disappears in this problem.

a. Graphical solution. An x-y diagram is constructed as shown by Fig. 50. A step corresponding to one actual plate is begun at the upper end of the operating line, where $y = 0.1$. The vertical step AB ends at a point 25 per cent of the way toward the equilibrium curve (the x axis in this case) and is followed by a horizontal step BC ending at the operating line. In this way the composition of the gas entering the second plate above the bottom of the column is found to be 0.075 mole fraction. The required value of y_2 is reached after eight steps.

The lower end of each step ends on a straight line which passes through the points $0.75y_2$ and $0.75y_1$. This line may be thought of as a fictitious equilibrium curve which may be used as though the actual plates are theoretical plates. The same type of construction, using a fictitious equilibrium curve, may be used even though both operating and equilibrium lines are curved.[18]

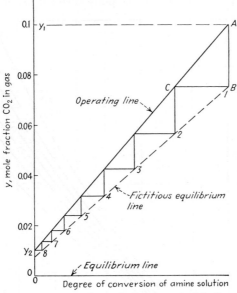

FIG. 50. Determination of number of actual plates required in the absorption of carbon dioxide in ethanolamine solution.

b. Analytical solution. Using Eq. (236)

$$N_{P'} = \frac{\ln (0.10/0.01)}{-\ln (1 - 0.25)} = 8.0 \text{ actual plates}$$

It should be noted that the concept of the theoretical plate and that of the over-all plate efficiency have no significance here. One theoretical plate would be more than sufficient to accomplish the desired absorption. If the step corresponding to a theoretical plate were begun at the lower end of the operating line, any finite value of the over-all plate efficiency would allow the step to end at the upper end of the operating line.

The *point efficiency* is more closely related to the resistance to interphase diffusion than any other plate efficiency. It is defined by the equation

$$E_{OG} = \frac{y_c' - y_d'}{y_{ec}' - y_d'} \tag{238}$$

where the y's are taken above and below a single point on the plate.

y_c' = mole fraction solute in the vapor leaving a small area of plate c.

y_d' = mole fraction solute in the vapor entering the same small section of plate c.

y_{ec}' = mole fraction solute in equilibrium with the liquid present on a small area of plate c.

The composition of the liquid is usually assumed to be uniform along any vertical line perpendicular to the plate surface; *i.e.*, it is assumed that

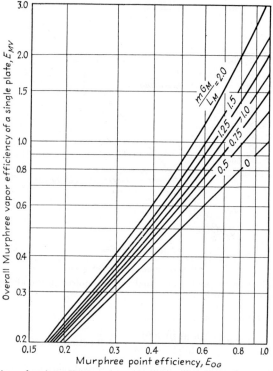

FIG. 51.   Relation of point efficiency to over-all Murphree efficiency; vapor mixed under each plate.

the liquid is thoroughly mixed in the vertical direction.   By definition, the point efficiency cannot exceed 100 per cent.

Particularly on a broad plate, where the horizontal path along which the liquid flows is several feet, the concentration of solute in the liquid may change gradually from the value x_b at the weir, where the fresh liquid is distributed evenly across the plate, to x_c at the overflow weir.*   In a

* On small plates only a few inches in diameter the violent bubbling action may cause large amounts of spray to be thrown backward opposite to the main liquid current.   Under these conditions all the liquid on the plate will have essentially the same

iarge absorber, therefore, the vapor which flows through the bubble caps near the upstream weir contacts liquid leaner than that which flows through the caps near the overflow weir. Even though the vapor which enters the plate may be uniform in composition, that which contacts the leaner liquid will experience a greater decrease in solute concentration.

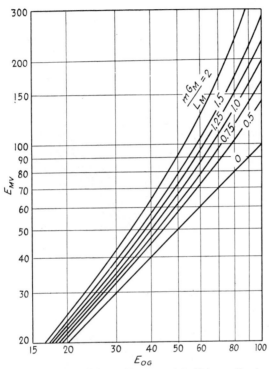

Fig. 52. Relation of Murphree efficiency E_{MV} to point efficiency E_{OG} for conditions where there is no blending of liquid on the plates and no blending of vapor between plates. Parallel flow of liquid on successive plates.

Since the Murphree vapor efficiency is equal to 100 per cent when the *average* composition of the vapor leaving the entire plate is equal to the composition in equilibrium with the *richest* liquid, y_{ec}, the Murphree vapor efficiency may exceed 100 per cent and is always greater than the point efficiency.

W. K. Lewis, Jr.,[282] has derived relations between the Murphree vapor efficiency and the point efficiency for the following conditions:

---

composition as the liquid leaving, x_c, and the Murphree efficiency of the plate will be equal to the point efficiency.

> *a.* Vapor entering the plate is uniform in composition, or the vapor is mixed completely between plates
> *b.* Vapor unmixed between the plates
> > (1) Liquid flows in the same direction across successive plates
> > (2) Liquid flows in opposite directions across successive plates

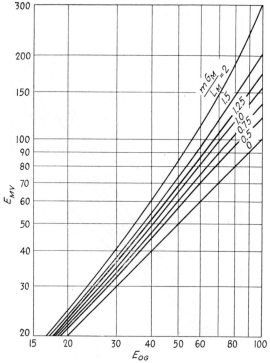

Fɪɢ 53.   Relation of Murphree efficiency E_{MV} to point efficiency E_{OG} for conditions where there is no blending of liquid on the plates and no blending of vapor between plates. Flow of liquid in opposite direction on successive plates.

Figures 51 to 53 show the results of these calculations.   Case *a* applies to the bottom plate of every column.   Cases *b*-(1) and *b*-(2) represent plates located some distance above the base of the column.   For these plates a permanent distribution pattern of vapor concentrations has been established by the action of the lower plates.   Kirschbaum,[246] Hausen,[179] and Colburn[88] have obtained similar results.

When a concentration gradient is present, the plates in a column give a crossflow type of contacting action, rather than a truly stagewise action, which is assumed in the concept of the theoretical plate.   This type of action is intermediate between the truly countercurrent action assumed in analyzing packed columns and stagewise equilibrium contact.

Lewis' case *a* results in[282]

$$E_{MV} = \frac{y_c - y_d}{y_{ec} - y_d} = \frac{L_M}{mG_M} \left(e^{E_{OG}mG_M/L_M} - 1 \right) \tag{239}$$

When the change in the liquid composition across a plate occurs in a stepwise manner as the liquid flows from one pool to another,

$$E_{MV} = \left(\frac{L_M}{mG_M} \right) \left[\left(\frac{mG_M E_{OG}}{kL_M} + 1 \right)^k - 1 \right] \tag{240}$$

where k is the total number of pools. The following table illustrates the progressive increase of the Murphree efficiency from a value equal to E_{OG} as k varies from 1 to infinity, in the case $mG_M/L_M = 0.7$:

k	E_{MV}
1	$0.80 = E_{OG}$
2	0.91
3	0.96
5	1.00
8	1.05
∞	1.07

The point efficiency would be 100 per cent, were it not for the resistance to interphase transfer. If we assume, as before, that the liquid is well mixed vertically, the vapor which flows through a small area on the plate changes in composition just as though it passed through a small packed tower or agitated tank throughout which the liquid has a constant composition. When Eq. (219) is applied to this case ($mG_M/L_M = 0$),

$$N_{OG} = \ln \frac{y_d' - y_{ec}'}{y_c' - y_{ec}'} = -\ln (1 - E_{OG}) \tag{241}$$

or

$$E_{OG} = 1 - e^{-N_{OG}} \tag{242}$$

This equation depends on the assumption that the product of the transfer coefficient per unit area and the interfacial area per unit of liquid volume is constant along the vertical path of integration. If resistance to transfer is present in both phases,

$$N_{OG} = -\ln (1 - E_{OG}) = \frac{K_G a h}{G_M} = \frac{h/G_M}{(1/k_G a) + (mP/\rho_M)(1/k_L a)} \tag{243}$$

or

$$\frac{1}{-\ln (1 - E_{OG})} = \frac{1}{N_G} + \frac{mG_M}{L_M} \frac{1}{N_L} \tag{244}$$

where $N_G = k_G aPh/G_M$, the number of transfer units based on the gas-film resistance, and $N_L = \rho_M k_L ah/L_M$, the number of transfer units based on the liquid-film resistance. Figure 54 is a plot of this equation. It shows that the point efficiency is greater, the smaller the resistance of each phase. When there are only a few gas-film transfer units (N_G small), the liquid-film resistance has little effect.

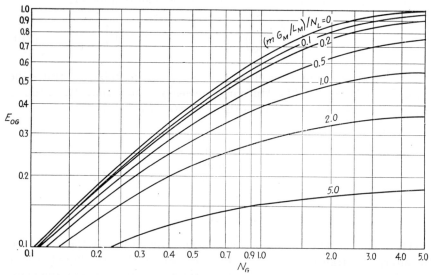

Fig. 54. Relationship between E_{OG}, N_G, and N_L, according to Eq. (244). E_{OG} = local or transfer efficiency on a gas basis, and N_G and N_L are numbers of gas and liquid transfer units.

In the case of a gas of low solubility the value of m in Eq. (244) is very large, and the second term dominates the right side of the equation. The point efficiency is extremely small under these circumstances, inasmuch as the vapor composition does not change appreciably as the gas flows through the tray. The liquid may come close to equilibrium, however. It is more logical in this case to reverse the roles of liquid and vapor, keeping in mind the progressive change in liquid composition toward equilibrium with the vapor as the liquid stream flows across the plate. It is logical, therefore, to define a new Murphree plate efficiency E_{ML}, in terms of liquid compositions, by means of the equation

$$E_{ML} = \frac{x_b - x_c}{x_b - x_{ec}} \tag{245}$$

where x_b = composition of liquid leaving tray b
$\quad x_c$ = composition of liquid leaving tray c
$\quad x_{ec}$ = composition of liquid in equilibrium with *average* exit vapor stream from tray c

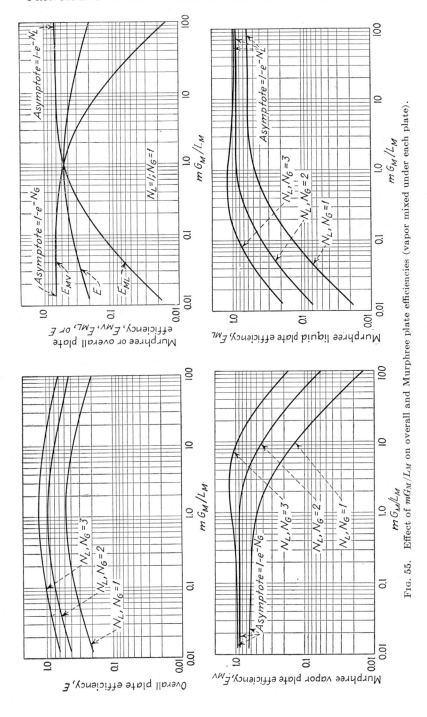

FIG. 55. Effect of mG_M/L_M on overall and Murphree plate efficiencies (vapor mixed under each plate).

This efficiency is similar to the Murphree vapor efficiency E_{MV} of the whole tray, across which a drop in liquid concentration takes place, rather than to the point efficiency. The relation between the two is

$$E_{ML} = \frac{E_{MV}}{E_{MV} + \dfrac{1 - E_{MV}}{mG_M/L_M}} \tag{246}$$

Figure 55 shows the dependence of the Murphree liquid and vapor efficiencies, as well as the over-all efficiency for an entire column, on the number of transfer units for each phase, N_G and N_L, and on mG_M/L_M. When m and also mG_M/L_M are very large, as in oxygen stripping from water, the value of E_{ML} is very nearly equal to $1 - e^{-N_L}$. Experimental measurements of E_{ML} for absorption or desorption of slightly soluble gases may be used, therefore, for computing N_L.

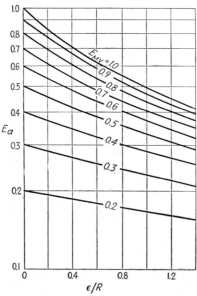

When liquid is carried by entrainment from one tray to the one next above, the strong liquid from the lower plate is mixed with weaker liquid. This action tends to destroy the desired countercurrent contact, with the result that the apparent Murphree vapor efficiency E_a of a tray in the presence of entrainment is lower than it would be otherwise. Colburn[85] has derived a simple, approximate relation showing the effect of the amount of entrainment, ϵ, and the gas-liquid ratio on the apparent vapor efficiency. The equation is

Fig 56. Relation of apparent Murphree plate vapor efficiency E_a to dry vapor efficiency E_{MV}, to moles entrainment ϵ per mole dry vapor, and to the reflux ratio $R = L_M/G_M$, according to Eq. (247).

$$E_a = \frac{E_{MV}}{1 + (\epsilon G_M/L_M)E_{MV}} \tag{247}$$

A plot of this equation is shown by Fig. 56 (see also Sherwood and Jenny).[419]

HEAT EFFECTS IN GAS ABSORPTION

The design procedure described on the preceding pages has assumed that the location of the equilibrium line on the p-c or the x-y diagram is known.   Since gas solubility depends on the temperature of the solvent, the equilibrium line cannot be located for the whole tower until the temperature of the solvent is known at every value of the solvent concentration.   When a very dilute gas is contacted with a large quantity of solvent, the heat effect accompanying solution of the soluble material may be so small in comparison with the sensible-heat capacity of the liquid that substantially isothermal operation will result.   In actual practice, however, there are many cases in which the solvent temperature rises appreciably.   Examples are the drying of air by contact with strong sulfuric acid, the absorption of sulfur trioxide in sulfuric acid, and the solution of hydrochloric acid gas in water to make concentrated muriatic acid.   In the last case, the quantity of heat which is liberated when HCl dissolves is so great that its removal becomes a controlling factor in the design of equipment for acid production.[345]

In most cases it is a relatively simple matter to correct for the change in temperature due to the heat of solution or condensation of the vapor. This correction is possible because the heat liberated is a function of the change in composition of the liquid, so if the heat capacity of the solvent is known, the relation between temperature rise and concentration may be calculated easily.   An equilibrium curve of gas composition vs. liquid composition may then be constructed, which takes into account the temperature variation through the column.

The rate of heat liberation is usually largest in the bottom of the tower, where the solute is absorbed more rapidly.   This has the effect of lifting the upper end of the equilibrium curve, as indicated by Fig. 57.   The lower end of the curve, corresponding to the upper, dilute end, of the absorber may remain straight, the slope corresponding to the initial solvent temperature.

The equilibrium curve EF, corresponding to the actual temperatures existing in the column, is located by first calculating the temperature rise for each value of x between x_2 and x_1.   The curve EF is then used in the design calculations.   If the liquid-film resistance controls the rate of absorption but the temperature of the liquid is the same at the interface as in the bulk of the liquid, the equilibrium line will be $E'F'$; but the procedure will be the same.   The variation of the liquid-film resistance with temperature may be allowed for in the graphical integration for tower height, since the relation between temperature and liquid concentration is obtained in order to place the equilibrium curve.

Allowance for cooling of the solvent due to heat loss from the column is more complicated, because the cooling is a function of column length rather than of liquid composition.   In theory, the equilibrium curve may be placed by trial, however, until graphical integration shows a relation between length and concentration which leads to a temperature-concentration relation agreeing with the assumed location of the equilibrium curve.

Since the minimum rate of liquid circulation required for good recovery of the solute gas is determined by the location of the upper end of the operating line, it is sometimes economical to provide special means for cooling the liquid in the base of the column. This may consist of coils laid on the bottom trays and supplied with cooling water or a refrigerant.

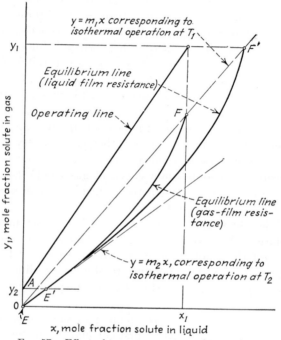

FIG 57.   Effect of temperature on equilibrium line.

Alternatively, it may be more desirable to divert the liquid stream through an external heat exchanger, or "intercooler," and then to return it to the next lower tray or section of the column.

If the rich gas enters the absorber cold, the liquid may be cooled just before it leaves by transferring sensible heat to the gas. A similar effect occurs if the solvent is volatile and the entering gas is not saturated with respect to the solvent. When water is the absorbent liquid, evaporation of water into the unsaturated entering gas may have a large cooling effect, owing to the large latent heat. In either of these cases, the liquid will be warmer at a point within the tower than at either end. Occasionally, the heat effects of this sort may be so large that the operating and equilibrium lines for the solute may cross, with the result that the solvent may be evaporated from the liquid in a lower part of the tower and condensed higher up.

Illustration 24. A gas containing 41.6 per cent NH_3 by volume at 68°F. is to be scrubbed with water to recover 99 per cent of its NH_3 content. If the water enters at 68°F. and if heat loss from the absorber is assumed to be negligible, what will be the minimum water rate, expressed as pounds water per pound gas mixture treated? What will be the corresponding maximum liquor strength obtainable? For heats of solution, see the International Critical Tables, Vol. V, page 213.

Solution

$$NH_{3gas} + nH_2O_{liq} \rightarrow (NH_3 + nH_2O)_{sol}$$

At 68°F. the heat of solution $(-Q)$ is related to the heat of formation $(a' + nb')$ of solution by

$$45.8676 + n(286.103) = a' + nb' + Q, \quad \text{kilojoules/g. mole}$$

n, g. moles H_2O	a'	b'	$-Q$, kilo-joules/g. mole NH_3	$-Q$, p.c.u./lb. mole NH_3	x, mole fraction NH_3	Adiabatic temp. rise, °F.	Liquid temp., °F.
1	66.12	293.4	27.55	6600	0.5	338	406
2.33	76.17	287.13	32.69	7820	0.3	238	306
4	78.09	286.46	33.62	8040	0.2	164	232
9	79.68	286.17	34.41	8220	0.1	83	151
19	80.31	286.11	34.64	8290	0.05	41.6	109.6
49	80.64	286.11	35.77	8580	0.02	17.1	85.1

Neglecting the change in sensible heat of the air and gaseous NH_3, and assuming that no water is vaporized and that the heat capacity of the ammonia solution is the same as that of liquid water, a heat balance shows that $\Delta T = -Q/(18)(1 + n)$. The liquor temperature is obtained by adding the temperature rise to the inlet temperature of 68°F. The mole fraction of NH_3 in the gas at equilibrium is then plotted vs. liquor strength, each point corresponding to the actual temperature resulting from the heat of the solution. The result is shown by Fig. 58.

$$Y_1 = \frac{0.416}{1 - 0.416} = 0.711 \text{ moles } NH_3/\text{mole air}$$

$$Y_2 = (0.01)(0.711) = 0.00711; \quad y_2 = \frac{0.00711}{1 + 0.00711} = 0.00710$$

Reading from the equilibrium curve of Fig. 58 where $y_e = y_1 = 0.416$, $x_1 = 0.088$, which is the maximum liquor strength. The corresponding mole ratio is $X_1 = 0.0965$ lb. mole NH_3/lb. mole H_2O. The minimum water rate $= (0.99)(0.711/0.0965) = 7.3$ lb. moles water per lb. mole of air or $(7.3)(1 - 0.416) = 4.26$ moles/mole of entering gas mixture, corresponding to the maximum liquor strength (and equilibrium at gas inlet).

Maximum liquor strength $= 0.088$ mole fraction, or **8.2** weight per cent ammonia.

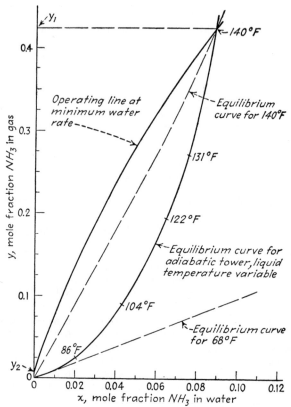

FIG. 58.   Equilibrium curve modified to allow for heat of solution of solute.

SIMULTANEOUS MASS AND HEAT TRANSFER IN PACKED ABSORBERS

The effects of absorption of the solute, vaporization of the solvent, and sensible-heat transfer between the gas and the liquid, all taking place simultaneously, may be allowed for by a step-by-step procedure if necessary. The calculations involved are tedious, however, and are mainly of theoretical interest.

Consider a differential section of the column, as shown by Fig. 59. For the sake of simplicity, assume that the gas and liquid solutions are dilute, so that G_M and L_M remain substantially constant. Assume also, for simplicity, that all the resistance to diffusion of both solute and evaporating solvent is in the gas phase, and that the temperature of the interface is the same as that of the bulk of the liquid, T. The following differential equations express the rates of change of the concentrations of solute and solvent in the gas, y and y'', respectively:

$$-\frac{dy}{dN_M} = y - y_e \tag{248}$$

$$-\frac{dy''}{dN_M''} = y'' - y_e'' \tag{249}$$

where N_M represents the number of transfer units for interphase mass transfer of the solute and N_M'' represents the number of transfer units for the solvent. Similarly, the rate of change of the gas temperature is given by

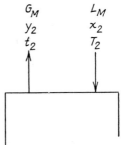

$$-\frac{dt}{dN_H} = t - T \tag{250}$$

where N_H represents number of transfer units for heat transfer. Each increment of height is expressed as an increment in the number of transfer units; each is related to the actual height increment dh by

$$dh = \frac{G_M}{k_GaP} dN_M = \frac{G_M}{k_G''aP} dN_M''$$

$$= \frac{C_pG}{ha} dN_H \tag{251}$$

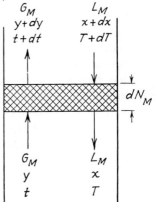

The transfer coefficients are related by the principle of similarity between mass and heat transfer. Thus,

$$\frac{k_G''a}{k_Ga} = \left(\frac{D_v''}{D_v}\right)^n = \alpha \tag{252}$$

and

$$\frac{ha/G}{k_GaP/G_M} = C_p\left(\frac{k}{C_p\rho_GD_v}\right)^n = \beta C_P \tag{253}$$

showing that

$$dN_M'' = \alpha\, dN_M; \qquad dN_H = \beta\, dN_M \tag{254}$$

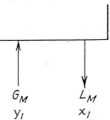

Fig. 59. Diagrammatic sketch of packed column.

and

$$-\frac{dy}{dN_M} = y - y_e \tag{255}$$

$$-\frac{dy''}{dN_M} = \alpha(y'' - y_e'') \tag{256}$$

$$-\frac{dt}{dN_M} = \beta(t - T) \tag{257}$$

A heat balance equating the heat leaving the differential section to that arriving leads to

$$\frac{dT}{dN_M} = \frac{G_M}{L_M C_L}\left(C_G \frac{dt}{dN_M} + Q \frac{dy}{dN_M} + Q'' \frac{dy''}{dN_M}\right) \qquad (258)$$

where Q and Q'' are the heats of solution of the solute and solvent vapors. A material balance leads to

$$\frac{dx}{dN_M} = \frac{G_M}{L_M}\frac{dy}{dN_M} \qquad (259)$$

Once all the concentrations and temperatures are known at one end of the packing, it is possible in principle to apply Eqs. (255) to (259) to successive thin slices of the packing, and thus to establish the profiles of gas and liquid concentrations or temperatures through the packing. If some of the concentrations or temperatures are not known at the ends, they may usually be found by over-all heat and material balances. In practice, the calculations are so tedious, except for very shallow beds of packing, that it may be desirable to calculate only the rates of change of the temperatures and concentrations at the top and bottom of the packing, and then to estimate the complete profiles very roughly. As an illustration, consider the absorption of acetone vapor from moist air in water under conditions similar to those reported by Othmer and Scheibel.[350]

Illustration 25. The following data correspond to Othmer and Scheibel's run 5, with slight adjustments to make material balances check: $t_1 = 58.8°F$.; $T_1 = 69.3°F$.; $y_1 = 0.0300$ mole fraction acetone in inlet gas; $y_1'' = 0.0116$ mole fraction water (assumed 70 per cent saturated); $x_1 = 0.0132$ mole fraction acetone in exit liquid; $y_{e1} = 0.0205$; $y_{e1}'' = 0.0240$; $t_2 = 72°F$.; $T_2 = 54.5°F$. water inlet temperature; $y_2 = 0.00231$ mole fraction acetone in exit gas; $y_2'' = 0.0265$ mole fraction water (assumed saturated); $x_2 = 0$; $y_{e2} = 0$; $y_{e2}'' = 0.0144$; $L_M/G_M = 2.47$; $Q = 18,000$ B.t.u per lb. mole acetone, evolved on solution of acetone vapor in dilute aqueous solution (the partial molal heat of solution of acetone at infinite dilution); $Q'' = 19,323$ B.t.u. per lb. mole water, evolved on condensation of water vapor; $C_L = 18$ B.t.u./ (lb. mole)(°F.); $C_G = 7$ B.t.u./(lb. mole)(°F.).

Comparing the Schmidt numbers $(\mu/\rho D_v)$ of acetone and water vapor diffusing through air (see Table III, page 20),

$$\alpha = \left(\frac{1.60}{0.60}\right)^{0.6} = 1.82$$

Also,

$$\beta = \left(\frac{1.60}{0.74}\right)^{0.6} = 1.59$$

Dividing Eq. (255) into Eqs. (256), (257), and (258) and multiplying each by L_M/G_M, we obtain

$$\frac{dy''}{dx} = \alpha \frac{L_M}{G_M} \frac{y'' - y_e''}{y - y_e} \tag{260}$$

$$\frac{dt}{dx} = \beta \frac{L_M}{G_M} \frac{t - T}{y - y_e} \tag{261}$$

$$\frac{dT}{dx} = \frac{Q}{C_L} + \frac{C_G}{C_L} \frac{G_M}{L_M} \frac{dt}{dx} + \frac{Q''}{C_L} \frac{G_M}{L_M} \frac{dy''}{dx} \tag{262}$$

At the bottom of the packing

$$\frac{dy''}{dx} = (1.82)(2.47) \frac{0.0116 - 0.0240}{0.0300 - 0.0205} = -5.86$$

$$\frac{dt}{dx} = (1.59)(2.47) \frac{58.8 - 69.3}{0.0300 - 0.0205} = -4330°F./\text{mole fraction}$$

$$\frac{dT}{dx} = \frac{18{,}000}{18} + \frac{7}{18} \frac{-4330}{2.47} + \frac{19{,}323}{18} \frac{-5.86}{2.47}$$

$$= -2230°F./\text{mole fraction}$$

At the top of the packing

$$\frac{dy''}{dx} = (1.82)(2.47) \frac{0.0265 - 0.0144}{0.00231 - 0} = 23.6$$

$$\frac{dt}{dx} = (1.59)(2.47) \frac{72 - 54.5}{0.00231 - 0} = 29{,}800°F./\text{mole fraction}$$

$$\frac{dT}{dx} = \frac{18{,}000}{18} + \frac{7}{18} \frac{29{,}800}{2.47} + \frac{19{,}323}{18} \frac{23.6}{2.47} = 16{,}000°F./\text{mole fraction}$$

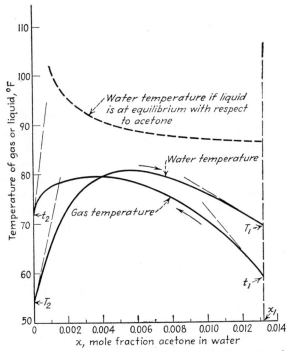

FIG. 60. Estimated temperature profiles in adiabatic absorption of acetone.

The equilibrium vapor pressures of acetone are based on the experimental activity coefficients shown by Fig. 41.[363]

Plots of the temperatures of the air and water against the mole fraction of acetone in the liquid start at the ends of the packing in the directions calculated above. These slopes are shown on Fig. 60. The complete temperature curves could be located by a step-by-step calculation, but for the purposes of this illustration they have simply been estimated. As an aid in locating these curves, it may be noted that the curve of gas temperature becomes horizontal at the point where it intersects the curve of the water temperature. The slope of the water-temperature curve at this point may be calculated roughly if it is assumed that the air remains saturated with water vapor.

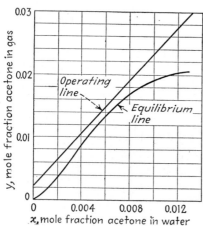

FIG. 61. Estimated equilibrium vapor compositions in the adiabatic absorption of acetone.

Once the water temperature is known as a function of the concentration of acetone, the equilibrium partial pressures of acetone over the aqueous solution may be determined and an x-y diagram constructed. Figure 61 is such a plot. The maximum liquid temperature at $x = 0.0057$ causes the diffusional driving force y-y_e to reach a minimum at this point.

Minimum Liquid Rate for an Adiabatic Tower. As shown by the calculations described in Illustration 25, the competing heat effects due to absorption of the solute and evaporation of the solvent may cause the liquid temperature to reach a maximum value at an intermediate point in the absorption tower. ("Hot spots" have been observed experimentally by noting the temperature of the metal shell enclosing the packing.) If the liquid is heated too much, the equilibrium and operating lines will touch, causing the equipment to become inoperable. Since the only way for removing the heat of solution of the solute in an adiabatic tower is by allowing the solvent to evaporate or to rise in temperature, it is obvious that an inoperable condition must be avoided by providing sufficient solvent to absorb all the solute and, *in addition*, to absorb the heat of solution.

Whereas in an isothermal tower, the minimum solvent rate is found as discussed on page 130 by considering the solubility of the solute at the exit liquid temperature only, in an adiabatic tower the operating and equilibrium lines may touch at an intermediate point. Even though the operating and the equilibrium lines are separated at the ends and an over-all heat balance is satisfied, the absorber will not have been proved operable until an intermediate equilibrium point has been proved not to exist.

The determination of the minimum solvent rate of an adiabatic tower does not appear to have been worked out in simple terms. At present one must resort to step-by-step calculations of fluid temperatures and compositions, starting from the base or the top of the packing, to determine whether the opposite end of the packing can be reached, using an arbitrarily chosen liquid rate.

In order to bring out these principles more clearly, the effects of changes in the liquid-gas ratio have been calculated for a typical case of adiabatic absorption of ammonia in water. The results show that the liquid rate must be 19 per cent greater than would be estimated by considering the terminal conditions alone.

Illustration 26. A packed absorption tower is to be designed for the removal of ammonia from air by adiabatic absorption in water. The gas entering the absorber contains 0.1 lb. mole/hr. of NH_3, 1 lb. mole/hr. of air, and is saturated with water vapor at its inlet temperature, 77°F. It is required that 95 per cent of the ammonia be absorbed in water, which enters at 61.3°F. Calculate the minimum water rate.

Solution. The composition of the entering gas is determined as follows:

Constituent	lb. moles/hr.	Mole fraction
Air..............	1	0.8813
NH_3.............	0.1	0.0882
H_2O.............	0.0346	0.0305
Total..........	1.1346	1.0000

The composition of the exit gas is estimated by assuming that it leaves at a temperature 7°F. higher than that of the inlet water and that the gas is saturated with water at this temperature.

Constituent	lb. moles/hr.	Mole fraction
Air..............	1	0.9707
NH_3.............	0.005	0.0048
H_2O.............	0.0252	0.0245
Total..........	1.0302	1.0000

An approximate over-all heat balance, based on Eq. (258), shows that

$$T_1 - 61.3 = \left(\frac{G_M}{L_M}\right)\left[\frac{7}{18}(77 - 69.8) + \frac{15,380}{18}(0.0882 - 0.0048)\right.$$
$$\left. + \frac{19,250}{18}(0.0305 - 0.0245)\right] = 80.5\frac{G_M}{L_M}$$

An over-all material balance shows that

$$x_1 = \frac{G_M}{L_M}(0.0890 - 0.0048) = 0.0842\frac{G_M}{L_M}$$

a. Approximate determination of minimum liquid rate. Equilibrium is reached at the base of the packed section if $y_1 = y_{e1} = (p_{e1}/x_1)(x_1/P)$. For dilute ammonia solutions, p_e/x is given as a function of temperature by the following data:

T_1, °F.	p_e/x_1, atm./mole fraction
50	0.64
68	1.03
84	1.65
104	2.54
122	3.80

The limiting gas-liquid ratio at which equilibrium is obtained is found by a cut-and-try calculation as follows:

G_M/L_M	T_1	p_e/x	x_1	y_{e1}
0.4	93.4	2.00	0.0336	0.0672
0.45	96.5	2.15	0.0379	0.0818
0.5	99.6	2.32	0.0421	0.0980

By interpolation, $y_{e1} = 0.0890$ when $G_M/L_M = 0.473$. The true limiting value of G_M/L_M is smaller, as shown below.

b. Determination of typical temperature profiles. As a trial solution, assume that $G_M/L_M = 0.38$ will give satisfactory operating conditions without equilibrium between the gas and liquid streams at any point in the packing. Over-all heat and material balances give $T_1 = 92.1°F.$, $x_1 = 0.0320$, and the other conditions at the base of the packing are listed above. A numerical, step-by-step integration is begun at the bottom of the packing, using Eqs. (255) to (259). For this case, the values of $\mu/\rho D_v$ are 0.74* and 0.60 for ammonia and water vapor, respectively, diffusing through air, giving $\alpha = 1.14$ and $\beta = 1.00$. The equations become

$$-\frac{dy}{dN} = y - y_e$$

$$-\frac{dy''}{dN} = 1.14(y'' - y_e'')$$

$$-\frac{dt}{dN} = t - T$$

$$\frac{dT}{dN} = 0.148\frac{dt}{dN} + 328\frac{dy}{dN} + 400\frac{dy''}{dN}$$

$$\frac{dx}{dN} = 0.38\frac{dy}{dN}$$

Figure 62 shows the variation of the temperature and ammonia content of the gas and liquid streams with position in the tower. The curves show that the equipment is operable at this liquid rate, even though the liquid temperature reaches a maximum value and the ammonia is absorbed relatively slowly at the corresponding point.

The dew point of the gas can be calculated from the mole fractions of ammonia and water vapor. It is interesting to note that, in the lower part of the packing, the gas is

* This value is based on the calculated value of D_v for ammonia in air, rather than the experimental value as given in Table III.

calculated to be cooler than its dew point, indicating that fog would form in this region. The consequent release of heat in the gas would tend to retard the fog formation, but the equations used in the calculations cannot be expected to apply under these conditions, since they are based on the assumption that mass and heat are transferred across the same interface and that all the heat of condensation or evaporation is released at the gas-liquid interface. Nevertheless, the calculated curves may be expected to represent the situation qualitatively.

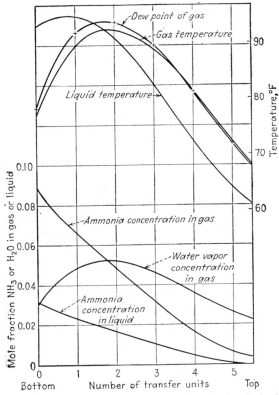

Fig. 62. Calculated temperature and composition profiles in adiabatic absorption of ammonia in water.

c. Determination of true limiting maximum value of G_M/L_M. By repeating the numerical integration procedure for other values of G_M/L_M, a set of curves is obtained similar to those of Fig. 62. Figure 63 shows several temperature profiles obtained in this way, based on terminal conditions only slightly different from those of parts *a* and *b* above. The corresponding operating and equilibrium lines are shown by Fig. 64. The limiting value of G_M/L_M lies between 0.39 and 0.40. Using the latter value, the top of the packing cannot be reached by calculating from the bottom, and vice versa. The liquid temperature does not pass through a maximum at the higher liquid rates, and the equilibrium curve has no point of inflection.

The value of G_M/L_M at which the liquid-temperature profile is horizontal at the bottom of the packing is of some interest. It is determined by setting $(dT/dN)_1$

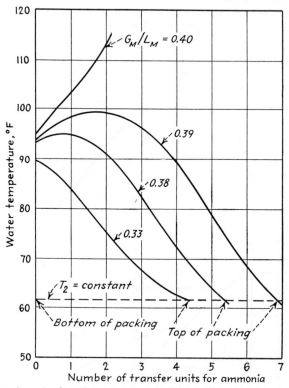

Fig. 63. Effect of varying liquid-gas ratio in the adiabatic absorption of ammonia in water.

equal to zero, determining T_1, x_1, y_{e1}, and y_{e1}'' from over-all heat and material balances. The calculations are summarized as follows:

$$\frac{L_M}{G_M}\left(\frac{dT}{dN}\right)_1 = 0 = \frac{7}{18}\left(\frac{dt}{dN}\right)_1 + \frac{15{,}380}{18}\left(\frac{dy}{dN}\right)_1 + \frac{19{,}250}{18}\left(\frac{dy''}{dN}\right)_1$$

$$0 = \left(\frac{7}{18}\right)(T_1 - t_1) + \frac{15{,}380}{18}(y_{e1} - y_1) + \frac{19{,}250}{18}(1.14)(y_{e1}'' - y_1'')$$

$$0.0882 - y_{e1} = \frac{19{,}250}{15{,}380}(1.14)(y_{e1}'' - 0.0305) + \frac{7}{15{,}380}(T_1 - 77) \qquad (262a)$$

$$T_1 = 61.3 + \frac{G_M}{L_M}\left[\frac{7}{18}(77 - 698) + \frac{15{,}380}{18}(0.0882 - 0.0048)\right.$$

$$\left. + \frac{19{,}250}{18}(0.0305 - 0.0245)\right]$$

$$= 61.3 + 81.0\frac{G_M}{L_M}$$

$$x_1 = 0.0834\frac{G_M}{L_M}$$

G_M/L_M	T_1 in °F.	x_1	y_{e1}	y_{e1}''	Eq. (262a)		
					Left side	Right side	Difference
0.35	89.8	0.0291	0.0530	0.0530	0.0352	0.0293	0.0059
0.40	93.8	0.0333	0.0672	0.0534	0.0210	0.0401	−0.0191
0.45	97.7	0.0375	0.0830				
0.50	101.9	0.0416	0.102				

By interpolation, it is found that dT/dN is zero at the bottom of the packing if $G_M/L_M = 0.362$. By the method of part a it is found that $y_{e1} = y_1$ if $G_M/L_M = 0.487$. The true limiting value, approximately $G_M/L_M = 0.395$, lies between.

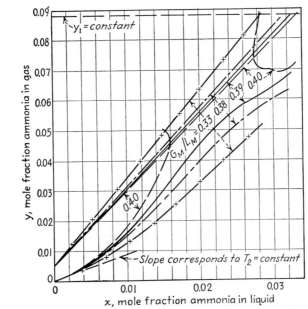

Fig. 64. Effect of varying liquid-gas ratio in the adiabatic absorption of ammonia.

As in a water-cooling tower, where the only solute present in the gas is the vaporized solvent and the inert gas is insoluble, Eqs. (248) to (258) may be simplified provided $\beta = 1$, *i.e.*, provided the ratio of h to k' is equal to the specific heat of the gas. These conditions have been discussed in detail in Chap. IV, but it remains to be shown how the equations developed there can be used for designing countercurrent water-cooling equipment. Owing to the use of the enthalpy potential, the calculations are quite similar to those already illustrated for isothermal absorbers and are demonstrated by the following example:

Illustration 26a. Calculate the cross-sectional area and the depth of packing required in a slat-packed water-cooling tower to cool 1000 gal./min. of water initially at 130°F. to 90°F. by countercurrent contact with air having a wet-bulb temperature of 70°F. The air rate will be 50 per cent greater than the minimum rate, and the height of a transfer unit for enthalpy transfer is 2.5 ft. The superficial air velocity will be 1000 lb./(hr.)(sq. ft.).

Solution. Referring to Fig. 30, Chap. IV, the enthalpy of the entering air is found to be 34 B.t.u./lb. To determine the minimum air rate draw a straight operating line on Fig. 30 tangent to the equilibrium curve and passing through the point (34 B.t.u./lb., 90°F.). Its slope is 2.8 B.t.u./(lb.)(°F.), from which the minimum gas rate is (1000)(8.33)/2.8 or 2980 lb./hr. The actual gas rate is (1.5)(2980) or 4460 lb./hr., and if the allowable gas mass velocity is 1000 lb./(hr.)(sq. ft.), the required tower cross section is 4.46 sq. ft.

The number of transfer units is calculated according to Eq. (145).

$$N_{OG} = \frac{xK'a}{G} = \int \frac{di_G}{i_L - i_G}$$

The enthalpy of the exit gas is found from an enthalpy balance, Eq. (149), to be

$$34 + (2.8/1.5)(130 - 90) = 109 \text{ B.t.u./lb.}$$

and the logarithmic-mean enthalpy driving force is

$$\Delta i_{l.m.} = \frac{(154 - 109) - (56 - 34)}{\ln \dfrac{154 - 109}{56 - 34}} = 32 \text{ B.t.u./lb.}$$

The number of transfer units is then

$$N_{OG} = \frac{109 - 34}{32} = 2.3$$

and the required packed height is

$$x = (2.5)(2.3) = 5.9 \text{ ft.}$$

Nomenclature for Chapter V

a = area of interphase contact, ft.^{2}/ft.^{3}

B = constant in Eq. (232)

c = solute concentration in the main body of the liquid, lb. moles/ft.^{3}

c_e = concentration of solute in liquid phase corresponding to equilibrium with gas, lb. moles/ft.^{3}

c_G = concentration of solute in gas phase, lb. moles/ft.^{3}

c_i = solute concentration in the liquid at the interphase boundary, lb. moles/ft.^{3}

c_1 = solute concentration in the liquid leaving the bottom (gas inlet), lb. moles/ft.^{3}

c_2 = solute concentration in the liquid fed to the top of a countercurrent absorption apparatus, lb. moles/ft.^{3}

C_G = molal heat capacity of gas, B.t.u./(lb. mole)(°F.)

C_L = molal heat capacity of liquid, B.t.u./(lb. mole)(°F.)

C_p = specific heat, Btu/(lb.)(°F.)

D_v = diffusion coefficient for gas (see Chap. I)

D_L = diffusion coefficient in liquid phase (see Chap. I), ft.^{2}/hr.

E = over-all plate efficiency, fraction

E_a = apparent vapor efficiency of a plate in the presence of entrainment, fraction

E_{ML} = Murphree liquid efficiency of a single plate, fraction

E_{MV} = Murphree vapor efficiency of a single plate

E_{CG} = Murphree point efficiency of single plate, fraction

G_M = superficial molar mass velocity of gas, lb. moles/(hr.)(ft.^{2})

G_M' = superficial molar mass velocity of inert gas, lb. moles/(hr.)(ft.^{2})

h = height of packed section of tower, ft.

H = Henry's law constant, p_e/c

H_G = height of an individual gas-phase transfer unit, ft.

H_L = height of an individual liquid-phase transfer unit, ft.

H_{OG} = height of an over-all gas-phase transfer unit, ft.

H_{OL} = height of an over-all liquid-phase transfer unit, ft.

k = number of "pools" in flow across plate

k_G = gas-film coefficient, lb. moles/(hr.)(ft.^{2})(atm.)

k_G' = gas-film coefficient, corrected for inert-gas concentration [see Eq. (169)]

k_Ga = gas-film coefficient on a volume basis, lb. moles/(hr.)(ft.^{3})(atm.)

$k_G'a$ = mass-transfer coefficient, corrected for mean partial pressure of inert gas, lb. moles/(hr.)(ft.^{3})(atm.) = $k_Ga(p_{BM}/P)$

k_L = liquid-film coefficient, lb. moles/(hr.)(ft.^{2})(unit Δc)

k_La = liquid-film coefficient on a volume basis, lb. moles/(hr.)(ft.^{3})(unit Δc)

K_G = gas-film coefficient, lb. moles/(hr.)(ft.^{2})(atm.)

K_Ga = over-all coefficient on a volume basis, lb. moles/(hr.)(ft.^{3})(atm.)

K_L = over-all coefficient, lb. moles/(hr.)(ft.^{2})(unit over-all Δc)

K_La = over-all coefficient on a volume basis, lb. moles/(hr.)(ft.^{3})(unit over-all Δc)

L_M = liquor rate, lb. moles/(hr.)(ft.^{2} column cross section)

L_M' = liquor rate, lb. moles solute-free solvent/(hr.)(ft.^{2} column cross section)

m = slope of equilibrium curve = dy_e/dx

M = mean molecular weight of gas; subscript 1 at bottom of packing

N_A = diffusion rate, lb. moles/(hr.)(ft.^{2})

N_G = number of individual gas-phase transfer units

N_H = number of transfer units for heat transfer

N_L = number of individual liquid-phase transfer units

N_{OG} = number of over-all gas-phase transfer units

N_{OL} = number of over-all liquid-phase transfer units

N_P = number of theoretical plates

N_P' = number of actual plates

N_T = number of transfer units

p = partial pressure of solute in main stream, atm.

p_{BM} = log mean of inert-gas pressures at film boundaries, atm.

p_i = partial pressure of solute at liquid-gas interface, atm.

p_e = pressure of solute in equilibrium with concentration of main body of liquid, atm.

p_1 = partial pressure of solute in gas entering, atm.

p_2 = partial pressure of solute in main gas stream at gas outlet, atm.

P = total pressure on system, atm.

Q = quantity defined in Table IX; also heat of solution (in Illustrations 24–26)

R = reflux ratio, L_M/G_M; gas-law constant = 1544 ft.-lb./(lb. mole)(°R)

S = quantity defined in Table IX

t = gas temperature, °F.

T = absolute temperature, °R., also liquid temperature, °F.

v = weight fraction of solute in solvent phase

V = volume of absorption apparatus, ft.^{3}

w = weight fraction of solute in nonsolvent phase

x = mole fraction of solute in liquid stream

x_e = mole fraction of solute in liquid at equilibrium with bulk of gas

x_i = mole fraction of solute in liquid at interface

x_1 = mole fraction of solute in liquid stream at concentrated end of countercurrent apparatus

x_2 = mole fraction of solute in liquid stream at dilute end of countercurrent apparatus

X = solute concentration in liquid, lb. moles solute/lb. mole solvent

X_c = solute concentration in the liquid on the cth plate from the top of the column, lb. moles solute/lb. mole solvent

X_e = solute concentration corresponding to equilibrium with the solute concentration in the main body of the gas, lb. moles solute/lb. mole solvent

X_1 = solute concentration of the liquid leaving the bottom (gas inlet), lb. moles solute/lb. mole solvent

X_2 = solute concentration of the liquid fed at the top (gas outlet), lb. moles solute/ lb. mole solvent

y = mole fraction of solute in gas stream

y'' = mole fraction solvent in gas stream

y_e = mole fraction of solute in gas at equilibrium with bulk of liquid

y_i = mole fraction of solute in gas at interface

y_1 = mole fraction of solute in gas stream at concentrated end of countercurrent apparatus

y_2 = mole fraction of solute in gas stream at dilute end of countercurrent apparatus

Y = solute concentration in gas, lb. moles solute/lb. mole inert gas

Y_c = solute concentration in gas leaving the cth plate, lb. moles solute/lb. mole inert gas

Y_e = solute concentration in gas corresponding to equilibrium with the concentration of the main body of the liquid, lb. moles solute/lb. mole inert gas

Y_1 = solute concentration of the gas entering the column, lb. moles solute/lb. mole inert gas

Y_2 = solute concentration of gas leaving the top of the column, lb. moles solute/lb. mole inert gas

α = ratio defined by Eq. (252)

β = ratio defined by Eq. (253)

Δ = difference, as in difference of concentrations used for driving force

ϵ = entrainment, lb. moles liquid/lb. mole dry vapor

ρ_L = density of liquid, lb./ft.^{3}

ρ_M = molal density of liquid, lb. moles/ft.^{3}

ρ_G = gas density, lb./ft.^{3}

γ = activity coefficient of solute in liquid solution, or deviation factor from Raoult's law

μ = viscosity, lb./(hr.)(ft.)

Problems

1. A plate tower is to be designed to strip propane from a nonvolatile oil by stepwise countercurrent contact with steam. The tower is to be operated at 280°F. and an absolute pressure of 20 p.s.i. There are to be two liquid feeds:

51.5 lb. moles/hr., containing 3 mole per cent propane

53.5 lb. moles/hr. of rich solution, containing 6.54 mole per cent propane

Each of these streams is to be introduced through pipes and valves at appropriate points. One pound mole per hour of superheated steam will be introduced at the bottom of the column, which is to contain enough plates to produce a stripped liquid containing 0.010 mole of propane per mole of nonvolatile oil.

a. Determine the minimum total number of theoretical plates in the column.

b. Specify the points where each feed should be introduced, calling the top theoretical plate No. 1.

c. What is the richest liquid on any plate?

d. Estimate the number of transfer units (over-all gas-film basis) required if a packed tower were substituted for the plate tower.

2. It is desired to design a tower packed with 1-in. ceramic Raschig rings to recover 99.5 per cent of the CO_2 from an inlet gas containing 5 mole per cent CO_2 and 95 mole per cent air, using CO_2-free water. The tower will be operated at atmospheric pressure at 68°F., and the maximum entering gas rate will be 3850 ft.^{3}/hr. Over the range involved Henry's law applies at equilibrium: $Y/X = m = 1410$, where Y is the mole ratio of CO_2 to air in the equilibrium gas phase and X is the mole ratio of CO_2 to water in the liquid phase.

It is agreed to use L_M/G_M (mole-ratio units) equal to $1.4m$, and to use an actual superficial air velocity equal to 50 per cent of the maximum allowable velocity at flooding.

a. Calculate the number of theoretical plates required by the stepwise method.

b. Repeat, using the Kremser equation.

3. A rich benzene-air mixture is to be treated in a tower packed with wood grids, using a nonvolatile hydrocarbon oil as solvent. The inlet gas contains 7.56 mole per cent benzene, and the oil has an average molecular weight of 210. Solubility of benzene in the oil follows Raoult's law: $p = P_v x$, where p is partial pressure of benzene over the solution, P_v is vapor pressure of benzene = 100 mm. at the tower temperature, and x is mole fraction of benzene in the oil.

What is the *minimum* oil rate as pounds of oil per minute if 90.9 per cent of the benzene is to be recovered from 600 lb. moles/hr. of inlet gas mixture? The oil fed contains no benzene. Total pressure = 760 mm.

4. A gas mixture containing 3.0 mole per cent benzene, 3.55 per cent toluene, and 2.48 per cent *o*-xylene is to be stripped in a packed column operated isothermally at 104°F. and 1 atm. total pressure. The absorbing liquid is a nonvolatile oil, and the column efficiency is such that 80 per cent of the toluene is recovered, with an inlet gas rate of 2000 lb. moles/hr. and a liquid rate of 145 lb. moles/hr.

What is the percentage recovery of benzene and of *o*-xylene?

At 104°F., the vapor pressures of the components are benzene 160.1 mm.; toluene, 59.1 mm.; *o*-xylene, 23.7 mm. Raoult's law and Dalton's law may be used in this case.

5. A tower packed to a height of 7.0 ft. is employed by an industrial company as a gas scrubber. A dilute air-ammonia mixture is drawn (under suction) by means of a fan through 1-in.-carbon-ring packing, countercurrent to water. Plant records indicate that operation of the tower has not been satisfactory, and the following data were taken in a test run on the unit:

Inlet gas rate . . . . 878 ft.^{3}/min. at 70°F. and 1 atm.

Gas composition inlet . . . . 4.93 per cent NH_3 by volume

Outlet . . . . 0.509 per cent NH_3 by volume

Inlet water rate . . . . 38.0 lb./min.

Exit liquid composition . . . . 0.0423 lb. NH_3/lb. water

Exit liquid rate . . . . 39.61 lb./min.

As plant engineer, interpret the above data and locate *where* the trouble, if any, occurs, assuming all measurements to be *accurate*. Assume K_Ga to vary as the 0.54 power of the gas rate; for purposes of calculation the operation may be assumed isothermal at 70°F. and 1 atm.

6. A burner gas containing 17 per cent SO_2 is scrubbed at atmospheric pressure in a packed tower 38 ft. tall. The water is at 68°F., and the water rate is 40 per cent greater than the theoretical minimum to absorb 80 per cent of the SO_2 in the entering gas. The data on the tower indicate that the present recovery of SO_2 is 80 per cent.

a. In order to reduce the nuisance and to increase the yield, it is proposed to install a second tower, an exact duplicate of the first, arranged so that the gas from the top of the first enters at the top of the second and flows through the second in parallel with the water. The same water and gas rates as at present will be used for the double-tower system as a whole. Assuming K_Ga to be the same for parallel as for counter-current flow, what per cent recovery can be expected? Water pumps and pipes can be installed to handle the water in whatever flow arrangement seems to be best. Assume the molecular weight of the inert gas to be 28.5. For purposes of an approximate calculation, assume the equilibrium for SO_2 in water at the tower temperature to be given by $Y = 15X$, where Y is pounds of SO_2 per pound of inert gas and X is pounds of SO_2 per pound of water.

b. Show the operating diagram for the double tower. Show operating and equilibrium lines on a Y-X diagram (diagrammatic only, not to scale).

7. *a.* A benzene-air mixture containing 8.12 mole per cent benzene is treated in an adiabatic packed tower, using a nonvolatile hydrocarbon oil as solvent. The tower is packed to a height equivalent to four perfect plates, and liquid and gas enter at 60°F. and 1 atm. The inlet gas rate is 3.96 ft./sec., and 1395 lb. of benzene-free oil (mol. wt. = 210) is fed per hr. per ft.² tower cross section. What per cent recovery of benzene is obtained in the tower?

b. It is proposed to remove the oil from the tower when 40 per cent of the total benzene has been absorbed, cool it to 60°F., and return it to the same point. What is the per cent recovery under this procedure?

Additional data:

Specific heat of oil = 0.4 B.t.u./(lb.)(°F.)
Latent heat of condensation of benzene = 182 B.t.u./lb.
The gas may be considered isothermal within the tower, and the benzene content of the oil may be neglected in calculating the temperature rise of the liquid.

8. An air-acetone mixture containing 2.5 per cent acetone by volume is treated with water in a countercurrent packed tower at 68°F. and 1 atm. With a water rate of 197 lb./min., the recovery of acetone is 98.0 per cent. The gas rate is 2000 ft.³/min.

It is now proposed to supply the tower with 2000 ft.³/min. of a gas containing 25 per cent acetone, with water rate and temperature unchanged. By what per cent must the tower height be changed to obtain the same 98 per cent recovery of acetone? Allow for variation of p_{BM} and K_Ga through the tower for the case of the rich gas. Assume K_Ga varies as the 0.8 power of the total gas flow.

9. Ammonia is to be absorbed from air at atmospheric pressure by means of a countercurrent packed tower, using a dilute solution of sulfuric acid as absorbent. In this system the gas film presents the controlling resistance, and $k_g = K_G$. An inlet gas rate of 800 lb./(hr.)(ft.²) and an acid rate of 1000 lb./(hr.)(ft.²) will be used. Under these conditions k_Ga is 18.0 lb. moles/(hr.)(ft.³)(atm.).

Determine the tower height needed for the absorption of (*a*) 50 per cent of the ammonia from an inlet gas containing 1.0 per cent NH_3 by volume in air; (*b*) 99 per cent of the NH_3 from the same gas; (*c*) 99 per cent of the NH_3 from a 5 per cent gas. Repeat for absorption in water not containing acid. Assume K_Ga to be 18.0. Assume the tower to operate at a constant temperature of 68°F.

10. Air containing 10 per cent ammonia vapor is to be scrubbed countercurrently with water in an absorption column. The inlet gas rate is 100 lb. moles/hr. of gas mixture, and the inlet liquor rate is 150 lb. moles/hr. of pure water. Assume that the temperature is constant at 77°F. and that the total pressure is 1 atm. The exit gas contains 0.5 per cent ammonia.

a. Calculate the number of pound moles of ammonia absorbed per hour and the number lost from the top of the column.

b. Calculate the mole fraction of ammonia in the exit liquor.

c. Calculate a table of values of x (liquid strength in mole fraction of ammonia) corresponding to gas compositions of $y = 0.02, 0.04, 0.06, 0.08$, where y is mole fraction of ammonia in gas. Make a plot of y vs. x.

d. Plot on the same chart a line for equilibrium values of y_e corresponding to values of x. Assume that Henry's law applies and that $Py_e/x = 750$ mm. Hg, where P is the total pressure in millimeters of mercury.

e. Calculate the number of transfer units required (1) using an over-all logarithmic-mean driving force, and (2) from Fig. 40.

f. Calculate the number of theoretical plates required, using Fig. 47.

11. Air containing 5 per cent ammonia vapor passes countercurrent to scrubbing water in a packed absorber. The inlet rate of the gas mixture equals 100 lb. moles/hr., and the inlet water rate equals 150 lb. moles/hr. Assume a constant temperature of 68°F. and atmospheric pressure. If the exit gas contains 0.2 per cent ammonia,

a. Calculate the pound moles of ammonia absorbed per hour.

b. Calculate the number of transfer units, using Fig. 40. At 68°F. $Py_e/x = 600$ mm., where P is the total pressure in millimeters of mercury.

c. If the packing is 1-in. Raschig rings and if a gas velocity of 700 lb./(hr.)(ft.²) is used, what height of tower is required?

12. A packed tower 8 ft. high operating at 1 atm. total pressure is found to remove 99 per cent of the ammonia from an air-ammonia mixture containing 6 per cent ammonia by volume. The gas rate is 128 lb./(hr.)(ft.²) of inert (air) at the gas inlet, and the tower is supplied with water at 68°F. at the rate of 188 lb./(hr.) (ft.²). Assuming isothermal operation, calculate the effect of separately doubling (*a*) the total pressure, (*b*) the gas supplied, (*c*) the water rate, on the tower height required to absorb 99 per cent of the ammonia in the entering gas. The necessary equilibrium data are as follows:

Partial pressure of NH_3, mm. Hg	12	18.2	24.9	31.7	50
Concentration in the liquid, lb. NH_3/lb. water	0.02	0.03	0.04	0.05	0.075

Note: Assume that the gas-film resistance controls the rate of transfer, but in part (*c*) neglect the effect on k_Ga of increasing the water rate.

13. A tower 6.07 in. in diameter, filled for 49.5 in. with 1-in. spheres, reduced the ammonia concentration from 4.52 to 1.29 per cent by volume of air fed at the rate of 113 lb./hr., by means of water supplied at the rate of 102.5 lb./hr. The strength of the ammonia solution obtained was 2.27 per cent by weight, at a temperature of 76.1°F., at which temperature $m = y_e/x$ may be taken as 0.99. Calculate an ammonia balance, as a percentage of that supplied in the air; calculate K_Ga in lb. moles/(hr.)(ft.³) (mole fraction) and H_{OG} in feet. The total pressure was atmospheric.

14. For the conditions of the above problem, estimate the desirable height of the tower to give the most economical recovery of the ammonia, taking its value at 5 cents per pound, the cost of the tower plus packing as 10 dollars per cubic foot, the cost of power as 0.8 cent per kilowatt hour, and the pressure drop per foot of height as 0.32 in. H₂O. Fixed charges may be taken at 30 per cent, and operation at 8400 hr./year will be assumed. Take the efficiency of power supplied to the air as 50 per cent.

15. For the conditions of Prob. 13 as to gas quantity and inlet concentration and as to water rate and outlet temperature, calculate the outlet gas and liquor strengths assuming that the 6.07-in. tower was packed for 15 ft. with 1-in. rings, and that for this packing the film values may be taken as $H_G = 4.5$ in. and $H_L = 22$ in. for the flow rates employed.

16. A slat-packed cooling tower is to be designed to cool 3000 g.p.m. of condenser water from 110 to 85°F. by means of air flowing up through the tower. Under the worst conditions the available air will be about 81 per cent saturated, with a wet-bulb temperature of 80°F.

Assume that the tower is made up of staggered, ¼- by 4-in. wood grids spaced 1.25 in. apart, and that values of H_G can be computed using Eq. (308), page 242 and assuming equality of the j factor and f'''. Assume the value of (H.T.U.)$_L$ representing resistance to heat transfer in the liquid phase is approximately the same as the mass transfer value for gas absorption by drip-point tile, as given by Fig. 129, page 290.

Calculate the height and cross-sectional area of the tower and the required volumetric capacity of the fan at the following ratios of air to water flow: (a) 1.25 times the minimum, (b) two times the minimum, (c) four times the minimum.

Based on an estimated annual tower cost of 1 dollar per cubic foot, a cost of delivered energy of 2 cents per kilowatthour, and operation 24 hr./day, 8 months a year, what are the optimum design conditions?

The pressure drop of air at atmospheric pressure and room temperature through this packing has been found to be 0.007 in. H₂O per ft. height at a superficial air velocity of 1000 lb./(hr.)(ft.²). This value is not affected by liquor rates up to 3000 lb./(hr.)(ft.²).

CHAPTER VI

DESIGN PRINCIPLES FOR MULTICOMPONENT SYSTEMS

The principles of the design calculations for the absorption of a single solute gas have been treated in the previous chapter. The graphical and analytical design methods there described may be extended without modification in principle to the treatment of design problems where several solute gases are absorbed simultaneously. Operating and equilibrium curves for each component are drawn on the same diagram, and the design is fixed by the fact that the calculation for each component must indicate the same tower volume or number of plates. The principle of the method is fairly simple, but practical difficulties are encountered in locating the equilibrium curves exactly when the liquid solution is not dilute, since the concentration of each solute affects the solubility of the other solutes.

Multicomponent absorption is sometimes encountered in the recovery of mixed solvent vapors, but it is in the recovery of natural gasoline and in the treatment of refinery gases that the problem is one of tremendous importance industrially. In these absorption problems of the petroleum industry the gas to be treated ordinarily consists of a mixture of methane and several of the lower hydrocarbons, principally aliphatics and olefins. The solvent used is almost invariably a light hydrocarbon oil, which is nonvolatile and in which the hydrocarbons to be absorbed are highly soluble. In the petroleum industry the apparatus used is usually of the plate type, and it is convenient, though not necessary, to employ the theoretical-plate concept in the design calculations.

Factors affecting the choice of economically optimum absorption equipment are discussed in the Appendix. This chapter is concerned with the principles of design calculations for specified operating conditions.

EQUILIBRIA FOR HYDROCARBON-OIL SYSTEMS

Before taking up the application of the graphical design method to multicomponent systems, it will be necessary to discuss the equilibrium relations employed in using the method for practical absorption problems of the petroleum industry. These relations are based on the laws of ideal solutions modified according to certain generalizations of the thermodynamic properties of the hydrocarbons encountered.

At low pressures Raoult's law, $p = P_v x$, and Dalton's law, $P = \Sigma p$, may be combined with Avogadro's law to give the equilibrium relation

$$p = P_v x = Py \qquad (263)$$

In these equations, p is the partial pressure of the solute in the gas phase, P_v is the vapor pressure of the pure component, P is the total pressure, and x and y represent the mole fractions of the solute in liquid and gas, respectively. Σp represents the sum of the partial pressures of the various components. Under conditions where the above relation applies, the compositions of vapor and liquid in equilibrium may be calculated. Even under atmospheric conditions, the deviations from Raoult's law may be appreciable, and at pressures of 400 to 500 p.s.i., at which many absorbers operate, Eq. (263) breaks down completely. The equation may be used to give correct results, however, if fugacities[155,278,437] are employed in place of the pressure terms P_v and P.

The term fugacity is defined by a thermodynamic equation for partial molal free energy, or "escaping tendency," and is discussed fully in standard texts on thermodynamics.[110,270,493] Its use is explained by the fact that the partial molal free energies of a compound in the vapor and liquid phases must be equal at equilibrium. In the present section we need be interested only in the use of the term in the calculation of high-pressure equilibria. At pressures low enough for the gas laws to apply, the fugacity becomes equivalent to the partial pressure. If we assume that fugacities follow simple mixture rules in both phases, we may substitute for P_v in Eq. (263) the fugacity f_P of the liquid, and for P, the fugacity f_π corresponding to the total pressure.* The solution law then becomes

$$f_P x = f_\pi y \qquad (264)$$

The quantities f_P and f_π may be looked upon as pressures corrected for the deviations of the compressibility from the perfect-gas laws, at the vapor pressure and at the total pressure, respectively. The fugacities to be used in this relation have been determined in two ways: by calculation from $P\text{-}V\text{-}T$ data on the pure hydrocarbons and by direct determination of vapor-liquid equilibria.

The $P\text{-}V\text{-}T$ data on the simpler straight-chain hydrocarbons have been satisfactorily correlated on the basis of the critical values of the individual hydrocarbons, *i.e.*, by a reduced equation of state.[99,109,155,271,490] This

---

* The fugacity of the pure liquid, f_P, is evaluated at the vapor pressure of the pure liquid, P_v, even though the liquid mixture actually is under a different pressure P. The effect of pressure on liquid fugacity is slight, however, and usually may be neglected. If desired, it may be calculated from an equation involving the molal specific volume of the liquid.[270]

correlation is in terms of the reduced pressure P_R, which is the ratio of the pressure to the critical pressure of the particular hydrocarbon; in terms of the reduced temperature T_R, which is the ratio of the absolute temperature to the critical temperature; and in terms of reduced volume V_R, or ratio of the specific volume to the specific volume at the critical conditions. The fugacities to be employed in Eq. (264) may be calculated from the P-V-T data if it is assumed that hydrocarbon liquids mix isothermally without heat effect or change in volume, and that the same is true of hydrocarbon vapors at constant pressure.

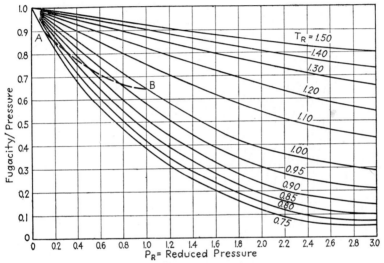

FIG. 65.   Fugacities of hydrocarbon vapors.

It is found that the fugacities calculated in this way may be correlated in terms of reduced pressure and reduced temperature, as was the case for the data on reduced volumes.[155,278,410]   Curves representing the resulting correlation, given by Lewis and Kay,[276] are reproduced in Fig. 65.   The ordinate is the ratio of fugacity to pressure, and the units of fugacity are the same as those of the pressure.   The curves above the line AB are based on the considerable amount of P-V-T data on the simpler straight-chain hydrocarbons.   The curves below the line AB and for values of T_R less than 1.0 are based on equilibrium data for several binary systems of the same hydrocarbons.   In plotting the latter data, f_P is obtainable from the plot in the region based on P-V-T data, and the other term is calculated from the data using Eq. (264).   This procedure is equivalent to a definition of the fugacity f_P of the liquid at temperatures above the critical.   Using the reverse procedure, the plot may be employed to calculate equilibria for hydrocarbons containing more than two carbon

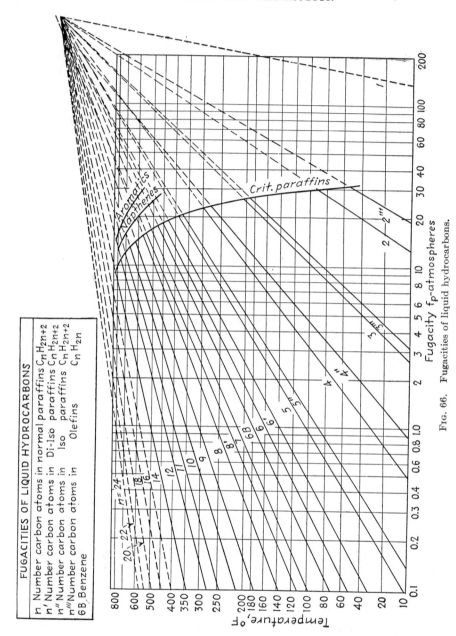

FUGACITIES OF LIQUID HYDROCARBONS

n Number carbon atoms in normal paraffins $C_n H_{2n+2}$
n' Number carbon atoms in Di-Iso paraffins $C_n H_{2n+2}$
n'' Number carbon atoms in Iso paraffins $C_n H_{2n+2}$
n''' Number carbon atoms in Olefins $C_n H_{2n}$
6B, Benzene

FIG. 66. Fugacities of liquid hydrocarbons.

atoms (propane and higher) with an accuracy of 5 to 8 per cent.[276] The deviations are greatest when the hydrocarbons differ appreciably in structure, as in a mixture of aromatic and paraffinic compounds; some deviations are observed for members within a homologous series when they differ considerably in molecular weight, as with methane and hexane.

The fugacity of a pure liquid may be obtained from its vapor pressure and Fig. 65, or obtained directly from Fig. 66. This latter is a plot of f_P vs. temperature constructed by Kay[240] in the manner of a Cox chart of vapor pressures. (As pointed out above, f_P approaches the vapor pressure at low temperatures.) The use of an extrapolated vapor pressure, together with Fig. 65, for f_P for methane leads to serious error, because ordinary temperatures are well above the critical temperature (344°R.), and at high values of T_R the correlation for the lower hydrocarbons is poor. In this range there appears to be a trend of deviations with the nature of the solvent and with the hydrocarbon. The data of Frölich *et al.*[146] on the solubility of methane at 77°F. in various hydrocarbons gave values of f_P ranging from 143 to 191 atm. when the solvent was butane, pentane, hexane, or octane at 18 to 100 atm. total pressure, and values of f_P from 270 to 555 atm. when

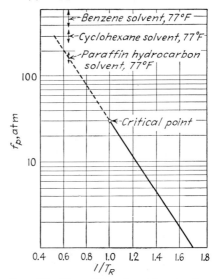

Fig. 67. Fugacities of methane extrapolated beyond the critical and compared with Frölich's solubility data.

the solvent was cyclohexane or benzene. These data are insufficient to show the variation of f_P with the character of the solvent, and the effect can only be estimated. The error involved in extrapolating vapor pressures above the critical may be reduced by carrying out the extrapolation on a plot of f_P vs. $1/T_R$ on semilogarithmic coordinates. Figure 67 shows such a plot for methane, with the critical point indicated. The lower right end up to the critical is based on vapor-pressure data, converted to f_P by Fig. 65. The upper dotted section is an extrapolation of the lower branch. The range of Frölich's data on the solubility of methane is indicated in the upper part of the plot. The extrapolated curve goes through the methane data for paraffin hydrocarbons, but the variation with solvent is evident.

The fugacities of light hydrocarbons have been computed by Benedict,

Webb, Rubin, and Friend,[30b] using the Benedict equation of state,[30a] which is capable of describing the volumetric behavior of paraffin hydrocarbons and their mixtures in both liquid and vapor phases up to high pressures. The fugacities in both liquid and vapor phases are found to deviate from the values expected from the Lewis fugacity rule when unlike components are present, even though only members of homologous series are involved. The deviations apparently depend on differences in molecular size and are greatest for methane. Figure 67a shows calculated

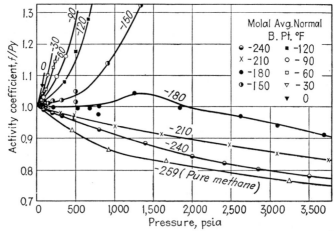

Fig. 67a. Effect of vapor phase composition on the fugacity of methane at 100°F. (*After Benedict, Webb, Rubin, and Friend.*)

fugacities of methane in various gaseous mixtures with other hydrocarbons. Comparison of the various curves with the lowest one, which represents pure methane, shows that methane has an abnormally large free energy when mixed with heavier molecules. It appears that the molal average normal boiling point of the condensed phase is sufficient to describe its composition for the purpose of correlating fugacities. Thus, methane apparently has the same fugacity in solutions with butane and with hexane, for example, provided the compositions are adjusted to give the same average boiling point. On this basis Benedict, Webb, Rubin, and Friend[30b] have prepared charts of K-factors for most of the light hydrocarbons, including correction factors to allow for the effect of composition of liquid and vapor phases. Copies are available from the M. W. Kellogg Company, New York. The corrections produce significant deviations from the K-factors based on the Lewis fugacity rule and listed in Table XI, especially for methane, ethane, and ethylene at all pressures, and for all compounds at pressures above 300 lb./sq. in. Values of K read from these charts agreee approximately with those listed in the last column of Table XI (below) for arbitrarily selected vapor and liquid compositions corresponding to average normal boiling points of $-100°F.$ and $+180°F.$, respectively. The values for methane and ethane would not agree, however, if the compositions had been different. Deviations for mixtures of paraffin and naphthenic or aromatic hydrocarbons involving possible chemical effects have not been calculated owing to the lack of constants for the equation of state.

TABLE X.   CRITICAL CONSTANTS FOR HYDROCARBONS

Compound	Critical temperature, °R.	Critical pressure, atm.	Reference
CH_4 methane	343.1	45.8	213
C_2H_4, ethylene	509.0	50.9	213
C_2H_6, ethane	549.3	48.8	213
C_3H_6, propylene	657.7	45.0	213
C_3H_8, propane	663.7	43.0	213
C_4H_8, 1-butene	756	40.0	49
C_4H_8, trans-2-butene	771	40.5	49
C_4H_8, isobutene	752	39.4	49
C_4H_{10}, n-butane	766	36.0	213
	766	37.5	49
C_4H_{10}, isobutane	736	35.9	49
	733	37.0	213
C_5H_{10}, 1-pentene	854	40.4	49
C_5H_{10}, 3-methyl-1-butene	837	33.9	49
C_5H_{10}, 2-methyl-2-butene	837	35.3	49
C_5H_{12}, n-pentane	846.5	33.0	49, 213
C_5H_{12}, isopentane	830	32.8	49, 213
C_5H_{12}, 2,2-dimethylpropane	823	33.0	49
C_6H_{12}, 1-hexene	929	....	49
C_6H_{12}, 2-hexene	931	....	49
C_6H_{14}, n-hexane	914	29.5	213
C_7H_{16}, n-heptane	972	26.8	213
C_8H_{18}, n-octane	1022	24.6	213
C_6H_6, benzene	1011.9	47.7	213

The fugacity plots represent a correlation of the physical properties of the common hydrocarbons, useful not only in the calculation of equilibria, but also as a basis for the calculation of various thermal properties. For convenience in using these plots, Table X summarizes the critical constants as given by the International Critical Tables[213] and other collections of data on hydrocarbons.[365]   In absorption and distillation practice, however, the relations plotted are of interest principally as a means of calculating the important equilibrium relations, for which purpose Eq. (264) may be written

$$y = \frac{f_P}{f_\pi} x = Kx \tag{265}$$

The procedure in obtaining values of K from the plots is simple but time-consuming, and for convenience tabulated values of K are given for various common hydrocarbons in Table XI. In each case the value of f was obtained from the Lewis curves of Fig. 65. For temperatures below the critical, f_P was obtained from Fig. 66. For temperatures above the critical, f_P was obtained from plots of f_P vs. $1/T_R$ given by Luke.[289] These are similar to Fig. 67.

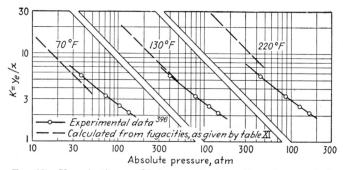

FIG. 68.   Vaporization equilibrium constants, methane in crystal oil.

Similar calculations of K have been carried out by others,[52,155,204] but the results disagree, especially for the light hydrocarbons, as shown by Table XII. It is evident that comparisons of the performance of absorption equipment must be based on consistent equilibrium data. The several sets of K's seem to be in reasonable agreement for hydrocarbons heavier than propane. For the lighter hydrocarbons, Lewis's values of K appear to be in agreement with recent experimental data,[396–398] as shown by Fig. 68.

Values of K are needed at pressures as high as 3000 p.s.i. for designing absorbers used in the recovery of natural gasoline from high-pressure gas fields. The heavier hydrocarbons are absorbed in an oil from which they are subsequently recovered by stripping. The residue gas is pumped back into the well to maintain the pressure in the subsurface formation and to prevent retrograde condensation of the heavier hydrocarbons in the sand. If the absorption is carried out at a high pressure of the same order of magnitude as the subsurface pressure, the expenditure of energy for pumping the lean gas leaving the absorber need not be so great as if the absorption pressure were low. On the other hand, the pressure of absorption should be below the critical pressure of the mixture of fluids inside the absorber, since all the values of K become equal to 1 at the critical pressure. At the critical state of the mixture the liquid and vapor phases become identical in composition and density, and there is no tendency for the heavier hydrocarbons to concentrate in the liquid phase in preference to the lighter ones.

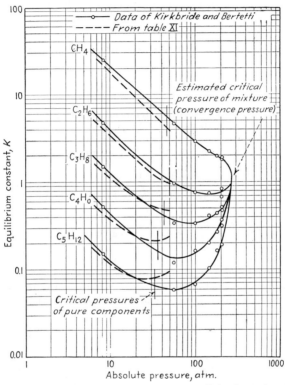

Fig. 69. Equilibrium constants for hydrocarbons in paraffinic absorption oil at 88 $\pm$ 4°F.

Figure 69 shows data on equilibrium vaporization constants, K's, for the lighter hydrocarbons in a paraffinic oil of molecular weight 220.[245] At low pressures the K values are seen to agree approximately with the data of Table XI. At high pressures the curves for the different compounds converge to the critical pressure of the mixture, which is usually higher than the critical pressure of any of the pure gaseous constituents.

Vink, Ames, David, and Katz[477] give K values for methane, ethane, and propane in crude oil, showing that two liquid phases—one hydrocarbon and one asphalt—plus one vapor phase, can exist under certain conditions. Roland, Smith, and Kavaler[393] determined equilibrium ratios for C_1 to C_2 in a system of natural gas and distillate at pressures up to 4000 p.s.i. Webber[492] reported K values for methane, ethane, propane, isobutane, n-butane, isopentane, n-pentane, and n-hexane in an absorption oil of molecular weight 183. His investigation covered temperatures from 33 to 180°F. and pressures from 100 to 5000 p.s.i. Particularly above 3000 p.s.i., he found that the equilibrium constants were dependent on the concentration of the oil as well as on that of volatile components. This is to be expected, since the critical pressure of the mixture depends on its composition and is in accord with the recent work of Benedict *et al.*[30a] Further high-pressure data are given by Katz and Hachmuth.[239]

Illustration 27. Calculate the value of K ($= y/x$) for n-butane at 5 atm and 150°F.

Solution. From Table X the critical temperature and pressure of n-butane are 766°R. and 36.0 atm., respectively.

$$T_R = \frac{150 + 460}{766} = 0.796$$

$$P_R = \frac{5}{36} = 0.139$$

From Fig. 65, $f_\pi/P = 0.88$; $f_\pi = (0.88)(5) = 4.4$ atm. From Fig. 66, at 150°F., $f_P = 6.15$ atm.

$$K = \frac{f_P}{f_\pi} = \frac{6.15}{4.4} = 1.4, \qquad \text{as given in Table XI}$$

Illustration 28. Luke[289] has experimentally determined the compositions of both gas and liquid phases for a mixture of hydrocarbons brought together and maintained at constant temperature and pressure until equilibrium was reached. A typical experiment showed the following vapor and liquid analyses (mole fractions) after the two phases had come to equilibrium with each other:

Component	x	y
CH_4...............	0.041	0.315
C_2H_4...............	0.015	0.033
C_2H_6...............	0.200	0.323
C_3H_6...............	0.115	0.072
C_3H_8...............	0.310	0.175
i-C_4H_{10}............	0.095	0.029
n-C_4H_{10}............	0.224	0.053

The observed temperature and pressure were 81°F. and 22 atm., respectively.

From the vapor analysis calculate the total pressure and the liquid analysis, and compare with the measured values. From the liquid analysis calculate the total pressure and the vapor analysis, and make a similar comparison. Repeat, using Raoult's and Dalton's laws in place of the calculation from fugacities.

Solution. The procedure in calculating the pressure from the vapor analysis is to tabulate values of K for an assumed pressure and then calculate values of x. If the assumed pressure is correct, the sum of the values of x will equal unity. Assume, for example, a pressure of 10 atm., and tabulate values of K obtained from Table XI.

Component	y	K	$x = y/K$
CH$_4$...............	0.315	17.6	0.018
C$_2$H$_4$.............	0.033	4.6	0.007
C$_2$H$_6$.............	0.323	3.0	0.107
C$_3$H$_6$.............	0.072	1.15	0.063
C$_3$H$_8$.............	0.175	1.0	0.175
i-C$_4$H$_{10}$...........	0.029	0.45	0.063
n-C$_4$H$_{10}$...........	0.053	0.33	0.162
			0.598

By trial it is found that at a pressure of 21 atm., the sum of the calculated values of x is very nearly unity:

Component	y	K	x (calculated)	x (observed)
CH$_4$..............	0.315	8.6	0.037	0.041
C$_2$H$_4$.............	0.033	2.4	0.014	0.015
C$_2$H$_6$.............	0.323	1.62	0.199	0.200
C$_3$H$_6$.............	0.072	0.68	0.106	0.115
C$_3$H$_8$.............	0.175	0.60	0.292	0.310
i-C$_4$H$_{10}$...........	0.029	0.28	0.103	0.095
n-C$_4$H$_{10}$..........	0.053	0.21	0.252	0.224
Total..........	.....	....	1.003	1.000

The calculated pressure, found by trial to be approximately 21 atm., checks the observed pressure of 22 atm. well within the accuracy of the values of K. The above table shows the excellent agreement of the calculated and observed liquid analysis.

Starting the liquid analysis and following a similar procedure, it is found that the vapor compositions total unity when values of K are employed for a pressure of 22 atm.

Component	x	K	y ($= Kx$)	y (observed)
CH$_4$..............	0.041	8.2	0.336	0.315
C$_2$H$_4$.............	0.015	2.3	0.035	0.033
C$_2$H$_6$.............	0.200	1.56	0.312	0.323
C$_3$H$_6$.............	0.115	0.62	0.072	0.072
C$_3$H$_8$.............	0.310	0.58	0.180	0.175
i-C$_4$H$_{10}$...........	0.095	0.28	0.026	0.029
n-C$_4$H$_{10}$..........	0.224	0.21	0.047	0.053
Total..........	1.000	....	1.008	1.000

Table XI. Values of K for the Lower Hydrocarbons, Calculated from the Fugacity Curves

Pressure, atm.	Temperature, °F.								
	60	80	100	150	200	300	400	500	600
Methane, CH_4									
0.5	296	340	380	490	610	870	1160	1450	1720
1	148	170	190	250	305	440	580	710	860
2	74	85	95	122	154	220	290	360	430
5	30	34	38	49	61	87	118	145	174
10	15	17	19	25	31	44	58	72	96
25	6.2	7.1	7.9	10	12.4	18	23	29	35
50	3.2	3.7	4.1	5.2	6.3	8.9	11.9	14.6	17.4
Ethylene, C_2H_4									
0.5	73	87	101	150	204	350	530	760	1020
1	37	43	51	75	101	170	270	390	510
2	18.5	22	26	37	51	87	134	192	258
5	7.5	8.9	10.4	15	21	35	54	77	106
10	3.9	4.6	5.3	7.7	10.5	20	27	39	52
25	1.8	2.0	2.3	3.3	4.4	7.3	11.0	15.5	21
50	1.1	1.2	1.4	1.8	2.3	3.8	6.8	7.9	10.4
Ethane, C_2H_6									
0.5	48	56	68	100	140	250	390	**570**	770
1	24	28	34	49	70	124	198	**290**	380
2	12	14	17	25	36	62	98	142	190
5	4.9	5.8	7.0	10	14.5	25	40	67	78
10	2.6	3.0	3.6	5.2	7.4	13	20	29	39
25	1.2	1.4	1.6	2.3	3.3	5.2	8.2	11.8	15.7
50	0.83	0.93	1.0	1.3	1.75	2.8	4.5	6.0	8.0
Propylene, C_3H_6									
0.5	15	20	24	39	61	120	200	310	430
1	7.7	10	12.2	20	31	59	100	154	215
2	4.0	5	6.3	10	15	30	50	78	109
5	1.7	2.2	2.6	4.1	6.2	12.3	20	31	44
10	0.94	1.15	1.4	2.2	3.3	6.3	10	15.9	22
25	0.50	0.60	0.73	1.05	1.5	2.7	4.3	6.5	9.0
50	0.40	0.49	0.57	0.76	1.0	1.5	2.4	3.5	4.7
Propane, C_3H_8									
0.5	13.2	17	21	35	52	100	168	260	370
1	6.8	8.6	10.8	17	25	50	86	132	188
2	3.4	4.4	5.5	8.7	13	24	44	66	94
5	1.5	1.8	2.3	3.6	5.3	10.3	17.4	27	38
10	0.8	1.0	1.23	1.9	2.8	5.3	8.8	13.2	19 0
25	0.44	0.54	0.65	0.95	1.3	2.3	3.7	5.5	7.6
50	0.37	0.44	0.53	0.72	0.91	1.34	2.0	2.9	4.2

TABLE XI.   VALUES OF K FOR THE LOWER HYDROCARBONS, CALCULATED FROM THE FUGACITY CURVES.   (*Continued*)

Pres-sure, atm.	Temperature, °F.								
	60	80	100	150	200	300	400	500	600
n-Butane, C_4H_{10}									
0.5	3.5	4.9	6.6	12.8	21	45	75		
1	1.8	2.5	3.4	6.4	10.4	23	37	70	
2	0.91	1.25	1.7	3.3	5.3	11.4	22	35	54
5	0.41	0.55	0.75	1.4	2.3	4.7	8.8	14.2	22
10	0.24	0.32	0.43	0.80	1.24	2.5	4.5	7.3	11
25	0.14	0.19	0.26	0.45	0.68	1.23	2.0	3.1	4.6
50	0.16	0.20	0.26	0.44	0.61	0.87	1.24	1.76	2.5
Isobutane, C_4H_{10}									
0.5	5.4	7.2	9.5	16.6	26	56	100	165	250
1	2.7	3.6	4.8	8.5	13	28	51	84	128
2	1.4	1.85	2.5	4.3	6.7	14	26	42	64
5	0.61	0.81	1.05	1.8	2.8	5.8	10.5	17	26
10	0.35	0.46	0.50	1.0	1.5	3.1	5.4	8.6	13
25	0.21	0.27	0.35	0.55	0.70	1.4	2.3	3.6	5.4
50	0.23	0.27	0.34	0.51	0.65	0.95	1.38	2.0	2.9
n-Pentane, C_5H_{12}									
0.5	0.92	1.4	2.0	4.6	8.5	23	40	80	
1	0.48	0.71	1.0	2.3	4.4	11.6	23	40	63
2	0.25	0.36	0.53	1.2	2.2	5.9	11.8	20	33
5	0.11	0.16	0.23	0.53	0.97	2.5	4.7	7.4	13.5
10	0.062	0.094	0.14	0.31	0.55	1.4	2.5	4.3	6.9
25	0.045	0.064	0.091	0.19	0.33	0.75	1.21	1.92	3.0
50	0.057	0.080	0.11	0.22	0.35	0.65	0.89	1.20	1.70
Isopentane, C_5H_{12}									
0.5	1.2	1.8	2.6	5.6	10.3	26	51	89	
1	0.62	0.91	1.3	2.9	5.2	13	26	48	69
2	0.32	0.47	0.67	1.5	2.6	6.7	13	22	35
5	0.15	0.21	0.30	0.65	1.1	2.8	5.4	9.0	14
10	0.09	0.127	0.18	0.38	0.65	1.4	2.8	4.6	7.0
25	0.058	0.081	0.11	0.23	0.39	0.80	1.3	2.1	3.0
50	0.076	0.10	0.14	0.26	0.40	0.70	0.95	1.24	1.74
n-Hexane, C_6H_{14}									
0.5	0.26	0.43	0.68	1.8	3.6	12.0	27	49	84
1	0.13	0.22	0.35	0.90	1.9	6.0	14	25	47
2	0.071	0.11	0.18	0.46	1.0	3.1	7.0	12.5	21
5	0.032	0.052	0.080	0.21	0.43	1.3	2.9	5.2	8.6
10	0.021	0.033	0.051	0.126	0.26	0.77	1.6	2.8	4.5
25	0.015	0.024	0.036	0.089	0.17	0.46	0.88	1.32	2.1
50	0.025	0.037	0.055	0.12	0.21	0.50	0.77	0.96	1.29

TABLE XI. VALUES OF K FOR THE LOWER HYDROCARBONS, CALCULATED FROM THE FUGACITY CURVES. (*Continued*)

Pressure, atm.	Temperature, °F.								
	60	80	100	150	200	300	400	500	600
n-Heptane, C_7H_{16}									
0.5	0.075	0.13	0.22	0.69	1.6	6.3	16.5	32	58
1	0.039	0.067	0.114	0.36	0.82	3.2	8.6	16.7	29
2	0.020	0.035	0.059	0.18	0.43	1.6	4.8	8.4	15
5	0.0094	0.016	0.027	0.085	0.20	0.72	1.82	3.4	6.0
10	0.0061	0.0106	0.018	0.053	0.12	0.43	1.04	1.80	3.2
25	0.0048	0.0081	0.014	0.040	0.087	0.28	0.62	1.00	1.5
50	0.011	0.017	0.027	0.070	0.14	0.36	0.67	0.83	1.05
n-Octane, C_8H_{18}									
0.5	0.025	0.044	0.076	0.27	0.77	3.4	11.2	22	39
1	0.013	0.023	0.039	0.14	0.39	1.7	5.4	11	20
2	0.0067	0.012	0.021	0.070	0.21	0.90	2.7	5.6	10
5	0.0032	0.0056	0.0096	0.032	0.093	0.40	1.15	2.4	4.3
10	0.0021	0.0037	0.0064	0.022	0.062	0.24	0.66	1.32	2.25
25	0.0018	0.0036	0.0051	0.017	0.045	0.18	0.45	0.78	1.16
50	0.015	0.021	0.030	0.064	0.11	0.29	0.58	0.78	0.92

The check obtained for both pressure and vapor analysis is probably within the accuracy of the methods of analysis employed.

In calculating the corresponding quantities, using Raoult's law, the vapor pressures are tabulated, and y/P_v calculated for each component. The sum of these ratios is the reciprocal of the total pressure [Eq. (263)].

Component	y	P, atm.	y/P_v	x (calculated)	x (observed)
CH_4..................	0.315	250*	0.00126	0.021	0.041
C_2H_4..................	0.033	70*	0.00047	0.008	0.015
C_2H_6..................	0.323	37.5	0.00862	0.146	0.200
C_3H_6..................	0.072	12.1	0.00595	0.099	0.115
C_3H_8..................	0.175	10.4	0.0168	0.284	0.310
i-C_4H_{10}..................	0.029	4.1	0.0708	0.121	0.095
n-C_4H_{10}..................	0.053	2.8	0.0190	0.321	0.224
			0.0592		

* Extrapolated considerably beyond critical.

The calculated pressure is the reciprocal of 0.0592, *i.e.*, 16.9 atm. Neither pressure nor composition as calculated checks well within the observed values.

Table XII. Comparison of Calculated Vaporization Equilibrium Constants

Component	Selected conditions		$K = y/x$					
	Temp., °F.	Abs. pressure, atm.	Brown et al.[52] (1935)	Katz and Hachmuth[239] (1937)	Brown[48] (1950)	Ragatz[382] (1948)	Gamson and Watson[155] (1944)	This book, following Lewis et al. (1937)
CH_4......	100	1	57	260	252	.....	......	190
		10	8.6	25.5	25.8	22	15.2	19
		50	2.8	5.5	....	5.1	.....	4.1
	300	1	73	....	286	.....	......	440
		10	11	....	30	.....	29	44
		50	3.6	....	....	.....	......	8.9
C_2H_6.....	100	1	24.5	40	38.5	.....	......	34
		10	2.9	4.1	4.0	4.2	3.9	3.7
		25	1.5	1.8	1.8	1.8	......	1.0
	300	1	55.5	....	94.0	.....	......	124
		10	6.5	....	10.2	.....	9.7	13
		25	3.4	....	4.5	.....	......	5.2
$n\text{-}C_3H_8$....	100	1	9.8	12	10.0	10.1	......	10.8
		10	1.13	1.27	1.22	1.38	1.24	1.23
		25	0.64	0.59	0.59	0.62	......	0.65
	300	1	30.5	....	41.0	.....	......	50
		10	4.1	....	4.9	.....	4.45	5.3
		25	1.8	....	2.35	.....	......	2.3
$n\text{-}C_4H_{10}$...	100	1	3.25	4.1	3.27	3.5	......	3.4
		10	0.41	0.46	0.39	0.40	0.43	0.43
		25	0.25	0.223	0.19	0.20	......	0.26
	300	1	18	....	20.5	.....	......	23
		10	2.1	....	2.6	.....	2.4	2.5
		25	1.17	....	1.3	.....	......	1.23
$n\text{-}C_5H_{12}$...	100	1	1.00	1.30	1.03	.....	......	1.0
		10	0.147	0.147	0.123	.....	0.157	0.14
		25	0.092	0.076	0.060	.....	......	0.091
	300	1	11	....	7.15	.....	......	11.6
		10	1.33	....	1.4	.....	1.37	1.4
		25	0.77	....	0.70	.....	......	0.75
$n\text{-}C_6H_{14}$...	100	1	0.35	0.50	0.34	.....	......	0.35
		10	0.055	0.058	0.045	.....	0.056	0.051
		25	0.036	0.033	0.023	.....	......	0.036
	300	1	6.1	....	6.0	.....	......	6.0
		10	0.80	....	0.76	.....	0.75	0.77
		25	0.49	....	0.39	.....	......	0.46

* Brown and Souders give correction factors for use with these K's. For very low concentrations of methane, for example, the corrected K is twice the value listed.

The corresponding computation, starting with the liquid analysis, is as follows:

Component	x	$P_v x$	y (calculated)	y (observed)
CH_4............	0.041	10.3	0.42	0.315
C_2H_4............	0.015	1.05	0.043	0.033
C_2H_6............	0.200	7.5	0.306	0.323
C_3H_6............	0.115	1.39	0.057	0.072
C_3H_8............	0.310	3.23	0.132	0.175
i-C_4H_{10}...........	0.095	0.39	0.016	0.029
n-C_4H_{10}.........	0.224	0.63	0.026	0.053

From the sum of partial pressures, P is 24.49 atm. This time the calculated pressure is only 11 per cent high, but the calculated analysis of the vapor is appreciably in error.

GRAPHICAL DESIGN METHOD

The graphical design method described in Chap. V was first applied to multicomponent systems by W. K. Lewis,[273] and it is a slight modification of Lewis's method that is outlined below. For convenience, concentrations will be expressed in molal stoichiometric units; X' represents the moles of one solute per mole of solute-free solvent at the top of the column, and Y' the moles of solute in the gas phase per mole of rich gas to be treated. The liquid rate will be represented by L', the moles of solvent per unit time, and the gas rate by G', the moles of gas to be treated per unit time. As before, the subscripts 1 and 2 will be used in referring to the rich and lean ends of the column, respectively. The material balance for any one component may be written

$$L'(X' - X_2') = G'(Y' - Y_2') \qquad (266)$$
$$L'(X_1' - X') = G'(Y_1' - Y') \qquad (267)$$

where X' and Y' represent the concentrations in the liquid and gas phases flowing across any imaginary horizontal plane located between any two trays of the column. In terms of molal stoichiometric units the equilibrium relationship, Eq. (265), becomes

$$\frac{Y'}{\Sigma Y'} = K \frac{X'}{1 + \Sigma X'} \qquad (268)$$

or

$$Y' = KX' \frac{\Sigma Y'}{1 + \Sigma X'} \qquad (269)$$

where $\Sigma Y'$ = sum of the values of Y' for the components present

$\Sigma X'$ = sum of the values of X' for each component except the solvent present in the liquid phase (X' is unity for the solvent)

In the special case of absorption from lean gases with large amounts of solvent, Eq. (269) reduces to

$$Y' = KX' \qquad (270)$$

The operation of a column treating a lean gas may be represented by a plot of Y' vs. X', with straight equilibrium curves for each component.

Each equilibrium curve will pass through the origin and have a slope K. Each component will have its own straight operating line, and these lines will be parallel, since the slope of each is L'/G'. Assuming the capacity coefficients on a molal basis to be the same for the various components, the ratio of the amount absorbed to the mean driving force must be the same for each component, and the location of each operating line is thus fixed by the size of the column. The required value of L'/G' is determined by the solubility of the least soluble compound present in the gas which it is desired to absorb completely.

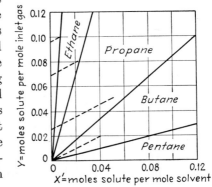

FIG. 70. Graphical construction for absorption of a lean gas containing several soluble constituents present in small amounts.

A typical diagram for absorption from a lean gas is shown as Fig. 70. The oil used as a solvent is assumed to be completely denuded ($X_2' = 0$), and the lower ends of the operating lines, at their intersections with the ordinate scale, indicate the composition of the treated gas with respect to each component. The percentage of each component absorbed may be determined by comparison of the values of Y' at the two ends of each operating line. Thus 50 per cent of the butane is absorbed, and the oil leaves the tower containing 0.05 mole butane per mole of solute-free oil. The operating line for propane is drawn parallel to that for butane and is placed so that the change in Y', i.e., $Y_1' - Y_2'$, divided by the mean driving force $\Delta Y'$ (mean vertical distance between operating and equilibrium lines) is the same as for butane. In the case illustrated by Fig. 70, the equilibrium lines are straight, and a logarithmic-mean $\Delta Y'$ may be employed. This may be obtained for butane by calculating the logarithmic mean of the values of $\Delta Y'$ at the two ends of the butane operating line. The propane line is then placed by trial so that $(Y_1' - Y_2')/\Delta Y_M'$ for propane is equal to the corresponding ratio for butane.

It is evident from the plot that the upper end of the operating line for propane must be very near the propane equilibrium curve, since the large slope of the latter curve reduces the amount absorbed and at the same time increases the driving force at the lean end of the column. In other words, the oil leaving the column is very nearly saturated with propane. In the case of ethane, the equilibrium curve is still steeper, and the oil leaving will be even more nearly saturated with ethane. The slope of the equilibrium curve for pentane is less than the slope of the operating line, so that the driving force is largest at the rich end of the column. The driving force at the rich end is fairly large compared with the total amount of pentane absorbed, and the operating and equilibrium curves will approach each other at the lean end, *i.e.*, the pentane content of the gas leaving the column is essentially in equilibrium with the oil entering, or substantially all the pentane is removed from the gas.

The "key component," in this case the butane, is defined as that component absorbed in appreciable amount, whose equilibrium curve falls most nearly parallel to the operating line, *i.e.*, the component having a value of K most nearly equal to L'/G'. In general, the composition of the gas with respect to components more volatile than the key component approaches equilibrium with the liquid phase at the rich end of the column, and the composition of the gas with respect to components less volatile than the key component approaches equilibrium with the oil entering. Thus, components heavier than the key component are absorbed nearly completely if the fresh solvent contains none of these components. Varying the oil-gas ratio will clearly change the nature of the key component; the optimum ratio is the one which will allow substantially complete absorption of the desired components.

The theoretical-plate method may be employed[435] to fix the various operating lines, as indicated by Fig. 71. This plot is quite similar to Fig. 70, with the addition of the steps used in counting theoretical plates. Assuming any one operating line to be fixed, as may be done by fixing the oil-gas ratio and fraction of the butane absorbed, the other operating lines must be drawn with the same slope and placed to give the same number of theoretical plates. Except for the method of placing the various operating lines, the construction is the same as that of Fig. 70.

Figure 71 serves to illustrate the differences in absorption distribution through the column for the various components. Starting at the ordinate scale at the left (representing the top of the column) and counting off one step for each component, the points c, c', c'', etc., on the various operating lines represent the composition of the gas entering and of the liquid leaving the top plate of the column. For ethane the composition of the gas entering the top plate (point c) is nearly equal to the composition of the gas entering the column, Y_1'. For pentane it is evident that no appreciable change occurs in the gas composition in passing through the top plate. It follows that the absorption of the more volatile components takes place in the upper part of the column, and that the less volatile components are absorbed in the lower section. The analysis of the oil-solute mixture on any plate may be determined by reading from the plot the values of X' for each of the various components on that plate.

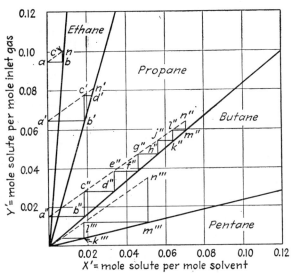

FIG. 71. Construction for counting theoretical plates in multicomponent absorption.

ALGEBRAIC METHOD

The method of calculation outlined above based on the theoretical-plate concept may be followed algebraically, using the Kremser formula[257,437] discussed in the preceding chapter. In terms of the molal stoichiometric units, this equation becomes

$$\frac{Y_1' - Y_2'}{Y_1' - m'X_2'} = \frac{(L'/m'G')^{N+1} - (L'/m'G')}{(L'/m'G')^{N+1} - 1} \tag{271}$$

where, as before, N represents the number of theoretical plates. It applies only when the equilibrium curve is a straight line through the origin with a slope m'. In the case of lean-gas absorption with a large amount of solvent, Eq. (270) applies, and $m' = K = y/x$. The left-hand side represents the ratio of the amount of solute absorbed to the amount which would be absorbed were the gas to leave in equilibrium with the entering oil, and consequently represents the efficiency of absorption of any one component. If the oil enters solute-free, as in Figs. 70 and 71, this ratio becomes equal to the fraction of the component entering the column which is absorbed. Where N, L', and G' are fixed, the fraction absorbed may be computed directly for each component, and the operating lines need not be placed by trial and error.

It is apparent from Eq. (271) that where m' is greater than L'/G' and N is large, the result is

$$\frac{Y_1' - Y_2'}{Y_1' - m'X_2'} = \frac{L'}{m'G'} \tag{272}$$

This is also evident from Fig. 72* which represents Eq. (271). The same conclusion may be reached by referring to Fig. 70 or 71, from which it follows easily by simple geometry that, in those cases where equilibrium is reached at the rich end of the column, the change in Y', divided by Y_1',

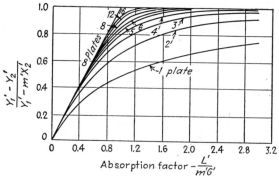

FIG. 72. Relation between column performance and number of theoretical plates [Eq. (271)].

is equal to the ratio of slopes of operating and equilibrium curves. It is usually convenient to estimate the fraction absorbed for each of the more volatile components by use of Eq. (272). The procedure is satisfactory in the case of those components for which the value of m' is three to four times the value of m' for the key component.

Furthermore, it is apparent that, where m' is small compared with L'/G', and N is large, the right-hand side of Eq. (271) reduces to unity, which means that the gas leaves in equilibrium with the entering oil. This is also shown by Fig. 72 and is apparent by inspection from Figs. 70 and 71. For the least volatile components, therefore, equilibrium at the lean end of the column may be assumed. If the oil used is solute-free, this corresponds to complete absorption of these components.

Where $L'/m'G' = 1$, the right side of Eq. (271) becomes indeterminate. It may be shown, however, that for this condition

$$\frac{Y_1' - Y_2'}{Y_1' - m'X_2'} = \frac{N}{N + 1} \tag{273}$$

* Figure 47, Chap. V, is a plot of the same equation.

It is seen that the computations are simple for the relatively volatile and nonvolatile components. It is only for the key component, and for the components on either side of the key component with respect to volatility, that the graphical method or the use of Eq. (271) is necessary.

APPLICATION OF GRAPHICAL METHOD TO THE ABSORPTION OF RICH GASES
ISOTHERMAL COLUMN

Because of the variation through the column of the amount of solutes carried by the oil, the equilibrium lines are curved, their curvature depending on the fraction of the gas absorbed and on the relative amounts of gas and liquid. This is evident from the equilibrium relation

$$Y' = KX' \frac{\Sigma Y'}{1 + \Sigma X'} \tag{269}$$

For lean gases and high oil rates, the fractional term may be assumed to approximate unity, as was done in the preceding section; but for rich gas or for low oil rates, the variations in the terms $\Sigma Y'$ and $1 + \Sigma X'$ must be allowed for, unless the total flow rates on a molar basis should be equal at some level in the absorber. Where the column is supplied with oil containing no dissolved solute, the equilibrium line may be located by two facts: (*a*) the slope at the origin is $K\Sigma Y_2'$, as found by differentiating Eq. (269); and (*b*) a point on the equilibrium curve for conditions at the rich end of the column is determined by substituting Y_1' or X_1', $\Sigma Y_1'$, and $\Sigma X_1'$ in Eq. (269). $\Sigma Y_1'$ is unity by definition, and $\Sigma X_1'$ may be calculated if the total moles of all components absorbed in the column is known. In many practical problems the curvature of the equilibrium lines is not serious, and the lines may be placed with sufficient accuracy if the slope at the origin and the location at the rich end are known in each case. The error involved in locating these lines is negligible except for the key component, for which certain additional calculations described below may be necessary. The equilibrium lines are straight over the entire range, even for rich gas or low oil rates, providing the total moles of liquid flowing is equal to the total moles of gas passing any point in the column. (If the flow rates are equal at any one point, they are equal at all points in the column.)

The exact location of the equilibrium lines is determined by the total absorption, and the amount absorbed is dependent on the equilibrium relations. Consequently the procedure is necessarily by trial and error, although it is possible to reduce the necessary computations greatly if a logical method is employed for the first estimates. For the volatile components, the absorption is determined by the location of the equi-

librium curve at the rich end of the column, and the shape and exact
location of the remainder of the curve are unimportant.   For the absorption of these volatile components from a lean gas, the performance of the
column was shown above to be

$$\frac{Y_1' - Y_2'}{Y_1' - m'X_2'} = \frac{L'}{m'G'} \tag{272}$$

In Eq. (272), m' represents the slope of a straight line through the origin
and through a point on the equilibrium curve at the rich end of the
column.   If the solvent supplied is solute-free, X_2' is zero, and the relation gives the fraction absorbed.   Allowing for the solvent effect of dissolved solute and neglecting the solute content of the liquid, this becomes

$$\frac{Y_1' - Y_2'}{Y_1'} = \frac{L'(1 + \Sigma X_1')}{K_1 \Sigma Y_1'G'} = \frac{L'(1 + \Sigma X_1')}{K_1 G'} \tag{274}$$

where $K_1 \Sigma Y_1'/(1 + \Sigma X_1')$ has replaced m' in Eq. (272), K_1 referring to
the value of K at the bottom of the absorber.   The moles of total gas
to be treated, G', is usually specified, but the moles absorbed, $L'\Sigma X_1'$,
must first be estimated.   This is best done by assuming straight equilibrium curves of slope K, and using Eq. (271) to estimate the fraction
absorbed for each component.   If the performance of the tower with
respect to one component is specified, Eq. (271) or Fig. 72 may be used
first to estimate the required number of perfect plates and then to
estimate the absorption of the other components.   This procedure leads
to an estimate of the total absorption of all components, and consequently
of the value of $\Sigma X_1'$, which may be employed to repeat the calculation,
this time using $L'(1 + \Sigma X_1')/KG'$ in place of $L'/m'G'$.

This second calculation will be very nearly correct, except for the key
component and possibly one component on either side of the key component.   For these it is necessary to construct a plot, placing the equilibrium lines from the known slope at the origin and from the known location of the curve at the rich end, and placing the operating lines by trial
until the correct number of plates is counted.   A new value of the total
absorption is obtained by addition.   If this is appreciably different from
that obtained by the first trial, a third calculation should be made, using
the corrected value of $\Sigma X_1'$.

In many cases it is possible to make a rough guess of the absorption by
inspection from the gas analysis.   Where this can be done, the first trial
calculation using a straight equilibrium curve may be omitted.   More
than three trials are very seldom required, and in cases where the total
moles of oil leaving the column is approximately the same as the total

moles of the gas entering, the equilibrium curves are nearly straight, and the first trial is sufficient.

The use of the inlet gas as a "basis" for all gas compositions is simple and convenient. The distance from equilibrium at any point in the tower expressed as a $\Delta Y'$ is not, however, strictly proportional to the diffusional driving force called for by the diffusional equations. The plate concept is commonly used in this type of absorber, however, and the choice of basis for expressing concentrations has no effect on the calculation of the number of the theoretical plates.

The design calculation outlined above for multicomponent systems may be summarized in the form of a list of steps given below in order. This tabulation assumes that the problem is to calculate the performance of a given column, having given the operating conditions, solvent and gas rates, and composition of the feed gas. Minor modifications of this procedure allow the calculation of the number of theoretical plates when the performance of the column is specified, etc.

1. Determine from Table XI, or other sources, the values of K for each component for the conditions prevailing in the column.

2. Calculate L' and G', the moles of fresh solvent and inlet gas per unit time.

3. Make a rough estimate of the total absorption, as moles per 100 moles feed gas.

4. Calculate $\Sigma X_1'$, based on this estimate of the total absorption. Calculate values of $L'(1 + \Sigma X_1')/KG'$, and employ Eq. (271), using these ratios in place of $L'/m'G'$, to obtain a second estimate of the absorption of the very volatile and the nonvolatile components.

5. For the key component (or components) construct a plot of Y' vs. X', and draw a line with a slope $K\Sigma Y_2'$ through the origin.* Locate the point (Y_1', X_1') (equilibrium) from Eq. (269), and draw the equilibrium curve in its approximate position.

6. Locate the operating line for the key component with a slope L'/G', and in a position above the equilibrium curve corresponding to the proper number of theoretical plates. From this line read off Y_2' for the key component, and calculate the moles of that component absorbed.

7. Add the moles of the components absorbed to obtain a third estimate of the total absorption. If this differs appreciably from the value obtained under step 4, repeat steps 4, 5, and 6.

The procedure just outlined is not difficult to follow, but it is suggested that the following illustrative problem be studied carefully if a clear understanding of the method of calculation is desired.

---

* This assumes the oil fed to contain none of the key component. Where this is not the case, the procedure must be modified as indicated in a later section.

Illustration 29. A 24-plate absorber is designed to operate at 470 p.s.i.g., treating 18,780,000 ft.^{3}/24 hr. (1 atm., 60°F.) of a gas containing 83.02 per cent CH_4, 8.41 per cent C_2H_6, 4.76 per cent C_3H_8, 0.84 per cent i-C_4H_{10}, 1.66 per cent n-C_4H_{10}, 0.61 per cent i-C_5H_{12}, 0.16 per cent n-C_5H_{12}, and 0.54 per cent C_6H_{14} and higher. The tower will be supplied with 111,840 gal./24 hr. of a denuded oil having an average molecular weight of 161 and a specific gravity of 0.8363 at the temperature at which it is metered. The tower will operate with an average oil temperature of 87°F. Assuming the Atkins and Franklin[11] value of 18 per cent for the over-all plate efficiency (see below), calculate the composition of the treated gas.

Solution

$$\text{Inlet gas} = \frac{18,780,000}{359}\frac{492}{520}\left|\frac{\text{lb. moles/day}}{\frac{1}{(24)(60)}}\right. = 34.4 \text{ lb.moles/min.}$$

$$\text{Inlet oil} = \frac{111,840}{(24)(60)}\left|\frac{\text{g.p.m.}}{\frac{(8.33)(0.8363)}{161}}\right. = 3.36 \text{ lb.moles/min.}$$

$$\text{Operating pressure} = 1 + \frac{470}{14.7} = 33 \text{ atm.}$$

Because of the high proportion of methane and ethane in the gas, the total absorption will not be large, even at this relatively high pressure. Assume 10 moles absorbed per 100 moles inlet gas. Values of K are obtained from Table XI by interpolation (graphically) for 87°F. at 33 atm. The tabulation of the values of K completes steps 1, 2, and 3.

$$\Sigma X_1' = \frac{10}{100} \times 34.4 \left|\frac{\text{moles absorbed/min.}}{\times \frac{1}{3.36}}\right. = 1.02 \text{ moles/mole oil}$$

$$\frac{L'(1 + \Sigma X_1')}{G'} = \frac{3.36(1 + 1.02)}{34.4} = 0.197$$

Values of $L'(1 + \Sigma X_1')/KG'$ are tabulated and used in place of $L'/m'G'$ in Eq. (271) to calculate the absorption of each component. The number of theoretical plates, N, is taken as 4.3, corresponding to the assumed plate efficiency of 18 per cent. For n-C_4H_{10}, for example,

$$\text{Fraction absorbed} = \frac{0.94^{5.3} - 0.94}{0.94^{5.3} - 1.0} = 0.79$$

Component	Mole per cent	K	$\dfrac{L'(1 + \Sigma X_1')}{KG'}$	Per cent absorbed	Moles absorbed
CH_4..................	83.02	5.7	0.035	3.5	2.9
C_2H_6..................	8.41	1.2	0.164	16.4	1.4
C_3H_8..................	4.76	0.51	0.386	38.6	1.8
i-C_4H_{10}..............	0.84	0.27	0.73	67	0.6
n-C_4H_{10}..............	1.66	0.21	0.94	79	1.3
i-C_5H_{12}..............	0.61	0.09	2.19	100	0.6
n-C_5H_{12}..............	0.16	0.072	2.74	100	0.2
C_6H_{14}..................	0.54	.....	.....	100	0.5
					9.3

Since the total absorption checks closely the assumed value of 10 moles, the calcula- tion may be continued with step 5, a more careful treatment of the key component. The previous calculation showed the key component to be n-butane, for which it is

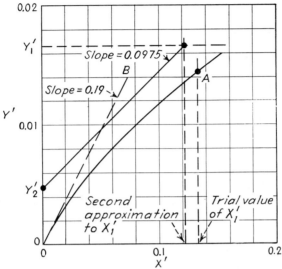

Fig. 73. Curved equilibrium line for key component obtained in case of low oil rate (Illustration 29).

necessary to plot equilibrium and operating lines. The slope of the equilibrium curve at the origin is

$$K(\Sigma Y_2') = (0.21)(1 - 0.093) = 0.19$$

The dotted line OB of Fig. 73 is drawn with this slope. The value of Y' in equilibrium with X_1' is obtained from Eq. (269):

$$Y' \text{ (equilibrium)} = 0.21 \frac{(1.3)(34.4)}{(100)(3.36)\left(1 + \frac{9.3}{100}\right)\left(\frac{34.4}{3.36}\right)} = 0.0144$$

This locates one point on the equilibrium curve near the rich end of the column, as shown by the point A on Fig. 73. The equilibrium curve is drawn in its approximate position, starting at the origin with the slope OB and curving off to pass through A.

The slope of the operating line is $L'/G' = 3.36/34.4 = 0.0975$. A straight line with this slope is placed by trial in a position such that 4.3 steps corresponding to theoretical plates can be stepped off between operating and equilibrium curves.

The n-butane content of the gas leaving the column is read as the intercept of the operating line with the Y' axis as $Y_n' = 0.0045$. The moles of n-butane absorbed is consequently $1.66 - 0.45 = 1.21$, vs. 1.3 previously estimated. The corrected total absorption is 9.2 moles, checking the original estimate sufficiently closely so that further computations are not necessary.

The composition of the gas leaving the column may now be calculated.

Component	Feed, mole per cent	Moles absorbed	Moles in exit gas	Mole per cent in exit gas	
				Calculated	Observed
CH_4...................	83.02	2.9	80.1	88.4	88.7
C_2H_6................	8.41	1.4	7.0	7.7	6.9
C_3H_8................	4.76	1.8	3.0	3.3	3.5
i-C_4H_{10}..............	0.84	0.56	0.28	0.31	0.42
n-C_4H_{10}..............	1.66	1.21	0.45	0.49	0.47
i-C_5H_{12}..............	0.61	0.6	0.00		
n-C_5H_{12}..............	0.16	0.2	0.00		
C_6H_{14}................	0.54	0.5	0.00		
			90.83		

The conditions described in Illustration 29 are those of a test reported by Brown and Souders,[50] in which an actual natural gasoline absorber was tested under the conditions described. The measured analysis of the exit gas is given in the last column of the table for comparison with the calculated composition. The agreement between calculated and observed compositions of the treated gas is seen to be quite good. The calculations show 73 per cent absorption for n-butane, whereas the actual absorption was about 69 per cent. This discrepancy is probably within the accuracy of the analysis for the small quantity of n-butane in the lean gas.

Similar calculations for hydrocarbon absorbers have been presented by Jackson and Sherwood,[216] who found that over-all tower performance in several tests was consistent with plate-efficiency data obtained in small laboratory equipment.

Available data on plate efficiencies for absorbers are presented in Chap. VII. The low value found in the above example is consistent with other data. Distillation columns usually give plate efficiencies which are considerably higher than 18 per cent, but it must be remembered that simple liquid mixtures flowing through such columns are at their boiling points and therefore have viscosities of the order of 0.2 to 0.3 centipoise, whereas the viscosity of the liquid phase in an absorber may be several times greater and the plate efficiency correspondingly lower.

Although the plate efficiency may be somewhat different for the different hydrocarbon gases, as discussed in Chap. VII, the numbers of moles of the gases heavier or lighter than the key component which are absorbed are almost independent of the plate efficiencies of these components, since the number of theoretical plates is usually sufficient to absorb substantially all of the heavier gases or to allow the lighter ones to reach almost complete equilibrium with the exit oil. Thus, only the recovery of the key and adjacent components is affected by the value of plate efficiency; conversely, test data for an absorber can be expected to give reliable plate-efficiency data only for the key component.

The effect of changes in the equilibrium data on the computed plate efficiency is brought out by the fact that Brown and Souders[50] calculate an over-all plate efficiency of 50 per cent from these same data using different values of K.[52]

The equilibrium curve for the key component may be placed much more accurately if an additional point, corresponding to the middle of the column, is located. The absorption of the components more volatile than the key component will take place in the upper part of the column; the absorption of the less volatile will take place on the lower plates. Consequently $1 + \Sigma X'$ for the middle plate may be estimated closely, and by using Eq. (269) the coordinates of a point on the equilibrium curve at about the middle of the column can be found. This additional calculation removes some of the uncertainty in placing the curved equilibrium line for the key component and improves the accuracy of the method. If the key component is one of the least volatile constituents, almost all the curvature will occur near the origin (see Fig. 73); if the key component is one of the most volatile constituents, the equilibrium line will follow the original slope (*OB* of Fig. 73) for a considerable distance from the origin.

ALLOWANCE FOR THERMAL EFFECTS

In an adiabatic absorber almost all the heat of solution of the dissolved gases must be compensated for by an increase in the sensible heat of the liquid stream. If the resulting temperature rise of the solvent as it flows through the tower becomes too great, the vapor pressure of the dissolved hydrocarbons over the exit oil may become excessively high. This situation resembles that described in Chap. V in connection with the determination of the minimum solvent-flow rate, and similar considerations apply.

The latent heats of condensation of hydrocarbons are relatively small, however, and as the gases dissolve in liquids of very similar molecular structure, the heats of mixing are negligibly small. Consequently, the temperature rise of the solvent passing through the column is not large unless the quantity of solvent is small, as in absorbers which operate at high pressure, or unless a large fraction of the rich gas is recovered.

Commercial natural-gasoline absorbers are sometimes operated so that the stream of oil is diverted through a heat exchanger, or "intercooler," and then returned to the column, in order to remove the heat of solution.

This sometimes proves to be economically attractive. In one series of commercial tests, the use of an intercooler increased the absorption from 25.1 to 36.8 per cent of the total moles of gas entering.[216] The rate of absorption was more than twice as great in the bottom half of the column when an intercooler was used as when the column was operated adiabatically.

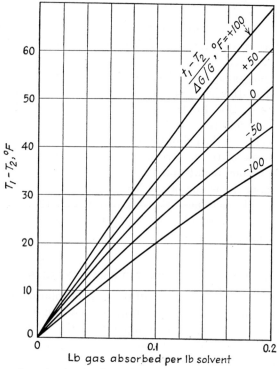

FIG. 74. Temperature rise due to absorption of dissolved solutes; oil absorption of light hydrocarbons.

Figure 74 may be used for approximate predictions of the temperature rise of the solvent in a natural-gasoline absorber which operates at a pressure lower than about 10 atm. This chart is based on a latent heat of 160 B.t.u./lb. for all hydrocarbons condensed and on heat capacities of 0.5 and 0.46 B.t.u./(lb.)($°$F.) for the rich oil and the rich gas, respectively. The lean gas is assumed to leave at the temperature of the lean oil, and the sensible heat gained or lost by the gas is allowed for by means of the parameter $(t_1 - T_2)/(\Delta G/G)$. (All flow rates are expressed in pounds rather than in pound moles.) It might be expected that the temperature rise of the solvent in a high-pressure absorber would be relatively large, owing to the low oil-gas ratio. The effect of pressure on the enthalpy of hydrocarbon vapors, however, is such that the heat of solution is smaller. At 33 atm. the temperature rise may be only 40 per cent as great as indicated by the curve.[52] The temperature rise for such cases must be computed from an enthalpy balance involving actual thermal data for the hydrocarbons under pressure.

It sometimes happens that the rise in oil temperature due to condensation is sufficient to cause stripping of one or more components previously absorbed in the cooler upper section. The composition of the oil with respect to these particular components then goes through a maximum on the middle plate of the column. The effect is illustrated by Fig. 75, on which the lines E_1, E_2, E_3, E_4 are equilibrium lines for one particular solute for the temperatures prevailing on the top four plates. AB represents the operating line, and $ACDFG$ is the usual construction for stepping off the first two plates. The abscissa at F represents the composition of the liquid on the second plate, and the ordinate at G the gas rising from the third plate. The composition of the liquid on the third plate is next

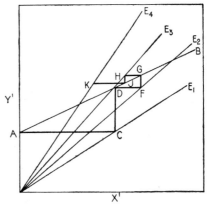

Fig. 75. Nonisothermal conditions, with stripping on the lower plates.

determined by moving to the left to the E_3 line at H. Beyond the point G the operating line is below the equilibrium curves, and the component is stripped from the oil. The concentration in the oil of the component in question is a maximum on the second plate, where the concentration is indicated by the abscissa at F.

The stripping action in the lower section of an absorption tower is not obtained in the adiabatic absorption of a single solute, except in some cases where the gas enters hot. The stripping effect is obtained for certain components in a multicomponent mixture only because the temperature of the solvent increases as it flows through the apparatus, owing to condensation of other components. Heat supplied to the column from outside would cause the same effect.

The effect just described should not be confused with the occurrence of maximum mole fraction with respect to one component frequently obtained in the central portion of a multicomponent column because of the varying concentrations of other components. In an isothermal column it is quite possible for the composition of the oil, with respect to a component of intermediate volatility, to reach a maximum near the middle of the column because of the diluent effect of the nonvolatile components absorbed in the lower section. In this case the concentration of the particular components falls off in the lower section, although the amount of the component dissolved in the oil may continue to increase on the lower plates. The concentration decreases, although no stripping occurs.

Design of Adiabatic Absorption Columns. Methods of allowing for the variations of the amounts of the liquid and vapor streams as absorption takes place have been outlined on pages 199 to 203 of this chapter for the calculation of natural-gasoline absorbers. Although the effects of changing flow rates on the curvature of the equilibrium line for the key component have been brought out, no methods have been presented for allowing for the effect of the changing liquid temperature on the gas solubility. It should be obvious that fluid compositions and temperatures can be calculated throughout an adiabatic absorber by making material and enthalpy balances around each successive theoretical plate, starting either at the bottom or the top of the absorber. Though rigorous, this procedure is too tedious and lengthy for many problems in which absorbers must be designed roughly. While plate-to-plate calculations may be desirable for the final precise design, simpler, less exact methods are desirable for exploratory calculations used in the location of optimum conditions of operation.

Basically, the problem reduces to that of estimating the liquid-temperature profile in the absorber. Several rough rules have been proposed for this purpose. Horton and Franklin[202] have suggested that over-all material and heat balances can be used in conjunction with an assumed average temperature of isothermal operation to estimate the compositions, flow rates, and temperatures of the streams entering and leaving the absorber, as outlined above; and that the temperatures and flow rates inside the tower may be estimated in the second approximation to the design by assuming that the fractional change in the vapor rate is the same for each theoretical plate. That is,

$$\frac{(G' \Sigma Y_c')}{(G' \Sigma Y_b')} = \left(\frac{G'}{G' \Sigma Y_2'}\right)^{1/N} \tag{275}$$

where G' = molal vapor rate of wet gas entering tower
$G' \Sigma Y_2'$ = molal vapor rate of lean gas leaving tower
$G' \Sigma Y_c'$ = molal vapor rate of gas leaving plate c inside the tower
$G' \Sigma Y_b'$ = molal vapor rate of gas leaving plate b inside the tower (note that plate b is the plate just above plate c)
N = total number of theoretical plates in the tower

Knowing $G'\Sigma Y_c'$, $L'(1 + \Sigma X_b')$ may be calculated from a material balance based on all components.

It is further assumed that the change of the liquid temperature from one theoretical plate to the next is given by

$$\frac{T_1 - T_b}{T_1 - T_2} = \frac{G' - G'\Sigma Y_c'}{G' - G'\Sigma Y_2'} \tag{276}$$

where T_1 = temperature of the exit rich oil

T_2 = temperature of entering lean oil

T_b = temperature of oil leaving plate b inside the column

Horton and Franklin[202] give a modified form of the Kremser equation [compare Eq. (271) above and Eq. (277) below] containing the absorption factor A_m for each of the N theoretical plates, rather than a single average factor. Each of the values of $L'(1 + \Sigma X_c')/K_cG'\Sigma Y_c'$ may be calculated using the above assumptions regarding flow rates and temperatures. The same authors also propose a shorter method in which the unmodified Kremser formula, Eq. (271), is used with an average effective absorption factor for the whole column. The flow rates and temperatures used in evaluating this average factor are different for each component being absorbed. For the key component, for which the average absorption factor is within the range 1.0 to 4.0, the values of $L'(1 + \Sigma X_c')$, $G'\Sigma Y_c'$, and K_c are those for plate c located near the bottom of the column at a level such that 70 per cent of the trays are above, *i.e.*, $c = 0.7N$. Conditions on the bottom plate are used in evaluating A_c for the lightest components, for which $L'(1 + \Sigma X_c')/K_cG'\Sigma Y_c'$ is between 0 and 0.1. For $L'(1 + \Sigma X_c')/K_cG'\Sigma Y_c'$ between 0.1 and 0.4, $c = 0.9N$; between 0.4 and 1.0, $c = 0.8N$; and above 4.0, $c = 0.6N$.

The method is relatively simple to apply. Examples given by Horton and Franklin[202] show that the absorption of each of the components of the gas estimated by either of the approximate methods agrees fairly well with the results of plate-to-plate calculations. Figure 76 shows the results of one of the plate-to-plate calculations given by Horton and Franklin for an absorber having four theoretical plates. It is seen that the oil-temperature profile and the variation of total vapor and liquid rates estimated by means of Eqs. (275) and (276) agree fairly well with the results of the plate-to-plate material and enthalpy balances. The absorption of the key component, *n*-butane in this case, was found, using the step-by-step method, to be 0.9185 times the number of moles of butane at the gas inlet. By the shorter, rough method the corresponding figure was 0.921.

Figure 76 shows that the numbers of moles in the liquid of the lighter gases, methane, ethane, and propane, go through maximum values within the column, indicating that these components are absorbed in the cold oil near the top of the column and stripped from the oil on a lower tray as the liquid temperature increases. The Kremser formula, used with an assumed constant absorption factor, is not capable of accounting for effects such as these. On the other hand, the effects are unimportant so far as the over-all recovery of each component is concerned; the correct recovery is obtained if the correct exit liquid temperature is estimated, since the exit oil is very nearly at equilibrium with the inlet gas.

Liquid-temperature profiles are not always so simple as that shown by Fig. 76. If the inlet gas is much colder than the oil leaving the absorber, the transfer of sensible heat from the oil to the gas as the gas temperature rises inside the tower may cause the liquid to cool as it flows across the lowest trays, resulting in a maximum in the curve of oil temperature vs. plate number. Brown and Souders[50] report measurements of the temperature of the liquid flowing from each tray of a high-pressure absorber.

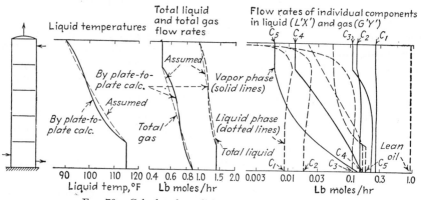

FIG. 76.   Calculated conditions in adiabatic absorber.

The oil temperature had a maximum value inside the column, owing to the low liquid-gas ratio employed at high pressure and the consequently greater ratio of the total heat capacity of the gas relative to that of the liquid. It is impossible to estimate a temperature profile having a maximum by using Eqs. (275) and (276), and the assumption suggested by Horton and Franklin should be used with caution when the molal liquid-vapor ratio is low and the gas enters much colder than the exit oil.

Edmister[125] has extended the approximate design method of Horton and Franklin, using the same assumptions for estimating the internal flow rates and temperatures, as given by Eqs. (275) and (276). For an absorber having two theoretical plates it is possible to derive an exact expression for the average effective absorption factor for the column, A_E', in terms of the values of A_e ($= L'(1 + \Sigma X_e')/K_cG'\Sigma Y_e'$) for the two plates. By making material balances around each of the N plates of an absorber, and after eliminating the $N-1$ intermediate gas compositions from the N equations so obtained, it is found that[202]

$$\frac{Y_1' - Y_2'}{Y_1'} = \frac{A_N A_{N-1} A_{N-2} \cdots A_1 + A_{N-1} A_{N-2} \cdots A_1 + \cdots + A_1}{A_N A_{N-1} A_{N-2} \cdots A_1 + A_{N-1} A_{N-2} \cdots A_1 + \cdots + A_1 + 1}$$
$$- \frac{L'X_2'}{G'Y_1'} \frac{A_{N-1} A_{N-2} \cdots A_1 + A_{N-2} \cdots A_1 + \cdots + A_1 + 1}{A_N A_{N-1} A_{N-2} \cdots A_1 + A_{N-1} A_{N-2} \cdots A_1 + \cdots + A_1 + 1} \tag{277}$$

or

$$\frac{Y_1' - Y_2'}{Y_1'} = \left(1 - \frac{L'X_2'}{A'G'Y_1'}\right) \frac{A'_E{}^{N+1} - A_E'}{A'_E{}^{N+1} - 1} \tag{278}$$

which defines A_E' and A'. For a two-plate absorber,

$$\frac{A'_E{}^3 - A_E'}{A'_E{}^3 - 1} = \frac{A_1(A_2 + 1)}{A_1(A_2 + 1) + 1} \tag{279}$$

$$\frac{A'_E{}^3 - A_E'}{A'(A'_E{}^3 - 1)} = \frac{A_1 + 1}{A_1(A_2 + 1) + 1} \tag{280}$$

where the subscripts 1 and 2 refer to the lower and upper trays, respectively.

Clearing Eq. (279) of fractions and removing the common factor $A_E' - 1$, we obtain

$$A'_E{}^2 + A_E' - A_1(A_2 + 1) = 0 \tag{281}$$

which is a quadratic equation in A_E'. The solution is

$$A_E' = \sqrt{A_1(A_2 + 1) + 0.25} - 0.5 \tag{282}$$

From Eq. (280) we find that

$$A' = \frac{A_1(A_2 + 1)}{A_1 + 1} \tag{283}$$

Edmister[122] uses Eq. (282) for finding the effective average absorption factor for a column of N plates by replacing A_1 with A_N. He finds that corrections are required to make this value of A_E' give the same result as Eq. (277), however, and has computed the value of the correction corresponding to certain arbitrarily assumed variations of temperature and flow rates.[124] Nevertheless, Eq. (282), without additional corrections, seems to give better agreement with point-to-point calculations than do the approximate methods of Horton and Franklin.[202]

Illustration 30. An absorber[216] receives a wet gas having the following composition:

Component	Mole Fraction
H_2S	0.0369
CH_4^*	0.4488
C_2H_4	0.0423
C_2H_6	0.2110
C_3H_6	0.0652
C_3H_8	0.1071
C_4H_8	0.0292
C_4H_{10}	0.0349
C_5+	0.0246
	1.0000

* Includes hydrogen and nitrogen.　Average molecular weight = 14.3.

The absorber has 19 trays, and the plate efficiency for the key component is estimated to be 34 per cent.　The lean oil is completely stripped and enters at 55.5°F.　Between the ninth and tenth trays from the bottom, the oil is diverted to an intercooler, from which it is returned to the tower at 48.6°F.　The gas enters at 41.8°F.　The oil rate at the intercooler is 1007 lb. moles/hr. (162,031 lb./hr.), and the inlet gas rate is 1075 lb. moles/hr. (30,181 lb./hr.).　The tower operates at 6.23 atm. absolute.　The oil leaving the intercooler has the following composition:

Component	Mole Fraction
H_2S	0.0077
CH_4^*	0.0142
C_2H_4	0.0070
C_2H_6	0.0538
C_3H_6	0.0280
C_3H_8	0.0426
C_4H_8	0.0013
C_4H_{10}	0.0016
C_5	0.0046
Lean oil	0.8392
	1.0000

* Includes hydrogen and nitrogen.　Average molecular weight = 14.3.

Using Edmister's[124] average effective absorption factor, estimate the fraction of each component absorbed in the lower section of the column.

Solution.　Assuming for a first, trial solution that 240 lb. moles/hr. of gas are absorbed, the value of $G'\Sigma Y_2$ is 835 lb. moles/hr. and $L' = (1007)(0.8392) = 845$ lb. moles/hr.　Assuming that the average molecular weight of the gases absorbed is 40, 9600 lb./hr. of gas are dissolved.

The temperature rise of the oil is found from Fig. 74.　This assumes that the gas leaves this section of the tower at the temperature of the inlet liquid.　The coordinates plotted in Fig. 74 are

$$\frac{\text{Lb. gas absorbed}}{\text{Lb. solvent}} = \frac{9,600}{162,031} = 0.0582$$

$$\frac{t_1 - T_2}{\Delta G/G} = \frac{41.8 - 48.6}{9600/30,181} = -21.4°F.$$

For these values, Fig. 74 gives $\Delta T = 16.5°F.$, from which $T_1 = 65.1°F.$

According to Edmister's assumptions regarding variations of temperature and flow rates, Eq. (275), the ratio of the total gas-flow rate entering and leaving a single theoretical plate is

$$(835/1075)^{1/(9)(0.34)} = 0.920$$

The quantity of gas leaving the first theoretical plate is

$$G' \Sigma Y_c' = (1075)(0.920) = 989 \text{ lb. moles/hr.}$$

The ratio of total liquid flow leaving the bottom plate to the total gas flow leaving the bottom plate is

$$\frac{L'(1 + \Sigma X_c')}{G' \Sigma Y_c'} = \frac{1007 + 240}{989} = 1.260$$

The quantity of total gas leaving the second theoretical tray is

$$(1075)(0.920)^2 = 910 \text{ lb. moles/hr.}$$

The total liquid-flow rate from the third tray is

$$L'(1 + \Sigma X_a') = 1007 + 240 - (1075 - 910) = 1082 \text{ lb. moles/hr.}$$

The ratio of total liquid to total gas flow leaving the top plate is, therefore,

$$\frac{L'(1 + \Sigma X_a')}{G' \Sigma Y_a'} = \frac{1082}{835} = 1.298$$

From Eq. (276)

$$\frac{65.1 - T_a}{65.1 - 48.6} = \frac{1075 - 910}{1075 - 835}$$
$$T_a = 53.8°F.$$

For all components lighter than propane, the absorption factor will be evaluated at the exit oil temperature, while the inlet oil temperature will be used for pentane. The absorption factor for butene is calculated as follows:

$$T_c = 65.1°F., \qquad K_c = 0.50, \qquad A_c = 2.5 \qquad \text{(bottom tray)}$$
$$T_a = 53.8°F., \qquad K_a = 0.43, \qquad A_a = 3.0 \qquad \text{(top tray)}$$

From Eq. (282),

$$A_E' = \sqrt{(2.5)(3.0 + 1) + 0.25} - 0.5 = 2.70$$

Values of A_E' for propane and butane are calculated similarly, with the following results:

Component	K at exit oil temperature (65.1°F.)	K at inlet oil temperature (48.6°F.)	A_E' Eq. (282)	$\frac{Y_1' - Y_2'}{Y_1 - KX_2'}$	A' Eq. (283)	$\frac{L'X_2'}{A'G'Y_1'}$	$\frac{Y_1' - Y_2'}{Y_1'}$	$(Y_1' - Y_2')G'$, lb. moles/hr.	
								Calculated	Observed[216]
H_2S......	3.0	.....	0.46	0.43	.....	.....	0.24	9.5	7.0
CH_4......	25	.....	0.050	0.050	.....	.....	0.02	9.7	55.0
C_2H_4.....	6.3	.....	0.20	0.19	.....	.....	0.04	1.8	3.3
C_2H_6.....	4.2	.....	0.30	0.28	.....	.....	0.058	13.2	19.0
C_3H_6.....	....	.....	0.918	......	0.939	0.428	0.345	24.2	24.9
C_3H_8.....	....	.....	1.05	......	1.07	0.348	0.505	58.3	42.3
C_4H_8.....	....	.....	2.70	......	2.86	0.015	0.957	30.2	30.2
C_4H_{10}.....	....	0.28	3.78	0.985	.....	.....	0.974	36.6	35.7
C_5........	....	0.085	15.3	0.9997	.....	.....	0.989	26.2	26.5
Total...	....	.....	......	......	.....	.....	.....	209.7	243.9

The calculation could be improved by making a more accurate heat balance than that on which Fig. 74 is based and by assuming a smaller number of moles absorbed, as indicated by this first trial.

The conditions of this illustrative example are those of an actual test reported by Jackson and Sherwood.[216] The total number of moles of gas actually absorbed was 244, and the measured exit oil temperature was 62.0°F.

Nomenclature for Chapter VI

A = absorption factor, $L'(1 + \Sigma X')/KG' \Sigma Y'$

A'_E = effective absorption factor for a nonisothermal column [compare Eq. (282)]

A' = effective absorption factor for a nonisothermal column [compare Eq. (283)]

f = fugacity, atm.; subscript π denotes fugacity of the pure component as a vapor at the total pressure of the mixture, and P denotes fugacity of the pure liquid under its own vapor pressure

G' = inlet gas rate, lb. moles/hr.

$\Delta G/G$ = vapor absorbed, lb./lb. inlet vapor, for use in Fig. 74

K = equilibrium vaporization ratio, y/x; subscript c refers to value at the temperature of plate c

L' = inlet solvent rate, moles/hr.

m' = slope of the equilibrium curve relating Y' and X' for vapor and liquid phases in equilibrium

N = total number of theoretical trays in absorber

p = partial pressure, atm.

P = total pressure, atm.

P_R = reduced pressure

P_v = vapor pressure, atm.

t = temperature of the vapor, °F.; subscript c refers to the vapor leaving plate c

T = temperature of the liquid, °F.; subscript c refers to the temperature of the liquid flowing from plate c

T_R = reduced temperature

V_R = reduced specific volume

x = mole fraction in the liquid phase

X' = moles of solute in the liquid per mole of solute-free liquid fed to the top of the absorber; subscript 2 denotes value in the entering liquid stream, c denotes values in stream leaving plate c, and 1 denotes value in liquid leaving the absorber

y = mole fraction in the vapor phase

Y' = moles of solute in the gas per mole of inlet gas; subscript 2 denotes value in the exit gas, 1 denotes value in entering gas, c denotes value in gas flowing from plate c

$\Delta Y'$ = mean driving force in units of Y'

$\Delta Y_m'$ = logarithmic mean $\Delta Y'$

$a, b, c, \ldots n$ = subscript designating plate location; plate a is top plate

Problems

1. A refinery gas containing 80 per cent methane, 8 per cent ethane, 5 per cent propane, 4 per cent n-butane, 2 per cent n-pentane, and 1 per cent n-hexane or higher, is absorbed in a 24-plate column operating at 60°F., with 1 mole of denuded absorption oil fed to the column for each mole of treated gas leaving the column. If the over-all plate efficiency is 25 per cent, what pressure must be used to recover 96 per cent of the butane?

2. A gas containing 60 per cent methane, 30 per cent *n*-butane, and 10 per cent nitrogen is compressed at 80°F. from 1 atm. until 30 per cent of the butane has been liquefied.

a. What is the final pressure?

b. What is the composition of the resulting liquid expressed in mole per cent methane?

3. A gas containing 86 mole per cent C_2H_6, 9 per cent C_3H_8, and 5 per cent *n*-C_4H_{10} is treated in a tower operating under a pressure of 45 p.s.i.g. The absorber oil is completely stripped and has a molecular weight of 180. The average temperature is 100°F. The tower contains 10 perfect plates, and 90 per cent of the butane is absorbed.

a. What is the oil-gas ratio required, expressed as pounds of oil per 1000 ft.³ of rich gas at 60°F. and 1 atm.?

b. What percentage of the propane is removed from the gas?

c. Make a plot of butane and propane recovery vs. the number of plates from the top of the tower.

4. A refinery proposes to treat a gas with absorbent oil in a 19-plate absorber fitted with an intercooler between the tenth and eleventh plates from the top. A lean oil of molecular weight 185 will be fed to the tower at 56°F. at a rate of 847 lb. moles/hr. The intercooler will cool the oil to 49°F. and return it to the tower. The total pressure will be 77 p.s.i.g. The wet-gas rate will be 1075 lb. moles/hr., and the out gas will have the following composition in terms of mole per cent: H_2S, 3.69; CH_4, 44.88; C_2H_4, 4.23; C_2H_6, 21.10; C_3H_6, 6.52; C_3H_8, 10.71; C_4H_{10}, 3.49; C_5, 2.46. Assume K for H_2S to be the same as for *n*-C_4H_{10}, and assume C_4H_8 to be 1-butene, with a value of K equal to 85 per cent of K for *n*-C_4H_{10}.

Making allowance for the variation in plate efficiency with composition (see Chap. VIII), estimate the composition of the treated gas. Assume the tower temperature constant at 59°F.

Note that these are the conditions of Illustration 30, but the suggested approach is different.

5. A plate absorber having the equivalent of 10 theoretical trays is used to treat a refinery gas containing 78 per cent CH_4, 6 per cent C_2H_6, 7 per cent C_3H_8, 5 per cent *n*-C_4H_{10}, and 4 per cent *n*-C_5H_{12} and higher. The column operates under pressure at 100°F., with an oil rate (completely denuded) of 431 lb. per 1000 ft.³ inlet gas (gas measured at 60°F. and 1 atm.), and absorbs 91 per cent of the *n*-C_4H_{10}.

Assuming the absolute pressure to be increased by 39 per cent, calculate the new per cent recovery of propane. The molecular weight of the oil is 186.

6. A gas containing 86 mole per cent CH_4, 9 per cent C_3H_8, and 5 per cent *n*-C_4H_{10} is treated in a tower operating at 45 p.s.i.a. pressure at 100°F. The tower contains 10 perfect plates, and the denuded oil is supplied at the rate of 108 moles per 100 moles inlet gas. It is found that 90 per cent of the butane and 34 per cent of the propane are absorbed.

What propane recovery could be expected if the total pressure were doubled, the other conditions remaining unchanged?

7. A rich mixture of refinery gases containing 30.1 per cent methane, 24.4 per cent ethylene, 20.3 per cent *n*-butane, 11.7 per cent isopentane, and 13.5 per cent heavier components, taken as n-heptane, is to be stripped in a plate tower, using a nonvolatile oil as absorbent. The tower is operated isothermally at 100°F. and 18 atm. total pressure. Denuded oil is fed to the tower at the rate of 76.3 moles per 100 moles inlet gas.

a. How many theoretical plates are required if 40.3 per cent of the isopentane is to be removed from the gas?

b. What is the composition of the gas leaving the tower under these conditions?

8. Casing-head gasoline is often made by scrubbing natural gas with an oil of low volatility and then stripping the absorbed hydrocarbons from the oil. It is desired to absorb 95 per cent of the butane from a natural gas whose composition in per cent is as follows: CH_4, 89.5; C_2H_6, 6; C_3H_8, 2; C_4H_{10}, 2; and C_5H_{12}, 0.5. The absorber will operate at a pressure of 25 atm. absolute and at a constant temperature of 100°F.

a. Estimate the minimum ratio of absorbent oil to rich gas.

b. Determine the number of theoretical plates required for $L'/G' = 0.26$ mole inlet oil per mole entering gas mixture.

c. Estimate the percentage of each component absorbed under these conditions.

CHAPTER VII

GAS-ABSORPTION EQUIPMENT

Filters, heat exchangers, distillation columns, dryers, and many other types of chemical engineering equipment are ordinarily designed mechanically and fabricated by equipment-construction companies, to be purchased by the manufacturing plant. Absorption equipment, also, is erected according to this procedure to some extent, especially in the case of large bubble-tray absorbers which do not differ essentially from distillation units of the same type (see Fig. 78). Other types of absorbers, including packed towers and units of special design, are often designed and built by engineers connected with the plant in which they are to be installed. The details of construction are determined by the chemical properties of the fluids being handled and by the difficulty of the absorption job to be accomplished. As a result of the wide variety of purposes and specifications of absorbers, a large number of quite different types have been built and used. The objective of each design, however, is the provision for intimate contact of gas and liquid over a large interphase surface; with low first cost and low operating and maintenance expense.

The various types of absorbers may be divided roughly into three groups: (a) packed towers, (b) bubble-cap or -tray towers, and (c) miscellaneous types, including spray chambers and agitated vessels. The first cost includes foundations; tower shell; packing material; solvent charge, pumps, blowers, piping ducts, accessory heaters, coolers, and heat exchangers; and solvent-recovery system, if needed. The operating costs include power for circulating gas and solvent, maintenance, labor, steam for regenerating the solvent, cooling water, solvent make-up, and the value of the material which remains unabsorbed and is lost. Abbreviated methods for choosing the economically optimum operating conditions and equipment dimensions are presented in the Appendix.

PACKED TOWERS

The most common type of absorption equipment for small-scale operations is the packed tower. It consists of a vertical shell set on an adequate foundation and filled with one of numerous types of inert packing materials. Figure 77 shows the construction of a typical ceramic tower (shown without packing). The operation is usually countercurrent, the

217

solvent being distributed over the packing at the top of the tower and passing down over the packing in thin liquid films, while the gas passes up through the free space between the wetted particles of packing.   In place of one very tall tower it is customary to employ several shorter towers in series, the gas passing from the top of the first tower to the bottom of the second, etc., while the liquor is pumped in the opposite direction, as from the bottom of the second to the top of the first, etc.   This type of opera-tion is common practice in the low-pres-sure absorption of nitric oxide in the man-ufacture of nitric acid.

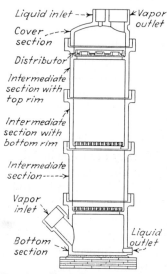

In some cases the liquor rate is neces-sarily small compared to the gas flow, and if the tower has a cross section adequate to handle the gas, there may not be enough liquid to wet the packing thoroughly. One method of overcoming this difficulty is to recirculate the liquor through the tower so that the quantity of liquor circu-lated hourly is several times the actual net hourly throughput.   When this is done in a single tower, the advantage of counter-current action is largely lost, and the use of several shorter towers is resorted to in an effort to simulate true countercurrent action.   With this design the liquor moves from tower to tower, countercurrent to the flow of gas.   If the liquor throughput is small compared to the liquor recircu-lated, the change in liquor concentration from top to bottom of any one tower will be small, and it is not important that the gas pass up through each tower.   In order to save on gas mains in such cases the gas may be allowed to pass alternately up and then down through successive towers.

Fig. 77. Typical ceramic absorp-tion-tower shell. (*General Ceram-ics and Steatite Corp., Kearney, N. J.*)

Individual towers are sometimes as high as 80 ft. and as large as 30 ft. in diameter.   Because of the enormous weight of the wetted packing in large towers and the necessity of allowing for wind pressure, the founda-tions are heavy and costly.   The requirements of foundations for self-supporting towers are discussed by Sandstrom.[399]   It is advisable to have the diameter small compared to the packed height, and where the ratio of diameter to height is greater than one-fifth, special care must be taken to ensure proper initial distribution of gas and liquor flow through the pack-ing.   Even after being distributed uniformly over the top of the packing the liquid has a tendency to flow toward the tower wall. In a tall tower it may be necessary to divide the packing into several sections with a device above each which will collect the liquid from the wall and redistribute it to the packing.

The packing rests on a brick checkerwork or metal grid, below which the gas is introduced. A part of the weight of the packing may be supported by the shell in a tall tower, but the packing support should be strong enough to bear the entire weight. A crude packing support may

Fig. 78. Plant for absorption of hydrocarbons for use in gasoline manufacture. (*Lummus Co., New York.*)

be made by stacking several large pieces of packing on each other. The packing may be crushed by alternate contractions and expansions of the shell if cyclic temperature changes occur.

Above the packing is the liquor-feed distributor, which may be any one of several types (see Fig. 79). If the liquid enters through the same openings by which the gas leaves, the cross-sectional area provided for gas flow must be sufficient to prevent flooding at the distributor. A better plan is to provide separate openings for the liquid and gas. For adequate initial distribution, the liquid should be subdivided into a number of separate streams equal to $(D_t'/6)^2$, where D_t' is the tower diameter in inches.[74] This can be done by installing a system of troughs and weirs[326] or by introducing the main liquid stream onto a horizontal tray having several liquid-overflow tubes ("downcomers") extending through the tray. The tops of these tubes must be leveled carefully during fabrication and installation, but the adjustment is not so critical if each tube is notched at the top, where the liquid overflows.

Spray nozzles, preferably the solid-cone type, make excellent distributors but may be clogged by solid particles suspended in the solvent. Alternatively, the liquid can be dispersed into a crude spray by allowing an open-ended pipe to direct a stream at a target laid on the packing.

Fig. 79.   Liquid-feed distributor plates.   (*Maurice A. Knight, Akron, Ohio.*)

Since absorption towers find wide application in chemical plants, particularly for acid manufacture, a common construction material is acidproof ceramic ware. Towers up to 5 ft. in diameter are constructed of cylindrical tower sections which fit together, as shown in Fig. 77. Larger towers are made of acidproof brick or of steel lined with an acidproof brick or special plastic coating. Chamber sulfuric acid plants use lead shells lined with acidproof brick. Modern plants producing nitric acid by oxidation of ammonia employ towers having shells made of chromium-steel alloy, and towers for this purpose were among the first large structures fabricated of stainless steel in this country. Ordinary steel is used in the petroleum industry, where the corrosion difficulties are less serious and plate towers are more common than packed.

The acidproof brick for the shells of the larger towers are bonded with an acidproof mortar, usually having a sodium silicate base. Various grades of chemical stoneware may be obtained, that for contact with acid being high in silica, low in iron oxide, alumina, and alkaline earths, thoroughly vitrified, and nonabsorbent. In general the porous materials are more resistant to temperature changes, and denser materials more resistant to acid. In addition to packing material and shells for the smaller towers it is possible to obtain acidproof chemical-stoneware pipes, liquor-distributing plates, valves, pumps, and blowers. Pipes, valves, and other small pieces may also be had in hard rubber. A general discussion of tower construction for acid plants is given by Fairlie.[135]

PACKING MATERIALS

A very large number of packing materials have been used or suggested for use in absorption towers. The earliest packings were lump materials such as coke or broken rock, screened to size to eliminate small particles which might plug a gas passage. These materials are still used, but in recent years a number of manufactured packings have been placed on the market and have found favor, particularly where acid-resistant materials are required. The individual particles of the manufactured packings have general dimensions of from $\frac{3}{8}$ to 6 in. and are usually hollow, so that, when they are dumped or packed in a tower, there will be less tendency for channeling of gas and liquor than in the case of the broken materials, the resistance to gas flow will be low, and the wetted surface per unit volume will be large. Most of these newer packings are patented, and their first cost is considerably greater than for broken materials.

The various criteria of an ideal packing are discussed in detail by Butcher,[61] Fairlie,[135] and by Badger and McCabe.[14] Basically, however, the requirements are three:

1. Low cost per cubic foot
2. High absorption capacity, as indicated by high allowable gas and liquor rates and high capacity coefficients $K_L a$ or $K_G a$ under the operating conditions
3. Low maintenance, implying low resistance to gas flow

In addition, the packing naturally must have a long life under the existing corrosion and thermal conditions. Manufacturers of packings can usually supply data on percentage of free volume, surface per unit volume, etc., but sometimes lack the really fundamental data on resistance to gas flow, and the capacity coefficients for the purpose at hand. Since high capacity coefficients are usually obtained with the smaller packing sizes, for which the resistance to gas flow is large, the best packing is necessarily a compromise having moderate absorption capacity and moderate resistance to gas flow. There is, however, a range of sizes within which the capacity coefficients are nearly independent of size, as shown in Chap. VIII. Within this range, large packings are preferred because of their smaller pressure drop. Popular sizes include 1-, 1.5-, and 2-in. Raschig rings and Berl saddles, 3-in. spiral tile, and ceramic or wood grids.

Fig. 80. Porcelain Raschig rings. (*Lapp Insulator Co., Inc., LeRoy, N. Y.*)

Figures 80 to 82 illustrate a few of the many types of manufactured packings, and Table XIII summarizes the physical characteristics of those pictured as well as of several not shown. The weight per cubic foot is important in connection with the design of the foundations, shell, and supporting grid for the packing. The percentage of free volume is roughly indicative of the resistance to gas flow, although sometimes misleading in this respect. For example, $\frac{1}{4}$-in. spheres have a very much greater resistance to gas flow than 3-in. spheres, and yet the percentage of free volume is the same for both, providing that the arrangement of the packing is the same. Even though the cross section available for flow is the same for both sizes, the mean diameter of the channels through the packing is greater for the larger spheres.

Pressure losses accompanying flow of air at atmospheric pressure through several commercially important dry packing materials are compared by Fig. 83. The larger random packings generally have more free space and give correspondingly smaller friction losses at the same superficial gas velocity. The stacked packings offer even less resistance to air flow than dumped packings having the same free space.

Fig. 81. Random-packed Berl saddles. (*Maurice A. Knight, Akron, Ohio.*)

The data on surface per cubic foot of tower volume are only very roughly indicative of the absorption capacity; the values given are for dry packing and are much larger than the active wetted area, as discussed below.

The stability of the packing, or angle of repose of a pile, is of importance in designing the tower shell. Some of the larger cylindrical and rectangular shapes are practically self-supporting when stacked in the tower and exert little side thrust on the walls.

Possibly the most popular packing is the hollow cylinder, or Raschig ring (see Fig. 80). These are made of glass, carbon, ceramic materials, or metal. They are usually "dumped" into the tower, although the larger sizes may be "packed" in regular horizontal tiers or courses. In placing dumped packing, the shell of a tall tower may be filled temporarily with water and the packing pieces dropped into the liquid to reduce breaking. Packing in tiers is usually reserved for the larger spiral and partition tiles. Raschig rings, Lessing rings, and other cylindrical pieces are almost always made with height equal to diameter. When dumped into the tower, the mass is homogenous and the tendency for channeling of the gas and liquid streams is minimized.   Packings constructed of slats, tiles, or glass plates on edge have both high surface per cubic foot and high free volume but are not so widely used as Raschig rings because of the labor of stacking and the channeling resulting from broken units.   In comparing

FIG. 82.   Drip-point grid tile—single unit and several units arranged in checker pattern. (*General Refractories Co., Philadelphia.*)

first costs of packing, the installation costs should always be included. The shape of the individual piece will sometimes suggest the likelihood of the liquor following its natural tendency to work over to the walls of the tower (see below). Stacked or packed hollow cylinders, for example, provide little opportunity for the liquor to work sidewise in the tower, whereas dumped packings provide the liquor with a possible velocity component toward the wall.

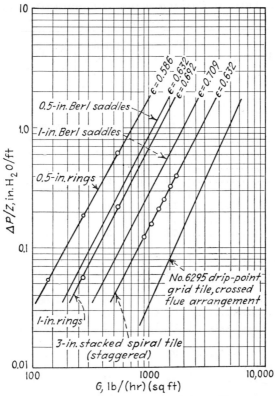

Fig. 83. Pressure drop for air flow through dry packings. Air at atmospheric pressure, 70°F. (*Data of Tillson, and of Molstad.*)

The mechanical-energy loss corresponding to the pressure drop of the gas goes partly to turbulence and partly to true skin friction. In a packed tower most of the loss is in turbulence, since the gas changes direction so frequently. Either increased turbulence or increased skin friction tends to thin the surface-gas film and promote interphase diffusion, but experience in heating air with surfaces of various shapes shows clearly that a given energy loss due to skin friction is more efficient in promoting heat transfer than is the same loss due to turbulence in the main body of the gas. By analogy, therefore, it would appear that the best packings might be those for which the pressure drop due to skin friction is high compared to that due to turbulence. This is true in streamline sections, in which the gas does not change direction, and high coefficients are obtained by using high gas velocities.

A simple packing meeting these conditions is a bundle of vertical tubes without headers, with spacers to maintain passages between the tubes

TABLE XIII. PHYSICAL CHARACTERISTICS OF COMMERCIAL TOWER PACKING MATERIALS*

Packing	Per cent free space, ϵ	Specific surface, a_v ft.^{2}/ft.^{3}	Number units/ft.^{3}	Bulk density, lb./ft.^{3}
Raschig rings:				
Stoneware:				
⅜ in.	53	148	26,000	65
½ in.	53	114	10,700	65
1 in.	68	58	1,330	45
1½ in.	68	36	380	45
2 in.	83	29	165	24
Carbon:				
¼ in.	55	212	85,000	46
½ in.	74	114	10,600	27
1 in.	73	58	1,350	27
1½ in.	67	38	400	34
2 in.	73	29	170	27
3 in.	78	19	49	23
Steel:				
0.6 in.	95.7	100	7,000	
1 in.	91.8	65	1,550	
2 in.	94.4	32	190	
Aluminum:				
2 in.	92	28	......	13.7
Berl saddles:				
½ in.	68	141	15,000	45
1 in.	69	79	2,300	42
1½ in.	70	50	650	42
Spiral tile (stacked):				
3-in. single spiral or tri-				
angular centers	58	40	63	60
3-in. triple spiral or tri-				
angular centers	50	50	63	69
Stoneware balls:				
1 in. diameter	40.8	43	1,975	80–90
½ in. diameter	24.3	109	15,700	80–90

* Based on information from Maurice A. Knight Co., Akron, Ohio; U.S. Stoneware Co., Akron, Ohio; National Carbon Co., Inc., Cleveland, Ohio.

having the same hydraulic mean radius as the interior of the tubes. A preliminary test of this packing has been made by one of the authors, and it was found to give excellent capacity coefficients with very low pressure drop. According to Fig. 105, Chap. VIII, the H.T.U. for such a packing should be approximately equal to $50D_e$, where D_e is the equivalent hydraulic diameter. Wood or ceramic grids installed with the vertical channels in line and Fiberglas pads installed with fibers vertical also meet the conditions approximately.

To obtain the maximum scrubbing efficiency of a packed tower, both gas and liquid streams should be distributed uniformly over the tower cross section. If this can be achieved, the maximum area of the packing will be wet and will be useful for interphase contact. In other words, K_Ga will have its maximum value. Moreover, there will be no liquid or gas streams which by-pass the packing and undergo negligible changes in composition; neither will there be streams which flow too slowly and become saturated too quickly. Both effects must be taken into account when discussing the effect of maldistribution on performance. The latter effect is especially important in operations where operating and equilibrium lines approach closely, *i.e.*, where the uniformly distributed liquid and vapor must approach equilibrium with each other in order to achieve the over-all composition changes expected. The more closely uniform distribution can be approached, the smaller will be the limitations on equipment performance from both causes; anything that can be done to make liquid distribution more uniform will help in each of the two ways.

The factor a is defined as the square feet of active wetted surface per cubic foot of packed volume. It is necessarily an average value, since the degree of wetting of the packing varies from point to point within the column. It is by no means proportional to the total specific surface of dry packing, a_v, although the smaller packing sizes will naturally tend to give more wetted surface per unit volume. This lack of proportionality is due primarily to three causes: (*a*) uneven distribution of liquor over the cross section of the column, (*b*) failure of the liquid to wet all of each individual particle, and (*c*) inactive surface at points of contact of packing particles, at which the liquor remains stagnant and soon becomes saturated with solute.

The fraction of the total external packing surface which is wetted and which is not inactive owing to stagnation of the liquid at points of contact of packing particles has not been measured directly. It may be estimated indirectly, however, by comparing the value of k_Ga for the irrigated packing with the value of this product measured by Taecker and Hougen[450] in a recent experiment in which specially constructed, porous Raschig rings and Berl saddles were soaked in water and then dried by blowing air through them. The value of $k_G a$ was calculated from the constant rate of drying and was expressed by the equations

$$j_D = 1.070 \left(\frac{G \sqrt{a_p}}{\mu} \right)^{-0.41} \tag{284}$$

for Raschig rings and

$$j_D = 0.855 \left(\frac{G \sqrt{a_p}}{\mu} \right)^{-0.34} \tag{285}$$

for Berl saddles. In these equations, a_p represents the total external and internal surface area of one packing piece. Introducing a_v, the total surface area (100 per cent wet) of the packing pieces contained in 1 ft.³ of packed space,

$$H_G = \frac{0.935}{a_v} \left(\frac{G \sqrt{a_p}}{\mu} \right)^{0.41} \left(\frac{\mu}{\rho D_v} \right)^{2/3} \tag{286}$$

for rings and

$$H_G = \frac{1.170}{a_v} \left(\frac{G \sqrt{a_p}}{\mu} \right)^{0.34} \left(\frac{\mu}{\rho D_v} \right)^{2/3} \tag{287}$$

for saddles. The values of a_v and a_p for the packings used by Taecker and Hougen are given by Table XIV. Using these data, the following equa-

TABLE XIV

Packing	Nominal size, in.	$\sqrt{a_p}$, ft.	a_v, ft.²/ft.³
Raschig rings..........	½	0.1028	122
	1	0.2102	58
	2	0.4193	29
Berl saddles..........	¼	0.0492	274
	½	0.0938	155

tions may be developed for the completely wetted packings.

$$H_G = 0.0204 G^{0.41} \tag{288}$$

for 1-in. rings and

$$H_G = 0.0543 G^{0.41} \tag{289}$$

for 2-in. rings.

The fraction of the total packing surface which is effective in an irrigated bed of the same packing may be estimated by comparing the above empirical equations with the following equation based on rates of continuous evaporation of water from 1.5-in. rings [compare Eq. (337), Chap. VIII]:

$$H_G = \frac{1.01 G^{0.31}}{L^{0.33}} \tag{290}$$

Assuming that Eq. (290) applies to both 2-in. and 1-in. rings, comparison with Eqs. (288) and (289) shows that for 1-in. rings the fraction of the total packing area which is wetted effectively at $G = 250$ lb./(hr.)(ft.²) is 35 per cent at $L = 1000$ and 76 per cent at $L = 10,000$ lb./(hr.)(ft.²). The fraction effectively wetted depends mainly on the liquid rate and very slightly on the gas velocity. Taecker and Hougen's data[450] have been used recently by Weisman and Bonilla[496] for estimating the fraction of the packing wetted in McAdams, Pohlenz, and St. John's[314] experiments on water evaporation from irrigated rings, and in their own experiments on water evaporation from solid spheres. The results are qualitatively similar to those presented here, but the estimated wetted areas are larger. The area available for heat transfer to the evaporating liquid is greater than that for mass transfer, as some of the heat from the gas can enter the packing through the dry areas. Other information on wetted areas is given by Van Krevelen[473] and by Grimley.[166]

Direct measurements of the extent of wetting of the packing surface have been made by Mayo, Hunter, and Nash[307] by means of an ingenious experimental technique. These investigators employed a small tower packed first with ½- by ½-in. and then with 1- by 1-in. Raschig rings made of paper, and circulated water containing a red dye. After running the apparatus for 10 or 15 min., the liquor feed was stopped, the packing removed and dried, and the wetted surface estimated by measuring the colored areas of the paper. The rings were made of double thicknesses of paper, so that they might be divided and the dyed areas measured on both inner and outer surfaces of the cylinders. The tower was fitted with a paper liner, so that the wetted surface of the tower wall could be measured. It was found that the exterior ring surfaces were wetted slightly more than the interior surfaces, and that below the top layer of packing the wall was wetted to a larger extent than the packing. Since a perforated-plate distributor was used for the feed, the percentage of both ring and wall surface wetted decreased from the top toward the bottom of the packing. The liquid tended to flow away from the center of the tower toward the walls, where it apparently formed rivulets.

The percentage of the total packing surface wetted increased steadily as the liquid feed was increased up to the flooding point, as shown by Fig. 84. In this figure D_t represents the inside diameter of the column and Z the distance from the top of the packing. Just below the flooding point the packing was incompletely wet, but the fraction wetted increased abruptly to 100 per cent as flooding occurred. Although the data shown by Fig. 84 were taken with no gas flowing through the packing, separate experiments showed that below the flooding point countercurrent flow of gas had no effect either on the volume of liquid adhering to the packing or on the wetted area. The average thickness of the liquid layer on the packing, obtained by dividing the holdup by the wetted area, was therefore dependent on the liquid rate but not on the gas rate.

These results emphasize the point that the surface of the packing is only partially wetted, even though the liquor is flowing over the packing with a uniform distribution over the cross section of the tower.

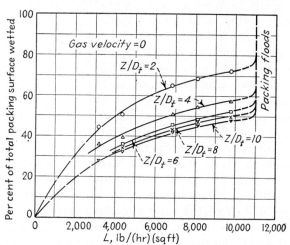

Fig. 84. Variation of wetted area with liquid rate in packed tower, using 0.5-in. rings in a 3-in.-diameter tower fed with water. (*Data of Mayo, Hunter, and Nash.*)

The third factor listed above as influencing the factor a, namely, the extent to which the wetted surface may be inactive owing to stagnant liquid films at points of contact of the packing, has not been the subject of a quantitative study. Mayo, Hunter, and Nash estimate that some 10 per cent of the actual wetted surface may be inactive for this reason.

Later extensive measurements of liquid holdup in tower packings[221] have confirmed that below the flooding point gas-flow rate has no measurable effect on the volume of liquid held by the packing. The liquid rate does have an effect, however, as shown by Fig. 85. For liquids other than water, values read from Fig. 85 should be corrected in direct proportion to the 0.1 power of the viscosity and inversely as the 0.78 power of liquid density and the 0.3 power of the surface tension.

An experimental study of liquor distribution over various packings has been reported by Baker, Chilton, and Vernon.[17] These investigators passed air and water through a number of common packing materials and collected the water draining from the bottom at each of several small cross-sectional areas of the column. By using various heights of packing they obtained data indicating the liquor distribution over the tower cross section at different distances from the top. In all tests they used a water rate of 500 lb./(hr.)(ft.²).

With packing particles large compared to the tower diameter, these data confirmed the previous results of Kirschbaum[247] in showing a marked tendency for the liquor to concentrate near the walls and for the center of the column to run nearly dry. With large ratios of tower diameter to packing size, Baker, Chilton, and Vernon[17] found that this tendency was negligible. For example, in a 6-in. column into which water was fed through a single central-point inlet over ½-in. broken-stone packing, the

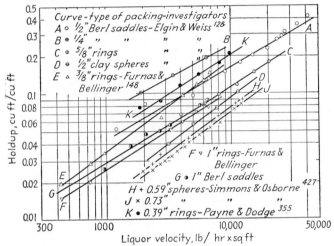

FIG. 85. Liquid holdup in packed towers (water). (*From Jesser and Elgin.*)

water had assumed a fairly uniform distribution at a point 4 ft. from the top, and the distribution did not change appreciably between points 4 and 15 ft. from the top, as shown by Fig. 86. When the same packing was used in a 3-in. column, however, over 70 per cent of the water was found in the 25 per cent of the cross section adjoining the wall, at the same elevation 4 ft. from the top. Using a ¾-in. broken-stone packing, definite segregation of water near the wall was observed when using the 6-in. tower.

Baker, Chilton, and Vernon[17] conclude that reasonably uniform liquor distribution is obtained with either regular or irregular solid packing materials, provided the ratio of tower diameter to packing size is greater than 8 to 1. When this ratio was greater than 8, they found that multiple-point liquor distribution at the top improved the uniformity of flow only in the top 4 ft. of packing of the 3- and 6-in. towers. With a 12-in. tower, using ¾-in. spheres and a central-point liquor feed, uniform distribution was not obtained until a depth of nearly 10 ft. was reached.

This result indicates the necessity of proper feed distribution in the larger towers, in which channeling due to poor initial distribution would be serious unless the tower were very tall.

In tests with fabricated rings and other hollow packing the results were similar to those obtained with solid packings in that the water was driven to the walls of the column if the ratio of column diameter to particle size

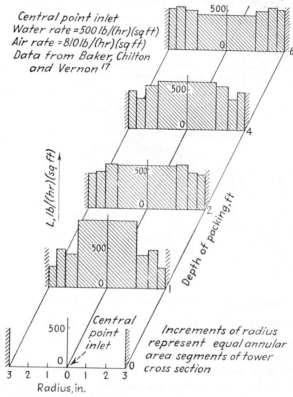

FIG. 86. Liquid distribution in a 6-in. column packed with ½-in. broken stone packing.

was small. With 1-in. Lessing rings in a 12- or 24-in. tower, fairly uniform liquor distribution was obtained, although multiple-point feed distributors were found to be necessary. Variations in gas or vapor velocity were found to have little effect on liquor distribution in the packing except as the flooding point was approached, when more even distribution was obtained. Changes in liquor rate over the ordinary range had but little effect on the uniformity of distribution.

In the absorption of a very soluble gas from a dilute mixture with other inert gases, it is sometimes desirable to operate with a very low liquor-gas ratio. With a reasonable gas rate the liquor rate per square foot of tower cross section will then be very low and uniform distribution of the liquor feed over the packing almost impossible to achieve. There seems to be no definite minimum liquid rate required to wet the packing; not all the exposed surface is wet under most operating conditions. As the liquid rate is decreased, the effective wetted area is reduced gradually, there being no definite point at which the packing ceases completely to be effective. Superficial liquid rates as low as 150 to 250 lb./(hr.)(ft.^{2}) have been employed in test absorbers.[3,253]

Complete wetting of the inside surface of a vertical copper wetted-wall tube has been obtained at water-flow rates as low as 56 lb./(hr.)(ft. wetted perimeter), according to Holmes,[201] and 70 lb./(hr.)(ft.), according to Dukler.[120] Complete wetting of a 2-ft.-wide, vertical, stainless-steel surface required a water flow of 300 lb./(hr.)(ft.).[119] Addition of a detergent did not reduce the minimum rate. According to Grimley[166] surface ripples on falling water films do not disappear until the flow rate has been reduced below 17 lb./(hr.)(ft.), corresponding to a Reynolds number of 25. Friedman and Miller[144] were able to keep their 1-in. glass tube wet at water rates as low as 2.3 lb./(hr.)(ft.).

One solution of the difficulty involved when the required liquid flow is small, as described above, is to recirculate the solution through the tower, returning several times as much liquor as is actually fed to the system. This has the disadvantage that the average liquor strength throughout the tower is increased, and the gas leaving is not in contact with fresh solvent. For a specified recovery the tower must then be larger. Another method is to flood the tower at intervals with accumulated feed liquor, allowing the gas to react with the liquor draining from the packing while another liquor-feed charge is collecting. This intermittent-feed method requires a special feed device. The problem does not occur with tray absorbers, which have a definite liquid holdup that is relatively independent of the liquid-flow rate.

Tour and Lerman[461] have studied the spread of water from a point source into a bed of packing so large that the liquid does not reach the tower walls. Based on the concept that each liquid stream has an equal chance of flowing outward toward the wall or inward toward the center line as it is divided in flowing over a packing piece, it would be expected that after several divisions of the initial stream the distribution of flow rate with radius would be Gaussian, *i.e.*, like a normal bell-shaped error curve. Although the assumption of equal opportunities for the stream to be deviated one way or the other does not represent the exact situation for the flow problem, the flow-distribution data were found to follow the error law, according to which

$$L = L_{av} \frac{cD_t'^2}{4Z} e^{-cR^2/Z} \tag{291}$$

The spreading constant c is different for different random packings. A few of the numerical values of c computed by Tour and Lerman[461] from the data of Baker, Chilton, and Vernon,[17] from the data of Hurter,[210] and from their own data are listed in Table XV.

TABLE XV.   PACKING CONSTANTS FOR UNCONFINED LIQUID DISTRIBUTION ACCORDING
TO TOUR AND LERMAN[461]

Type of packing	Packing size, in.	Packing constant c, ft./in.^{2}
Berl saddles..........	0.5	0.23
	1.0	0.15
Raschig rings:		
Stoneware..........	0.5	0.21
Porcelain..........	1.0	0.25
Lessing rings..........	1	0.26
Clay spheres..........	0.5	0.33
	0.75	0.40
	1	0.31
Broken stone..........	0.25	0.17
	0.5	0.19
	0.75	0.22

c is a measure of the tendency for the liquid to spread horizontally. The larger c, the smaller the tendency for the liquid to spread.   One-inch saddles appear to be more effective in promoting spreading than 1-in. rings, and clay balls are less effective than either.   Some of the results indicate that spreading is less rapid in $\frac{3}{4}$-in. packings than in either larger or smaller sizes.   If separate liquid streams originating at neighboring point sources may be assumed independent of each other in their flow, *i.e.*, if the flow distribution from each has the same characteristics as though the other source were absent, then the distribution of liquid from an area source like a perforated plate or spray distributor may be found by the superposition principle.   According to this principle, the distribution for the area source is found by adding together the distribution functions from an infinite number of point sources.   Such calculations have been carried out by Tour and Lerman.[461]

Sherwood[414] has used the results of Tour and Lerman to compute the weighted average value of the absorption coefficient $K_L a$ for a non-uniformly irrigated packing.   The results are of interest for the case of absorption of a gas in a solvent which exerts no back pressure.   The more complicated problem of the effect of nonuniformity of liquid flow on the changes of the average gas composition over a packed bed when the liquid exerts an equilibrium back pressure does not appear to have been solved.

Additional data on liquid distribution have been reported by Uchida and Fujita.[467]

PRESSURE DROP THROUGH PACKINGS

Apart from general maintenance, the power required to force the gas through the packing frequently represents the principal operating cost of a packed tower. The power cost is proportional to the product of the gas rate and the pressure drop through the tower, so data on pressure drops at various gas rates are of first importance for design purposes. Since no thoroughly satisfactory method has yet been developed for correlating

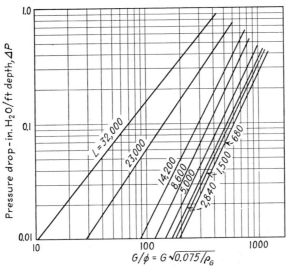

Fig. 87. Pressure drop for 2-in. ceramic Raschig rings (dumped). (*Data of Tillson.*)

the pressure drop for hollow commercial packing with the countercurrent flow rates of gas and liquid, the simplest and most accurate procedure for equipment design is to refer to plots of pressure drop against flow rate for the common commercial packings.[363] The most reliable data available are those of Tillson,[459] who has made extensive pressure-drop measurements in a 20-in.-diameter column, which is sufficiently large to minimize wall effects. Figure 87 summarizes his results for 2-in. Raschig rings, and Fig. 88 presents the data of Sarchet[400] for 1-in. rings.

The behavior of a packed column as the rate of gas throughput is increased is best described by reference to a plot of pressure drop vs. gas velocity, as shown by Fig. 88. For the dry packing, the pressure drop increases as the 1.8 power of the air mass velocity, indicating that the flow through the packing material is turbulent. Up to the gas velocity at "loading," approximately the same variation of ΔP with gas velocity is observed with countercurrent liquid flow. There is no sudden change in the appearance of a transparent column at the "loading point," but at this characteristic gas velocity the pressure drop begins to increase rapidly with increasing gas rate until a point is reached at which the liquid begins to build up in an agitated layer on top of the packing. The loading

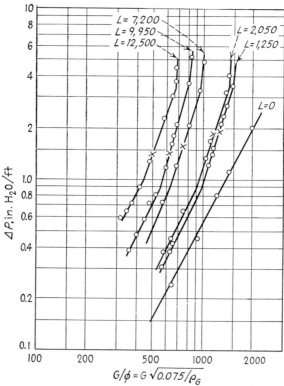

FIG. 88. Pressure drop for flow of water and air through 1-in. Raschig rings. (*Data of Sarchet.*) Points marked *x* indicate visual build-up of water over packing.

points are indicated by x's on the figure. Further increase in the gas rate causes the packing to "flood." This occurs at the point where the pressure-drop curve turns abruptly upward. The estimation of flooding velocities and their correlation with gas velocity will be discussed more thoroughly below. The pressure drop at the flooding point is found to lie between 1.5 and 4.0 in H_2O per ft. for many commercial packings.

PRESSURE DROP FOR DRY PACKING

Some degree of success has been achieved in correlating the pressure drop through a dry bed of packing with the gas-flow rate, the physical properties of the gas, and the dimensions of the pieces of packing. In

1931 Chilton and Colburn[77] presented an excellent survey of the data then available and added certain new data on various solid packings, mostly of small sizes. They pointed out that most of the pressure drop in the turbulent range is due to contraction and expansion losses and changes in direction as the gas flows through the irregular orifices formed by the packing particles, and estimate that only some 10 per cent of the drop is due to true skin friction. Contraction losses, expansion losses, and skin friction are all proportional approximately to the square of the gas rate, so an empirical correlation based on the Fanning equation for friction in pipes is not unsound. The relation is written

$$\frac{\Delta P}{Z} = \frac{2f'' A_w A_p A_L G^2}{\rho_G g_c D_p}\qquad(292)$$

where ΔP = pressure drop, p.s.f.

G = mass velocity of the gas based on the total cross section of the tower, lb./(hr.)(ft.²)

g_c = gravitational conversion factor, 4.169×10^8 (lb. mass)(ft.)/(lb. force)(hr.²)

ρ_G = gas density, lb./ft.³

D_p = nominal size of a packing particle, ft.

Z = depth of packing, ft.

A_w = wall-effect factor, dimensionless

A_p = correction factor for hollow packing

A_L = correction for the wetting of the packing by the solvent circulated; unity for dry packing

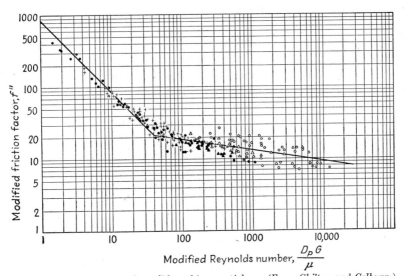

FIG. 89. Friction factors for solid packing particles. (*From Chilton and Colburn.*)

Figure 89 shows the data presented by Chilton and Colburn. The dimensionless friction factor f'' is plotted against a modified Reynolds number D_pG/μ, following the method of plotting commonly used for friction in pipes. The passage diameter is replaced by the nominal particle size. Equation (292) is dimensionally sound, and any self-consistent set of units may be employed. In English units, μ for air at 70°F. is 0.0436 lb./(ft.)(hr.).

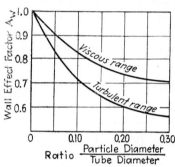

FIG. 90. Wall-effect factor [Eq. (292)].

The figure shows the correlation to be not particularly good, some deviations from the curve being almost 100 per cent in the turbulent range. It must be remembered that the plot includes data[9,34,59,147] on irregular-shaped broken particles as well as geometrically regular shapes such as spheres. The two branches of the curve are typical of friction-factor plots, the left branch with a negative slope of 1.0 representing the viscous-flow region in which ΔP varies as the first power of G, the first power of μ, inversely as the square of D_p, and independently of ρ_G at constant linear velocity.

The wall-effect factor has been measured by Furnas[147] for solid particles but may be taken as unity for hollow packing. Furnas' data are shown by Fig. 90. For the same nominal packing size, the space in a bed of hollowing packing is larger, and the factor A_p is accordingly smaller than unity. Figure 91 shows White's correlation of data[499] for hollow rings and saddles.

It seems probable that, if the hydraulic mean diameter of the channels between the packing instead of the nominal particle size could be introduced into the Fanning equation, the correlation of pressure-drop data for different packings could be improved. If it is assumed that the gas flows through a number of parallel, continuous, winding channels which, together, account for the entire open space in the bed, the hydraulic radius of these channels may be calculated from the surface area of the packing and the free space between the solid particles. If Z' is the length of the average channel, n the number of channels per square foot of bed cross section, D_e the equivalent diameter of the channel, and ϵ the fraction free void space in the packing,

$$\text{Volume of channels} = n\frac{\pi D_e^2}{4}Z' = \epsilon Z \qquad (293)$$

and

$$\text{Surface area of channels} = n(\pi D_e)Z' = a_v Z \qquad (294)$$

Dividing Eq. (293) by Eq. (294),

$$\frac{D_e}{4} = \frac{\epsilon}{a_v} \qquad (295)*$$

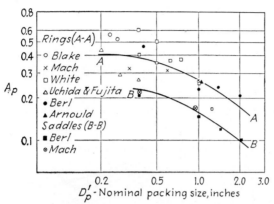

FIG. 91. Correction factor A_p for rings and Berl saddles.

The free cross section available for gas flow is smaller than the total bed cross section. If S' is the average free cross section and S is the total cross section,

$$S'Z = \epsilon SZ \qquad (296)$$

from which it follows that the average linear velocity in the bed, u', is related to the superficial velocity u by

$$u' = u \frac{S}{S'} = \frac{u}{\epsilon} \qquad (297)$$

Introducing these relationships into the following form of the Fanning equation:

$$\frac{\Delta P}{Z} = 2f'u'^2 \frac{\rho_G}{D_e g_c} \qquad (298)$$

* Alternately, if the packing pieces are solid spheres, the surface exposed per cubic foot of packed space is $n'\pi D_p^2$, where n' is the number of spheres per cubic foot. The volume of the solid per cubic foot is $n'(\pi D_p^3/6)$, and the total volume, assumed equal to 1 ft.³, is also $n'(\pi D_p^3/6)/(1 - \epsilon)$. The specific surface area of the packing is, therefore,

$$\frac{n'\pi D_p^2}{n'(\pi D_p^3/6)/(1 - \epsilon)} \qquad \text{or} \qquad \frac{6(1 - \epsilon)}{D_p}$$

From Eq. (295) it follows that $D_e = \frac{2}{3} D_p(\epsilon/1 - \epsilon)$.

we obtain

$$\frac{\Delta P}{Z} = \frac{f'}{2} \frac{G^2}{\rho_G g_c} \frac{a_v}{\epsilon^3} \tag{299}*$$

the Reynolds number, $D_e G'/\mu$, becomes

$$\frac{D_e G'}{\mu} = \frac{4G}{a_v \mu} \tag{300}*$$

Figure 92 shows pressure-drop data for a variety of hollow and solid packing materials plotted on the basis indicated by Eqs. (299) and (300).

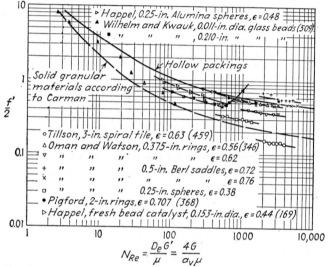

FIG. 92. Correlation of pressure drop across dry packing for air. (*Method of Carman.*)

The correlation of the data is only slightly better than that indicated by Fig. 89, which was based on the nominal particle size and did not include the packing porosity or the packing surface, except indirectly through the correction factor A_p. It is apparent that not all the effects of packing dimensions have been allowed for in the variables plotted. Oman and Watson[346] were able to reduce the scatter of their own data for solid

* In terms of the particle diameter D_p for solid spheres

$$\frac{\Delta P}{Z} = 3f' \frac{G^2}{\rho_G g_c} \frac{1 - \epsilon}{D_p \epsilon^3} \tag{301}$$

$$N_{Re} = \frac{D_e G'}{\mu} = \frac{2}{3} \frac{D_p G}{\mu} \frac{1}{1 - \epsilon} \tag{302}$$

For the viscous region, where f' is inversely proportional to N_{Re}, the pressure drop varies with the porosity and the packing size according to the group $[(1 - \epsilon)^2/\epsilon^3]$ $(1/D_p{}^2)$, in agreement with the Carman-Kozeny equation[66,254]. Other functions of porosity have been developed theoretically[169] and empirically.[20,53,267-269,346] granules and small hollow packings by changing the exponent on the fraction void space in Eq. (299) to 1.7 rather than 3. Equation (299) and Fig. 92 give the same pressure drop as their correlation at $\epsilon = 0.64$, which is approximately equal to the values of void space for many open packing materials. According to their correlation, the pressure drop for packings having ϵ greater than 0.64 is higher than that predicted by Fig. 92 and conversely. Although Oman and Watson were successful in correlating their own data when the exponent on ϵ was changed, their results do not agree with the few data on large packings which have been published by other investigators and for which values of ϵ and a_v were given. The open circles on Fig. 92 represent data for stacked 3-in. spiral tile obtained by Tillson.[459] These points fall even below the line of Carman, owing to the fact that changes in direction are much less frequent when the gas stream flows through the continuous channels of stacked packing than the tortuous channels of random packings. Packings like 3-in. tile can be stacked in layers either in the continuous-flue arrangement or with the tiles located randomly in each layer. The specific packing surface and the free space would be expected to be nearly the same for both arrangements, but the number of changes in direction and, consequently, the pressure drop would be smaller for the continuous-flue arrangement.

Figure 92 cannot be used for estimating pressure drop unless the porosity ϵ and the specific surface a_v are known. If the friction factor f' is constant, $\Delta P/Z$ is proportional to a_v/ϵ^3. Values of a_v and ϵ are listed by various manufacturers of packing, but the actual values for the installed packing depend on the method of filling the tower. Lobo, Friend, Hashmall, and Zenz[286] find that a_v/ϵ^3 is smaller if the packing is dropped into a tower filled previously with liquid than if it is poured dry into an empty container. The latter procedure is used by most manufacturers for measuring a_v and ϵ. If the packing is shaken after having been placed in a tower by the wet method, a_v/ϵ^3 may be higher than the manufacturer's figure, however. Table XIII lists typical values of packing constants. Lobo *et al.* give the following empirical equations for estimating ϵ for commercial ceramic Raschig rings:

For the "dry-packed" method,

$$\epsilon = 1.046 - 0.658M \tag{303}$$

for the "wet-packed, shaken" method,

$$\epsilon = 1.009 - 0.626M \tag{304}$$

for the "wet-packed, unshaken" method,

$$\epsilon = 1.029 - 0.591M \tag{305}$$

where

$$M = \frac{1 - (C/B)^2}{(AB^2)^{0.017}} \tag{306}$$

where A = ring height, in.

B = outside diameter of ring, in.

C = inside diameter of ring, in.

These equations should not be used for $M < 0.2$ or for very thick-walled or solid cylinders. a_v increases in proportion to $1 - \epsilon$ as a given mass of packing is consolidated.

For any grid packing, Johnstone and Singh[231] give the following equations for the dry pressure drop:

$$\frac{\Delta P}{Z} = \frac{2f''' \rho_G u'^2}{g_c D_e} \tag{307}$$

$$f''' = 0.08 \left(\frac{D_e u' \rho_G}{\mu} \right)^{-0.2} + 0.52 \left(\frac{D_b}{D_s} \right)^{1.5} \left(\frac{D_e}{D_g} \right)^{0.75} \tag{308}$$

where u' = actual velocity based on open or free cross section of grid packing

D_e = equivalent diameter of passages, equal to four times free volume divided by the area of the flat surfaces parallel to the mean flow direction

D_b = thickness of grid members

D_g = height of individual grid members

D_s = horizontal clearance between grid members

Illustration 31. Estimate the pressure drop across a 1-ft.-deep bed of 2-in., dry, carbon Raschig ring packing in a 31.5-in.-diameter column at G = 1000 lb./(hr.)(ft.²) of air at 70°F. and 1 atm., (*a*) using the method of Carman (Fig. 92), and (*b*) using the method of Chilton and Colburn (Fig. 89). The dimensions of the packing pieces are such that a_v = 28.4 ft.²/ft.³ and ϵ = 0.707.

Solution.   *a.* The Reynolds number is computed according to Eq. (**300**).

$$N_{Re} = \frac{4G}{a_v \mu} = \frac{(4)(1000)}{(28.4)(0.0436)} = 3230$$

From Fig. 92,

$$\frac{f'}{2} = \frac{\Delta P}{Z} \frac{g_c \rho_G}{G^2} \frac{\epsilon^3}{a_v} = 0.50$$

from which

$$\frac{\Delta P}{Z} = \frac{(0.50)(1000)^2(28.4)}{(0.0747)(4.169 \times 10^8)(0.707)^3} = 1.27 \text{ lb./(ft.²)(ft.)}$$

or

$$\frac{\Delta P}{Z} = \frac{(1.27)(12)}{(62.3)} = 0.25 \text{ in. H}_2\text{O/ft.}$$

b. According to the Chilton-Colburn method, the Reynolds number based on the nominal packing size is

$$\frac{D_p G}{\mu} = \frac{(2)(1000)}{(12)(0.0436)} = 3820$$

From Fig. 89

$$f' = \frac{1}{2} \frac{\Delta P}{Z} \frac{\rho_G g_c}{G^2} \frac{D_p}{A_w A_p A_L} = 11$$

From Fig. 91, $A_p = 0.17$; from Fig. 90, $A_w = 0.80$ at $D_p/D_t = 0.063$.

$$\frac{\Delta P}{Z} = \frac{(2)(11)(1000)^2(12)(0.80)(0.17)}{(0.0747)(4.169 \times 10^8)(2)} = 0.58 \text{ lb.}/(\text{ft.}^2)(\text{ft.})$$

or

$$\frac{\Delta P}{Z} = \frac{(0.58)(12)}{62.3} = 0.11 \text{ in. } H_2O/\text{ft.}$$

c. The pressure drop actually observed during a test made under these conditions was 0.27 in. H_2O per ft. As shown by Fig. 87, Tillson[459] also observed $\Delta P/Z = 0.27$ in. H_2O per ft. using very similar ceramic rings ($\epsilon = 0.816$)

Illustration 32. Estimate the pressure drop across a 1-ft.-deep bed of wood-grid packing at a superficial air mass velocity of 2000 lb./(hr.)(ft.²). The air temperature is 70°F., and the total pressure is 1 atm. The grids are made from parallel boards on edge 0.25 in. thick, 4 in. wide in the direction of gas flow, spaced 1.25 in. apart.

Solution. The volume of the space between adjacent boards per inch of distance along the grids is $(4)(1.25) = 5$ in.³; the surface parallel to the flow direction area is $(2)(4) = 8$ in.; and the equivalent diameter D_e is $(4)(5)/(8) = 2.5$ in.

Since $D_b = 0.25$ in., $D_s = 1.25$ in., and $D_g = 4$ in.,

$$\mu = (0.018)(2.42) = 0.0435 \text{ lb.}/(\text{ft.})(\text{hr.}); \qquad \rho_G = 0.075 \text{ lb.}/\text{ft.}^3$$

$$G' = \frac{(2000)(1.25 + 0.25)}{1.25} = 2400 \text{ lb.}/(\text{hr.})(\text{ft.}^2)$$

$$N_{Re} = \frac{D_e G'}{\mu} = \frac{(2.5)(2400)}{(12)(0.0435)} = 11,500$$

$$f''' = (0.08)(11,500)^{-0.2} + 0.52 \left(\frac{0.25}{1.25}\right)^{1.5} \left(\frac{2.5}{4}\right)^{0.75} = 0.0449$$

$$\frac{\Delta P}{Z} = \frac{2f''' \rho_G (u')^2}{g_c D_e} = \frac{2f''' G'^2}{\rho_G g_c D_e}$$

$$= \frac{(2)(0.0449)(2400)^2(12)}{(0.075)(4.169 \times 10^8)(2.5)} = 0.0792 \text{ lb.}/(\text{ft.}^2)(\text{ft.})$$

or

$$\frac{(0.0792)(12)}{62.3} = 0.0153 \text{ in. } H_2O/\text{ft.}$$

The measured value[231] of ΔP was 0.02 in. H_2O per ft. The calculation of the friction factor shows that the form drag, represented by the second term on the right of Eq. (308), accounts for the largest part of the friction. The pressure drop is low, however, compared to large-sized irregular packing materials. For example, 3-in. spiral tile, stacked staggered, would have a dry pressure drop of about 0.9 in. H_2O per ft. at the same superficial gas velocity.

PRESSURE DROP FOR WET PACKING

In the ordinary operation of a packed tower the liquid circulated over the packing occupies an appreciable fraction of the voids and reduces the mean free cross section open to passage of the gas. At a constant superficial gas velocity, therefore, the actual gas velocity is increased, and the pressure drop is appreciably greater than when the packing is dry.* This is in qualitative accord with the function of void space included in Eq. (299), although the prediction of the effect from the liquid holdup according to Eq. (299) gives values that are too low. The empirical correction factor A_L of Eq. (292) is plotted in Figs. 93 and 94 based on the

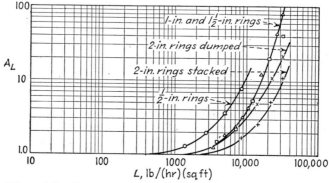

FIG. 93. Effect of liquid rate on pressure drop for ceramic Raschig rings. (*Data of Tillson.*)

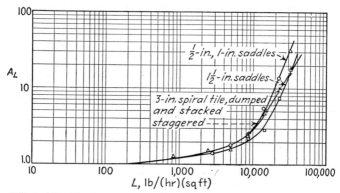

FIG 94. Effect of liquid rate on pressure drop for ceramic Berl saddles. (*Data of Tillson and Mach.*)

data of Tillson[459] for water and air. A_L represents the ratio of the observed pressure drop to that obtained at the same gas velocity with dry packing. The points at the extreme left represent packing wet and drained, with no water actually being circulated. At the extreme right the curves turn sharply upward and, if continued, would be asymptotic to the abscissa representing the flooding velocity. In general, A_L decreases with increased particle size and increases with liquor rate. It

---

* Uchida and Fujita[467] give empirical equations for the pressure drop as a function of the void space in the wet packing.

increases sharply as either gas or liquor velocity corresponding to flooding conditions is approached.

It should be emphasized that the data on A_L plotted in Figs. 93 and 94 are only for water and do not apply when the liquor circulated is viscous or has physical properties differing widely from those of water. Schoenborn and Dougherty[404] found that at a constant gas-flow rate the pressure drop was smaller, the higher the liquid viscosity.

Illustration 33. Estimate the pressure drop through 10 ft. of packing in a tower 1 ft. in diameter packed with 1-in. Raschig rings. Assume the gas to be air at 70°F. flowing at a superficial mass velocity of 325 lb./(hr.)(ft.²) and the liquor to be practically pure water flowing at the rate of 10,000 lb. per hr. per ft.² tower cross section.

Solution. Referring to Eq. (292), G is 325 and g_c is 4.77×10^8. The abscissa of Fig. 89 is $(1/12)(325/0.0436) = 242$; f'' is 17; and A_w is obtained from Fig. 90 as 0.74. A_p is 0.27 from Fig. 91, and A_L is 3.8 from Fig. 93. Hence

$$\Delta P = \frac{(2)(17)(0.74)(0.27)(3.8)(325^2)(10)}{(4.17 \times 10^8)(\frac{1}{12})(0.075)}$$

$$= 10.5 \text{ p.s.f.}$$

$$= (10.5)\frac{(12)}{62.3} = 2.0 \text{ in. } H_2O$$

According to the data of Sarchet,[400] as given by Fig. 88, the pressure drop should be $(0.35)(10) = 3.5$ in. H_2O.

ECONOMIC GAS VELOCITY*

When an absorption tower is to be designed for treating a given quantity of gas per hour, the cross-sectional area is determined by the superficial gas velocity which is chosen. The larger the gas velocity which is selected, the smaller will be the tower diameter but the larger will be the cost of pumping the gas against the tower pressure drop. The economic gas velocity and the economic tower diameter are the values which minimize the total annual cost, including the fixed charges of the tower as well as the cost of power for operating.

Regardless of the economic optimum gas velocity calculated by balancing costs, the gas velocity should not exceed the flooding velocity. In fact, a margin of 40 to 50 per cent of the flooding velocity should be allowed in designing equipment for continuous service.

Expressing the pressure drop across the packing as

$$\Delta P = \frac{b'ZG^s}{\rho_G} \tag{309}$$

the annual cost of power becomes

$$\frac{c_2'\theta b'ZG^{s+1}S}{\rho_G^2}$$

* The material in this section follows closely a development given by A. P. Colburn.[83]

where c_2' = cost of energy delivered to the gas stream, dollars per foot-pound

θ = hours of operation per year

S = cross-sectional area of packed section, ft.^{2}

The annual cost of the tower itself is

$$c_1 SZ$$

where c_1 is annual fixed charges in dollars per cubic foot of packed space (including cost of shell and erection). The total annual cost is

$$\text{T.A.C.} = \frac{c_2'\theta b' Z S G^{s+1}}{\rho_G{}^2} + c_1 SZ \qquad (310)$$

while the annual cost per unit of total gas throughput and per foot of tower height is obtained by dividing Eq. (310) by GSZ. The result is

$$\frac{\text{T.A.C.}}{(\text{Lb./hr.})(\text{ft.height})} = \frac{c_2'\theta b' G^s}{\rho_G{}^2} + \frac{c_1}{G} \qquad (311)$$

Differentiating with respect to G and setting the derivative equal to zero,

$$\frac{s c_2'\theta b' G^{s-1}}{\rho_G{}^2} = \frac{c_1}{G^2} \qquad (312)$$

or

$$G_{\text{opt}} = \left(\frac{c_1 \rho_G{}^2}{s c_2'\theta b'}\right)^{1/(s+1)} \qquad (313)$$

If we introduce the following more convenient terms,

$\phi = (\rho_G/0.075)^{\frac{1}{2}}$, the density correction factor

c_2 = cost of power, dollars per kilowatt hour

b = pressure drop, in. H$_2$0/ft., at G/ϕ = 1000 lb./(hr.)(ft.^{2})

and let $s = 2$, we obtain the final equation

$$G_{\text{opt}} = 2680 \phi^{\frac{4}{3}} \left(\frac{c_1}{c_2\theta b}\right)^{\frac{1}{3}} \qquad (314)$$

In terms of the optimum gas velocity, the total annual cost per unit of packed volume is found from Eq. (310)

$$\frac{\text{T.A.C.}}{\text{Ft.}^3} = c_1\left[1 + \frac{1}{s}\left(\frac{G}{G_{\text{opt}}}\right)^{s+1}\right] \qquad (315)$$

while at the optimum velocity G_{opt} the annual cost of fixed charges plus power per unit throughput and per transfer unit becomes

$$\frac{\text{T.A.C.}}{(\text{T.U.})(\text{lb./hr.})} = 2^{\frac{1}{3}}\frac{3}{2}\left(\frac{c_1{}^2 c_2'\theta b'}{\rho_G{}^2}\right)^{\frac{1}{3}} H_{OG}$$

$$= \frac{H_{OG} c_1{}^{\frac{2}{3}}(c_2\theta b)^{\frac{1}{3}}}{1787\phi^{\frac{4}{3}}} \qquad (316)$$

This shows that the cost of a given operation for fixed charges and power varies directly as H_{OG}, is slightly less sensitive to the unit investment charge, and varies only slightly as the unit cost of energy.

Both the flooding velocity and the economic velocity are related to the pressure drop. It is therefore not surprising that for many packings the two velocities are of the same order. The calculated optimum velocity may exceed the flooding velocity, however, for expensive packings which have low pressure drop, *i.e.*, high c_1 and low c_2. In this case the design obviously would not be made according to Eq. (314), but the gas rate should be fixed arbitrarily at about half the flooding velocity.

Illustration 34. Calculate the economic optimum gas velocity for a packed absorber handling essentially pure methane vapor at 70°F. and 10 p.s.i.g. The tower is filled with 1-in. ceramic Raschig rings, the liquid rate is 1000 lb./(hr.)(ft.²), operation takes place 8400 hr./year, electricity costs 1 cent per kilowatthour, and the annual cost of packing, shell, and erection is $3.60 per cubic foot (approximately 5-year amortization period).

Solution. From Fig. 88 the pressure drop for this packing at $L = 1000$, $G/\phi = 1000$ is 0.9 in. H_2O per ft. $= b$.

$$\rho_G = \frac{16}{359}\frac{492}{530}\frac{14.7 + 10}{14.7} = 0.0695 \text{ lb./ft.}^3$$

$$\phi = \sqrt{\frac{0.0695}{0.075}} = 0.963$$

$$G_{opt} = (2680)(0.963)^{4/3}\left[\frac{3.60}{(0.01)(8400)(0.9)}\right]^{1/3}$$

$$= 923 \text{ lb./(hr.)(ft.}^2)$$

This is below the flooding velocity for this packing, 1550 lb./(hr.) (ft.²), but above the loading velocity, 900 lb./(hr.)(ft.²)(compare Fig. 85). Operation would therefore be feasible at the optimum velocity, but it would be safer to reduce the velocity to the value at loading or below. At 775 lb./(hr.)(ft.²) velocity the annual cost of equipment and power per cubic foot would be

$$3.60[1 + (0.5)(^{775}\!/_{923})^3] = (3.60)(1.296) = \$4.66$$

compared with $5.40 per cubic foot of packing for operation at the optimum velocity. Since the volume of the packing required is considerably greater at this lower velocity, the total cost of power and packing is, of course, larger.

MAXIMUM ALLOWABLE LIQUID AND GAS RATES IN PACKED COLUMNS

The behavior of a packed column near the loading and flooding points is described in detail by Elgin and Weiss.[128] As the gas velocity is increased near the flooding point, the holdup of the liquid phase increases rapidly. For a ring-packed column irrigated with water, a layer of liquid appears on top of the packing at the flooding point, and the gas bubbles through this liquid layer. When oil is used instead of water, the liquid layer sometimes does not appear, but the liquid is entrained in quantity by the gas that flows from the packing. For Berl saddle packings, the liquid phase may become continuous at a point just above the packing support, or slugs of foaming liquid may surge through the packing, as observed by Bain and Hougen.[15]

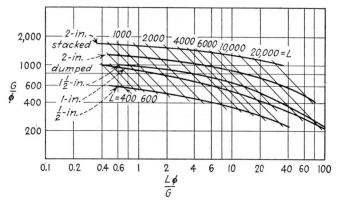

FIG. 95.   Loading velocities for Raschig ring packing.   (*Data of Tillson.*)

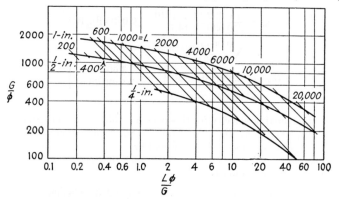

FIG. 96.   Flooding velocities for ceramic and carbon Raschig rings.

The flooding point has been defined as the gas velocity at which a liquid layer forms on top of the packing, as the second break point on a log-log plot of pressure drop vs. gas velocity, and also as the point at which the measured holdup increases abruptly. The visual flooding point is usually slightly less than that obtained from pressure-drop measurements (compare Fig. 88).

There is no marked change in the appearance of a column as the loading point is reached, though there is evidence that the liquid holdup increases when the gas velocity is greater than at loading. At this point the pressure drop through the packing begins to increase faster than in proportion to the 1.8 power of the gas rate.

For each liquid rate through the packing there is a definite gas rate at which loading will occur and another at which flooding takes place. These gas velocities are lower, the greater the liquid rate. Larger, more open packings flood at a higher velocity than smaller, more dense packings. Figures 95 to 98 are based on the data of Mach,[291] White,[499]

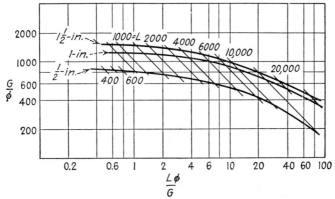

Fig. 97. Loading velocities for Berl saddle packing. (*Data of Tillson.*)

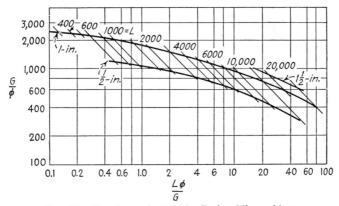

Fig. 98. Flooding velocities for Berl saddle packing.

Sarchet,[400] Bain and Hougen,[15] Sherwood, Shipley, and Holloway,[422] Uchida and Fujita,[467] Elgin and Weiss,[128] Schoenborn and Dougherty,[404] and Tillson,[459] using water and air in equipment filled with Raschig rings and Berl saddles. The plots are constructed with the gas velocity G in both ordinate and abscissa for easy use in design calculations. The ratio L/G is usually determined by the gas solubility and therefore is known before either G or L is known separately. This method of plotting has the disadvantage that the large effect of liquid velocity on the flooding velocity at high liquid rates is not apparent.   This behavior may be seen by following the lines of constant L on the figures.

Loading velocities for drip-point grid tile have been measured by Molstad, Abbey, Thompson, and McKinney.[326]   Data for other packings are given by Perry.[363]

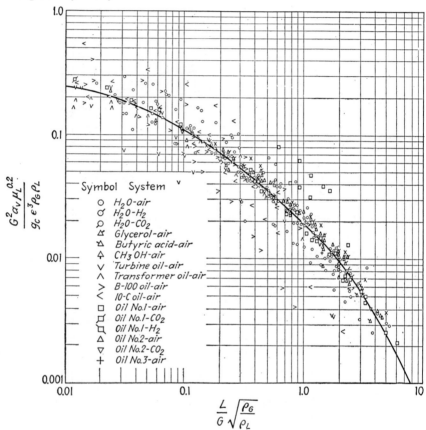

Fig. 99.   Generalized correlation of flooding velocities for packed towers.   (*After Lobo et al.*)

Theoretical discussions of flooding in packed equipment and a generalized correlation of limiting velocities with fluid properties and packing dimensions are given by Elgin and Weiss,[128] (compare Bain and Hougen[15]), Bertetti,[31] and by Sherwood, Shipley, and Holloway.[422] Sherwood *et al.* introduce the packing dimensions in a way very similar to that followed by Carman in correlating dry-pressure-drop data.   The square of the linear gas velocity through the mean free area of the packing is divided by the hydraulic mean diameter of the channels, resulting in the group $u^2 a_v / g_c \epsilon^3$. This may be thought of as the mean kinetic energy per pound of the gas divided by the hydraulic radius. This group is used in constructing Fig. 99, which also includes the viscosity and density of the liquid and the density of the gas. Variations in the surface tension of the liquid were found to have only a very slight effect. Figure 99 is taken from a paper by Lobo, Friend, Hashmall, and Zenz,[286] who conclude that average deviation of the experimental points from the curve is only 11.5 per cent when the measured values of a_v / ϵ^3 are used. This is a smaller deviation than that obtained when using the characteristics of the packing as reported by the manufacturers.

Figure 99 gives the same information for packings in general that Figs. 95 to 98 provide for packings of particular types. The generalized correlation also includes the physical properties of the fluids, while Figs. 95 to 98 are based on data taken using water and air. Each of the figures uses the ratio of the liquid-flow rate to the gas-flow rate in the abscissa. The gas rate but not the liquid rate appears in the ordinate. The fact that data for a variety of packings fall along a single line on Fig. 99 indicates that the lines on Figs. 95 to 98 for various packings could be superimposed by vertical displacement. Inspection of the figures shows that this is indeed true.

The fact that the line of Fig. 99 has a negative slope at high values of L/G means that in this region G^2 is being plotted against G, or that L is constant. In other words, as the liquid rate is increased, a point is reached at which a small increase in L is sufficient to prevent any gas whatever from flowing countercurrently through the packing. According to Fig. 99, this limiting value of L is proportional to $(\rho_L^2 \epsilon^3 / a_v \mu_L^{0.2})^{1/2}$.

Flooding velocities in vertical, empty tubes for countercurrent flow of water and air are given by Perry,[363] based on the data of Holmes.[201]

Illustration 35. Estimate the flooding velocity for a packed absorber filled with 1-in. ceramic Raschig rings. The calculation is to be made for the absorption of acetone vapor from air by water at 86°F. at 1 atm. total pressure. Data on the packing are $a_v = 58$ ft.^{2}/ft.^{3}, $\epsilon = 0.73$.

Solution. The solubility of acetone in water at 86°F. corresponds to $m = 2.64$. In order for substantially complete removal of the acetone to be possible, mG_M / L_M must not exceed unity. Choosing 0.7 as a satisfactory value, $L/G = (18/29)(m/0.7) = 2.34$. At 86°F., the gas density is approximately

$$\rho_G = \frac{28.9}{359} \frac{492}{546} = 0.0725 \text{ lb./ft.}^3$$

so that the gas-density correction factor becomes

$$\phi = \left(\frac{0.0725}{0.075} \right)^{1/2} = 0.984$$

$$\frac{L\phi}{G} = (0.984)(2.34) = 2.30$$

According to Fig. 96, $G/\phi = 1200$ lb./(hr.)(ft.²), and $G = (1200)(0.984) = 1180$ lb./(hr.)(ft.²) at flooding.

The calculation will be repeated on the basis of the generalized flooding correlation of Fig. 99.   The abscissa is

$$\frac{L}{G} \sqrt{\frac{\rho_G}{\rho_L}} = 2.34 \left(\frac{0.0725}{62.3}\right)^{\frac{1}{2}} = 0.08$$

From Fig. 99, the ordinate is 0.11, and

$$G = u\rho_G = \sqrt{\frac{0.11\rho_G\rho_L g_c\epsilon^3}{a_v\mu_L^{0.2}}}$$

$$= \sqrt{\frac{(0.11)(0.0725)(62.3)(4.17 \times 10^8)(0.73)^3}{(58)(1)^{0.2}}}$$

$$= 1157 \text{ lb./(hr.)(ft.²)}$$

The tower would be designed for a fraction of this velocity, say, $\frac{1}{2}$, or for the economic optimum velocity if the latter is not too high.   Choosing 600 lb./(hr.)(ft.²) as the gas velocity, the liquid rate would be $(600)(2.34) = 1403$ lb./(hr.)(ft.²). L is also cut in half, so $G = 600$ is somewhat less than half the new flooding velocity.   If desired, the conditions for operation at exactly one-half the flooding velocity can be computed by trial and error.

PLATE TOWERS

Plate towers are employed frequently in cases where the solvent and gas are noncorrosive and ordinary steel construction is satisfactory. Their use is borrowed from distillation practice, and they are operated very much like rectifying columns.   Where the scale of operation is large they are usually considered more economical and more certain in operating characteristics than packed columns.

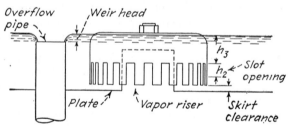

Fig. 100.   Diagrammatic sketch of plate and bubble cap.

The gas to be treated enters at the bottom, passing up through the tower and bubbling through the liquid on each plate.   The solvent is fed at the top and overflows from plate to plate through vertical overflow pipes connecting each plate with that next below.   Figure 100 shows a diagrammatic sketch of a plate and a single bubble cap.   Although some columns are built with a single large cap as much as 2 ft. in diameter, it is more common to have a number of small 3- to 6-in. caps on each plate. The gas from below enters the caps through the risers and, depressing the liquid level inside the caps, escapes into the liquid on the plate through the notches or slots in the periphery of each cap. The gas passes through these notches or slots at high speed and passes into, and up through, the liquor pool in the form of irregular bubbles of all sizes and shapes. The gas is broken up into bubbles so small that the interphase surface is large and rapid absorption is promoted. Furthermore, the violent agitation of the liquid and the escape of gas from its surface causes considerable foam and splashing, so that the gas space between the plates may operate as a spray chamber when the gas velocity is high.

A wide variety of caps is available, from small 3-in. caps with vertical $\frac{3}{16}$-in. slots, to large cast-iron hemispherical caps with 2-in. V notches designed for use with slurries which would clog the small slots.

The usual vertical spacing on the trays is from 6 in. to 3 ft., depending on the tendency of the liquid to foam and splash from one plate to the next and on the pressure drop across the tray.[244] In the larger columns the shell may be provided with manholes at each plate to allow occasional cleaning of the tower. Vertical tray spacings of 6 to 18 in. are usually employed in columns installed indoors, at some sacrifice in allowable vapor velocity.

The liquid-overflow pipes on successive plates are usually placed at alternate sides of the column. Thus the liquor overflowing from the plate above must pass across the plate to reach the overflow weir. Even with this arrangement there is some tendency for "short-circuiting" of the liquor directly from one overflow pipe to the next. This difficulty may be overcome at least partially by various baffle arrangements designed to guide the liquor across the plate.

In addition to caps, sieve and porous plates may be used to obtain a similar bubbling action. Sieve plates are metal sheets punched with small holes and must be held absolutely level or serious channeling will result. Furthermore, they operate properly only within a rather narrow range of gas velocities. Porous plates are used for aerating sewage and are extremely effective in breaking up the gas into fine bubbles. Except for deep liquid pools, most of the pressure drop is through the plate and not through the liquid, so the importance of maintaining the plate level is not so great as for the sieve plates. The pressure drop depends on the porosity and on the gas-flow rate. The overflow pipes dip into a liquid seal on each plate, but if the pressure drop through the plate is greater than the liquid head between plates, the vapor will go up the overflow pipes and the column cease to function. At a superficial velocity of 1.0 ft./sec. the pressure drop through a commercial "coarse" ceramic plate is about 25 in. H_2O, which means that the plates in the column would have to be spaced at least this far apart.

At high gas rates in a plate column the mechanical entrainment of liquid from one plate to the next becomes serious, resulting in a dilution of the liquor which has just been concentrated.   Data reported by Sherwood and Jenny[419] show the quantitative effect of entrainment of water by air in an 18-in. column with seven 4-in. caps placed on $5\frac{1}{4}$-in. centers. With a plate spacing of 9 in., the entrainment was found to be a little greater than 0.1 lb. water per lb. air at a superficial velocity of 3 ft./sec. It was shown that this amount of entrainment would have relatively little effect on the performance of the column (see also Rhodes[389]).   Additional entrainment data are given by Holbrook and Baker,[199] by Pyott, Jackson, and Huntington,[381] and by Peavy and Baker.[358]   It seems probable that entrainment plays no important role in plate-column absorbers at any gas velocity below that at which the column ceases to function because of priming (transport of foaming liquid up the column from one plate to the next) or because of liquor backing up the overflow pipes.

The equation of Souders and Brown[436] for the allowable superficial vapor velocity in a tray absorber was derived originally on the assumption that the frictional drag of the vapor on suspended liquid droplets must not exceed the average weight of a droplet.   Thus it was found that

$$u = K_V \sqrt{\frac{\rho_L - \rho_G}{\rho_G}} \qquad\qquad (317)$$

where u is the superficial gas velocity based on the entire tower cross section and expressed in feet per second, ρ_L is the liquid density in pounds per cubic foot, ρ_G is the gas density in the same units, and K_V is an empirical constant based on operating experience.   The constant is found to vary with the plate spacing and with the depth of the liquid over the tops of the slots in the bubble caps.   Carey[63] lists values corresponding to generally accepted commercial conditions and notes that general practice in the design of hydrocarbon absorbers involves the use of vapor velocities only 65 to 80 per cent of those used in similar distillation equipment.

Equation (317) may be looked upon as an empirical representation of conservative commercial practice.   For ordinary operating conditions, especially for absorbers, ρ_G is much smaller than ρ_L, and the latter does not vary very much.   The only quantities besides K_V in Eq. (317) which vary to a significant degree are u and ρ_G.   Introducing $\rho_L = 49$ lb./ft.^{3} as a representative average value of liquid density and multiplying by $\sqrt{\rho_G}$, Eq. (317) becomes

$$F = u \sqrt{\rho_G} = 7K_V \qquad\qquad (318)$$

The "F factor," $u \sqrt{\rho_G}$, has also been used for empirical correlation of allowable vapor velocities.   It is especially useful because in the turbulent range the pressure drop across the apparatus is a unique function of F. In this simplified form, the equation of Souders and Brown may therefore be looked on as an empirical representation of the column pressure drop which will ensure satisfactory operation.   A somewhat more useful quantity than the F factor for many absorption design problems is related to F as follows:

$$\frac{G}{\phi} = 986u \sqrt{\rho_G} \tag{319}$$

where G is the superficial vapor mass velocity and ϕ is equal to $\sqrt{\rho_G/0.075}$. Table XVI is based on Carey's[63] tabulation of K_V values.

TABLE XVI.   ALLOWABLE VAPOR VELOCITIES FOR BUBBLE-CAP ABSORBERS*

Plate spacing, in.	$u \sqrt{\rho_G}$ (or G/ϕ)			
	Liquid-seal depth, in.			
	0.5	1	2	3
6	0.15–0.3 (150–300)			
12	0.6–0.8 (590–780)	0.5–0.6 (490–590)	0.35–0.5 (350–490)	
18	1.0 (980)	1.0 (980)	0.8 (780)	0.6 (590)
24	1.3 (1270)	1.2 (1180)	1.1 (1080)	1.0 (980)
30	1.4 (1370)	1.3 (1270)	1.3 (1270)	1.2 (1180)
36	1.4 (1370)	1.4 (1370)	1.3 (1270)	1.3 (1270)

* Based on tabulation of Carey,[63] using $\rho_L = 49$ lb./ft.³

Illustration 36.   Estimate the allowable vapor velocity for a plate column having a plate spacing of 24 in. and a 1-in. seal depth, using the conditions of Illustration 35.
   Solution.   The conditions of the problem are $\rho_G = 0.0725$ lb./ft.³ and $\phi = 0.984$. From Table XVI, the allowable $G/\phi = 1180$ at these conditions.   This corresponds to $G = 1160$ lb./(hr.)(ft.²), which is very nearly equal to the flooding velocity of the packed towers.   The plate tower would therefore be smaller in diameter.

LIQUID FLOW ACROSS BUBBLE TRAYS

After the tower diameter has been chosen on the basis of the allowable vapor velocity, the tray design should be considered from the viewpoint of the resistance to flow of liquid across it.   For towers designed for handling large quantities of liquid, for example, low-pressure towers absorbing a slightly soluble gas, the limitations of liquid flow may be more serious than those which ordinarily fix the vapor velocity.   As the diameter of the tower increases, the quantity of gas which can be put through it at the same velocity and the quantity of liquid needed for treating the gas both increase as the square of the diameter.   The average width of the liquid-flow path increases only as the first power of the diameter, however, and the distance across the tray which the liquid must travel is larger.   The result is that the liquid may not be able to flow across without getting so deep at the entrance weir that the caps near this weir stop bubbling.   Part of the liquid may even leak through the risers of these caps, thus by-passing two trays.

Figure 101 is an idealized sketch of a plate which operates so near the point of instability that only a very few bubbles of gas flow from the cap

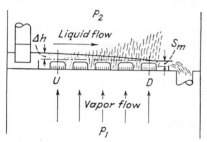

at U.   The difference in liquid depth, Δh, is needed to overcome the resistance to liquid flow across the rough, irregular channel as well as to provide the momentum required to carry the gas bubbles forward a short distance in the direction of liquid flow.   The pressure of the gas is uniformly equal to p_1 under the plate and to p_2 above the plate. The pressure difference is made up of the pressure drop through the dry

Fig. 101.   Idealized sketch of a plate operating near point of instability. (*From Kemp and Pyle.*)

plate as well as the pressure required to overcome the liquid head above the tops of the slots.   Expressing pressures in units of the equivalent depth of the clear liquid that flows across the plate, the total pressure drop at U and at D can be subdivided as follows:

$$\Delta p_U = \Delta p_D$$
$$\Delta h + S_m = \Delta p_0 + \psi S_m \qquad (320)$$

where Δp_0 = pressure drop at zero seal, *i.e.*, when the clear liquid surface
         is level with the tops of the slots
   S_m = minimum depth of clear liquid above the tops of the slots
   ψ = ratio of weight of aerated liquid over tops of slots at D to
         weight of clear liquid
  Δh = hydraulic "gradient"

This is the condition for stability of the operation of the plate.   When the value of Δh is greater than that indicated by Eq. (320), the upstream caps will not bubble; when Δh is less, all the caps will bubble.   If Δh is fixed, the pressure drop at zero liquid seal must exceed the value

$$\Delta p_0 = \Delta h + (1 - \psi)S_m \qquad (321)$$

for stable operation.   Depending on the value of ψ, stability can exist when Δp_0 is greater than or equal to Δh.   In actual practice ψ may be about 0.7, and for deep seals such as are often employed to provide a large cross section for liquid flow, $(1 - \psi)S_m$ may influence stability as much as Δh.

Figure 102 shows the data of Kemp and Pyle[241] for water and air using a plate section containing 16 rows of standard 3-in.-diameter bubble caps

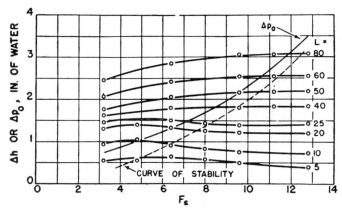

FIG. 102. Sample plot of effect of F_s on hydraulic gradient as used in preparation of liquid-handling capacity charts. Sixteen rows of 3-in. caps, flush, on $4\frac{1}{4}$-in. equilateral triangular centers; minimum seal constant at 1.0 in. (*From Kemp and Pyle.*)

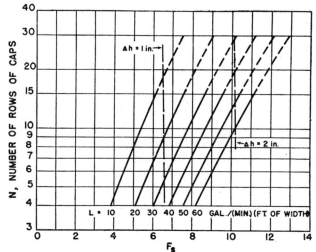

FIG. 103. Sample liquid-handling capacity chart for 3-in. caps, flush, on $4\frac{1}{4}$-in. equilateral triangular centers, at constant minimum seal of 1.0 in. (*From Kemp and Pyle.*)

located on 4.25-in. equilateral centers and with the depth of clear liquid at the discharge weir 1 in. above the tops of the slots. The figure shows both the values of Δh for this tray at various liquid and gas rates and also Δp_0. The gas velocity is expressed in terms of the slot F factor, *i.e.*, the product of the square root of the gas density by the gas velocity through the slots, assuming that the liquid surface inside the caps is depressed to the bottom of the slots.   For this particular arrangement of caps, the slot area (3.12 in.^{2}/cap) was 20 per cent of the active tray area.   The figure shows that stable operation is obtained below and to the right of the dashed line, along which Δh is at every point slightly less than Δp_0, in agreement with Eq. (321).   Similar data were also obtained using differ-

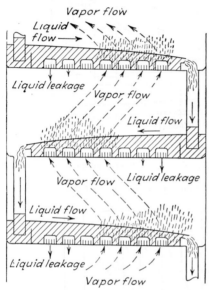

ent numbers of rows of caps in the liquid path, leading eventually to Fig. 103.   This shows the influence of both number of rows and liquid rate on the slot F factor required for critical stability.

When handling liquids other than water, Kemp and Pyle[241] recommend multiplying the value of F_s read from Fig. 103 by $\sqrt{\rho_L/62.3}$. This was arrived at empirically from tests using perchloroethylene, in which it was found that, at the same volumetric liquid-flow rate, Δh was independent of ρ_L, but Δp_0 was greater for the denser liquids. The pressure drop through the dry plate is obviously independent of liquid density, while the extra pressure drop owing to the presence of liquid around the slots is propor-

Fig 104.   Sketch of plates with excessive hydraulic gradient and backflow of vapor. *(From Kemp and Pyle.)*

tional to ρ_L.   The square-root effect which was found empirically is therefore qualitatively reasonable.   In general, denser liquids require larger gas rates for stability.

Figure 104 shows the appearance of a column which is operating in the unstable region.   The poor vapor distribution increases the pressure drop and decreases the efficiency of contact between vapor and liquid.   Stable operation usually can be obtained by increasing the pressure drop through the dry plate, increasing the spacing between caps, increasing the minimum seal depth, raising the caps off the plate, decreasing the number of rows of caps in the path of the liquid, and lowering the liquid flow per foot of plate width.   Additional data on the hydraulic characteristics of trays have been presented by Good, Hutchinson, and Rousseau,[163] and a correlation of such data has been attempted by Davies.[101]

COMPARISON OF PLATE AND PACKED TOWERS FOR GAS ABSORPTION

The relative merits of the plate tower and packed tower for a given purpose are properly determined only by comparison of the cost figures resulting from detailed designs for each type. However, it may be worth while to summarize in a general way their relative advantages and disadvantages. This may be done briefly as follows:

1. For acids and other highly corrosive solutions the packed tower is simpler and cheaper to construct than the plate tower built of glass, acid-resisting alloy steel, or other material.

2. The pressure drop of the gas in passing through the packed tower can be considerably less than for a plate tower designed for the same duty.

3. The plate column avoids serious channeling difficulties of gas and liquor streams.

4. The plate column can be designed to handle liquor rates which would flood the ordinary packing.

5. A plate tower fitted with manholes can be cleaned of accumulated sediment which would clog many packing materials and necessitate costly removal and refilling of the tower.

6. The plate tower lends itself readily to cooling of the liquor to remove a large heat of dilution, either by cooling coils on the plates or by external coolers through which the liquor is passed in flowing from one plate to the next.

7. The liquor holdup in the packed tower is considerably less than in the plate tower.

8. The total weight of the plate tower is usually less than for the packed tower designed for the same duty.

9. Temperature changes are apt to do more damage to the packed tower than to the plate tower.

Nomenclature for Chapter VII

a = wetted specific surface area of packing, ft.^{2}/ft.^{3}

a_v = specific surface area of dry packing, ft.^{2}/ft.^{3} packed volume

a_p = surface area of one piece of packing, ft.^{2}

A = height of Raschig ring, in.

A_p = correction factor for packing pressure drop for hollow packing, dimensionless

A_L = correction factor for packing pressure drop for wetting of the packing by the solvent, dimensionless

A_w = wall-effect correction factor for packing pressure drop, dimensionless

b = pressure drop through packing at G/ϕ = 1000 lb./(hr.)(ft.^{2}), in. H_2O/ft.

b' = constant in equation for pressure drop across packing [see Eq. (309)]

B = outside diameter of Raschig ring, in.

c = spreading constant for liquid distribution in packed tower, ft./in.^{2}

c_1 = annual fixed charges per cubic foot of packed space, dollars per year.

c_2 = cost of power delivered to gas stream flowing through packing, dollars per kilowatthour

c_2' = cost of energy for forcing gas through packing, dollars per foot-pound

C = inside diameter of Raschig ring, in.

D_b = thickness of wood grids, ft.

D_e = equivalent hydraulic diameter of channels through streamline packing

D_g = height of wood grid, ft.

D_p = nominal size of a packing piece, ft.

D_p' = nominal size of a packing piece, in.

D_s = horizontal distance between adjacent wood grids, ft.

D_t = inside diameter of packed column, ft.

D_t' = inside diameter of packed tower, in.

D_v = diffusivity, ft.²/hr.

f''', f'', f' = friction factors for flow of gas through packing, dimensionless [see Eqs. (308), (292), and Eq. (298), respectively]

F = "F factor," defined as $u \sqrt{\rho_G}$, (ft./sec.)(lb./ft.³)$^{1/2}$

F_s = "F factor" based on total area of slots, (ft./sec.)(lb./ft.³)$^{1/2}$

g_c = gravitational conversion factor = 4.169×10^8 (lb. mass)(ft.)/(hr.²)(lb. force)

G = superficial mass velocity of gas flowing through packing, lb./(hr.)(ft.²)

G_M = gas flow rate, lb. moles/(hr.)(sq. ft.)

G' = true average mass velocity of gas through channels in packing, lb./(hr.)(ft.²)

Δh = "hydraulic gradient," *i.e.*, difference in elevation of clear liquid surface at upstream and downstream zones on bubble tray, in. of liquid flowing

H_G = height of a transfer unit for the gas film, ft.

H_{OG} = height of an over-all gas-phase transfer unit, ft.

j_D = j factor for diffusion, equal to $(k_G P/G_M)(\mu/\rho_G D_v)^{2/3}$

k_G = individual gas-film transfer coefficient lb. moie/(hr.)(ft.²)(atm.)

$k_G a$ = individual gas-film absorption coefficient, lb. moles/(hr.)(ft.³)(atm.)

$k_G a$ = over-all gas-phase absorption coefficient, lb. moles/(hr.)(ft.³)(atm.)

$k_L a$ = over-all liquid-phase absorption coefficient, lb. moles/(hr.)(ft.³)(lb. mole/ft.³)

K_V = empirical constant in Souders and Brown equation for allowable superficial vapor velocity, ft./sec.

L = superficial liquid rate, lb./(hr.)(ft.²)

L_M = liquid rate, lb. moles/(hr.)(sq. ft.)

m = slope of equilibrium curve, dy_e/dx

M = quantity related to Raschig ring, dimensionless [see Eq. (306)]

n = number of channels through packing per square foot

N_{Re} = Reynolds number, $D_p G/\mu$

Δp_0 = pressure drop across bubble tray with the level of clear liquid at the top of the slots, in. of liquid flowing

ΔP = pressure drop across packing, p.s.f.

P = total pressure, atm.

R = radius of a point in a packed tower where the superficial mass velocity is measured, in.

s = slope of a log-log plot of packing pressure drop vs. gas mass velocity

S = cross sectional area of packing, ft.²

S' = average free cross-sectional area through the packing, ft.^{2}

S_m = minimum seal depth, *i.e.*, height of clear liquid over the tops of the slots at the overflow weir, in. of liquid flowing

u = superficial gas velocity, ft./hr.

u' = average linear velocity of gas through the channels through packing, ft./hr.

x = mole fraction solute in liquid

y_e = mole fraction solute in gas, in equilibrium with x

Z = distance from the top of the packing, or tower height, ft.

Z' = average length of channels through packing, ft.

ϵ = fraction of free void space within the packing, ft.^{3}/ft.^{3}

ϕ = correction factor for gas density, dimensionless, equal to $\sqrt{\rho_G/0.075}$

θ = hours of operation of packed column per year

μ = viscosity of gas, lb. mass/(hr.)(ft.)

μ_L = viscosity of liquid, centipoises

ψ = aeration factor, ratio of weight of aerated liquid over last downstream cap to weight of clear liquid at weir

ρ_G = density of gas, lb./ft.^{3}

ρ_L = density of liquid, lb./ft.^{3}

Problems

1. Estimate the pressure drop (in. H$_2$O) through a tower packed to a height of 30 ft. with (a) 1-in. broken quartz; (b) wooden grids, 2 in. high, staggered with a pitch of 0.625 in.; (c) 1-in. Raschig rings.

The tower cross section is 5 ft.^{2}, liquor rate 11,500 lb./hr., and air rate 3000 lb./hr. Temperature if 70°F., and total pressure 1 atm.

2. A gas containing 2 per cent acetone in air (by volume) enters an isothermal packed tower with a superficial velocity of 2.0 ft./sec. at 68°F. and 1 atm. Estimate the pressure drop (p.s.i.) through 15 ft. of ½-in. Raschig ring packing if the water velocity is (a) 1.5 times the theoretical minimum for 99 per cent absorption (based on infinite tower height); (b) 75 per cent the flooding velocity for the given gas rate.

3. Equation (313) for the optimum gas velocity in an absorber has been derived on the assumption that the H.T.U. is independent of G. The equation gives no information regarding the increase in cost when the gas velocity is different from the optimum value. Find an equation for the limits of G within which the annual cost does not exceed the minimum value by more than 10 per cent of the minimum value, the total quantity of gas treated being held constant. What is the ratio of the gas velocity to its optimum value at each of these limits if s equals 2?

4. An absorption tower is to be employed to recover 97 per cent of the acetone contained by an air-acetone mixture containing 2 mole per cent acetone, using water as a solvent. The gas to be handled flows at the rate of 3000 ft.^{3}/min. at 68°F. and 1 atm., and the water rate will be 1.20 times the theoretical minimum. Calculate the tower height, tower cross section, and theoretical fan power in horsepower if the tower is packed with 1-in. Raschig rings. Both gas and liquid rates will be 60 per cent of flooding rates for the same gas-liquid ratio.

CHAPTER VIII

PERFORMANCE OF ABSORPTION EQUIPMENT

The design of equipment for gas absorption, like that for many other unit operations, involves the use of data on the gas solubility or phase equilibria as well as kinetic information on the resistance to mass transfer at an interface. These data are incorporated in a design procedure which is based on energy and material balances as outlined in Chaps. V and VI. The quantity of solvent required and the maximum degree of recovery of the solute can be determined when the equilibrium data are known; no rate data are needed. The calculation of equipment dimensions is a different matter, however. Even though the equipment size can be computed in terms of the number of transfer units or theoretical trays required, the actual size is not known until the H.T.U. or the tray efficiency is available. The purpose of this chapter is to summarize the data of this type which have been reported in the literature. A generally useful theory for predicting such data for all types of equipment has not yet been developed, though notable steps have been taken in this direction.[157,473]

A general discussion of phase equilibria belongs to the field of thermodynamics and is outside the scope of this book, except for the solutions of hydrocarbons which flow through natural-gasoline absorbers and which are discussed in Chap. VI. Many of the important equilibrium data are available in standard handbooks.[212,259,363,408] Methods of extending meager data to the conditions appropriate for gas absorption have also been presented.[64,362] Reference may be made to an extensive review and catalogue of existing information on gas solubilities.[297]

DATA ON WETTED-WALL COLUMNS

The performance of wetted-wall columns is of interest not only because of the direct utility of the data in many practical problems of engineering design, but also because the results obtained with such columns throw light on the mechanism of mass transfer for the systems studied. The interfacial area is fixed and definite, as it is in almost no other continuous apparatus, and the turbulence conditions in the gas stream are standard and reproducible.

The theory applicable to this case and most of the available data for vaporization of pure liquids into air streams were discussed in Chap. III, where it was shown that the data are correlated by the equation

$$\frac{k_c D}{D_v}\frac{p_{BM}}{P} = 0.023\left(\frac{DG}{\mu_G}\right)^{0.83}\left(\frac{\mu_G}{\rho_G D_v}\right)^{0.44} \tag{108}$$

For the special case of a dilute mixture of solute gas and air at 1 atm. and 68°F., for which μ_G and ρ_G may be taken as for air, and p_{BM} may be taken as 1 atm., the following equivalent equations result:

$$k_G P = 0.00063\,\frac{D_v^{0.56}}{D^{0.17}}\,G^{0.83}, \qquad \text{lb./(hr.)(ft.}^2)(\text{mole fraction}) \tag{322}$$

$$H_G = 13.6\,\frac{D^{1.17}G^{0.17}}{D_v^{0.56}}, \qquad \text{ft.} \tag{323}$$

where D is the tube diameter in feet, G is in lb./(hr.)(ft.²), and D_v is in square feet per hour. For water evaporating into air,

$$H_G = 1.97(D')^{1.17}V_G^{0.17}, \qquad \text{ft.} \tag{324}$$

where D' is the tube diameter in inches and V_G is the average gas velocity in feet per second.

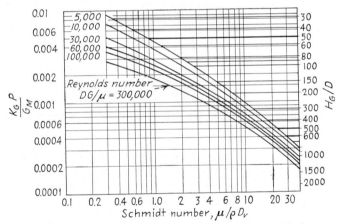

FIG. 105. Theoretical values of mass-transfer coefficient and H.T.U. for a wetted-wall column. (*After Boelter, Martinelli, and Johassen.*)

Figure 105 shows the ratio H_G/D, i.e., the H.T.U. expressed in pipe diameters, as a function of the Schmidt number for various values of the gas Reynolds number. This figure is based on the theoretical equation of Boelter, Martinelli, and Johassen,[40] which is similar to the theoretical relations discussed in Chap. III. It predicts values of H_G about 20 per cent larger than Eq. (108).

Equations (108) and (322) to (324) may be used for absorption or vaporization in a wetted-wall column with gas-film resistance controlling, provided that normal turbulence conditions exist, as in a long straight pipe. If extra turbulence is present owing to flow conditions at the gas inlet or to turbulence promoters in the gas stream, the values of k_G will be higher. Greenewalt[164] studied the effect of various inlet gas nozzles in the absorption of water vapor from air by sulfuric acid in a wetted-wall tower and found that for a given air flow there was a definite trend in k_G with the degree of turbulence induced by the inlet nozzle used. Certain

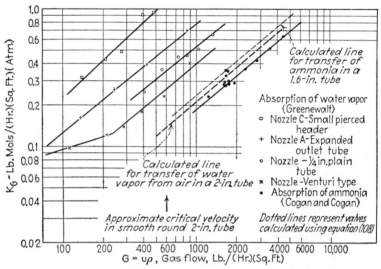

FIG. 106. Mass-transfer rates in wetted-wall tubes having turbulence promoters. (*Data of Greenewalt and Cogan and Cogan.*)

of his data are shown in Fig. 106, the four upper lines representing the data obtained with four different nozzles. The uppermost line was obtained using a header pierced with several small holes to supply the air at the bottom of the column. The lowest of the four curves was obtained with a venturi-type inlet nozzle, used to minimize entrance turbulence. The tower was only 31 in. long, however, and even this latter inlet tube induced enough turbulence to give results somewhat higher than predicted by Eq. (108), represented by the lower dotted line. Greenewalt's data for the venturi-type inlet nozzle show a marked break at a mass velocity of 230, corresponding to a Reynolds number of about 900. This is doubtless the critical velocity for the apparatus, the flow being streamline or viscous at lower air rates.

Figure 106 also shows the data of Cogan and Cogan[82] for the absorption of ammonia from air by water in a 1.6-in.-i.d. wetted-wall tower provided with a calming section to eliminate entrance turbulence effects. These data fall approximately 20 per cent below the line predicted by Eq. (108). The group of points at mass velocities from 1600 to 1700 represents a series of runs with varying ammonia concentrations in the gas, obtained at approximately the same Reynolds number. It was found that k_G increased with increasing ammonia concentration in the gas, an effect only partially explained by the decreased partial pressure of air in the film, p_{BM}.

No attempt will be made to present and correlate all the existing data on absorption in wetted-wall apparatus. Nevertheless, the work of Hollings and Silver[200] on absorption of NH_3 and SO_2 from air and city gas in water or various solutions, the work of Haslam, Hershey, and Kean[173] and of Haslam, Ryan, and Weber[174] on absorption of SO_2 from air in water, and the work of Krebs[256] on absorption of SO_2, Cl_2, and H_2S in water and various buffered solutions may be mentioned as being of interest to those doing further work in this area. As a general expression for the gas-film coefficient, Eq. (108) is doubtless the best available, although this relation applies only when there is a minimum of turbulence caused by the gas entering the tower.

Relatively little is known regarding the factors which influence the liquid-film resistance in wetted-wall towers, probably because this resistance usually is considerably smaller than that in the gas phase. In certain applications, however, such as absorption or stripping of slightly soluble gases, the liquid phase may contain the major resistance.

Theoretical treatment of the problem of absorption in the liquid layer is complicated by the presence of waves at the liquid surface. These are found at liquid Reynolds numbers larger than about 4, even though the flow of the film may have many of the characteristics of laminar motion up to a Reynolds number of 2100. While these waves have a negligible effect on the average thickness of the liquid layer,[144,243] which is determined by the velocity gradient at the solid boundary, and only a small effect on the rate of heat conduction through the entire liquid layer,[308] they are of paramount importance in determining the rate of gas absorption. The reason is that a thin layer of liquid near the liquid-gas interface has sufficient capacity to absorb substantially all the dissolved gas, the molecules of solute penetrating only a short distance into the liquid within the region where the waves have their greatest influence. As a result, the observed rate of absorption of a slightly soluble gas may be several times the rate expected from the simple diffusion theory.

Based on the assumptions that no waves are present at the surface, that the distribution of velocities through the film is parabolic, that the initial liquid concentration is uniform, and that the interfacial concentration is uniform, the equation for the diffusion of solute into the liquid[367] shows that

$$\frac{c_i - c_{av}}{c_i - c_0} = 0.7857 \exp(-5.121p) + 0.1001 \exp(-39.21p)$$
$$+ 0.0360 \exp(-105.6p) + 0.0181 \exp(-204.7p) + \cdots \quad (325)$$

where $p = D_L\theta/B_F^2$ and θ is the time of exposure of the liquid surface. A similar expression was derived by Vyazovov.[483] When the time of contact of the liquid layer with the dissolving gas is short enough, Eq. (325) reduces to

$$\frac{c_{av} - c_0}{c_i - c_0} = \sqrt{\frac{6}{\pi}} \left(\frac{D_L Z}{B_F^2 u_{av}}\right)^{1/2} \quad (326)$$

which may also be derived, as shown by Hatta and Katori,[177] by assuming that the solute diffuses into a semiinfinite layer of liquid which moves with a uniform velocity equal to the surface velocity of the actual layer. In terms of a mass-transfer coefficient based on the loganithmic-mean driving force, Eq. (326) is equivalent to

$$k_L = \sqrt{\frac{6}{\pi}} \sqrt{\frac{D_L u_{av}}{Z}} = \sqrt{\frac{6}{\pi}} \sqrt{\frac{D_L \Gamma}{\rho_L B_F Z}} \quad (327)$$

and to

$$H_L = \sqrt{\frac{\pi}{6}} \sqrt{\frac{B_F Z \Gamma}{\rho_L D_L}} \quad (328)$$

These equations are equivalent to Eq. (121) of Chap. III, where the film thickness B_F has been calculated from the equation for laminar flow along a vertical surface,

$$B_F = \left(\frac{3\mu\Gamma}{\rho^2 g}\right)^{1/3} \quad (329)$$

If the length of the surface, Z, is great enough or the mean velocity of flow, $\Gamma/\rho B_F$, small enough for the diffusing solute molecules to penetrate the liquid layer completely, all the terms on the right of Eq. (325) are negligible in comparison with the first. In this case the corresponding expressions for the loganithmic-mean mass-transfer coefficient and the H.T.U. are

$$k_L = 3.41 \frac{D_L}{B_F} \quad (330)$$

$$H_L = 0.29 \frac{\Gamma B_F}{\rho D_L} \quad (331)$$

Figure 107 shows the data of Grimley,[166] Hatta and Katori,[177] and Vyazovov[483] for the absorption of CO_2 in water flowing down vertical or inclined surfaces, as well as data obtained by Hodson,[196] Henley,[181] Miller,[324] and Richards[390] for absorption of oxygen or hydrogen in vertical columns. The three solid lines at the upper right of the figure correspond to Eq. (328) evaluated for a vertical surface and for oxygen absorption in water at 77°F. Within this range the theoretical value of H_L for a surface inclined at an angle θ from the vertical may be found by multiplying

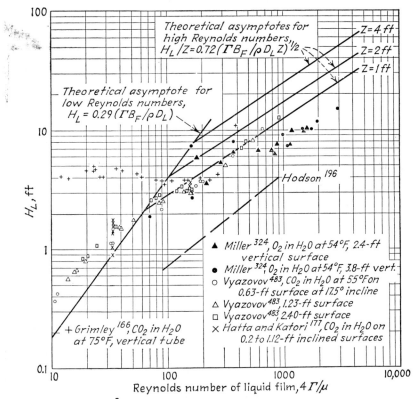

FIG. 107. Liquid-film resistance in absorption of gases in wetted-wall columns. Theoretical lines are calculated for oxygen absorption in water at 77°F.

the ordinate of Fig. 107 by $(\cos \theta)^{-\frac{1}{6}}$. Comparison of the experimental data with the theory shows that the resistance to mass transfer into the water films on vertical surfaces is substantially less than would be expected from the theory. At low flow rates the data of Grimley[166] indicate resistances even larger than would be expected from the theory. This discrepancy may be due to incomplete wetting of the surface by the liquid film at these low rates. The deviation of the data from the theoretical line is caused by the influence of surface waves, and these do not form immediately when the liquid begins to flow in film form. It may be expected, therefore, that the data for short surfaces will agree more closely with the theory than those for long surfaces. This is confirmed by the results obtained by Hatta and Katori[177] and by Vyazovov[483] using short inclined surfaces.

The theory predicts that the absorption coefficient is proportional to the square root of the liquid-diffusion coefficient. This has been confirmed experimentally in an approximate way for wetted-wall tubes[390] and, if true, indicates that, at a constant velocity of flow, k_L should depend on the liquid temperature in proportion to $(T/\mu)^{1/2}$. The liquid-film resistance expressed in terms of the equivalent partial-pressure driving force, H/k_L, may not vary so rapidly with temperature as does k_L itself, owing to the counter-balancing effect of the decrease in gas solubility with increasing temperature.

Illustration 37.   Estimate theoretically the value of the liquid-film H.T.U. for the absorption of oxygen in a water film at 77°F. which flows down a vertical surface 30 in. long at a rate of 100 lb./(hr.)(ft.) based on the width of the surface.   The diffusion coefficient may be taken as 8.0×10^{-5} ft.^{2}/hr. and the kinematic viscosity as 0.035 ft.^{2}/hr.

Solution.   From Eq. (329) the film thickness is calculated as follows:

$$B_F = \left[\frac{(3)(0.035)(100)}{(62.3)(4.17 \times 10^8)} \right]^{1/3} = 0.00074 \text{ ft.}$$

According to Eq. (327)

$$H_{L,a.m.} = \left[\frac{(\pi)(0.00074)(30)(100)}{(6)(62.3)(12)(8.0 \times 10^{-5})} \right]^{1/2} = 4.4 \text{ ft.}$$

At this flow rate the Reynolds number of the liquid layer is

$$N_{Re} = \frac{4\Gamma}{\mu} = \frac{(4)(100)}{(0.035)(62.3)} = 184$$

The calculated values agree with the upper lines on Fig. 107.   The experimental value would be perhaps one-half as great.

SPRAY TOWERS

While rates of evaporation of liquids from the surface of droplets have been shown to be rapid, even when the drop diameter is too large for the surface curvature to affect the vapor pressure, it is not easy to achieve efficient contact between a gas and a liquid in a spray chamber, especially when the absorption job is a difficult one requiring countercurrent action. Sprays are usually produced by forcing the liquid stream through a nozzle under pressure.   The drops which are formed may leave the nozzle with a velocity on the order of 50 ft./sec.   If they are small, the drops are quickly slowed down by air friction and may be easily carried out of countercurrent apparatus with the exit gas stream.   On the other hand, if the drops are large, they may quickly strike the walls of the chamber, since most nozzles produce a conical spray.

The problem of designing an efficient spray contactor reduces to that of providing sufficient interfacial area in the spray chamber in the form of drops of a size suitable for easy handling in the gas stream. Johnstone and Williams[233] have estimated the interfacial area present in a spray chamber into which the liquid droplets of the sizes produced by a com-

mercial spray nozzle are injected vertically downward along straight lines parallel to the axis of a countercurrent air stream. The smaller droplets slow down owing to air friction but are quickly swept up by the larger droplets. Even in this idealized situation, where the liquid is assumed not to strike the walls, the interfacial area of the spray per unit of tower volume decreases with increasing distance from the nozzle. Calculated interfacial areas for a liquid rate of 500 lb./(hr.)(ft.²) and countercurrent gas velocities of 5 to 10 ft./sec. ranged from 0.1 to 0.2 ft.²/ft.³. These results are surprisingly small, since an empty, wetted-wall cylinder 20 ft. in diameter would expose 0.2 ft.²/ft.³, and smaller tubes present even larger areas per unit of volume. Actually, the spray is produced almost at a point, and at the same total liquid rate the rate of coa-

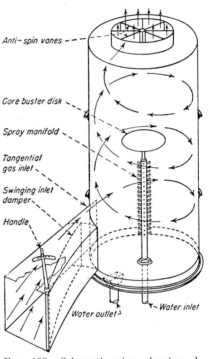

Anti-spin vanes

Core buster disk

Spray manifold

Tangential gas inlet

Swinging inlet damper

Handle

Water outlet

Water inlet

Fig 108. Schematic view showing elements of cyclonic-spray scrubber. (*From Kleinschmidt and Anthony.*)

lescence of droplets would be expected to be more rapid than that calculated, owing to the high spray concentration. This greater probability of collision is offset, however, by the influence of a parallel current of air which is entrained by the spray and which keeps the small drops from slowing down until the spray is dispersed.

Figure 108 illustrates a centrifugal spray apparatus in which the spray droplets are thrown to the wall by centrifugal force before they are swept out the top of the chamber by the gas stream.[250] This apparatus is more flexible in operation than one in which gravity is the only force promoting drop motion relative to the gas, and possible gas velocities may be as high as 2400 lb./(hr.)(ft.²) without excessive entrainment.[226]   The apparatus gives a crossflow type of contact, however, and is incapable of producing an effect greater than that of about one theoretical stage.

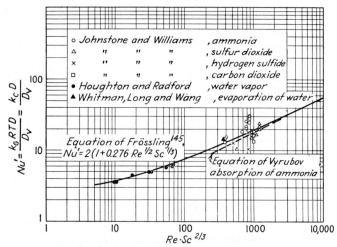

FIG. 109.   Gas-film resistance in the absorption of gases from air by single drops.

In spite of the difficulties which are encountered in the estimation of the interfacial area in a spray chamber, the problem does not appear to be insuperable, and after further information becomes available, it may be possible to employ in equipment design data on mass-transfer rates for individual drops.

Rates of evaporation of pure liquids from spherical surfaces were discussed in Chap. III.   Additional data are available on rates of absorption of gases by droplets, and Fig. 109 shows that, for situations in which most of the resistance is in the gas phase, these data agree with the correlation presented previously.

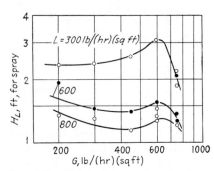

FIG. 110.   Rates of mass transfer in a countercurrent spray chamber. Desorption of oxygen from water at 86°F.; 31.5-in.-diameter spray tower; 52.5 in. from spray nozzles to air inlet; six Sprayco 5-B nozzles.

Absorption of slightly soluble gases in liquid droplets has usually been thought to proceed at a low rate, because of the low values of liquid-diffusion coefficient appropriate for the stagnant interior of a drop.   For a short exposure of a drop to a soluble gas, diffusion theory indicates that the change in concentration should be given approximately by

$$\frac{c - c_0}{c_i - c_0} = \frac{12}{\sqrt{\pi}} \left(\frac{D_L\theta}{D_p{}^2}\right)^{\frac{1}{2}} \tag{332}$$

This is in agreement with Bosworth's data[44] for CO_2 absorption in a spray of viscous sugar solution containing lime. The amount of CO_2 absorbed when the drops fell vertically from rest increased with the $\frac{1}{4}$ power of the distance fallen, and therefore with the $\frac{1}{2}$ power of the time of exposure, θ. Guyer, Tobler, and Farmer[168] absorbed CO_2 in drops of pure water which also fell short distances from rest. Their data conform approximately to Eq. (332). Other evidence indicates, however, that there is circulation of liquid within drops of nonviscous fluids, owing to surface friction caused by relative motion of a gas or owing to the persistence of motion origi-

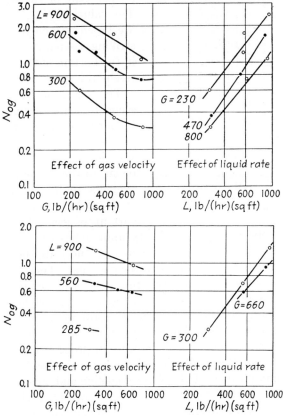

Fig. 111. Rates of mass transfer in countercurrent spray chamber. Absorption of ammonia in water: 31.5-in.-diameter spray tower; six Sprayco 5-B nozzles in 26-in. high tower.

nating in the spray nozzle. Thus, while it has sometimes been assumed that spray equipment would be especially unsuitable for the absorption or stripping of slightly soluble gases, recent data on spray chambers indicate that they may compare favorably with other types of equipment for such applications.

Figures 110 to 112 show data[369] for the absorption of ammonia, evaporation of water, and stripping of oxygen from water in a 31.5-in.-diameter spray chamber measuring either 26 or 52 in. from a concrete spray-collection basin in the bottom to the six 5-B Sprayco solid-cone nozzles at the top. Although the nozzles were inclined slightly toward the axis of the chamber to reduce the amount of spray striking the wall, the water running from the wall of the taller spray chamber amounted to 60 to 80 per cent of the water sprayed. The values of H_L given by Fig. 110 are based on analyses of the spray striking a separate collecting basin in the bottom of the tower and represent the spray effect alone.

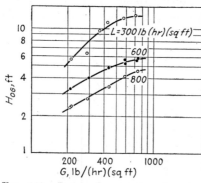

FIG 112. Rates of mass transfer in a countercurrent spray chamber. Humidification of air; 31.5-in.-diameter spray tower; 52.5 in. from spray nozzles to air inlet; six Sprayco 5-B nozzles. Note that the H.T.U. is based on an enthalpy driving force.

The value of H_L for the spray seems to decrease slightly at first as the air velocity is increased. After passing through a minimum value, H_L increases slightly, probably owing to the tendency of the spray droplets to be blown toward the walls of the chamber by the rising current of gas. The value of H_L decreases sharply as the gas velocity approaches the point where the holdup of spray in the chamber is increased and water begins to be carried out the top of the chamber with the exit gas. These data show also that at a constant gas velocity the number of transfer units due to the spray is approximately proportional to the rate at which liquid is sprayed into the chamber. It therefore seems that the interfacial area increases about in proportion to the volume of spray present in the chamber at any instant, the increased effect of coalescence of drops at higher spray pressures being offset by the smaller initial average drop size.

Data on humidification of air or water cooling and on ammonia absorption in the same spray apparatus are also shown by Figs. 111 and 112. In both cases the value of H_{OG} increases as the gas velocity increases, and the number of transfer units is approximately proportional to the liquid rate.

A reduction in the height of the spray chamber reduces the number of transfer units obtained for all three cases, but the reduction is proportionately less than the change in the volume of the chamber. A few typical figures are listed in Table XVII. It may be concluded from these data that the rate of interfacial transfer at the drop surface is most rapid just after the drops are formed at the spray nozzle.

TABLE XVII.   EFFECT OF SPRAY-CHAMBER HEIGHT ON NUMBER OF TRANSFER UNITS FOR OXYGEN STRIPPING AND AMMONIA ABSORPTION

L	G	N, number of transfer units		Ratio, $\dfrac{N \text{ for 26 in.}}{N \text{ for 52 in.}}$
		52-in. tower	26-in. tower	
		N_{OL}, oxygen stripping		
900	300	3.6	2.7	0.75
900	600	3.7	2.7	0.73
600	300	2.6	1.93	0.74
600	450	2.5	1.93	0.77
600	600	2.3	2.00	0.88
300	300	1.8	1.22	0.68
				0.76 av.
		N_{OG}, ammonia absorption		
900	300	2.0	1.30	0.65
900	600	1.3	1.00	0.77
600	300	1.24	0.74	0.60
600	450	0.92	0.66	0.72
600	600	0.78	0.63	0.81
300	300	0.49	0.30	0.61
290	340	0.72	0.45	0.63
				0.68 av.

It is interesting to compare the mass-transfer efficiency of a spray chamber with that of a duplicate chamber filled with a packing material. Table XVIII shows such a comparison for ammonia absorption and also for oxygen stripping.

It will be noted that a spray chamber is reasonably efficient for an operation in which the liquid-phase resistance predominates, in contrast to what has frequently been assumed. A taller packed tower probably would be considerably more efficient than a similar spray chamber, however, as appreciable countercurrent action evidently does not take place in a spray chamber. The gas appears to be so thoroughly mixed that it has nearly the same composition throughout. It seems very likely that spray chambers will be limited in application to those operations, such as air conditioning or deaeration of water, which require very few transfer units.

TABLE XVIII. COMPARISON OF SPRAY CHAMBERS AND PACKED COLUMNS FOR MASS TRANSFER WITH CONTROLLING LIQUID-FILM RESISTANCE

G	L	Spray tower	Packed tower, 2-in. rings
52-in. depth of packing		N_{OL} for oxygen at 86°F.	
450	900	3.6	5.0
450	650	2.7	5.3
450	350	1.5	5.7
26-in. depth of packing			
450	900	2.7	2.5
450	600	1.95	2.7
450	300	1.2	2.9
52-in. depth of packing		N_{OG} for ammonia	
500	500	0.7	1.35
800	500	0.6	1.13
500	1000	1.6	2.06
800	1000	1.1	1.72
26-in. depth of packing			
500	500	0.55	0.67
800	500	0.48	0.57
500	1000	1.18	1.03
800	1000	0.91	0.86

Experiments on a spray chamber of the centrifugal cyclone type, similar to that shown by Fig. 108, have been reported by Johnstone and Silcox.[230] Their apparatus was a scale model of a large smokestack. It consisted of a tapered cylinder 14 ft. high, varying in diameter from 28.5 in. i.d. at the bottom to 20.5 in. at the top. From 20 to 50 small hollow-cone spray nozzles were fastened to a vertical manifold 6 ft. long located on the axis of the chamber at the bottom. The gas entered the tower tangentially at the base through a rectangular nozzle 13½ in. high and 4½ to 12 in. wide. Sulfur dioxide was absorbed from air in 0.6N sodium carbonate solution. The spray nozzles were pointed in the direction of the spiraling gas stream, so that the spray droplets moved quickly to the walls, where they were collected and drained to the base of the tower. The amount of absorption which took place on the walls was determined in a separate series of experiments in which the spray nozzles were shut off and the alkaline liquid was distributed only over the wall. For the experiments in which the sprays operated, the number of over-all gas-phase transfer units was determined by assuming no back pressure of SO_2. The number of transfer units due to the spray alone was calculated by subtracting the number due to the wall from the total number observed. For the experimental conditions, the wall accounted for 0.12 to 0.26 out of a total of 0.63 to 3.4 units.

Figure 113 shows typical results of these experiments in terms of the number of transfer units for the spray as a function of the gas rate based on the tower cross section. Different numbers of nozzles were used, but all the nozzles operated at 67 ± 2 p.s.i.g. pressure. The agreement between the data obtained when using 35 nozzles concentrated on the lower half of the manifold and those obtained when the same number of nozzles was distributed uni-

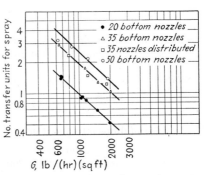

Fig. 113. Number of transfer units for centrifugal-cyclone-spray scrubber. (*Data of Johnstone and Silcox.*) Absorption of sulfur dioxide from air in sodium carbonate solution; tower diameter = 20 in.; liquid rate = 1 lb./min. per nozzle.

formly along the whole manifold suggests that there was negligible interference between adjacent sprays due to collisions between droplets. The data shown on Fig. 113, as well as data obtained with different widths of the tangential entrance nozzle and also data obtained by Johnstone and Kleinschmidt[226] using a similar tower 10.5-ft. in diameter, are correlated by the equation

$$N_{OG} = 62.8 \frac{LD_t P}{G_e^{0.8} S D_d N_{Sc}^{2/3}} + 0.0064 \frac{A_w P}{G_e^{0.37} S N_{Sc}^{2/3}} \qquad (333)$$

where a_w = wetted area of wall, ft.^{2}
P = total pressure, atm.
G_e = mass velocity through tangential entrance, lb./(hr.)(ft.^{2})
S = cross-sectional area of gas entrance nozzle, ft.^{2}
N_{Sc} = Schmidt number for gas, $\mu_G/\rho_G D_v$
D_t = diameter of spray chamber, ft.
D_d = mass-median diameter of spray droplets, microns

The first term in Eq. (333) gives the effect of the spray; the second, that of the walls. Values of D_d at 67 p.s.i. nozzle pressure are 175 and 595 microns, respectively, for nozzles having 0.046-in.- and 0.187-in.-diameter orifices. At constant pressure, D_d is approximately proportional to the orifice diameter.[369] Kleinschmidt[249] also discusses the estimation of the efficiency of dust collection in spray chambers.

Additional data on spray absorbers have been reported by Johnstone and Williams,[233] Kowalke, Hougen, and Watson,[253] Haslam, Ryan, and Weber,[174] Hixson and Scott,[194] Niederman, Howe, Longwell, Seban, and Boelter,[341] and Boelter and Hori.[39]

Illustration 38. Estimate the H.T.U. for evaporation of water from a uniform spray composed of droplets 175 microns in diameter, assuming the drops to fall vertically downward at their terminal velocities relative to a countercurrent stream of air. The mass velocity of the liquid is 1000 lb./(hr.)(ft.²) and that of the gas is 200 lb./(hr.) (ft.²).

Solution. The volume of each drop is

$$\frac{\pi}{6}(0.0175)^3 = 2.8 \times 10^{-6} \text{ cc.}$$

The number of drops introduced into the spray chamber per unit of time is

$$\frac{(1000)(28,310)}{(62.3)(2.8 \times 10^{-6})(3600)} = 4.51 \times 10^7 \text{ drops/sec.}$$

The area of each drop is $(0.0175)^2$, or 9.6×10^{-4} cm.², or 1.03×10^{-6} ft.². The total interfacial area introduced into the tower each second is $(1.03 \times 10^{-6})(4.51 \times 10^7)$ = 46.5 ft.²/sec.

The terminal velocity of a 175-micron water droplet in air at 70°F. is 1.9 ft./sec. This is the velocity relative to the rising gas, which moves at a velocity of 200/ (0.075)(3600), or 0.74 ft./sec. The downward velocity of the droplets relative to the chamber walls is, therefore, $1.9 - 0.74 = 1.16$ ft./sec., and the time required to traverse each foot of tower height is $1/1.16 = 0.86$ sec. The interfacial drop-surface area present in each cubic foot of tower volume is $(46.5)(0.86) = 40$ ft.²/ft.³

The Reynolds number of the falling droplet is

$$N_{Re} = \frac{(0.0175)(1.9)(30.5)}{0.155} = 6.54$$

where 0.155 is the kinematic viscosity of air in square centimeters per second. The Schmidt number for water vapor in air is 0.60, and the abscissa of Fig. 109 is (6.54) $(0.60)^{2/3} = 4.65$. From the figure, or from Fig. 22, $k_G R T D_d / D_v P$ is 3.2. Using 0.256 cm.²/sec. for D_v, we find

$$k_G = \frac{(3.2)(0.256)(1)}{(82.06)(298)(0.0175)} = 1.91 \times 10^{-3} \text{ g. mole/(sec.)(cm.}^2)(\text{atm.)}$$

or

$$k_G = \frac{(0.00191)(3600)(30.5)^2}{(454)} = 14.1 \text{ lb. moles/(hr.)(ft.}^2)(\text{atm.)}$$

We now calculate the product $k_G a$ and, finally, H_G.

$$k_G a = (14.1)(40) = 564 \text{ lb. moles/(hr.)(ft.}^3)(\text{atm.)}$$

$$H_G = \frac{G_M}{k_G a P} = \frac{200}{(28.9)(56.4)(1)} = 0.0123 \text{ ft.}$$

According to Fig. 112, H_G is approximately $52/(12)(2.5)$, or 1.7 ft., for these conditions, showing that the drops must be larger and less numerous than the calculated values, their velocities must be greater, or some of the gas must fail to contact the liquid.

AGITATED VESSELS

While gas may be dispersed through a liquid in a tank simply by forcing it through a porous gas sparger,[406] it is sometimes economical to increase the degree of dispersion and, consequently, the rate of solution of the gas by introducing it from the open end of a tube located just below a spinning propeller. Equipment of this type usually operates batchwise and is limited to the equivalent of one theoretical plate because of the thorough mixing of the liquid. It is especially useful, however, when a slurry or an emulsion must be treated with a gas.

The holdup of gas in the liquid has been measured by Foust, Mack, and Rushton[142] by observing the rise in the average liquid-surface level due to presence of the dispersed gas phase. For the dispersion of air in water by means of a turbine-type impeller simultaneously upward and downward, they found that the average contact time θ per foot of liquid depth varied according to the equation

$$\theta = c \left(\frac{P_v}{V_G}\right)^{0.47}, \quad \text{sec.} \tag{334}$$

where P_v = power input to impeller shaft, hp./ft.^{3} unaerated liquid volume

V_G = superficial air velocity, ft./sec.

c = 1.26 to 1.65

Observed contact times varied from 0.4 to 2.5 sec./ft. at superficial air velocities from 0.08 to 0.02 ft./sec., and Eq. (334) was found to apply approximately to vessels as large as 8 ft. in diameter as well as to small, laboratory-sized tanks. The calculated contact time per foot cannot exceed the reciprocal of the velocity of rise of individual bubbles.

It is desirable to operate with as large a contact time as possible in a situation where the process being carried out is limited by the finite rate of a chemical reaction. However, the data of Cooper, Fernstrom, and Miller[98] show that when liquid-phase diffusion is the limiting process, the rate of the process depends on agitator power and dimensions in a way which is somewhat different from the dependence of contact time on these variables as indicated by Eq. (334). These authors compared the performance of agitators on the basis of the observed rate of oxidation of sodium sulfite solution containing copper ions as a catalyst. The rate of oxygen absorption from air was found to be independent of the sulfite and sulfate concentrations below $1N$. Below a superficial "loading" velocity of approximately 0.1 ft./sec., the over-all gas-phase absorption coefficient was proportional to $V_G^{0.67}$ and to nearly the first power of the power per unit of liquid volume. Figure 114 shows the proportions of the apparatus tested, and Fig. 115 shows the data obtained with a vaned-disk impeller. The dashed line on the figure represents data obtained with simple flat-bladed paddles in tanks 9.5 in. and 8.0 ft. in diameter.

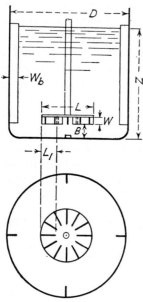

Fig. 114. Proportions and arrangement of apparatus used by Cooper, Fernstrom, and Miller for gas absorption in agitated vessel. $D/L = 2.5$; Z/D variable; $W/L = 0.1$; $B/D = 0.3$; $L_1/L = 0.35$; $W_b/D = 0.08$ to 0.10.

At low rates of energy consumption the flat paddle seems to give slightly superior performance, but an impeller of this type evidently is not capable of dispersing more than about 70 ft.³ gas per hr. per ft.²

Packed towers and agitated vessels may be compared with respect to power requirements and absorption efficiency if the over-all gas-phase coefficients of Cooper *et al.*[98] are converted to liquid-phase coefficients, by assuming that the oxygen dissolves in the sulfite solution without reaction according to the same gas-solubility relations that apply for oxygen in pure water. Carlson[64] has carried out such calculations. He finds that the highest absorption rate observed by Cooper *et al.* is equivalent to a liquid-phase coefficient of 5250 lb. moles per hr. per ft.³ per mole fraction O_2 in the liquid at a power input to the agitator shaft of 330 ft.-lb./min. in a 9.5-in.-diameter vessel. An additional 150 ft.-lb./min. was required to force the air to the bottom of the liquid, making the total power consumption 480 ft.-lb./min., exclusive of friction. In a packed tower operated to absorb oxygen in a large volume of water at the same rate, 1500 ft.-lb./min. would be required to pump the liquid to the top of the packing. So little gas would be absorbed that almost no power would be needed to force the air through the packing.

In this example the agitated tank has a slight advantage in size over a packed tower. In another case involving gases of greater solubility, however, the agitated vessel would be at a disadvantage, owing to the limited superficial gas velocities at which gas bubbles are able to rise through the liquid.

PACKED TOWERS

In spite of the large volume of experimental data which have appeared since 1935 on the mass-transfer characteristics of tower packings, no completely descriptive theory of interphase mass transfer in such apparatus has yet been developed. In order to simplify the situation as much as possible, most investigators have preferred to work with systems which undergo no chemical reaction during absorption or for which the chemical reaction in the liquid is so rapid and so complete that the influence of liquid-phase resistance is eliminated. It is not easy to select systems for study which meet the conditions of these two extremes. For example, even the reaction of carbon dioxide with concentrated sodium hydroxide solution appears not to proceed rapidly enough to

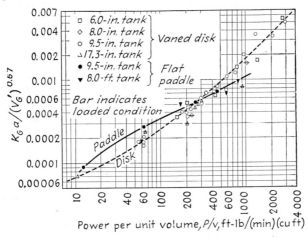

Fig. 115. Gas-absorption characteristics of mechanical agitator-dispersers. (*Data of Cooper, Fernstrom, and Miller.*) Absorption of oxygen from air into an aqueous solution originally 1.2N with respect to sodium sulfite. Average liquid temperature, 86°F. *Note:* On this figure V_G' is the superficial gas velocity in feet per hour.

eliminate diffusional resistance in the liquid,[455] and the absorption of chlorine in water[480] appears to be affected as much by the rate of production of hypochlorite and chloride ion as by the rate of diffusion across the interface.

The systems for which the most reliable data have been obtained thus far are those which involve no chemical reaction with the solvent whatever, such as the absorption or desorption of oxygen or hydrogen in water, or those involving a small equilibrium degree of completion of the chemical reaction, such as the absorption of carbon dioxide in water. Under the experimental conditions which are convenient in the laboratory, absorption of these slightly soluble gases is controlled by the liquid-phase resistance, and the most reliable data available apply to this condition.

One of the outstanding differences between packed absorbers and the empty, wetted-wall tubes to which diffusion theory has been applied so successfully, is the unknown wetted area in the former. This area must undoubtedly vary with the liquid-flow rate, causing the rate of mass transfer per unit volume of packing to vary with flow rates, owing both to the variation in the characteristics of fluid films surrounding the packing pieces and to the variation in the interfacial area. The data indicate clearly that the surface of contact of the two phases bears no simple relation to the total surface of the packing material. Workers in England[166] and in Holland[473] have preferred to allow empirically for the gradual change in wetted area as the liquid rate through the packing is increased. Most workers in this country have preferred, however, to report data obtained on packed columns more directly in terms of the volumetric transfer coefficient or the value of the height of a transfer unit, as discussed in Chap. V. There seems to be some justification for this latter procedure in the fact that rates of transfer in different packings do not vary in proportion to the total surface area of the packed beds.

The upper limit of the mass-transfer rate which can be approached when the packing is completely wet can be found from the data of Gamson, Thodos, and Hougen,[154] Wilke and Hougen,[511] or Taecker and Hougen,[450] who evaporated water into air from beds of wet porous cylinders or fabricated packing pieces. These data have been summarized in Chap. III and used in Chap. VI to estimate the effective packing area. Hurt[209] has reported similar results from experiments on the evaporation of naphthalene into air or hydrogen. While such data are useful for analyzing the mass-transfer characteristics of catalyst beds used for chemical reactions, they are of little practical value in connection with continuous absorbers, since there appears to be no way to estimate accurately the effective wetted area of irrigated packing.

In estimating the size of a commercial gas absorber, it is most desirable to have data on over-all mass-transfer coefficients for the system to be used obtained at flow velocities suitable for the design. Such data should be taken with apparatus of pilot-plant or semiplant size to avoid abnormal wall effects, the tower diameter being at least eight or ten times the packing size. In the absence of such information, however, it is best to estimate the over-all transfer resistance from the values for the separate films by using either of the equations

$$H_{OG} = H_G + \frac{mG_M}{L_M} H_L \tag{335}$$

$$H_{OL} = H_L + \frac{L_M}{mG_M} H_G \tag{336}$$

These equations do not apply to those cases in which the rate of absorption is limited by a slow chemical reaction; these special cases are considered in another chapter.

Gas-phase Resistance. The methods which have been used for experimental study of this case are (a) vaporization of pure liquids into an inert-gas stream as the liquid flows over the packing, (b) absorption of a gas in a liquid in which it is very soluble, and (c) absorption of a gas in a liquid with which it reacts chemically and from which no equilibrium back

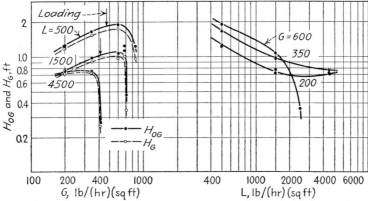

FIG. 116. Values of H.T.U. for absorption of ammonia in water—$\frac{3}{8}$-in. ceramic Raschig rings. (*Data of Fellinger.*)

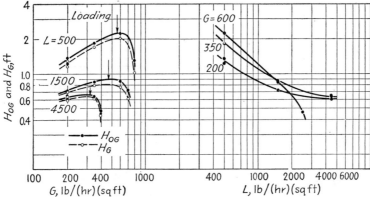

FIG. 117. Values of H.T.U. for absorption of ammonia in water—$\frac{1}{2}$-in. ceramic Raschig rings. (*Data of Fellinger.*)

pressure is exerted, owing to a rapid, irreversible chemical reaction. Ammonia absorption in water was thought at one time to constitute a case of pure gas-film resistance, owing to the extremely high solubility of this gas, but it now appears that this is only approximately true. Nevertheless, data on ammonia absorption are themselves reliable and extensive and will be presented in some detail.

Fellinger[139] determined rates of absorption of ammonia and reported

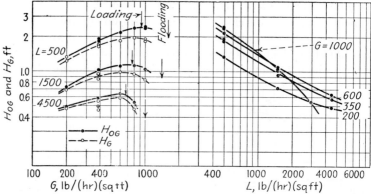

FIG. 118.   Values of H.T.U. **for** absorption of ammonia in water—1-in. ceramic Raschig rings. (*Data of Fellinger.*)

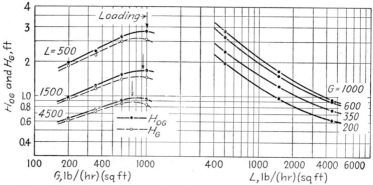

FIG. 119.   Values of H.T.U. for absorption of ammonia in water—1½-in. ceramic Raschig rings. (*Data of Fellinger.*)

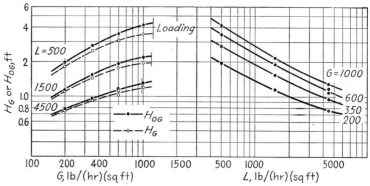

FIG. 120.   Values of H.T.U. for absorption of ammonia in water—2-in. ceramic Raschig rings. (*Data of Fellinger.*)

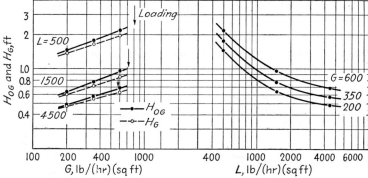

FIG. 121. Values of H.T.U. for absorption of ammonia in water—½-in. ceramic **Berl** saddles. (*Data of Fellinger.*)

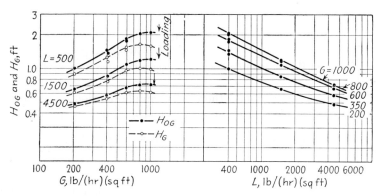

FIG. 122. Values of H.T.U. for absorption of ammonia in water—1-in. Berl saddles. (*Data of Fellinger.*)

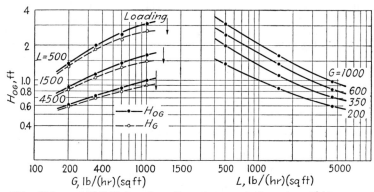

FIG. 123. Values of H.T.U. for absorption of ammonia in water—1½-in. ceramic **Berl** saddles. (*Data of Fellinger.*)

what are apparently the most complete and consistent data available. His results are shown by Figs. 116 through 124. The figures also show the values of H_G calculated from Fellinger's data by allowing for the liquid-film resistance as estimated from data on oxygen absorption taken under similar flow conditions.[418]

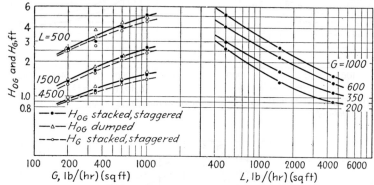

FIG. 124. Values of H.T.U. for absorption of ammonia in water—3-in. triple-spiral tile. (*Data of Fellinger.*)

According to Fellinger's data there is no simple relation between packing size and H_{OG}. This is brought out by the third column of Table XIX.

TABLE XIX. EFFECT OF PACKING SIZE ON H.T.U.

Packing	Total packing surface area, ft.²/ft.³	H_{OG} for NH₃ absorption in H₂O*	H_L for O₂ absorption from H₂O†
⅜-in. ceramic Raschig rings.............	148	1.01	0.95
½-in. ceramic Raschig rings.............	114	0.87	0.90
1-in. ceramic Raschig rings..............	58	1.00	0.95
1½-in. ceramic Raschig rings............	36	1.30	1.02
2-in. ceramic Raschig rings..............	29	1.62	1.17
3-in. triple-spiral tile....................	42	1.87	1.31
½-in. ceramic Berl saddles..............	141	0.81	0.91
1-in. ceramic Berl saddles..............	79	0.85	0.91
1½-in. ceramic Berl saddles............	50	1.17	0.80

* Based on $G = 400$ lb./(hr.)(ft.²), $L = 1500$ lb./(hr.)(ft.²); data of Fellinger.[139]
† Based on $L = 3000$ lb./(hr.)(ft.²); data of Sherwood and Holloway.[418]

In a few cases, such as the absorption of acid gases (except CO_2) in caustic solutions and the vaporization of water into air, it seems clear that all the resistance to transfer must be in the gas phase. If it were not for the fact that such experiments are difficult to carry out because the gas stream comes nearly to equilibrium with the liquid after passage through a relatively shallow bed of packing, data obtained in such experiments could be considered to represent the true gas-film resistance for irrigated packed beds. The shallow beds of packing which must be used to obtain measurable driving forces, however, probably cause abnormal end effects which influence the results.

Experiments in which water was evaporated into air using a 20-in.-diameter tower filled with 8 in. of 1½-inch ceramic Raschig ring packing were carried out by Sherwood and Holloway.[417] These data, as well as

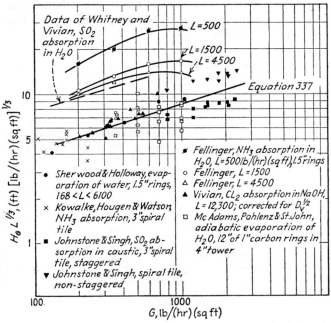

FIG. 125. Correlation of data on gas-film resistance to mass transfer for packed towers.

the results of Johnstone and Singh[231] from experiments in which sulfur dioxide was absorbed in caustic solution using 3-in. spiral-tile packing, the results of Vivian[479] on chlorine absorption in sodium hydroxide solution, and the data of McAdams, Pohlenz, and St. John[314] on adiabatic vaporization of water into air, are shown by Fig. 125. The data cover a range of liquid rates from 168 to 6100 lb./(hr.)(ft.²) and are represented by the equation

$$H_G = \frac{1.01 G^{0.31}}{L^{0.33}} \quad \text{ft.} \tag{337}$$

Within the accuracy of the data there was no effect of the packing dimensions. Equation (337) and the lower line on Fig. 125 are equivalent to the line recommended by Sherwood and Holloway.[417]

Figure 125 also shows values of H_G derived from Fellinger's ammonia-absorption experiments. According to these data the apparent gas-film resistance for ammonia absorption appears to be abnormally large; after correcting for the normally expected liquid-phase resistance, the remaining resistance is considerably greater than that expected from the evaporation and other gas-film data. Conversely, if the data on water evaporation and SO_2 or Cl_2 absorption in alkali are accepted for the gas-film resistance, then the liquid-phase resistance for ammonia is abnormally large. The discrepancy between gas-phase transfer data obtained from different sources is brought out by Table XX, which is based on some of the same data plotted in Fig. 125.

TABLE XX.   COMPARISON OF GAS-PHASE RESISTANCE TO MASS TRANSFER
DETERMINED BY DIFFERENT METHODS

Packing	Flow conditions	H_G, ft.	
		From experiments on vaporization of H_2O into air, or absorption followed by rapid chemical reaction*	From experiments on absorption of NH_3 in H_2O, corrected for liquid-film resistance normally expected†
1.5-in. rings......	$G = 500, L = 1500$	0.62	1.30
1.5-in. rings......	$G = 1000, L = 1500$	0.77	1.45
3-in. spiral tile...	$G = 500, L = 1500$	0.62	1.80
3-in. spiral tile...	$G = 1000, L = 1500$	0.77	2.40

* Calculated from Eq. (337).
† From data of Fellinger, as given by Figs. 119 and 121.

A part of the discrepancy between the H_G values listed in columns three and four of Table XX may be due to end effects, which are likely to have been present in some of the experiments leading to the data in column three, but it seems possible that the explanation is to be found partly in the chemical reaction which takes place between ammonia and water in the liquid phase. If the chemical reaction takes place at finite velocity, the equilibrium at the interface is that between dissolved but unreacted NH_3 and gaseous NH_3. As suggested first by Vivian and Whitney[480] and as discussed below, this phenomenon has the effect of reducing the available driving force below that expected from the usual equilibrium solubility data involving both reacted and unreacted forms of NH_3. This results in an abnormally large apparent value of H_L. Further work is needed before the situation will be understood thoroughly. In the meantime it seems wisest to recommend values of H_G read from Figs. 116 through 124 for use in conservative design practice.

According to the theory developed in Chaps. IV and V, changes in temperature are expected to have a negligible effect on H_G. Dodge and Dwyer,[111] Molstad, McKinney, and Abbey,[328] and Kowalke, Hougen, and Watson[253] have observed a slight increase in H_G with an increase in temperature, ranging from 0.2 to 0.7 per cent/°F. based on data for ammonia absorption in water.

For different gases H_G should be taken proportional to $(\mu_G/\rho_G D_v)^{1/2}$. Available data are contradictory. Johnstone and Singh[231] found that rates of absorption of SO_2 in NaOH solution, absorption of NH_3 in aqueous acetic acid, and evaporation of water into air from wood grids varied

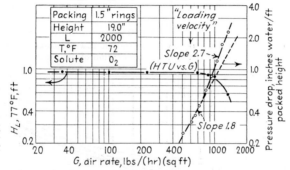

FIG. 126. Effect of gas velocity on liquid-film H.T.U. (*Data of Sherwood and Holloway.*)

according to $(\mu_G/\rho_G D_v)^{2/3}$. On the other hand, Sherwood and Holloway[417] report data obtained by Mehta and Parekh[317] on rates of vaporization of pure liquids, including water, into air in a 3.6-in.-diameter tower filled with 5 in. of $\frac{3}{8}$-in. porcelain Raschig rings; these data show that the exponent on the Schmidt group should be 0.17. An exponent of 0.5 is approximately in accord with the data of Gilliland and Sherwood[161] for vaporization in empty tubes and also with the theory outlined in Chap. III.

Sherwood and Holloway[417] summarize data from several sources on the effects of adding small amounts of wetting agents to the liquid flowing over a packing in order to depress its surface tension. They conclude that the reduction in surface tension has no effect on H_G but that the liquid-phase resistance is increased by the presence of large organic molecules at the interface.

Liquid-phase Resistance. Absorption or desorption of oxygen from water in packed towers provides an experimental technique which is relatively simple and accurate for the determination of H_L or $K_L a$. Extensive data obtained by Sherwood and Holloway[418] have been checked independently by several other investigators.[105,328,480,505] The original data are shown by Figs. 126 to 128. Below the gas velocity at which loading begins, the value of H_L is independent of G, as shown by Fig. 126. Figures 127 and 128 show how H_L varies with L for Berl saddles and Raschig rings, respectively.

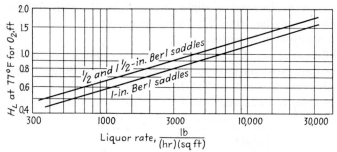

FIG. 127. Liquid-film resistance to mass transfer in towers packed with ceramic Berl saddles. (*Data of Sherwood and Holloway.*) Desorption of oxygen from water at 77°F.

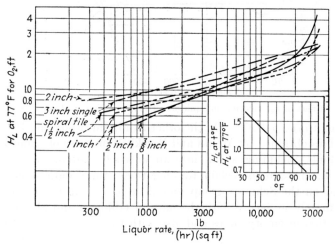

FIG. 128. Liquid-film resistance to mass transfer in towers packed with ceramic Raschig rings and tile. (*Data of Sherwood and Holloway.*) Desorption of oxygen from water at 77°F.

In contrast with the gas-phase resistance, H_L varies considerably with the liquid temperature. The variation may be allowed for through the equation

$$H_L = \frac{1}{\alpha}\left(\frac{L}{\mu_L}\right)^n \left(\frac{\mu_L}{\rho_L D_L}\right)^{0.5} \tag{338}$$

where the value of α varies from 80 to 550 for the different packings studied and n is between 0.22 and 0.46. A simpler method is to multiply the value of H_L from Figs. 127 and 128 by $e^{-0.013(t-77)}$, where t is the liquid temperature in degrees Fahrenheit. The small plot at the right of Fig. 128 shows the temperature effect graphically.

The effect of the chemical nature of the solute is taken care of by the factor $D_L^{0.5}$ in Eq. (338), which is based mainly on data taken with hydrogen. Although the exponent on D_L is somewhat uncertain, owing in part to lack of certainty in the values of D_L for liquid systems, the value 0.5 agrees with the theoretical effect for absorption of gases in falling liquid films. It is assumed that a fresh liquid surface is exposed as the liquid stream flows onto each piece of packing, after which the liquid film flows quietly along the exposed packing surface; hence Eq. (328) is applicable successively to each packing piece and leads to just the variation with D_L which is observed.

The liquid rates at which the lines on Figs. 127 and 128 deviate from straight lines are near the rates at which loading occurred in the experiments. The increase in H_L may be due to the tendency of the liquid to bridge across the spaces formerly filled with air. Normally an increase in L will lead to a tower of smaller diameter in order to handle the same liquid flow; but if H_L increases in proportion to L, the required tower height would increase proportionately as L increases and the required volume of packing would remain constant. Since more power would be required to lift the liquid to the top of the packing and for pumping the gas, operation of equipment at liquid rates greater than the break points would be uneconomical if the diffusional resistance is principally in the liquid.

Another type of ceramic packing which is useful because of the low pressure drop, high liquid-handling capacity, and reasonably low resistance to mass transfer is the ceramic drip-point grid. This closely resembles wood grids, which may be made as required from wood slats, but is fabricated from chemically inert ceramic material (see Fig. 82). Extensive data for such packing pieces have been reported by Molstad, McKinney, and Abbey,[328] and some of the results are given by Figs. 129 and 130. It is interesting to notice that the checker arrangement of the square grid units is nearly as efficient as the crossed-flue and the continuous-flue arrangements. In the checker arrangement only 59 per cent as many packing pieces are used, however, since the packing pieces in each layer are arranged in a checkerboard pattern, each packing piece being surrounded in a horizontal layer by four blank spaces and four other pieces, which it touches at the corners. The pressure drop for this arrangement was the lowest of any studied by these authors. The continuous-flue arrangement gave nearly the same H_L and H_{OG} values as the crossed-flue arrangement for both oxygen desorption and ammonia

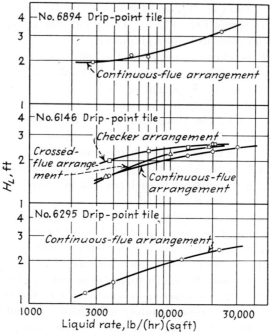

FIG. 129. Liquid-film resistance to mass transfer for ceramic grids. (*Data of Molstad, McKinney, and Abbey.*)   Absorption of O_2 in water at 77°F.

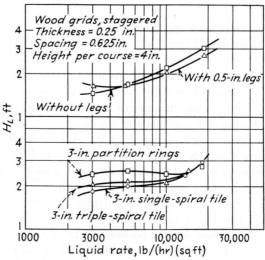

FIG. 130. Liquid-film resistance to mass transfer for wood grids, partition rings, and spiral tile. (*Data of Molstad, McKinney, and Abbey.*)   Absorption of O_2 in water at 77°F.

absorption, respectively, though the pressure drop for the continuous-flue arrangement was only 75 per cent as great.

Absorption of chlorine in water is an interesting case of predominating liquid-phase resistance which is in some respects abnormal owing to the influence of the chemical reaction which takes place between chlorine and water after the solute gas molecules have entered the liquid as molecular chlorine. The results of a study by Vivian and Whitney[480] are of interest in connection with the problems of purely physical absorption and are discussed as an intermediate case in Chap. IX.

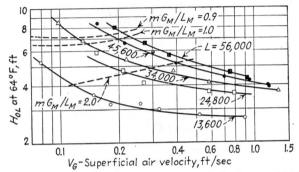

Fig. 131. Liquid-film resistance to mass transfer in packed columns at high liquid rates. (*Data of Cooper, Christl, and Peery.*)   Absorption of CO_2 in H_2O using 2-in. steel rings.

If a slightly soluble gas such as carbon dioxide is to be absorbed in water under conditions which will allow substantially complete removal from the gas, the liquid-gas ratio must be large enough to exceed m, *i.e.*, mG_M/L_M must be smaller than unity. At 68°F. and 1 atm. total pressure m is 1420 for CO_2 in water, and the ratio of weight flow rates, L/G, must exceed 880. Even at a gas mass velocity as low as 50 lb./(hr.)(ft.²) the liquid rate must exceed 44,000 lb./(hr.)(ft.²), and under these conditions special types of apparatus are sometimes used to achieve countercurrent action.[96]

If an ordinary packed column is operated at these abnormally high ratios of liquid- to gas-flow rate, the values of H_L predicted from Figs. 127 and 128 may be too low. Figures 131 and 132 show the data of Cooper, Christl, and Peery[97] for carbon dioxide absorption in water using a 30-in.-square tower filled to a depth of 86 in. with 2- by 2- by $\frac{1}{16}$-in. steel Raschig rings. Water rates ranging from 13,600 to 56,000 lb./(hr.)(ft.²) were employed, duplicating the conditions of commercial practice. Figure 131 shows that, when mG_M/L_M is less than unity, the value of H_{OL} may exceed 6 ft. at values of L ranging from 13,600 to 56,000, while Fig. 128 indicates that H_L should not be greater than 3 ft. for values of L up to 30,000. It might be expected that a part of the difference is due to the effect of gas-film resistance, which, according to Eq. (336), plays a part when $mG_M/L_M < 1$. As H_G should not exceed 0.1 ft. at these flow rates, according to Eq. (337), the explanation must be found elsewhere.

Cooper, Christl, and Peery[97] pointed out that the linear velocities of liquid and gas are approximately equal for the flow conditions of their experiment. Thus, at $L/G = 880$, V_L/V_G is found to be 1.06, based on the same channel cross section for both streams. Normally the linear gas velocity far exceeds the liquid velocity; at the loading velocity, for example, the gas tends to support the liquid in the packing. At these low gas velocities the gas does not have sufficient momentum to entrain the liquid but may be carried downward by the liquid. This reverse flow

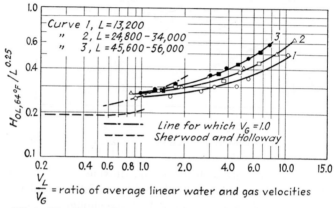

FIG. 132.   Effect of liquid-gas velocity ratio on H_{OL} for packed column.   (*Data of Cooper, Christl, and Perry.*)   Absorption of CO_2 in H_2O using 2-in. Raschig rings.

tends to mix the gas vertically within the tower and to destroy the desired countercurrent action. The H.T.U.'s plotted on Figs. 131 and 132 are computed on the assumption that the flow is countercurrent, and it is not surprising that the values of H_L are larger than the normal values. Figure 132 shows that the Cooper, Christl, and Peery data tend toward the results for the normal countercurrent case, shown by the horizontal dashed line, when the ratio of water to air velocity is small enough.

Resistance in Both Phases.   The system ammonia-water-air has been studied more frequently than any other in packed towers, owing probably to the relatively easy analytical procedure and to the comparatively simple experimental technique. The most reliable and complete set of data are those of Fellinger, which have already been presented by Figs. 116 to 124. The data of Molstad, McKinney, and Abbey,[328] Dodge and Dwyer,[111] Borden and Squires,[43] and Doherty and Johnson[112] agree approximately with those of Fellinger. Values of H_{OG} calculated from the experiments of Kowalke, Hougen, and Watson[253] are considerably lower, probably because of the effect of spray sections above and below the packing. Williams, Akell, and Talbott[513] reported results from a 6-in.-diameter tower filled with three 2-ft. sections of Fiberglas pads.

Most of the early work on ammonia absorption in water was directed toward the determination of the gas-phase resistance to mass transfer; it was thought that liquid-phase resistance would have no influence, owing to the very large solubility of ammonia. By plotting H_{OG} against mG_M/L_M, as suggested by Eq. (335), it was found[88] that at normal operating conditions (near $mG_M/L_M = 1$) H_{OG} may be much greater than

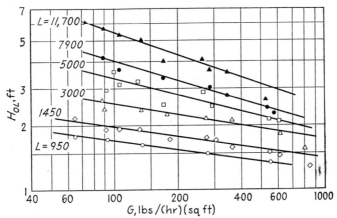

Fig. 133. Height of over-all liquid-phase transfer unit. Absorption of sulfur dioxide in water; 1-in. ceramic rings. (*Data of Whitney and Vivian.*)

H_G, the intercept on the vertical axis. As discussed above, the liquid-film resistance for ammonia appears to be higher than that for absorption of an inert, nonreactive gas.

Absorption of sulfur dioxide in water is a case of special interest, for the solubility of this gas is neither very high nor very low, and flow rates which are easy to achieve in a packed tower correspond approximately to mG_M/L_M equal to unity. Adams,[3] Haslam, Ryan, and Weber,[174] Jenness and Caulfield,[219] and Cantelo, Simons, Giles, and Brill[62] have investigated SO_2 absorption, but the most complete and self-consistent data available are those of Whitney and Vivian,[505] who used an 8-in. i.d. lead tower filled to a depth of 2 ft. with 1-in. ceramic Raschig rings. The liquor distributor and gas inlet device were designed to minimize end effects. Data were taken over a wide range of gas and liquid velocities and tower temperatures. Some of the results are shown by Figs. 133 and 134.

Whitney and Vivian utilized the fact that H_L had been found by Sherwood and Holloway[418] to be independent of the gas rate, while H_G

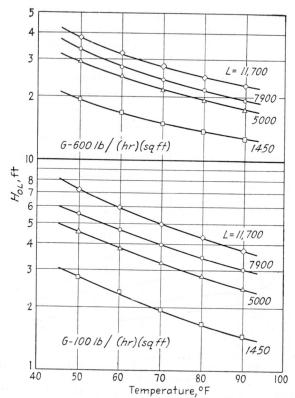

Fig. 134. Effect of temperature on height of over-all liquid-phase transfer unit. Absorption of sulfur dioxide in water; 1-in. ceramic rings. (*Data of Whitney and Vivian.*)

varies with both L and G, to compute values of the separate film resistances from their experimentally observed values of H_{OG}. The method is similar to the Wilson method[308] of analyzing over-all heat-transfer coefficients. In terms of H.T.U.'s the procedure is equivalent to the following:

From work on oxygen desorption[418] it is known that the liquid-film resistance is independent of the gas velocity up to the loading point. Thus,

$$H_L = \gamma L^n \qquad (339)$$

From Eq. (337),

$$H_G = \beta \frac{G^p}{L^q} \qquad (340)$$

Introducing these expressions into Eq. (336),

$$H_{OL} = \gamma L^n + \frac{29/18 \beta (1/m') L^{1-q}}{G^{1-p}} \qquad (341)$$

In this equation, m' is not the customary Henry's law coefficient, y_e/x, but is defined as the *slope* of the equilibrium curve, dy_e/dx. The derivation leading to addition of resistances according to Eq. (336) is valid if the equilibrium line is straight for the range of concentrations between the points (y_{e2}, x_2) and (y_1, x_{e1}); the equilibrium line need not go through the origin. The solubility data for SO_2 in water fulfill this more general condition.

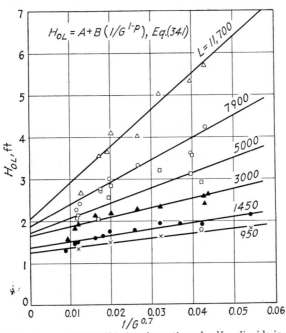

FIG. 135.   Analysis of over-all H.T.U.'s for absorption of sulfur dioxide in water at 70°F. using 1-in. Raschig rings.   (*Data of Whitney and Vivian.*)

At constant L and constant temperature, Eq. (341) is the equation of a straight line, the variables being H_{OL} and $1/G^{1-p}$. The correct value of p must be found by trial such that the data give a straight line when plotted. The best value of p for these data is 0.3, which corresponds very closely with the value in Eq. (337). Figure 135 shows some of the data plotted in this way. The final equation for H_{OL} is

$$H_{OL} = 0.37L^{0.18} + \frac{(29/18)(1.24)(1/32.4)L^{0.75}}{G^{0.7}} \qquad (342)$$

where $m' = 32.4$ at 70°F., $\gamma = 0.37$ ft., and $\beta = 1.24$ ft. The constant exponents on L in the two terms on the right are found by logarithmically cross-plotting slopes and intercepts from Fig. 135 against L.

From oxygen-absorption data, for 1-in. Raschig rings according to Fig. 128

$$H_L = 0.13L^{0.25}, \qquad \text{ft.} \tag{343}$$

which differs somewhat from the first term of Eq. (342). At $L = 1000$, H_L is 1.28 ft. according to the SO_2 data and 0.73 ft. according to the oxygen data; at $L = 10,000$ the corresponding figures are 1.94 ft. and 1.3 ft., respectively. Here also, as in the case of ammonia absorption, the chemical reaction of the solute with the solvent seems to make the apparent liquid-phase resistance abnormally large. The explanation for this deviation is to be found in the work of Vivian and Whitney on chlorine absorption, discussed in Chap. IX.

Based on the last term of Eq. (342), the following relationship for H_G is derived:

$$H_G = \frac{1.24G^{0.3}}{L^{0.25}} \tag{344}$$

which may be compared with Eq. (337), and with Fellinger's over-all H.T.U.'s for ammonia absorption, as shown by Table XXI. This com-

TABLE XXI. COMPARISON OF GAS-FILM H.T.U.'s FOR 1-IN. RASCHIG RINGS

Conditions	H_G, ft.		
	Whitney and Vivian,[505] SO_2 absorption	Eq. (337)	Fellinger,[139] NH_3 absorption
$G = 500, L = 1000$........	1.42	0.69	1.3
$G = 500, L = 5000$........	0.95	0.41	0.58

parison shows that the equation derived from the SO_2 experiments gives H_G values which are definitely too large. The accuracy of Eq. (344) is questionable, however, as the major resistance to SO_2 absorption was in the liquid film in the experiments which led to this equation. Nevertheless, there is approximate agreement with the individual gas-film H.T.U.'s derived from the ammonia data. Even greater emphasis may be placed on this agreement when it is realized that the constant in Eq. (344) was found to be substantially independent of temperature, in agreement with theory, while the constant in Eq. (343) was found to decrease with increasing temperature at nearly the same rate as that found by Sherwood and Holloway[418] for oxygen desorption.

Additional data for specific systems in which both resistances are important have been reported by Molstad and Parsley[329] for absorption of ethanol from air in water and by Scheibel and Othmer,[403] Othmer and

Scheibel,[350] and White and Othmer[501] for the absorption of acetone from air in water.

Illustration 39.   Estimate the value of H_{OG} for the absorption of acetone from air in dilute aqueous solution using a packed column filled with 1-in. ceramic Raschig rings.   The flow rates through the packing will be $G = 616$ lb./(hr.)(ft.^{2}) and $L = 1181$ lb./(hr.)(ft.^{2}).   The liquid temperature will be 86°F.

Solution.   a. Estimation of H_G for acetone-air mixture.   For 1-in. rings a conservative value of H_G is found from the data on ammonia-air mixtures given by Fig. 118 as

$$H_G = 1.2 \text{ ft.}$$

The value of $\mu_G/\rho_G D_v$ for mixtures of acetone and air is 1.59, whereas the value for ammonia-air mixtures is 0.78.   The corrected value of H_G is estimated as

$$H_G = (1.2)\left(\frac{1.59}{0.78}\right)^{1/2} = 1.7 \text{ ft.}$$

b. Estimation of H_L for acetone-water solutions.   From Fig. 128, H_L for oxygen in water at 77°F. is 0.77 ft.   The liquid-phase diffusivity of acetone in water is assumed to be 3.5×10^{-5} ft.^{2}/sec., while that for oxygen in water is 7.0×10^{-5} ft.^{2}/sec., both at 68°F.   We assume that both diffusion coefficients are affected by temperature in the same way, so that their ratio at 86°F. is the same as at 68°F.   The estimated value of H_L for the acetone-water system at 86°F. is

$$H_L = (0.77)\left(\frac{1.80}{0.9}\right)^{0.47} e^{-0.013(86-77)}$$
$$= 0.95 \text{ ft.}$$

c. Estimation of H_{OG}.   This step requires that we know the value of mG_M/L_M. From Fig. 41, the activity coefficient of acetone in dilute aqueous solution is 7.1; the corresponding value of m is $(7.1)(283/760) = 2.64$, where 283 is the vapor pressure of pure acetone in millimeters of mercury.

$$H_{OG} = H_G + H_L \frac{mG_M}{L_M}$$
$$= 1.7 + 0.95 \frac{(2.64)(616)(18)}{(29)(1181)}$$
$$= 1.7 + (0.95)(0.855) = 1.7 + 0.81 = 2.5 \text{ ft.}$$

For these conditions $(0.81/2.5)(100)$ or 32 per cent of the total resistance is in the liquid phase.

PLATE COLUMNS

Owing to the stagewise type of contact which takes place in bubble-plate towers, performance data for such equipment are usually expressed in terms of the plate efficiency.   The efficiency may be defined in different ways, and the corresponding numerical values of the efficiency are different, as discussed in Chap. V.   The "over-all efficiency" is most convenient for design purposes, since it may be used directly to find the number of actual trays required by dividing it into the required number of theoretical trays.   The fractional approach of the vapor stream to equilibrium with the liquid at one point on a tray, called the point efficiency, or the transfer efficiency, is more directly related to the resistance to transfer between the phases which contact each other, however, and is to be preferred for interpreting experimental data on absorbers. The different efficiencies are interrelated, as discussed in Chap. V, so that the over-all efficiency can usually be calculated, once the point efficiency is known. For small columns, where the liquid on a tray is thoroughly mixed, and when the operating and equilibrium lines are almost parallel, the two efficiencies are equal. Most of the data available from tests of plant-sized equipment are reported as over-all efficiencies, while data from small, laboratory-sized columns may be reported in both ways.

In commercial distillation columns handling binary mixtures the plate efficiency usually is 65 per cent or greater. It is not uncommon, however, to find efficiencies for commercial hydrocarbon absorbers as low as 10 per cent. This may appear surprising at first, since distillation and gas absorption do not differ outwardly; in each case the vapor is bubbled through the liquid on a bubble tray or sieve tray. The large difference in efficiency is due mainly to the different characteristics of the fluids. Liquids at their boiling points, including simple binary mixtures, usually have low viscosities on the order of 0.2 to 0.3 centipoise. In an absorption column, on the other hand, the liquid temperature is not fixed by the composition and the total pressure, and the viscosity may be several centipoises or higher, depending on the nature of the solvent. The influence of liquid viscosity on efficiency is explained by its effect on the rate of diffusion in the liquid phase and on the resistance to mass transfer across the fluid films at the interface.

Table XXII lists available data on over-all and Murphree point efficiencies of commercial absorbers and gives some of the details of construction of the equipment. The efficiencies given for the hydrocarbon absorbers are those for the key components, usually propane or butane. (These are the only ones for which significant values can be computed, owing to "pinches" at the top or bottom of the absorber for the heavier and lighter components, respectively.) The vapor rate is given in terms of the F factor, defined by

$$F = V_G \sqrt{\rho_G} \qquad (345)$$

where V_G = superficial vapor velocity based on tower cross section, ft./sec.

ρ_G = vapor density, lb./ft.^{3}

The effect of viscosity just described is brought out by the table. For example, consider the absorption of propylene in heavy naphtha, in gas oil, and in a mixture of gas oil plus lubricating oil,[489] in each of which the

TABLE XXII. PLATE EFFICIENCIES FOR BUBBLE-TRAY ABSORBERS*

System	Average temp., °C	Pressure, p.s.i.a.	Average liquid viscosity, centipoises	$m = \frac{y_e}{x}$	$\frac{L_M}{G_M}$	Col. diam., in.	No. plates	Plate spacing, in.	No. caps per plate	Size of caps, in.	Slot area, % of tower cross section	Static seal depth, in.	Range of F factor, $(\text{lb./sec.})/(\text{ft.}^3)^{1/2}$	Plate efficiency, % Over-all	Plate efficiency, % Murphree	Ref.
C_1–C_5 in 220 M.W. oil	38	78	0.81	0.68–0.93 for C_4	1.0	72	21	20	50	6.5	9.8	2		18		11
C_1–C_6 in 161 M.W. oil	34	485	0.42	0.27 for C_4	0.185		24							49 for n-C_4 / 50		51
H_2S, C_1–C_6 in 185 M.W. oil	38 / 15	60 / 92	0.42 / 1.9	0.83–0.94 for C_3	1.16–1.24	108	10 / 19	30	92	6.31	8.04	0.75	0.18	26–27 for C_3		216
C_1–C_6 in 206 M.W. oil	52	255	0.40		0.05	48	24	18					1.04	42		115
C_1–C_6 in 157 M.W. oil	53	260	0.41		0.25	60	16	30					1.05	39		115
C_1–C_6 in 164 M.W. oil	51	265	0.50		0.25	60	16	30					1.24	38		115
C_1–C_6 in 201 M.W. oil	49	260	0.48		0.08	48	24	18					0.76	36		115
C_1–C_6 in 135 M.W. oil	59	267	0.22		0.4–0.5	60	16	30					0.46	56		115
C_1–C_6 in 135 M.W. oil	55	254	0.31		0.3–0.4	48	24	18					0.49	50		115
C_1–C_6 in 250 M.W. oil	47	94	0.41		0.5	48	24	18					0.88	10		115
i-C_4H_8 in heavy naphtha	26	66	0.97	0.61	0.45	2	1		1	2	10	0.75	0.6		36	489
i-C_4H_8 in gas oil	25–37	66	3.9–5.4	0.65–0.95	0.45	2	1		1	2	10	0.75	0.6		17	489
i-C_4H_8 in gas oil + lube oil	24	66	20.6	0.50	0.45	2	1		1	2	10	0.75	0.6		9–10	489
C_2H_6 in heavy naphtha	18–43	46–66	0.74–1.10	1.95–3.29	0.47–0.73	2	1		1	2	10	0.75	0.6		22–24	489
C_2H_6 in gas oil	24–48	66	2.8–5.8	2.34–3.67	0.52	2	1		1	2	10	0.75	0.6		11–13	489
C_3H_6 in gas oil + lube oil	23–41	66	10.5–21.5	1.92–2.70	0.34	2	1		1	3	10	0.75	0.6		5–11	489
H_2O evaporation into air	20–31	14.7–55	0.8–1.0			2	1		5				0.2–0.8	85–92	65–85	387
NH_3 in H_2O	11–17	14.7		0.52–0.69	2.9–16	18	1		7	4	10.6	0.375	0.08–0.46		69	489
NH_3 in H_2O	10–12	14.7		1030–1100	2.2–16	18	1		7	4	10.6	0.375	0.08–0.46		1.8–2.6	489
CO_2 in H_2O	13–59	14.7	1.20–0.48	1150–3330	6.3–41	5	4	11	7	3.5	15.2	1.5	0.2–1.5		1.5–3.5	489
CO_2 in H_2O	25	14.7	0.9	1640	14–22	5	4	11	1	3.5	15.2	1.5	0.33		2.0	489
CO_2 in H_2O-glycerol solution			1.2	1840											1.6	489
			1.7	2080											0.96	489
			2.4	2340											0.96	489
			3.7	2720											0.65	489
CO_2 in sodium carbonate-bicarbonate solution; sodium normality = 1.7N; conversion to bicarbonate = 35%	60	14.7					15		1						7	503

* From "Chemical Engineers' Handbook," courtesy of J. H. Perry and McGraw-Hill Book Company, Inc.

gas solubility is about the same. As the liquid viscosity increases from around 0.9 to 15 centipoises, the plate efficiency drops from 23 to 8 per cent. These effects have been brought out by Drickamer and Bradford,[115] on the basis of extensive data on plant columns, and by Walter and Sherwood[489] for laboratory equipment.

An even greater variation of efficiency shown by the tabulated data is seen when a value of 65 to 85 per cent for ammonia absorption in water is compared with 1.5 to 3.5 per cent for the absorption of carbon dioxide in water. Here the liquid viscosity is the same for each case, and the difference is due to the effect of gas solubility. This is consistent with the concepts of diffusion between phases, since it has been shown that for constant flow conditions in the apparatus the contribution of the liquid phase to the over-all gas-film resistance is greater, the lower the solubility of the gas. For carbon dioxide the principal resistance to mass transfer is in the liquid phase, as in packed towers.* The efficiency based on gas compositions is correspondingly low. Gas solubility, expressed in the table by the value of m, has an effect similar to that of liquid viscosity; reducing the former or increasing the latter increases the effect of liquid-film resistance to interphase transfer.

Figure 136 shows the data from Table XXII plotted against the product $m\mu_L$, according to the procedure suggested by O'Connell.[343] The data for water solutions lie consistently above those for hydrocarbons, possibly indicating that diffusion of hydrocarbon solutes is more difficult through the oils of higher molecular weight, even when the viscosity is the same as that of water, or that the higher pressures in all the hydrocarbon columns caused the efficiency to be abnormally low. There seems to be little doubt, however, that viscosity and solubility have equally important effects. It should be realized that factors of plate construction, such as slot width, seal depth, and relative slot area, may affect the efficiency, especially for plates of unorthodox design.

The most thorough understanding of plate-efficiency data is probably to be found in a study of the factors affecting resistances in the separate phases. The point efficiency was shown in Chap. V to be related to the over-all gas-phase absorption coefficient K_Ga, to the molar mass velocity G_M, and to the effective liquid depth Z_V, by the equation

$$E_{OG} = 1 - e^{-K_Ga Z_V/G_M} = 1 - e^{-N_{OG}} \tag{346}$$

* Under economical operating conditions the necessary flow rates of liquid and vapor will be different for "key" components of different solubility. Although no data are available to prove the point, it may be that plate efficiencies for CO_2 absorption in water would be somewhat higher at the large liquid-flow rates required to absorb this slightly soluble gas.

or

$$- \ln (1 - E_{OG}) = \frac{K_G a Z_V}{G_M} = N_{OG} \qquad (347)$$

The over-all coefficient $K_G a$ may be expressed as the combination of the individual coefficients $k_G a$ and $k_L a$, leading to the equation

$$\frac{1}{- \ln (1 - E_{OG})} = \frac{G_M}{k_G a Z_V} + \frac{m G_M}{L_M} \frac{L_M}{\rho_M k_L a Z_V} \qquad (348)$$

or

$$\frac{1}{- \ln (1 - E_{OG})} = \frac{1}{N_G} + \frac{m G_M}{L_M} \frac{1}{N_L} \qquad (349)$$

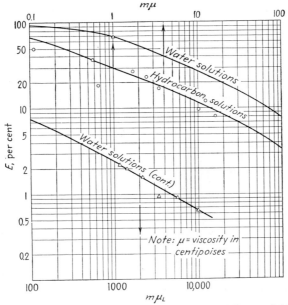

FIG. 136. Correlation of plate efficiencies of gas absorbers with gas solubility and liquid viscosity according to method of O'Connell.

For E_{OG} small, $-1/\ln(1 - E_{OG})$ is approximately equal to $1/E_{OG}$. Equation (349) is similar in many respects to the familiar relation for addition of individual film resistances to obtain the over-all resistance to transfer between phases, Eq. (335). The rate of absorption of a readily soluble gas, for which m is small, is limited principally by the resistance of the gas phase; that of a slightly soluble gas, by the liquid phase. Figure 54 shows these relationships graphically. Large values of $(m G_M / L_M) / N_L$, corresponding to predominating liquid-phase resistance, lead to a maximum value of the efficiency expressed in terms of gas compositions, E_{OG}, which

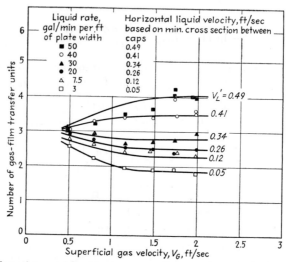

Fig. 137. Effect of gas and liquid rates on gas-film transfer units for bubble tray, using flush caps; weir 2.25 in. above plate, 1.125 in. above slots. (*Data of Gerster et al. and of Bonnet.*)

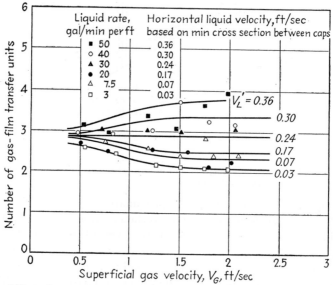

Fig. 138. Effect of gas and liquid rates on gas-film transfer units for bubble tray, using flush caps; weir 3.25 in. above plate, 2.125 in. above slots. (*Data of Gerster et al. and of Bonnet.*)

is approximately equal to $N_L/(mG_M/L_M)$. The Murphree efficiency defined in terms of liquid compositions, E_{OL}, is nearly equal to $N_L/(1 + N_L)$. The relationships between the various efficiencies have been shown by Fig. 55 in Chap. V. Owing to the influence of gas solubility, experiments designed to yield values of N_L and N_G for bubble trays are usually carried out using slightly soluble and readily soluble gases, respectively.

Adiabatic vaporization of water into air furnishes a case for which there is no liquid-film resistance, since the liquid temperature is uniform, *i.e.*, m is effectively zero. Values of the plate efficiency observed in experiments of this type can be used to calculate values of N_G in Eq. (349). Figures

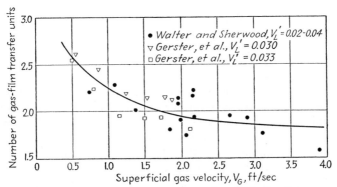

FIG. 139. Comparison of bubble-tray humidification data.

137 and 138 show the data of Gerster, Colburn, Bonnet, and Carmody[158] and those of Bonnet,[42] who used a 13-in.-diameter tray having 13 bubble caps in three rows. At a liquid rate of about 0.3 ft.³ per sec. per ft.² liquor cross section normal to the direction of liquid flow, or 40 g.p.m. per ft. plate width, the number of transfer units is substantially independent of the gas velocity or the F factor. At high or at low liquid-flow rates, however, the number of transfer units varies slightly with gas velocity. Figure 139 shows a comparison with similar data obtained by Walter and Sherwood[489] using a smaller apparatus. In spite of a considerable difference in the depth of clear liquid over the slots—1.0 in.[489] compared with 3.6 in.[158]—the number of gas-film transfer units is the same for the two trays at comparable gas-flow rates.

The effect of changing a few of the plate design factors on the 13-in.-diameter tray of Gerster *et al.*[158] is brought out by Table XXIII. The table shows that at low liquid rates nearly the same number of transfer units was obtained with the caps raised ¾ in. off the tray as with zero skirt clearance, even though part of the liquid must have flowed underneath the raised caps at the higher liquid rate. At 60 g.p.m. the number of transfer units is higher for the raised caps, suggesting that this arrangement would be preferred because of its lower hydraulic resistance to liquid flow.

TABLE XXIII. EFFECT OF LIQUID DEPTH ON GAS-FILM RESISTANCE FOR BUBBLE TRAYS*

(Superficial gas velocity = 1.8 ft./sec.)

Skirt clearance, in.	Weir height, in.	Height of weir over top of slots, in.	Liquid rate, g.p.m.	N_G
¾	4	2⅛	18.4	2.6
			60	5.2
0	3¼	2⅛	20	2.5
			60	4.1†

* Data of Gerster, Colburn, Bonnet, and Carmody.[158]
† Extrapolated from Fig. 137.

Comparison of values of N_G read from Figs. 137 and 138 shows that raising the overflow weir may either increase or decrease the number of transfer units. This is true either for constant total liquid flow, expressed in gallons per minute, or at constant liquid horizontal velocity, indicating that the effective liquid depth Z_V, whatever dimension it may be, is not equal to the vertical distance from the tops of the slots to the top of the weir or to the surface of the flowing, clear liquid. Walter and Sherwood[489] studied the effect of slot width and found that N_G was proportional to the $-\frac{1}{3}$ power of this dimension.

The effect of the physical properties of the vapor on N_G has not been studied experimentally, but it seems logical to suppose, by analogy with packed and wetted-wall columns, that

$$N_G = N_{G'} \left[\frac{(\mu_G/\rho_G D_v)'}{\mu_G/\rho_G D_v} \right]^{\frac{1}{2}} \tag{350}$$

The symbols without the prime represent data for water and air; the primed symbols are for another system.

The resistance of the liquid phase on bubble trays has been studied experimentally by dissolving or stripping slightly soluble gases from water. Figures 140 to 142 show results obtained by Gerster, Colburn, Bonnet, and Carmody[158] and by Bonnet,[42] using a small 13-in.-diameter tray, and by Hess,[183] using a 4-ft.-long section of a tray from a plant tower. The data are plotted in terms of H_L' the length of a transfer unit measured in the direction of liquid flow, based on measurements of rates of desorption of oxygen from water. The flow rate is expressed in terms of the superficial liquid velocity in the horizontal direction, based on the area through which the unaerated liquid would flow, the area occupied by the bubble caps being excluded. This choice of the length of the path of liquid flow across the plate for computing H_L' is not arbitrary; it is the logical one for the situation where the liquid contacts a gas of constant composition and is the necessary choice if the liquid mass velocity is based

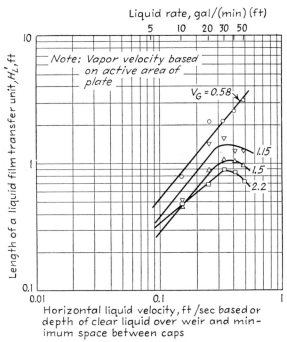

Fig. 140. Effect of gas and liquid velocities on length of a liquid-film transfer unit for bubble tray. (*Data of Bonnet.*) Thirteen-inch-diameter column; 1.5-in.-diameter caps with no skirt clearance; weir 2.25 in. high, 1.125 in. above tops of slots.

on the vertical cross section of the liquid pool. This may be seen from the following: The number of liquid-film transfer units is given by

$$N_L = \frac{\rho_M Z_V k_L a}{L_M} \tag{351}$$

where Z_V = the vertical effective liquid depth

L_M = liquid molar mass velocity, based on horizontal tower cross section

But the liquid mass velocity may also be based on the vertical cross section of the channel through which the liquid flows, S_v, rather than on the tower cross section S_H. Thus

$$L_M' = L_M \frac{S_H}{S_v} \tag{352}$$

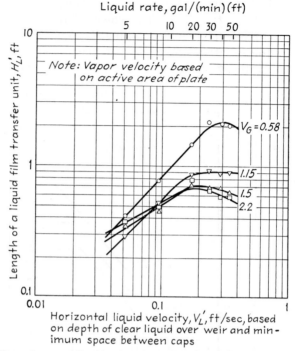

FIG 141. Effect of gas and liquid velocities on length of a liquid-film transfer unit for bubble tray. (*Data of Bonnet.*) Thirteen-inch-diameter column; 1.5-in.-diameter caps with no skirt clearance; weir 3.25 in. high 2.125 in. above tops of slots.

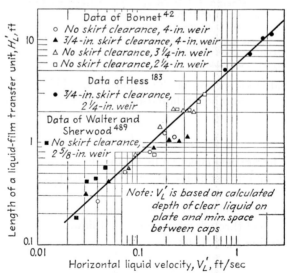

FIG. 142. Correlation of oxygen and carbon dioxide desorption data for bubble trays—length of a liquid-film transfer unit vs. liquid rate at superficial gas velocity of 0.6 ft./sec.

and

$$N_L = \frac{Z_V \rho_M k_L a}{L_M} = \frac{Z_V \rho_M k_L a S_H}{L_M' S_v} = \frac{Z_H \rho_M k_L a}{L_M'} \tag{353}$$

since

$$Z_V S_H = Z_H S_v \tag{354}$$

where Z_H is the length of the horizontal path across the tray. At a constant liquid rate L_M' the wider the tray, the larger N_L and the greater the change in liquid composition. It should be emphasized that this effect is separate from the improvement in Murphree vapor efficiency usually associated with larger trays owing to the presence of a concentration gradient on the tray and to the reduced intensity of lateral mixing of the liquid. Thus, to estimate E_{MV} for a tray using a known value of H_L', the plate width would be used first to calculate N_L according to Eq. (353); then this value would be used together with N_G to calculate E_{OG}; finally, the effect of the concentration gradient would be allowed for according to the method of W. K. Lewis, Jr.,[282] to obtain E_{MV} (see Figs. 51 to 53, Chap. V).

Figures 140 and 141 show that the H.T.U. for the liquid phase increases with increasing liquid rate, especially at low gas velocities. At high velocities, however, a point is reached at which an increase in L produces no change, or even a slight decrease, in the resistance to interphase transfer. The maximum resistances are greater for the shallower liquid pool. Figure 142 shows that at a low gas velocity the data of Hess[183] on a large plant-sized tray having 6-in.-diameter bubble caps agree with the data on the smaller, 13-in.-diameter, laboratory column when the latter are extrapolated to the high liquid rates which were employed with the larger equipment. Figure 142 also shows similar data taken by Walter and Sherwood[489] using a column having an active tray area of only 5 in.². This comparison indicates that the diameter of the caps is relatively of little significance and that the horizontal distance traversed by the liquid and the horizontal liquid velocity are the significant variables rather than the total liquid rate per unit of tray area or the effective vertical depth of liquid. Although the flow rates for the plant-scale and the laboratory trays do not overlap, it is assumed that tray efficiencies approaching 100 per cent would be observed with the longer tray at low liquid velocities, owing to the large number of transfer units available.

All the available data indicate that increasing the gas velocity causes the resistance of the liquid phase to decrease. This effect is shown by data obtained by Walter and Sherwood,[489] using 18-in.-diameter and 5-in.-square trays, as plotted in Fig. 143. At low gas rates the larger tray gave smaller H_L' values, but at velocities in the range of customary industrial practice, above 1 ft./sec. superficial velocity, the larger and smaller trays gave comparable values of H_L'. This agreement despite differences in liquid-seal depth is to be expected if the bubbling action at these high gas rates is such as to produce the same interfacial area per square foot of tray area regardless of the liquid volume on the tray. The negative slope of the lines on Fig. 143 is nearly equal to unity, suggesting that the interfacial area is roughly proportional to the gas volumetric rate. This is in contrast to a packed column, where the interfacial area depends mainly on the liquid rate and where the value of H_L is independent

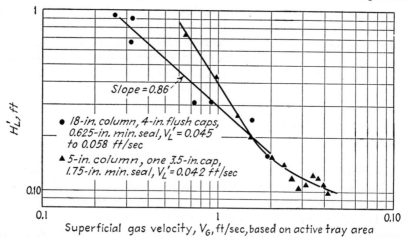

Fig. 143. Effect of gas velocity on H.T.U. for liquid phase in plate column. (*Data of Walter and Sherwood.*) Carbon dioxide absorption or desorption in water.

of V_G. A larger *number* of transfer units was obtained with the tray having the longer flow path. The figure shows again that the value of H.T.U. calculated by dividing the number of transfer units into the horizontal path length is the significant value to use in comparing trays of different size.

The effects of liquid temperature and liquid viscosity on tray efficiency were also investigated by Walter and Sherwood,[489] using the system CO_2-water in their 5-in.-square column. The results are shown by Fig. 144. The viscosity of the liquid was increased at constant temperature by adding up to 42 per cent of glycerol, with the result that H_L' increased from 0.29 to 0.53 ft., corresponding to an exponent of 0.43 on the viscosity. This is roughly the value expected if the interfacial area should be independent of viscosity. The liquid diffusivity is inversely proportional to the viscosity, suggesting that the mass-transfer coefficient is proportional to about the square root of diffusivity, as is normal for unsteady-state diffusion at short times of exposure.

No direct measurements of interfacial areas on bubble trays have been reported, but Van Krevelen and Hoftijzer[470] have measured the holdup of gas above a single submerged orifice as well as the diameters of the bubbles formed as a function of the gas velocity through the hole. Figure 145 shows a few of their data obtained by using liquids of varying physical

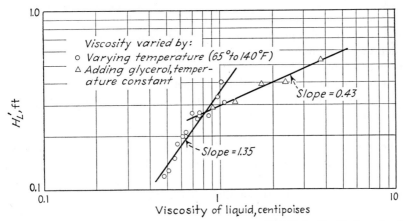

FIG 144. Effect of liquid viscosity and temperature on H.T.U. for liquid phase in plate column. (*Data of Walter and Sherwood.*) Desorption CO_2 from water and aqueous glycerol solutions in 5-in.-square column.

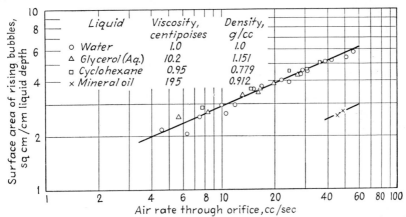

FIG. 145. Interfacial surface area of bubbles produced at a single submerged orifice 2.3 mm. in diameter. (*Data of Van Krevelen and Hoftijzer.*)

properties. The figure shows that, for liquid viscosities up to 10 centipoises, the liquid density, surface tension, and viscosity apparently do not affect the surface area of the bubbles which rise through the liquid. Although these results cannot be expected to apply quantitatively to interfacial areas on bubble trays, where foam and spray as well as bubble surfaces are present, it is nevertheless not surprising that the effect of liquid viscosity on tray efficiency is no greater than that expected from the change in the liquid-diffusion coefficient alone.

When the viscosity was decreased by heating the liquid, however, the effect on H_L' was more pronounced in the experiments of Sherwood and Walter,[489] corresponding to the 1.35 power of μ. To compare this effect with the influence of temperature on H_L for packed columns, it may be noted that H_L' is proportional to $e^{-0.015t}$, where t is the liquid temperature in degrees Fahrenheit. For packings the exponent is $0.013t$, which is nearly the same. The explanation for the larger changes in H_L' when the temperature was changed than when the viscosity was altered by changing liquid composition is very likely that other physical properties of the liquid have an influence on the interfacial area of the bubbles and foam.

The effects of static liquid depth and elevation of the caps above the plate are brought out by Table XXIV, which is based on the data of Gerster *et al.*[158] and those of Bonnet.[42] The data indicate that the resistance to transfer was slightly smaller when the caps were raised than when they were mounted directly on the plate. These results are similar to those obtained for the gas-phase resistance, suggesting that raising the caps a short distance may be generally advantageous. The table also shows that an increase in the depth of clear liquid above the tops of the slots did not always decrease the length of a transfer unit, though the trend in this direction was more definite than was the case when the gas-film resistance was the limiting one.

TABLE XXIV. EFFECT OF TRAY DESIGN FACTORS ON RESISTANCE OF LIQUID PHASE

Skirt clearance, in.	Weir height, in.	Height of weir over top of slots, in.	Superficial vapor velocity, ft./sec.	Horizontal liquid velocity, ft./sec.	Length of a liquid-film transfer unit H_L', ft.
¾	4	2⅛	0.58	0.1	0.66
0	3¼	2⅛	0.58	0.1	0.81
0	2¼	1⅛	0.58	0.2	1.2
0	3¼	2⅛	0.58	0.2	1.5
0	4	2⅞	0.58	0.2	1.1
0	2¼	1⅛	1.15	0.3	1.4
0	3¼	2⅛	1.15	0.3	0.90
0	4	2⅞	1.15	0.3	0.85

Illustration 40. Estimate the Murphree point efficiency and the Murphree vapor efficiency for a tray column of the type used by Gerster *et al.*[158] for distillation of methanol-water solutions at atmospheric pressure and 158°F. The important tray dimensions are:

Inside column diameter...................................... 13 in.
Distance of liquid travel across three rows of bubble caps.......... 7 in.
Average column width over area occupied by bubble caps.......... 12 in.
Height of overflow weir above plate............................ 4 in.
Height of overflow weir above slots............................ $2\frac{1}{8}$ in.

The flow rate of vapor corresponds to a column F factor, based on the entire column cross section, of 0.6. The apparatus operates at total reflux.

Solution. At total reflux the molal liquid and vapor rates are equal. Assuming a 50 mole per cent mixture, the vapor density is

$$\rho_G = \frac{(25)(492)}{(359)(618)} = 0.0555 \text{ lb./ft.}^3$$

and the molal vapor rate is

$$G_M = \frac{V_G \rho_G}{M_G} = \frac{F}{M_G} \sqrt{\rho_G} = \frac{(0.6)(3600)}{25 \sqrt{0.0555}} = 368 \text{ lb. moles/(hr.)(ft.}^2)$$

At total reflux the molal liquid rate will also equal 368 lb. moles/(hr.)(ft.²), and the volumetric rate of liquid flow will be

$$\frac{(368)(25)}{(62.3)(3600)(0.873)} = 0.0470 \text{ ft.}^3/\text{sec.}$$

The cross section of the liquid path is determined from the calculated depth of clear liquid over the weir and the minimum distance between caps. For a weir 8 in. long the head of liquid required to cause a flow of 0.047 ft.³/sec. is 0.92 in., making the total liquid depth 4.92 in. The caps were 1.625 in. in diameter. Five of them located on the tower diameter leave a channel $13 - (5)(1.625) = 4.875$ in. wide between caps. Thus the horizontal liquid velocity is

$$V_L' = \frac{(0.0470)(144)}{(4.92)(4.875)} = 0.283 \text{ ft./sec.}$$

The F factor based on the *active* area of the tray, *i.e.*, the space between the inlet and exit weirs within which the bubble caps are installed, is $(0.6)(0.785)(13^2)/(12)(7)$ or 0.946, and the corresponding velocity is

$$V_G = \frac{0.946}{\sqrt{0.0555}} = 4.01 \text{ ft./sec.}$$

From Fig. 138, N_G is estimated to be 3.25 for air and water. The Schmidt numbers of the two systems are not equal, and a correction for these physical properties must be applied. For air and water vapor $N_{Sc} = 0.60$, while for methanol and water vapor $N_{Sc} = 0.40$. Thus, for the methanol-water system,

$$N_G = 3.25 \left(\frac{0.60}{0.40}\right)^{\frac{1}{2}} = 4.0$$

At a horizontal liquid velocity of 0.283 ft./sec. and an air velocity of 4.01 ft./sec., desorption of oxygen from water at 70°F. gave $H_L' = 0.5$ ft., estimated from Fig. 141. The viscosity of water at 77°F. is 0.90 centipoise, while that of a 50 mole per cent aqueous methanol solution at the same temperature is 1.53 centipoises. According to Figure 144, the correction factor due to this change in viscosity is $(1.53/0.90)^{0.43}$, or 1.256. The effect on H_L' of the temperature change from 70 to 158°F. is estimated by multiplying the low-temperature value by $e^{-0.015(158-70)}$, or 0.268. The two liquid systems also have different diffusion coefficients. That for oxygen in water is 7.0×10^{-5} ft.²/hr. at 68°F., while the value for dilute aqueous methanol solutions is 5.0×10^{-5} ft.²/hr. at the same temperature. Thus,

$$H_{L}' = (0.5)(0.268)(1.256) \left(\frac{7.0}{5.0}\right)^{0.5} = 0.20 \text{ ft.}$$

and

$$N_L = \frac{7}{12} (0.20) = 2.9$$

At total reflux the operating and equilibrium lines are approximately parallel on the average, which means that mG_M/L_M is unity. Thus,

$$\frac{-1}{\ln(1 - E_{OG})} = \frac{1}{4.0} + \frac{1}{2.9} = 0.60$$

from which

$$E_{OG} = 0.81, \text{ or } 81\%$$

This is the estimated Murphree point efficiency. The resistance of the liquid phase is $1/(2.9)(0.60)$ or 57 per cent of the total.

If no lateral mixing of liquid took place on the tray, the Murphree vapor efficiency of the entire tray would be greater owing to the crossflow of liquid and vapor. If the vapor is unmixed between trays,

$$E_{MV} = \frac{e^{E_{OG}(mG_M/L_M)} - 1}{mG_M/L_M} = \frac{e^{0.81} - 1}{1} = 1.25 \text{ or } 125\%$$

It seems very unlikely that so small a tray could operate without some lateral mixing. The true efficiency will very likely be much closer to 81 per cent. The figure observed experimentally[158] was 85 per cent.

Illustration 41. Estimate the tray efficiency of an absorber which removes propane from a mixture of hydrocarbon gases by scrubbing with an oil under the following conditions:

Tower diameter............................ 9 ft.
Bubble-cap diameter....................... 6⅝₆ in.
Minimum clearance between caps............ 3.6 in.
Height of overflow weir above tray........... 2.5 in.
Height of overflow weir above top of slots.... 0.75 in.
Height of slots............................ 0.75 in.
Liquid rate at bottom of absorber........... 1192 lb. moles/hr., or 170,600 lb./hr.
Vapor rate entering absorber............... 1075 lb. moles/hr.
Average molecular weight of entering vapor... 23.1
Average tower temperature................. 55.5°F.
Oil viscosity at average temperature........ 1.9 centipoises
Absolute pressure in tower................. 6.25 atm.

Solution. The vapor density may be estimated from the law of ideal gases as an approximation.

$$\rho_G = \frac{23.1}{359} \frac{6.25}{1} \frac{492}{516} = 0.384 \text{ lb./ft.}^3$$

The cross-sectional area of the tower is $(0.785)(9)^2$ or 63.6 ft.², and the superficial vapor velocity is

$$V_s = \frac{(1075)(23.1)}{(63.6)(3600)(0.384)} = 0.282 \text{ ft./sec.}$$

For a column of this size the active tray area is nearly equal to the total cross-sectional area of the tower.

At a volumetric liquid-flow rate over the exit weir equal to

$$\frac{170,600}{(3600)(62.3)(0.8)} = 0.95 \text{ ft.}^3/\text{sec.}$$

and a weir length of 6 ft., the depth of clear liquid over the weir is calculated from the weir equation to be 1.57 in. Thus, the total depth of equivalent clear liquid above the tray is calculated to be 2.5 + 1.57, or 4.07 in. The horizontal liquid velocity, based on the minimum clearance between caps and on a depth of 4.07 in., is

$$V_L' = \frac{(170,600)(144)(9.9)}{(3600)(62.3)(0.8)(4.07)(100)(3.6)} = 0.924 \text{ ft./sec.}$$

where 100 represents the mean width of the liquid path in inches and 9.9 is the center-to-center spacing between caps in inches.

At these velocities the air-water system gave $N_G = 3.0$, according to Fig. 137. This must be corrected for differences in the physical properties of the gases. For mixtures of propane and methane the Schmidt number is estimated to be 1.3. Thus, the number of gas-film transfer units for the hydrocarbon system is estimated as

$$N_G = 3.0 \left(\frac{0.60}{1.3}\right)^{0.5} = 2.0$$

From Fig. 142 the length of a liquid-film transfer unit for oxygen desorption from water is about 5.5 ft. when the gas-flow rate is 0.6 ft.^{3}/(sec.)(ft.^{2}). This must be corrected for differences in temperature, diffusivity, and vapor velocity. In order to find H_L' for the oxygen-water system at 55°F., we multiply the value read from the figure at 70°F. by the factor $e^{-0.015(55-70)}$, or 1.25. At this same temperature the value of H_L' for the hydrocarbon system will be larger, owing to the lower diffusivity. No experimental values of the liquid-diffusion coefficient are available for this hydrocarbon system, but a rough estimate may be made by the method of Wilke.[510] The molecular volume of oxygen is 25.6 cc./g. mole and that of n-propane is 74.0 cc./g. mole, based on additive volumes as explained in Chap. I. At these molecular volumes the values of F ($= T/\mu D_L$) given by Wilke are $(2.85)(0.9)$ and 1.35 for propane in oil and for oxygen in water, respectively, at the same temperature. The makes the ratio of the liquid-diffusion coefficients

$$\frac{(D_L)_{O_2}}{(D_L)_{C_3}} = \frac{(2.85)(0.9)}{1.35} = \frac{1.9}{1.14} = 3.17$$

Assuming that the length of a transfer unit is proportional to the inverse square root of the diffusivity, as suggested by Fig. 142, the correction factor due to liquid diffusivity is 1.78. According to Fig. 143, the value of H_L' is proportional to the negative 0.86 power of the gas rate, at least approximately. The value of this quantity estimated for the hydrocarbon system under the conditions of the problem is

$$H_L' = (5.5)(1.25)(1.78) \left(\frac{0.60}{0.282}\right)^{0.86} = 23.4 \text{ ft.}$$

The length of the liquid path from weir to weir is estimated to be 90 in., giving

$$N_L = \frac{90}{(12)(23.4)} = 0.32$$

The solubility of propane in the hydrocarbon solution at this temperature and pressure corresponds to $K = m = 1.17$. Thus,

$$\frac{mG_M}{L_M} = \frac{(1.17)(1075)}{1192} = 1.056$$

The point efficiency is calculated as follows:

$$\frac{-1}{\ln(1 - E_{OG})} = \frac{1}{N_G} + \frac{mG_M}{L_M}\frac{1}{N_L} = \frac{1}{2.0} + \frac{1.056}{0.32} = 3.80$$

from which

$$E_{OG} = 0.23, \text{ or } 23\%$$

Assuming no lateral mixing of the liquid on the tray and perfect mixing of the vapor under each tray, the Murphree efficiency of the entire tray is

$$E_{MV} = \frac{e^{E_{OG}(mG_M/L_M)} - 1}{mG_M/L_M}$$
$$= \frac{e^{(0.23)(1.056)} - 1}{1.056} = 0.26, \text{ or } 26\%$$

The Murphree vapor efficiency given by Fig. 136 at $m = (1.17)(1.9) = 2.2$ is 22 per cent, which is slightly smaller than the value predicted. The difference is smaller than the probable precision of the method of prediction, however. The conditions chosen are those of a test reported by Jackson and Sherwood[216] in which the over-all efficiency for propane was about 26 per cent, as shown by Table XXII. As shown by Jackson and Sherwood[216] and as predicted by Eq. (349), the efficiency is smaller for the lighter, less soluble components, which have larger values of m.

Nomenclature for Chapter VIII

A_w = wetted area of wall, ft.^{2}

B_F = thickness of liquid film, ft.

c = concentration of dissolved solute in liquid film, lb. moles/ft.^{3}; subscript av. denotes weighted mean concentration; 0, initial uniform value; i, value at liquid-gas interface

D = inside diameter of tube, ft.

D' = inside diameter of tube, in.

D_d = mass-median diameter of spray drops, microns

D_p = droplet diameter or nominal diameter of packing piece, ft.

D_t = inside diameter of spray chamber, ft.

D_v = diffusion coefficient, ft.^{2}/hr.

D_L = diffusion coefficient for liquid phase, ft.^{2}/hr.

E_{MV} = Murphree vapor efficiency of a single tray

E_{OG}, E_{OL} = point efficiencies, fractional

F = "F factor," related to superficial gas velocity by Eq. (345)

g = acceleration due to gravity = 4.17×10^8 ft./(hr.^{2})

G = mass velocity of gas, lb./(hr.)(ft.^{2})

G_e = mass velocity through tangential entrance nozzle, lb./(hr.)(ft.^{2})

G_M = molar gas mass velocity, lb. moles/(hr.)(ft.^{2})

H = Henry's law coefficient

H_G = height of an individual gas-film transfer unit, ft.

H_L = height of an individual liquid-film transfer unit, ft.

H_L' = length of a transfer unit measured in the direction of liquid flow, ft.

$H_{L,\text{a.m.}}$ = H.T.U. for liquid film ft., based on arithmetic-average driving force

H_{OG} = Height of an over-all gas-phase transfer unit, ft.

H_{OL} = height of an over-all liquid-phase transfer unit, ft.

k_c = mass-transfer coefficient for vapor phase, lb. moles/(hr.)(ft.^{2}) (lb. mole/ ft.^{3})

k_G = mass transfer coefficient, lb. moles/(hr.)(ft.^{2})(atm.)

$K_G a$ = over-all mass-transfer coefficient, lb. moles/(hr.)(ft.^{3})(atm.)

k_L = liquid-film transfer coefficient, lb. mole/(hr.)(ft.^{2})(lb. mole/ft.^{3})

$k_L a$ = volumetric mass-transfer coefficient for liquid phase, lb. moles/(hr.)(ft.^{3}) (lb. mole/ft.^{3})

$k_{L,\text{a.m.}}$ = liquid-film coefficient, lb. mole/(hr.)(ft.^{3})(lb. mole/ft.^{3}), based on arith-metic-average driving force.

$K_L a$ = over-all liquid-film transfer coefficient, lb. mole/(hr.)(ft.^{3})(lb. mole/ft.^{3})

L = superficial mass velocity of liquid, lb./(hr.)(ft^2)

L_M = molar liquid mass velocity, lb. moles/(hr.)(ft.^{2})

L_M' = molar mass velocity of liquid flowing across tray, based on vertical cross-sectional area, lb. moles/(hr.)(ft.^{2})

m = slope of equilibrium line, y_e/x

m' = slope of straight portion of equilibrium line for SO$_2$-H$_2$O-air system. dy_e/dx

M_G = molecular weight

n = constant in Eq. (339).

N = number of transfer units; subscripts OG refer to over-all gas basis; OL, to over-all liquid basis

N_G = number of gas-film transfer units

N_L = number of liquid-film transfer units

N_{Re} = Reynolds number, based on drop diameter and properties of gas

N_{Sc} = Schmidt number of gas, $\mu_G/\rho_G D_v$

P = total pressure, atm.

P_{BM} = logarithmic-mean partial pressure of inert gas, atm.

p, q = constants in Eq. (341)

R = gas constant (atm.)(ft.^{3})/(lb. mole)(°R.)

S = cross-sectional area of gas entrance nozzle, ft.^{2}

S_v = vertical cross-sectional area of liquid channel on tray, ft.^{2}

S_H = cross-sectional area of liquid pool on tray, ft.^{2}

t = liquid temperature, °F.

T = absolute temperature, °R.

u_{av} = average velocity of liquid film, ft./hr.

V_G = superficial gas velocity, ft./hr., based on entire cross section for large towers, and on area of tray covered with bubble caps for small laboratory column

V_L = superficial liquid velocity based on tower cross section, ft./hr.

V_L' = horizontal velocity of liquid flowing across tray, based on vertical cross-sectional area excluding bubble caps, ft./sec.

x = mole fraction in liquid

Z = height of packed section or length of wetted surface, ft.

Z_H = length of horizontal path of liquid flow across a tray, ft.

Z_V = effective depth of liquid path (on tray), ft.

α = constant in Eq. (338)

β = constant in Eq. (340)

γ = constant in Eq. (339)

θ = time of exposure, hr.

ρ_G = density of gas, lb./ft.^{3}

ρ_L = density of liquid, lb./ft.^{3}

ρ_M = molar liquid density, lb. moles/ft.^{3}

x_e = mole fraction solute in liquid in equilibrium with gas

y = mole fraction solute in gas

y_e = mole fraction solute in gas in equilibrium with liquid

Γ = liquid-flow rate, lb./(hr.)(ft. wetted perimeter)

μ_G = viscosity of gas, lb. mass/(ft.)(hr.)

μ_L = viscosity of liquid, lb. mass/(ft.)(hr.)

CHAPTER IX

SIMULTANEOUS ABSORPTION AND CHEMICAL REACTION

The usual objective in the selection of an absorbent for scrubbing a gas is to find a liquid, possibly a solution, which has a very large capacity for absorbing the solute without building up an appreciable equilibrium back pressure. This can be accomplished readily by choosing a chemical with which the solute reacts irreversibly, as when an aqueous solution of sodium hydroxide is used to absorb carbon dioxide. The cost of fresh solvent is usually exorbitant, however, except for the treatment of traces of solute, and it is economically desirable to choose a solvent from which the dissolved gas may be expelled and the solvent regenerated. Most often the regeneration is accomplished by heating the solution to a temperature at which the solute becomes volatile, the solute being stripped by countercurrent contact with a vapor such as steam. Thus, in the commercial absorption of carbon dioxide gas, the scrubbing liquid may be an alkaline aqueous solution either of sodium carbonate or of an organic amine, each of which reacts reversibly with carbon dioxide. The equilibria are sensitive to temperature, however, and the loose chemical compound which is stable at the lower temperature may be decomposed by heating.

In the absorption of carbon dioxide by sodium or potassium carbonate solution the dissolved carbon dioxide reacts with the carbonate present, increasing the bicarbonate concentration. The resulting solution, high in bicarbonate, is heated to the boiling point, causing the decomposition of the bicarbonate, which reverts to the carbonate. After the water vapor evolved in the stripping operation has been condensed, the resulting gas is nearly pure carbon dioxide. The hot carbonate solution is cooled and used again to absorb more carbon dioxide. The over-all reaction involved is

$$Na_2CO_3 + CO_2 + H_2O \rightleftarrows 2NaHCO_3$$

When diethanolamine or triethanolamine is used as the alkaline agent, the amine carbonate is formed according to the over-all reaction

$$2RNH_2 + CO_2 + H_2O \rightleftarrows (RNH_2)_2H_2CO_3$$

The amines are relatively nonvolatile and have a high absorption capacity.   They are used extensively to remove carbon dioxide from water gas in the commercial manufacture of hydrogen.[445]

The same alkaline solutions may be used to remove other acid gases, such as hydrogen sulfide, the operations being very similar to the absorption of carbon dioxide.   For sodium carbonate solution and hydrogen sulfide the reaction is

$$Na_2CO_3 + H_2S \rightleftarrows NaHCO_3 + NaHS$$

The solution may be regenerated by chemical means instead of by heating.   This proves to be more economical in the removal of sulfur dioxide from flue gas by scrubbing with aqueous sodium sulfite solution.[232]   The sulfite is partially converted to a bisulfite by reaction with SO_2.   On addition of solid zinc oxide to the solution the original sulfite is regenerated, and the absorbed sulfite precipitates as the crystalline zinc sulfite according to the following reactions

$$NaHSO_3 + ZnO + 2\tfrac{1}{2}H_2O \rightarrow ZnSO_3 \cdot 2\tfrac{1}{2}H_2O + NaOH$$
$$NaOH + NaHSO_3 \rightarrow Na_2SO_3 + H_2O$$

After removal from the solution by filtration the crystals are calcined to produce ZnO and concentrated gaseous SO_2.

If the solvent contains an ingredient which reacts selectively with only one component of the gas mixture, a separation of the gaseous solutes may be accomplished.   Olefinic and acetylenic hydrocarbons react with aqueous solutions of cuprous salts to form nonvolatile, covalent compounds and may thereby be separated from the paraffinic constituents of the gas.[331,407]   The solubility of hydrocarbons in these solutions depends on the degree of unsaturation of the compound, diolefins being generally more soluble than olefins and acetylenes being very highly soluble.

The purpose of absorption may be to produce a chemical product in the liquid phase, rather than ultimate recovery of the solute unchanged. Thus, in the manufacture of nitric acid, gaseous oxides of nitrogen, oxygen, and water are contacted in a stainless-steel absorber under pressure in order to carry out the following reactions:

$$3NO_2 + H_2O \rightarrow 2HNO_3 + NO$$
$$2NO + O_2 \rightarrow 2NO_2$$

The latter takes place in the gas space between the trays, while the former occurs in the liquid.

Other industrially important absorption processes in which chemical reaction of the solute with the solvent is important include the removal of sulfur compounds by scrubbing with sodium arsenite solution (the Thylox process[372]) or by scrubbing with sodium phenolate solute,[372] the production of chlorinated-lime slurry by absorption of chlorine in milk of lime, and the absorption of SO_3 in water or dilute acid to produce sulfuric acid, or oleum. A few of the above processes will be considered in some detail after the discussion of the theory of the influence of chemical reaction on absorption rates.

EFFECT OF CHEMICAL REACTION ON ABSORPTION RATE

There is no sharp line dividing pure physical absorption from absorption controlled by the rate of a chemical reaction. Most cases fall in the intermediate range, the rate of absorption being limited both by the resistance to diffusion and by the finite velocity of reaction. Absorption of hydrogen or oxygen in water appears to be a case of purely physical absorption, since these gases are inert toward water. In many cases that have sometimes been considered to fall in the class of purely physical processes, however, there is a reaction between the solute and the solvent. Thus, in the absorption of ammonia, sulfur dioxide, or chlorine in water, a fraction of the dissolved molecules is present as ions resulting from a chemical reaction with the solvent. Even in these intermediate cases the equilibria between the various forms of the diffusing substance set up by the reactions and the rates of these reactions may affect the rate of absorption.

TABLE XXV. ABSORPTION COEFFICIENTS FOR CO_2 IN VARIOUS SOLVENTS
(Packed towers filled with Raschig rings)
Basis: $L = 2500$ lb./(hr)(ft.^{2}); $G = 300$ lb./(hr.)(ft.^{2}); $T = 77°F.$ (liquid temperature).

Liquid	K_Ga, lb. moles/(hr.) (ft.^{3})(unit Δy)	Reference
Water	0.05	418
1N sodium carbonate, 20 per cent of sodium as bicarbonate	0.03	148
3N diethanolamine, 50 per cent conversion to carbonate	0.4	100
2N sodium hydroxide, 15 per cent of sodium as carbonate	2.3	455
2N potassium hydroxide, 15 per cent of potassium as carbonate	3.8	439
Hypothetical solvent with no liquid-phase resistance	24.0	417

While some advances in the theory applicable to these cases have been made in recent years, the picture is still far from complete. It is not yet possible to state a priori whether a given case will be limited by diffusional or chemical resistance. Each case must be studied experimentally.

While most acid gases like SO_2, HCl, SO_3, and Cl_2 dissolve readily in water because of the effect of chemical reaction in which ionized products are produced, CO_2 dissolves slowly. In fact, owing to the small extent of the ionization reaction even at chemical equilibrium, its rate of solution is precisely what would be expected from the hypothesis that it does not react at all. Its rate of solution in sodium hydroxide is also lower than might be expected and can be explained only by assuming that the liquid-phase reaction proceeds slowly. Table XXV compares rates of absorption of carbon dioxide in various alkaline agents and shows that even the strongest alkali does not eliminate all the resistance in the liquid phase.

THEORY ON SIMULTANEOUS DIFFUSION AND REACTION

The kinetic theory of simultaneous diffusion and chemical reaction in the liquid phase has been developed by Hatta,[175,176] Davis and Crandall,[103] and others[55,494] based on the assumption that the resistance to diffusion is concentrated within a thin film adjacent to the gas-liquid interface. This film is assumed to have negligible capacity for holding the dissolved solute compared with the main body of the liquid, which is so thoroughly mixed that no concentration gradient exists within it.

The existence of such a film has not been proved for commercial absorption equipment such as packed or plate towers. The assumption of two such films, one in the gas and one in the liquid, is the basis of Whitman's two-film theory[502] and of the resulting concept of resistances in series, as it is outlined in Chap. III. Alternatively, however, it may be assumed that the solute diffuses from the interface into the liquid by an unsteady-state process, the amount of solute dissolving being limited by the time of exposure of the liquid surface and its area. It may be shown[298] that the customary expression for addition of reciprocals of "film" coefficients follows from such a theory when two stagnant phases are placed in contact for a limited time. Agreement between the Whitman two-film theory and absorption data cannot therefore be taken as proof of the existence of stagnant fluid films of negligible capacity at the interface. Higbie[185] has suggested the application of this unsteady-state-diffusion concept to the liquid layer which flows over the surface of a piece of packing. He points out that it leads to the conclusion that in the absence of chemical reaction the liquid-film absorption coefficient varies with the square root of the liquid diffusivity, in agreement with experimental data.[418] The theoretical prediction that k_L varies with the square root of the liquid-surface velocity cannot be checked using data on packed absorbers, owing to the unknown variation in a.

Thus, there are two bases for theoretical discussion of the kinetic problem, one depending on the assumption of physical films of negligible capacity but finite resistance, and the other depending on the assumption of unsteady-state molecular diffusion of the solute into the whole mass of liquid. It is not possible at present to decide from evidence available which concept is the more nearly correct. Neither appears completely justified. Truly stagnant films are hardly conceivable in industrial absorbers, and the presence of a stagnant film of negligible capacity seems less likely than a liquid layer capable of retaining the dissolved gas in the region near the interface. A thoroughly mixed main body of liquid in the liquid layer which adheres to the packing piece is inconceivable; as a matter of fact the greatest degree of turbulence must be present near the gas-liquid interface rather than adjacent to the solid packing. In wetted-wall columns these surface disturbances take the form of ripples, which cause diffusion to take place more rapidly than expected for molecular diffusion. Lacking a physical picture which is completely consistent with the facts, theories will therefore be presented on the basis of both concepts.

Theory of the Stagnant Film of Finite Thickness—Rapid Second-order, Irreversible Reaction. In the case of a rapid second-order, irreversible chemical reaction in the liquid phase, the conditions in the film are complicated by the fact that it is within the liquid film that the reaction occurs. For example, assume that a solute gas A is absorbed from a gas mixture by a solution of a substance B, which combines with A according to the equation

$$A + B \rightarrow AB \tag{355}$$

As the solution is first brought into contact with the gas, A will dissolve and react immediately with B at the phase boundary. The product AB will begin to diffuse toward the main body of liquid. The liquid near the surface will soon be depleted of B, which will begin to diffuse from the main body of the liquid toward the interface. The rapid removal of B from the zone near the surface makes it necessary for incoming A to diffuse through part of the liquid film to meet the substance B diffusing in the opposite direction. The zone of reaction between A and B will thus move away from the gas-liquid interface, taking up a position (stationary in this theory) such that the rate of diffusion of A from the gas phase is equal, mole for mole, to the rate of diffusion of B from the main body of the liquid. This process requires only a very short time, during which the absorption rate falls rapidly. Within a few seconds at the most, the reaction zone reaches this equilibrium position.

The following theory applies to the steady rate of absorption which is observed after the equilibrium reaction position is reached. Figure 146 is a diagrammatic sketch of the concentration gradients. Pressures or concentrations are plotted as ordinates, and the abscissa represents the position in the film. PQ represents the plane of the interface between gas and liquid phases. VW and UT are the outer boundaries of gas and liquid films, respectively. SR represents the equilibrium position of the reaction zone, to which A and B diffuse and from which the product AB diffuses toward the main body of the liquid. A diffuses through the gas film under the influence of the driving force $p - p_i$ and diffuses to the reaction zone owing to the driving force c_i in the liquid phase. B diffuses from the main body of the liquid to the reaction zone under the influence of the driving force q, and the reaction product AB diffuses back to the

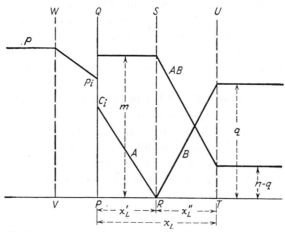

Fig. 146.   Idealized sketch of gradients in double film with irreversible instantaneous reaction following absorption.

main body of the liquid owing to the potential $m - (n - q)$. The solution is n-normal in free plus combined B and is q-normal in B, and consequently the normality with respect to AB is $n - q$. The reaction product tends to diffuse from reaction zone toward the gas phase as well as toward the main body of the liquid, but AB is assumed nonvolatile, and the concentration of AB is soon equalized through the section QS of the liquid film.

The diffusion equations derived in the previous chapter may be applied to the gas film and to both sections of the liquid film. Thus, for the gas film

$$N_A = k_G(p - p_i) \qquad (356)$$

Assuming the solvent concentration to be large compared with the concentrations of A, B, and AB, Eq. (356) may be written

$$N_A = \frac{D_A}{x_L'} (c_i - 0) \qquad (357)$$

for the first section of the liquid film. For the second section, SU,

$$-N_B = \frac{D_B}{x_L''} (q - 0) = +N_A \tag{358}$$

and

$$N_{AB} = \frac{D_{AB}}{x_L''} (m - n + q) = N_A \tag{359}$$

As before, the gas and liquid phases at the actual interface QP may be assumed to be in equilibrium, and since A does not react in the section of the film QS but dissolves physically, the equilibrium may be assumed to follow Henry's law approximately,

$$p_i = Hc_i \tag{360}$$

Since the molal diffusion rates of B and AB are equal, the potentials $[m - (n - q)]$ and q must be in inverse proportion to the respective diffusivities of AB and B, as found by combining Eqs. (358) and (359):

$$m - (n - q) = \frac{D_B}{D_{AB}} q \tag{361}$$

Equations (356) to (358), and (360) may be combined algebraically to eliminate p_i, c_i, m, n, x_L', and x_L''. The result is

$$N_A = \frac{(p/H) + (D_B/D_A)q}{(x_L/D_A) + (1/Hk_G)} \tag{362}$$

This equation states that the rate of absorption is proportional to the over-all driving force, as expressed by the sum of the two terms in the numerator, and inversely proportional to the over-all resistance, as expressed by the denominator. The first term of the denominator represents the combined resistances of both sections of the liquid film, and the second term represents the resistance of the gas film. Equation (362) states further that, for a constant gas composition and constant film conditions, the rate should be a linear function of the residual concentration of B in the liquid.

Equation (362) may be put in an equivalent and more useful form by eliminating gas-phase concentrations

$$N_A = \frac{c_{Ai} + (D_B/D_A)q}{x_L/D_A} \tag{363}$$

Defining the liquid-film coefficient on the basis of the liquid-film driving force $(c_{Ai} - 0)$, we find that

$$k_L = \frac{D_A}{x_L} \left(1 + \frac{D_B}{D_A} \frac{q}{c_{Ai}}\right) \tag{364}$$

In the absence of chemical reaction the coefficient is given by the quotient D_A/x_L, and the factor in parenthesis gives the affect of q on the apparent coefficient.

Since it is impossible for p_i to be negative, Eq. (356) cannot be expected to apply for conditions where p_i is less than zero. Solving Eqs. (356) and (362) for p_i,

$$p_i = \frac{k_G p - (D_B q/x_L)}{k_G + (D_A/H x_L)} > 0 \tag{365}$$

Hence

$$q < \frac{x_L k_G p}{D_B} \tag{366}$$

which is a necessary condition for the application of Eq. (362). When q is greater than $x_L k_G p/D_B$, p_i approaches zero, and absorption takes place at constant rate:

$$N_A = k_G p \tag{367}$$

The condition (366) expresses the critical value of q. If absorption is started using a solution in which the concentration of B is greater than this critical value, the rate of absorption will be constant as q decreases to the critical value. The rate will then fall off linearly with q as indicated by Eq. (362), assuming, of course, that p and other conditions are held constant.

The derivation of Eq. (362) follows that of Hatta,[175] who was interested in the batch absorption of CO_2 by KOH solutions. More complicated cases involving consecutive reactions may be treated by a relatively simple extension of the theory presented. Weber and Nilsson[494] discuss the case of simultaneous reactions, as in the absorption of CO_2 in a solution of calcium and sodium hydroxides.

Theory of the Stagnant Film of Finite Thickness—Slow First-order Reaction. If the reaction is not very rapid compared with the rate of diffusion, the zone of reaction will not be concentrated in a thin region, as shown by Fig. 146, but will be spread throughout the liquid film. Hatta[176] gives the following derivation for the absorption and simultaneous slow irreversible reaction of a solute A, with a large excess of the solvent.

The solute diffuses through the gas film under the influence of the driving force $p - p_i$. After entering the liquid phase, it starts to diffuse toward the main body of the liquid but immediately begins to react with the dissolved substance B. Since the diffusing current of solute is being depleted as it diffuses into the liquid, the gradient will be concave upward, as shown in Fig. 147. (The total rate of diffusion of reacted and unreacted forms of A is constant, however, as there is no accumulation of A in the film.)

If the rate equation for the reaction is known, the conditions of the process may be expressed mathematically. Assume, for example, that the reaction is first order* and that the rate of elimination of A is proportional to the concentration of A at any point, *i.e.*, that

$$-\frac{dA}{d\theta} = k_c c V \qquad (368)$$

where k_c is the specific reaction-rate constant, c is the variable concentration of A, and V is the liquid volume considered. Consider now a

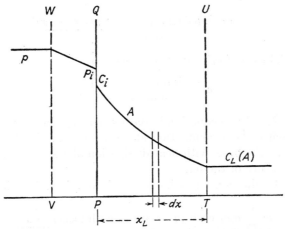

Fig. 147. Idealized sketch of film conditions for absorption followed by slow first-order reaction in the liquid film.

differential element, of unit area and of thickness dx, of the liquid film of thickness x_L. The rate of diffusion into this element will be

$$N_A = -D_A \frac{dc}{dx} \qquad (369)$$

at $x = x$. The rate of diffusion out of this element, at $x = x + dx$, will be

$$N_A = -D_A \left(\frac{dc}{dx} + \frac{d^2c}{dx^2} dx \right) \qquad (370)$$

The disappearance of A within the element, due to reaction with B, is

$$\frac{dA}{d\theta} = -k_c c \, dx \qquad (371)$$

* This may not be possible in any actual case but is sometimes approximated in practice and will be assumed here for illustrative purposes.

since the volume of the element is dx. The difference in diffusion rates in and out of the element must equal the rate of elimination of A by reaction with B, whence

$$D_A \frac{d^2c}{dx^2} = k_c c \qquad (372)$$

Assuming k_c constant throughout the film, the solution of this equation may be given as

$$c = A_1 e^{a_0 x} + A_2 e^{-a_0 x} \qquad (373)$$

where $a_0 = \sqrt{k_c/D_A}$. Substituting the limits $c = c_i$, at $x = 0$, and $c = c_L$, at $x = x_L$, the constants A_1 and A_2 are obtained and the solution becomes

$$c = \frac{c_L \sinh (a_0 x) + c_i \sinh [a_0 (x_L - x)]}{\sinh (a_0 x_L)} \qquad (374)$$

For the special case of $c_L = 0$, this reduces to

$$c = \frac{\sinh [a_0 (x_L - x)]}{\sinh (a_0 x_L)} c_i \qquad (375)$$

It is of interest that this equation is mathematically similar to the solution of the problem of heat conduction along a fin maintained at a constant temperature at the base, with heat dissipation along the fin proportional to the temperature of the fin.

The slope of the concentration curve is obtained by differentiating Eq. (374):

$$\frac{dc}{dx} = \frac{a_0 c_L \cosh (a_0 x) + a_0 c_i \cosh [a_0 (x_L - x)]}{\sinh (a_0 x_L)} \qquad (376)$$

The rate of diffusion into the liquid is obtained by multiplying the slope at $x = 0$ by the diffusivity D_A:

$$N_A = -D_A \left(\frac{dc}{dx} \right)_{x=0} = \frac{D_A a_0 [c_i \cosh (a_0 x_L) - c_L]}{\sinh (a_0 x_L)} \qquad (377)$$

and the rate of diffusion of A into the main body of the liquid is obtained similarly by substituting $x = x_L$:

$$N_A' = -D_A \left(\frac{dc}{dx} \right)_{x=x_L} = \frac{D_A a_0 [c_i - c_L \cosh (a_0 x_L)]}{\sinh (a_0 x_L)} \qquad (378)$$

Of the solute A entering the liquid phase, the fraction F reaching the main body of the liquid without reacting is given by

$$F = \frac{N_A'}{N_A} = \frac{c_L \cosh (a_0 x_L) - c_i}{c_L - c_i \cosh (a_0 x_L)} \qquad (379)$$

In the special case where the concentration of A in the main body of liquid is low, Eq. (377) may be written

$$N_A = \frac{bD_A(c_i - c_L)}{x_L} \tag{380}$$

where

$$b = \frac{a_0 x_L}{\tanh{(a_0 x_L)}} \tag{381}$$

Equation (380) is similar to Eq. (178), with k_L replaced by bD_A/x_L. Equation (180), for over-all resistance, becomes

$$\frac{1}{K_L} = \frac{x_L}{bD_A} + \frac{1}{Hk_G} \tag{382}$$

whence

$$N_A = \frac{c_e - c_L}{(x_L/bD_A) + (1/Hk_G)} \tag{383}$$

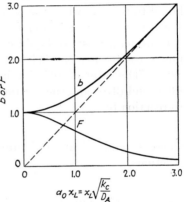

FIG. 148. Effect of chemical reaction in the liquid film on absorption coefficient and transfer of unreacted molecules into liquid phase.

This is the same as the equation for absorption through combined gas- and liquid-film resistances, except that the factor b has been introduced into the term representing liquid-film resistance. Figure 148 shows F and b plotted vs. $a_0 x_L$, as calculated from Eqs. (379) and (381) for the case of $c_L = 0$. When c_L becomes an appreciable fraction of c_i, F may still be calculated by Eq. (379), but Eq. (383) no longer applies, and Eq. (377) must be employed.

Figure 148 indicates that F, the fraction of the diffusing material getting through the film without reacting, decreases rapidly as $a_0 x_L$ increases. Low diffusivity, large film thickness, and high rate of reaction tend to increase the value of $a_0 x_L$, and most of the reaction occurs within the liquid film.

If the reaction rate is low, F is nearly unity, indicating that most of the diffusing material passes through the film without reacting. The variation in b is equally interesting. At high values of $a_0 x_L$, b becomes equal to $a_0 x_L$, and Eq. (383) reduces to

$$N_A = \frac{c_e - c_L}{(1/\sqrt{k_c D_A}) + (1/Hk_G)} \tag{384}$$

which indicates that, if $a_0 x_L$ is large because k_c is large, the gas film may become controlling. At low values of $a_0 x_L$, the factor b approaches unity, and Eq. (383) reduces to

$$N_A = \frac{c_e - c_L}{(x_L/D_A) + (1/Hk_G)} = \frac{c_e - c_L}{(1/k_L) + (1/Hk_G)} \qquad (384a)$$

Thus if the chemical reaction is slow, the absorption process becomes the same as for pure physical absorption, and the reaction takes place in the main body of the liquid.

Theory of Unsteady-state Absorption in the Stagnant Liquid—Slow First-order Reaction. During the period of initial exposure of the liquid to the gas, when the solute may accumulate in the liquid, an additional term must be included in Eq. (372).

Consider a prism of liquid near the interface, having a vertical side of unit cross section parallel to the interface and a thickness dx (see Fig. 147). The rates of diffusion in and out of this prism are given by Eqs. (369) and (370) and the net rate of disappearance per unit volume owing to reaction by

$$k_c c_A - k_c' c_B$$

where k_c and k_c' are the rate constants for the forward and reverse reactions,

$$A \rightleftarrows B$$

Since at equilibrium the opposing rates are equal, $k_c' = k_c/K$, where K is the chemical equilibrium constant. The rate of depletion of A from the prism is $-(\partial c_A/\partial\theta)\ dx$ in the unsteady state. Equating the rate of input of A by diffusion to the sum of the rates of output by diffusion, disappearance by reaction, and depletion, we obtain

$$D_A \frac{\partial^2 c_A}{\partial x^2} = k_c c_A - \frac{k_c}{K} c_B + \frac{\partial c_A}{\partial\theta} \qquad (385)$$

A similar material balance for B gives

$$D_B \frac{\partial^2 c_B}{\partial x^2} = \frac{k_c}{K} c_B - k_c c_A + \frac{\partial c_B}{\partial\theta} \qquad (386)$$

If the concentration of B is eliminated and the diffusivities are assumed equal, the following fourth-order, linear, partial-differential equation results:

$$D \frac{\partial^4 c_A}{\partial x^4} - k_c\left(1 + \frac{1}{K}\right)\frac{\partial^2 c_A}{\partial x^2} + \frac{1}{D}\frac{\partial^2 c_A}{\partial\theta^2} - 2\frac{\partial^3 c_A}{\partial\theta\,\partial x^2}$$
$$+ \frac{k_c}{D}\left(1 + \frac{1}{K}\right)\frac{\partial c_A}{\partial\theta} = 0 \qquad (387)$$

The product of the reaction is assumed to be nonvolatile; the interfacial concentration of A is assumed to be equal to the value in equilibrium with the gas, where the partial pressure of A is constant; the initial concentrations of A and B in the liquid before exposure to the gas are assumed uniformly equal to their equilibrium values; and the body of liquid is taken as effectively infinite. Thus, the following boundary conditions apply:

1. $c_A = c_i = p_A/H$ at $x = 0$

2. $\dfrac{\partial c_B}{\partial x} = 0$ at $x = 0$

3. $c_B = K c_A = \dfrac{K}{1 + K} c_0$, a constant, at $\theta = 0$

4. $c_B = K c_A = \dfrac{K}{1 + K} c_0$, a constant, at $x = \infty$

where c_0 represents the sum of the initial values of c_A and c_B, assumed to be in equilibrium with each other. The solution of Eq. (387), subject to these boundary conditions, may be obtained most readily by the Laplace transform method.[370] The result is given by

$$\frac{(K + 1)c_{\mathrm{av}} - c_0}{(K + 1)c_i - c_0} = \frac{3}{\sqrt{\pi}} \sqrt{\frac{D_L \theta}{B_F{}^2}} \left[\frac{f(K, k_c \theta)}{K + 1} \right] \qquad (388)*$$

where

$$f(K, k_c \theta) = K + 1 + \left[\frac{\pi K^5}{4(K - 1)(k_c \theta)} \right]^{\frac{1}{2}} \exp \left[\frac{k_c \theta}{K(K - 1)} \right]$$
$$\left\{ \mathrm{erf} \left(\frac{K k_c \theta}{K - 1} \right)^{\frac{1}{2}} - \mathrm{erf} \left[\frac{k_c \theta}{K(K - 1)} \right]^{\frac{1}{2}} \right\}$$
$$- \left[\frac{\pi K^3 (K + 1)}{4 k_c \theta} \right]^{\frac{1}{2}} \mathrm{erf} \left[\frac{(K + 1) k_c \theta}{K} \right]^{\frac{1}{2}} \qquad (389)$$

where $(K + 1)c_{\mathrm{av}}$ represents the average total concentration of solute in the liquid in both the reacted and the unreacted forms and c_{av} represents the average concentration of A after absorption if A and B were in chemical equilibrium at every point. Similarly, $(K + 1)c_i$ represents the total concentration of reacted and unreacted solute in the liquid if it was allowed to come to physical and chemical equilibrium with the gas. The following functional notation is used:

$$\exp(q) = e^q \quad \text{and} \quad \mathrm{erf}(q) = \frac{2}{\sqrt{\pi}} \int_0^q e^{-p^2} \, dp \qquad (390)$$

* A similar result was given recently by Danckwerts[100a] for the case of the irreversible reaction ($K = \infty$).

the latter being the "error function." For large values of $k_c\theta$, the approximate equivalent of Eq. (388) is

$$f(K,k_c\theta) = (1 + K)\left[1 - \frac{\pi^{1/2}}{2} K \left(\frac{K}{K+1}\right)^{1/2} (k_c\theta)^{-1/2} + \frac{K^3}{2(K+1)} (k_c\theta)^{-1}\right]$$

(391)

For small values of $k_c\theta$, approximately,

$$f(K,k_c\theta) = 1 + \frac{K^{1/2}(K+1)^{3/2}(K-1)^2 - K^4 + 3K^2 - 2K}{3(K-1)^2} k_c\theta$$ (392)

For the irreversible reaction $(K = \infty)$,

$$f(\infty,k_c\theta) = \frac{1}{2} \exp(-k_c\theta) + \sqrt{\frac{\pi}{4}} \left[\frac{1 + 2k_c\theta}{(k_c\theta)^{1/2}}\right] \text{erf}(k_c\theta)^{1/2}$$ (393)

When these equations are to be applied to absorption from a gas in a falling liquid film, the time of exposure is that of the liquid surface, which may be calculated from the surface velocity,

$$\theta = \frac{Z}{u_s} = \frac{2}{3}\frac{Z}{u_{av}}$$ (394)

where Z is the height of the surface. By means of a material balance on the liquid layer of thickness B_F the liquid-film absorption coefficient k_L is obtained as follows:

$$u_{av}B_F[(K+1)c_{av} - c_0] = k_LZ[(K+1)c_i - c_0]$$ (395)

and

$$\frac{k_LZ}{u_{av}B_F} = \frac{(K+1)c_{av} - c_0}{(K+1)c_i - c_0} = \frac{3}{\sqrt{\pi}}\left(\frac{D_L\theta}{B_F^2}\right)^{1/2}\left[\frac{f(K,k_c\theta)}{K+1}\right]$$ (396)

In these equations, as before, c_0 represents the concentration of total dissolved solute (both A and B forms) before exposure of the liquid surface, and $(K+1)c_i$ represents the concentration of total dissolved solute (both A and B forms) in a liquid in phase equilibrium and reaction equilibrium with the gas. This latter quantity is not the actual solute concentration at the interface, where chemical equilibrium may not exist. It is, however, the concentration which would be found in the usual static equilibrium experiment. The absorption coefficient k_L is therefore defined in Eq. (395) on the basis of total dissolved-solute concentrations as a driving force.

Comparison of Eq. (396) with Eq. (327), which was developed in Chap. VIII for purely physical absorption,

$$\frac{k_LZ}{u_{av}B_F} = \frac{3}{\sqrt{\pi}}\sqrt{\frac{D_L\theta}{B_F^2}}$$ (397)

shows that $f(K,k_c\theta)/(K + 1)$ is a multiplying factor which gives the effect of the chemical reaction on the coefficient for no reaction. Inspection of Eq. (392) shows that $f(K,k_c\theta)$ becomes equal to 1 for the condition of a very unfavorable equilibrium $(K = 0)$. Under this condition the correction factor to the absorption coefficient becomes equal to unity, as expected.

$f(K,k_c\theta)$ also becomes equal to unity when the equilibrium favors the production of B $(K > 0)$ but the reaction is extremely slow $(k_c\theta \sim 0)$. Equation (396) shows that under these conditions the absorption coefficient is *lower* than for purely physical absorption. Physically this is due to the fact that the solute dissolves at the interface in the A form and does not react immediately. The interfacial concentration is only p_i/H, therefore, rather than $(K + 1)(p_i/H)$, which is used in defining k_L. The

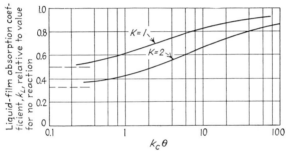

Fig. 149. Effect of chemical reaction on liquid-film absorption coefficient. First-order, reversible reaction.

driving force causing diffusion is smaller and the rate of absorption smaller, because of the reaction. In this connection see the discussion of Cl_2 absorption in water, below.

When the reaction is rapid $(k_c \to \infty)$ Eq. (391) shows that $f(K,k_c\theta)$ approaches $K + 1$ as a limiting value. The absorption coefficient then has its normal value, irrespective of K.

Figure 149 shows the effects of K and $k_c\theta$ on the absorption coefficient k_L, as defined by Eq. (395). Each line, corresponding to a constant value of K, shows the gradual transition between the abnormally low value of the coefficient when A reacts very slowly after it dissolves and the normal value when both A and B exist in equilibrium with gaseous A at the interface.

Figure 150 shows the variation of the total amount of solute absorbed with K and $k_c\theta$ for constant values of D_L, B_F, and Z/u_s. Increasing values of the reaction-rate constant and of the equilibrium constant increase the amount absorbed. Each curve approaches $K + 1$ as an upper limit, this being the maximum fractional increase possible. The curve for $K = \infty$ corresponds to the irreversible reaction, as in the reaction of CO_2 with NaOH. It is interesting to note that in this case Eq. (389) reduces approximately to

$$f(\infty, k_c\theta) = \left(\frac{\pi k_c\theta}{4}\right)^{1/2} \tag{398}$$

for large values of $k_c\theta$. The amount of solute absorbed then becomes

$$\frac{(K+1)c_{a\backslash} - c_0}{c_i - [c_0/(K+1)]} = \frac{k_L'Z}{u_{a\backslash}B_F} = \frac{3}{2}(D_Lk_c)^{1/2}\frac{\theta}{B_F} \tag{399}$$

where the concentration difference in the denominator is calculated from the amount of dissolved but unreacted solute at the interface and in the

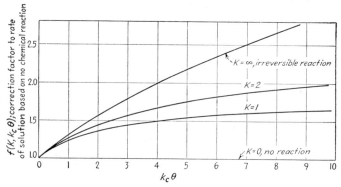

FIG. 150. Effect of chemical reaction on rate of absorption. Reversible, first-order reaction in liquid.

unexposed liquid and where k_L' is a pseudo liquid-film coefficient, *i.e.*, a coefficient based on a driving force expressed in terms of unreacted solute concentrations. For such situations it may be expected, therefore, that the influence of liquid rate, or time of exposure, will be different from the effect normally observed when no reaction occurs. In this connection see the discussion of CO_2 absorption in NaOH solution, below.

Theory of Unsteady-state Absorption in the Stagnant Liquid—Rapid Second-order, Irreversible Reaction. If the chemical reaction which takes place in the liquid, after the absorption of gaseous substance A, is

$$A + B \rightarrow AB$$

and if the rate of absorption of A is sufficiently rapid, the rate may be limited by the rate at which B can diffuse from the liquid toward the gas-liquid interface to react with A. The faster B is able to diffuse, the shorter the distance A will have to diffuse into the liquid to meet it. In contrast with the theory of the first-order reaction,

$$A \rightarrow C$$

which has already been discussed and for which the rate of absorption is independent of the concentration of B, the rate of absorption of A depends on the concentration of B in the second-order case.

The theory of the second-order reaction of finite reaction velocity does not appear to have been worked out. If the reaction rate is extremely rapid compared with the rate of diffusion of the reactants, the theory can be developed, however, as shown below. The results are comparable with Hatta's theory[175] of the steady-state diffusion through a "film" of finite thickness. The following theory has the advantage over Hatta's, however, of allowing for non-steady-state absorption effects and therefore, for the flow of the liquid film as absorption proceeds. The newer second-order theory bears the same relation to Hatta's reaction-zone theory (compare page 321) that the theory of unsteady-state diffusion and simultaneous first-order reaction bears to Hatta's theory (compare page 324) of steady-state diffusion and slow, simultaneous, first-order reaction in a film of finite thickness.

The derivation proceeds along lines suggested by Neumann's method[339] of calculating heat conduction in the formation of ice. As described by Ingersoll, Zobel, and Ingersoll,[211] the plane at which ice forms retreats continuously away from the surface when heat is being removed, the rate of retreat depending on the rate of heat conduction through the ice layer. In the absorption problem, the following liquid layer initially has a uniform concentration of B when it is exposed to a gas containing A. As A is absorbed, the B molecules which are near the interface are consumed in the reaction and are replenished by diffusion of additional B molecules from the main body of the liquid. Since the reaction is assumed to take place instantaneously when A and B are brought together, regardless of the concentrations in the reaction zone, the point where A and B molecules meet each other will move farther and farther away from the interface. The rate of absorption of A therefore grows progressively smaller as the molecules have to diffuse farther into the liquid in order to react.

There is no opportunity for A to react until it reaches the reaction zone at a distance x' from the interface. Thus, within the region $0 < x < x'$, the diffusion of A is governed by the differential equation

$$D_A \frac{\partial^2 c_A}{\partial x^2} = \frac{\partial c_A}{\partial \theta} \tag{400}$$

Similarly, B does not react with A until it reaches the point $x = x'$; for $x > x'$, the diffusion of B is governed by the equation

$$D_B \frac{\partial^2 c_B}{\partial x^2} = \frac{\partial c_B}{\partial \theta} \tag{401}$$

For short times of exposure of the liquid surface, concentrations of A and B vary only within a region near the interface, so that for these conditions we may assume without affecting the results significantly that the liquid layer is infinitely deep. Thus, Eq. (401) applies within the region $x' < x < \infty$.

Figure 151 shows profiles of the concentration curves for $A + B$ at

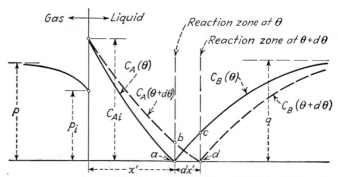

FIG. 151.   Concentration profiles for rapid second-order reaction in the liquid.

times θ and $\theta + d\theta$, the reaction zone having moved a distance dx' during $d\theta$. From the geometry of the small triangles abd and adc, it is seen that

$$ab = \frac{\partial c_A}{\partial \theta}\, d\theta = -\,\frac{\partial c_A}{\partial x}\, dx' \qquad (402)$$

$$cd = -\,\frac{\partial c_B}{\partial \theta}\, d\theta = \frac{\partial c_B}{\partial x}\, dx' \qquad (403)$$

from which it follows that

$$\frac{dx'}{d\theta} = -\,\frac{\partial c_B/\partial \theta}{\partial c_B/\partial x} = -\,\frac{\partial c_A/\partial \theta}{\partial c_A/\partial x} \qquad (404)$$

Equation (404) gives the relationship between the properties of the equations representing c_A and c_B, respectively, as functions of x and θ and the rate of movement of the reaction zone.

Solutions of Eqs. (400) and (401), which will be suitable if they can be made to satisfy the necessary boundary conditions, are

$$c_A = A_1 + B_1\, \mathrm{erf}\, \frac{x}{2\,\sqrt{D_A\theta}} \qquad (405)$$

$$c_B = A_2 + B_2\, \mathrm{erf}\, \frac{x}{2\,\sqrt{D_B\theta}} \qquad (406)$$

where the functional notation of Eq. (390) is employed. If Eqs. (405)

and (406) are differentiated and substituted into Eq. (404), setting $x = x'$, we obtain

$$\frac{dx'}{d\theta} = \frac{x'}{2\theta} \tag{407}$$

and, on integrating,

$$x' = 2\alpha^{\frac{1}{2}}\theta^{\frac{1}{2}} \tag{408}$$

where the constant of integration is taken as $2\sqrt{\alpha}$. Thus, the reaction zone moves away from the interface at a rate which decreases with increasing time. The constant α has to be determined from the other boundary conditions, which may be listed as follows:

1. $c_A = c_{Ai}$, a constant, when $x = 0$, $\theta > 0$
2. $c_B = q$, a constant, when $x = \infty$, $\theta \geq 0$
3. $c_B = q$, when $\theta = 0$, $x > 0$
4. $c_A = 0$, and $c_B = 0$, when $x = x'$, $\theta > 0$*

One additional boundary condition is needed to determine the five arbitrary constants A_1, A_2, B_1, B_2, and α. It may be developed by setting down the stoichiometric condition that 1 mole of A consumes 1 mole of B at the reaction zone. We make a stoichiometric material balance for a reaction time, $\Delta\theta$, as follows:

$$\text{Moles of } A \text{ diffusing from left} = -D_A \frac{\partial c_A}{\partial x}\Delta\theta$$

$$\text{Moles of } A \text{ appearing in } \Delta x' = -\frac{\partial c_A}{\partial x}\left(\frac{\Delta x'}{2}\right)^2$$

$$\text{Moles of } B \text{ diffusing from right} = +D_B\left(\frac{\partial c_B}{\partial x}\right)\Delta\theta*$$

$$\text{Moles of } B \text{ appearing in } \Delta x' = -\frac{\partial c_B}{\partial x}\left(\frac{\Delta x'}{2}\right)^2$$

In the limit, as $\Delta x'$ and $\Delta\theta$ approach zero, the second and fourth items become negligibly small in comparison with the first and third, so that the fifth boundary condition is expressed by

5. $D_A\dfrac{\partial c_A}{\partial x} + D_B\dfrac{\partial c_B}{\partial x} = 0$ at $x = x'$, $D_B \neq 0$†

The five boundary conditions lead to the following equations for determining the constants:

---

* This is true only if D_B is finite. Otherwise c_B will be uniformly equal to q for $x > x'$.

† If $D_B = 0$, $-D_A(\partial c_A/\partial x) = q(dx'/d\theta)$ at $x = x'$.

$$A_1 = c_{Ai} \tag{409}$$

$$A_2 + B_2 = q \tag{410}$$

$$A_1 + B_1 \operatorname{erf}\left(\frac{\alpha}{D_A}\right)^{\frac{1}{2}} = 0 \tag{411}$$

$$A_2 + B_2 \operatorname{erf}\left(\frac{\alpha}{D_B}\right)^{\frac{1}{2}} = 0 \tag{412}$$

$$B_1 \sqrt{D_A}\, e^{-(\alpha/D_A)} + B_2 \sqrt{D_B}\, e^{-(\alpha/D_B)} = 0 \tag{413}$$

The solution of this set of simultaneous equations leads to

$$B_1 = -\frac{c_{Ai}}{\operatorname{erf}(\alpha/D_A)^{\frac{1}{2}}} \tag{414}$$

$$\frac{q}{c_{Ai}} \frac{e^{(x/D_A)(1-r)}}{r} \operatorname{erf}\left(\frac{\alpha}{D_A}\right)^{\frac{1}{2}} + \operatorname{erf}\left(\frac{r\alpha}{D_A}\right)^{\frac{1}{2}} = 1 \tag{415}$$

where $r = D_A/D_B$.

The result is simplified considerably if A and B have equal diffusion coefficients, which is approximately true in practice. In this case,

$$\operatorname{erf}\left(\frac{\alpha}{D}\right)^{\frac{1}{2}} = \frac{c_{Ai}}{c_{Ai} + q} \tag{416}$$

For any ratio of D_A to D_B, Eq. (415) may be solved for α/D_A by cut-and-try methods and the four arbitrary constants determined. Figure 152

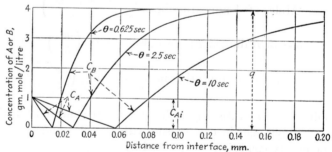

FIG. 152. Calculated concentration profiles during rapid second-order reaction in liquid film. Based on $D_A = 3.9 \times 10^{-5}$ ft.²/hr.; $D_B = 1.95 \times 10^{-5}$ ft.²/hr.

shows calculated concentrations of A and B for a particular set of physical conditions. The gradual movement of the reaction zone away from the interface is evident. It is interesting to note that the thickness of the zone near the interface in which the concentrations are sensibly affected up to 10 sec. exposure is only a few tenths of a millimeter.

The instantaneous rate of absorption is found by calculating the slope of the c_A curve at the interface. Thus

$$N_A = -D_A \left(\frac{\partial c_A}{\partial x}\right)_{x=0} = \frac{c_{Ai}}{\text{erf } (\alpha/D_A)^{1/2}} \left(\frac{D_A}{\pi\theta}\right)^{1/2} \qquad (417)*$$

and the average rate of absorption, up to a total time of exposure, θ, is given by

$$(N_A)_{\text{av}} = \frac{1}{\theta} \int_0^\theta N_A \, d\theta = \frac{c_{Ai}}{\text{erf } (\alpha/D_A)^{1/2}} 2 \left(\frac{D_A}{\pi\theta}\right)^{1/2} \qquad (418)$$

If the liquid-film transfer coefficient k_L is defined on the basis of a driving force equal to $c_{Ai} - 0$, we have

$$k_L = \frac{2}{\sqrt{\pi}} \frac{(D_A/\theta)^{1/2}}{\text{erf } (\alpha/D_A)^{1/2}} \qquad (419)$$

Under the simplifying assumption that $D_A = D_B$, we obtain, finally,

$$k_L = \frac{2}{\sqrt{\pi}} \left(1 + \frac{q}{c_{Ai}}\right) \left(\frac{D_A}{\theta}\right)^{1/2} \qquad (420)$$

It is interesting to observe that, according to Eq. (420), the liquid-film absorption coefficient increases linearly with the concentration of active reactant in the liquid, q, and decreases with increasing concentration of A at the interface. This effect is exactly that found from Hatta's two-zone, steady-state theory of diffusion through a film of constant thickness, but here the effect of the time of exposure of the liquid surface and the diffusivity of the solute are in agreement with experimental data, as will be shown below.

Equation (420) is limited by the assumption of equal diffusivities of the reacting molecules. Equations (414) and (415) may be solved by trial and error for $r \neq 1$, however. Figure 153 shows the results obtained for the case $D_A/D_B = 2$. It is seen that, to a close degree of approximation,

$$k_L = \frac{2}{\sqrt{\pi}} \left(1 + \frac{D_B}{D_A}\frac{q}{c_{Ai}}\right) \left(\frac{D_A}{\theta}\right)^{1/2} \qquad (421)$$

Thus, if A diffuses faster than B, k_L increases with the ratio q/c_{Ai}, though the rate of increase in k_L is not so rapid as for the case of equal diffusivities. Equations (415) and (421) lead to erroneous results if D_B is zero. A study of the case leads to the conclusion that k_L increases in proportion to $\sqrt{q/c_{Ai}}$, rather than to the first power of this ratio.

Summary of Theoretical Results on Absorption and Reaction. Theoretical results have been obtained for the following hypothetical situations:

* The same result was published recently by Danckwerts[100a] without discussion or mathematical development.

A. Steady-state diffusion and reaction in stagnant film of finite thickness

    1. Infinitely rapid second-order chemical reaction limited by diffusion of solute and reactant to a thin reaction zone [Eq. (362)]

    2. Slow first-order, irreversible reaction and simultaneous diffusion in the film [Eq. (380)]

B. Unsteady-state diffusion and reaction in a thick, flowing layer of liquid, the instantaneous absorption rate decreasing with increasing time of exposure

    1. Infinitely rapid second-order reaction limited by diffusion of solute and reactant to a thin reaction zone which starts at the interface and moves gradually into the liquid [Eq. (421)]

    2. Slow first-order, reversible reaction and simultaneous diffusion into the liquid [Eq. (388)]

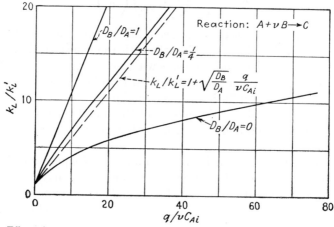

Fig. 153. Effect of concentrations of B and A in liquid on absorption coefficient. Second-order reaction $A + B \rightarrow C$.

For both of cases A-1 and B-1 the rate of the second-order absorption reaction is found to depend on the concentration of the active chemical in the liquid, q, as well as the concentration of the dissolved solute at the interface, c_{Ai}. Similarly, the over-all gas-film coefficient or the liquid-film coefficient is found to depend on the ratio q/c_{Ai}. Since there is assumed to be no limitation on the reaction rate except the rate of diffusion of the reactants, the liquid-film coefficient is found to increase without limit as q increases.

In both of cases A-2 and B-2 the rate of absorption is found to be independent of all concentrations except the concentration of dissolved solute at the interface. (If the reaction is a pseudo first-order type, which appears to be first order only because the second reactant is in large excess, the effective reaction-rate constant is proportional to q.) The absorption rate is limited both by diffusion and by the finite velocity of reaction, but the absorption coefficient should not depend on either q or c_{Ai}. If the reaction is pseudo first order, however, the coefficient will vary with q through its effect on the apparent k_c but will not vary with c_{Ai}.

Cases B-1 and B-2 differ from cases A-1 and A-2 in that it is not necessary in the former to conceive of a stagnant film of finite thickness capable of exerting resistance to diffusion but incapable of retaining any of the solute which dissolves, nor is a thoroughly mixed main body of liquid assumed.

EXPERIMENTS ON BATCHWISE ABSORPTION WITH REACTION

Most of the earliest attempts to study the kinetics of absorption under conditions such that chemical reaction influences the absorption rate were carried out using laboratory equipment similar to that shown in Fig. 154. These devices have the advantage over packed or plate columns that the interfacial area is known. However, the agitation which is usually provided in the liquid phase in order to produce a constant rate of absorption may make conditions in the zone of reaction quite different from those encountered in packed columns, where there is no means available for stirring the bulk of the liquid phase and where the solute which is absorbed at each exposure of the liquid stream is retained by the liquid surface itself. It is not surprising, therefore, that results obtained from such experiments have not proved of so much value in analyzing the mechanism of absorption in continuous absorbers as was hoped during the early development of this field.

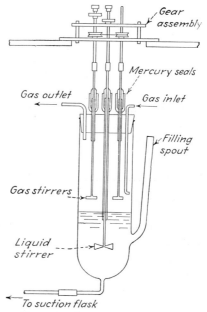

FIG. 154. Batch absorption vessel.

Jenny[220] used a batch absorber containing 700 cc. of liquid to absorb ethyl acetate and methyl formate in caustic solutions. Both phases were stirred, and mixtures of the esters with air were fed continuously to the gas space. The absorption rate was determined from analyses of liquid samples, which were removed periodically from the vessel, analyzed by means of a conductivity cell, and returned to the reactor. Jenny found that for both esters the rate of absorption remained constant throughout each run, which in some cases was continued until the residual OH$^-$ normality was less than 0.01. In the case of the ethyl acetate runs, appreciable time was required to obtain a constant reading in the conductivity cell, indicating the presence of unreacted ester in the sample withdrawn.

The results obtained with the two esters are summarized in Table XXVI. For comparison, the result of a test absorbing ammonia by water from air in the same apparatus is included.

TABLE XXVI. RATE OF ABSORPTION OF ESTERS BY NaOH SOLUTIONS*

Vapor	Initial NaOH normality	Partial pressure of solute in gas, atm.	Absorption rate, lb. moles/(hr.) (ft.²)	K_G, lb. moles/ (hr.)(ft.²) (atm.)
Ethyl acetate............	0 (water)	0.095	0.00294	0.0310
	0.5	0.046	0.00142	0.0308
	0.5	0.087	0.00254	0.0292
	0.5	0.095	0.00258	0.0272
	1.0	0.092	0.00274	0.0298
Methyl formate..........	0 (water)	0.094	0.0030	0.032
	0.5	0.088	0.00578	0.065
	0.5	0.090	0.0059	0.065
	0.5	0.130	0.00742	0.057
	1.0	0.084	0.0089	0.106
Ammonia................	0 (water)	0.052	0.0097	0.187

* Data of Jenny.[220]

For ammonia the gas-film resistance is presumably controlling because of the high solubility. Since for each ester the value of K_G for absorption by water is much less than for ammonia, it is apparent that the liquid film must represent a large part of the over-all resistance. In the case of the ethyl acetate the differences obtained with various strengths of caustic are probably within the experimental error, and it may be concluded that the occurrence of the chemical reaction does not affect the rate of absorption. The reaction is sufficiently slow to permit the ester to diffuse through the liquid film before reacting, and the result corresponds to the last case above, in which F is unity, and the theoretical relation reduces to the equation

$$N_A = K_L(c_e - c) \tag{422}$$

Methyl formate is absorbed by water at practically the same rate as is ethyl acetate, and it seems probable that the liquid-film resistance is again controlling. The reaction-rate constant for methyl formate and caustic is very much larger than for ethyl acetate and caustic, and the reaction in solution proceeds so rapidly that the OH^- ion concentration is depleted in the reaction zone. An increase in the caustic strength therefore increases K_G, as expected from Hatta's theory [Eq. (362)].

According to Eq. (362), K_G should vary linearly with the ratio of hydroxide normality to gas partial pressure. Figure 155 shows Jenny's methyl formate data plotted in this fashion. The straight line shows that the agreement with the theory is quantitative, at least within the range of q and p covered experimentally. The maximum value of K_G would be

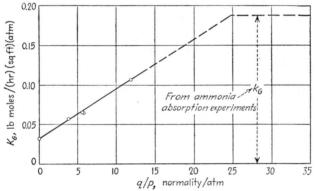

FIG. 155. Batch absorption of methyl formate in sodium hydroxide. (*Data of Jenny.*)

approximately the value of k_G, corresponding to K_G, observed in the ammonia experiment.

The results obtained with ethyl acetate do not afford a quantitative test of the theory of the slow first-order reaction, owing to the low reaction-rate constant. The theoretical prediction that the reaction should be without effect as long as k_c is small is confirmed, however. The higher absorption rates obtained with methyl formate may be explained on the basis of chemical reaction within the liquid film, and consequently a shorter distance for the ester to diffuse.

Jenny[220] also carried out a second series of experiments in which CO_2 was absorbed from mixtures with air in NaOH solutions using the same apparatus. Above $1N$ NaOH, the over-all absorption coefficient was constant at a value of 0.028 lb. mole/(hr.)(ft.²)(atm.), and according to the Hatta theory this should be the value of the gas-film coefficient. The rate of absorption of ammonia observed in a separate experiment corresponded to $k_G = 0.187$ lb. mole/(hr.)(ft.²)(atm.), so that the theory based on the infinitely rapid reaction fails to explain these results. It seems likely that the absorption in this case is limited by the rate at which CO_2 is able to combine chemically with OH^- ions. Under these conditions the over-all coefficient should be independent of both q and p, the concentration of OH^- ions at every point in the liquid reaction zone adjacent to the interface being large enough for the bimolecular reaction of CO_2 with OH^- ion to be effectively a first-order reaction.

Other experiments of a similar nature have been carried out by Hitchcock,[193] using CO_2 and either NaOH and KOH; by Hatta,[175] using CO_2 and KOH solutions; by Pozin,[378] using CO_2 in NaOH, KOH, or Na_2CO_3, as well as Cl_2 in NaOH, and also NH_3 in several organic and inorganic acids; and by Turkhan,[466] using CO_2 in NaOH. Pozin's extensive data all show that the rate of absorption is proportional to a linear combination of the partial pressure of the solute in the gas and the concentration of the reactant in the liquid, in agreement with the Hatta steady-state theory of the rapid second-order reaction [Eq. (362)] or with the unsteady-state theory [Eq. (421)].

CONTINUOUS ABSORPTION WITH SIMULTANEOUS REACTION

Absorption of a gas by a liquid chemical absorbent which flows as a thin film down a wetted-wall tower resembles the action of a continuously acting packed absorber more closely than does a batch experiment of the type already described. It may be expected that the rate of solution will decrease rapidly from a very large value when the liquid is first exposed to the gas. The average rate of absorption should depend on the time of exposure of the liquid surface to the gas and therefore on the velocity of flow and the length of the column.

It seems reasonable to suppose that in a packed absorber the liquid is rather thoroughly mixed each time it flows from one piece of packing to another. After each instance of mixing the fresh liquid surface absorbs an incremental quantity of solute at a steadily decreasing rate until the next mixing process takes place. The average resistance to absorption is therefore independent of the packed depth, since the packed bed is invariably several packing pieces deep. As the liquid flows down the tower, it experiences a series of mixing processes and unsteady-state absorption operations.

Stephens and Morris[443] described an interesting series of experiments in which a wetted-wall column of special design was used to absorb chlorine from air in aqueous solutions of ferrous and ferric chlorides, the ferrous iron being oxidized to ferric iron by chemical reaction in the liquid. In many ways the results confirm the unsteady-state theory of absorption and rapid, irreversible, second-order reaction described above.

Stephens and Morris made a preliminary series of experiments using a wetted-wall apparatus of ordinary design to absorb CO_2 in water. Because of the end effects (due to unsteady-state diffusion) which were detected when the length of the column was changed, it was decided to do further work using the apparatus shown by Fig. 156. As the liquid was

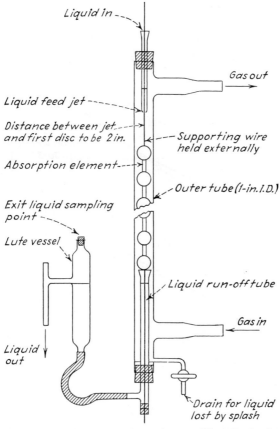

Fig. 156. Arrangements of disk absorption column. (*Used by Stephens and Morris.*)

stirred each time it flowed from one disk to another, the apparatus resembled a packed absorber, yet the total disk area was wet at all times and could therefore be used to calculate absorption coefficients.

Based on experiments in which CO_2 was absorbed in water and others in which Cl_2 was absorbed in ferric chloride solution, the liquid-film coefficient for physical absorption was related to the liquid-flow rate by the equations

$$k_L = 1.86 \times 10^{-2} \left(\frac{\Gamma}{\mu}\right)^{0.7} \qquad \text{for } \Gamma/\mu > 16 \qquad (423)$$

$$k_L = 3.24 \times 10^{-2} \left(\frac{\Gamma}{\mu}\right)^{0.5} \qquad \text{for } \Gamma/\mu < 16 \qquad (424)$$

which correspond to the lowest line on Fig. 157.

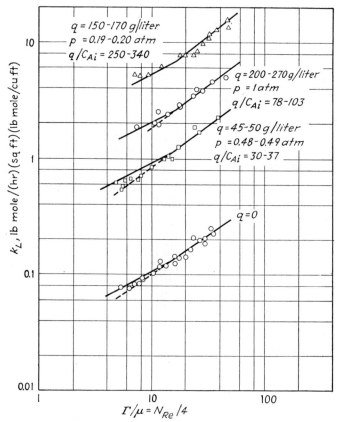

FIG. 157.   Absorption of chlorine in ferrous chloride solution; initial strength of solution = 377 g. FeCl₂/liter.   (*Data of Stephens and Morris.*)

According to the theory of flow of liquid layers, the surface velocity varies as $\Gamma^{2/3}$.   The time of exposure therefore varies as $\Gamma^{-2/3}$, and, according to Eq. (421), k_L should vary as $\Gamma^{1/3}$.   The effect of Γ given by Eqs. (423) and (424) is approximately twice that expected.   The difference is probably due to the fact that the frequent mixing which the liquid undergoes causes the effective diffusivity to vary with the flow rate.

Figure 157 also shows the data obtained by Stephens and Morris when the liquid contained $FeCl_2$. The effect of liquid rate is seen to be similar to that shown by the lowest line, which corresponds to purely physical absorption. Under the influence of chemical reaction, the coefficients are larger, the greater the concentration of $FeCl_2$ and the smaller the partial pressure of the gas. (The liquid-film coefficients were calculated on the assumption that the solubility of chlorine at the interface is the same as in pure $FeCl_3$ solution. A small correction was applied for the gas-phase resistance, which was determined experimentally by absorbing ammonia in water.)

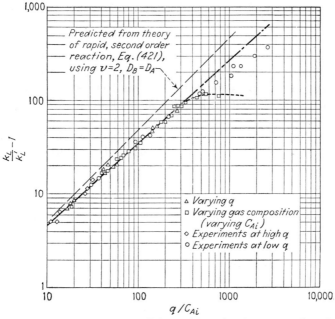

Fig. 158. Variation of absorption coefficient with ratio of concentration of $FeCl_2$ to concentration of dissolved Cl_2 at interface. (*Data of Stephens and Morris.*)

According to Eq. (421), the ratio of the liquid-film coefficient without reaction to that with reaction should depend on the ratio q/c_{Ai} and, for constant values of this ratio, should be independent of either q or c_{Ai} separately. The different curves on Fig. 157 are located relative to one another in the order of increasing values of q/c_{Ai}. Either concentration, taken by itself, would not correlate the effects observed, however. Figure 158 shows the results of approximately one-third of all the runs, the coefficient in each case being divided by the coefficient at the same value of Γ/μ but with no reaction. The figure shows that, indeed, the effect of the reaction is described by q/c_{Ai}, despite separate variations in the concentration of $FeCl_2$, the Cl_2 content of the gas, or the liquid-flow rate. The qualitative deduction from the theory is thus confirmed to a remark-able degree.

Quantitatively, the fractional increment in k_L above its value for no reaction should be a linear function of q/c_{Ai}. Thus, the slope of the line in Fig. 158 should be unity, theoretically. Actually, the slope is 0.83, and the coefficient is given by

$$k_L = k_L' \left[1 + (0.46) \left(\frac{q}{c_{Ai}} \right)^{0.83} \right] \qquad (425)$$

The fractional value of the coefficient inside the bracket could be explained by a lower diffusion coefficient for $FeCl_2$ than for chlorine in the liquid.

It may be observed that the data obtained at very low gas concentra-tions, under conditions such that the rate of absorption was low, deviate from the line in a direction such that the coefficient becomes almost independent of the gas composition. This lack of dependence is just what would be expected if the reaction should become slow and effectively first order under these conditions, its rate being limited by a finite value of the reaction-velocity constant k_c. For these conditions, Eq. (420) should be replaced by Eqs. (388) and (393). The reaction rate is of the same order or smaller than the rate at which B can diffuse toward the interface, with the result that the concentration of B is uniformly large throughout the film. The effective first-order reaction constant k_c then becomes $k_{II}q$, where k_{II} is the velocity constant of the second-order reac-tion. As a matter of fact, it seems plausible to suppose that the low exponent on q/c_{Ai} in the empirical expression [Eq. (425)] is due to the fact that the second-order reaction is not instantaneous, the influence of q/c_{Ai} being slightly less than that given by Eq. (420), owing to the fact that the reaction goes on to some extent throughout the liquid.

Additional measurements of absorption rates in a wetted-wall column have been reported by Pozin,[378] who studied the absorption of pure gaseous CO_2 or Cl_2 in 1 to 14 per cent NaOH in a column 1.3 cm. in diameter and 20 cm. long. The results were calculated as liquid-film coefficients, using the concentration of hydroxyl ion as a driving force. This procedure is justified by Eq. (421), which may be rewritten in the form

$$k_L'' = \frac{N_A}{q} = \frac{2}{\sqrt{\pi}} \left(\frac{c_{Ai}}{q} + \sqrt{\frac{D_B}{D_A}} \right) \left(\frac{3D_A u_{av}}{2Z} \right)^{\frac{1}{2}} \qquad (426)$$

where k_L'' is Pozin's coefficient, based on q as the driving force causing diffusion of the reactant B toward the interface, and where $3u_{av}/2Z$ has been substituted for the time of exposure, θ, *i.e.*, the surface velocity divided by the length of the column. Thus, the quantity k_L''/u_{av} should vary linearly with the reciprocal of the caustic concentration, the rate of variation being dependent on c_{Ai}, the concentration of dissolved solute at the interface. Table XXVII summarizes Pozin's data and shows that the coefficient k_L'' does vary in the direction expected, though the variation is less for Cl_2, which has the greater solubility, c_{Ai}. At any constant

TABLE XXVII

q, lb. moles NaOH/ft.^{3}	$1/q$	$k_L''/\sqrt{u_{av}}$*
Cl_2 absorption in NaOH solution		
0.0275	36.4	103
0.0640	15.6	92
0.0995	10.1	84
CO_2 absorption in NaOH solution		
0.0630	15.9	17.7
0.248	4.04	8.0

* The units of k_L'' are kg./(hr.)(m.²)(mole fraction NaOH); the units of u_{av} are m./hr.

value of q, $k_L'' \sqrt{u_{av}}$ was constant in spite of a variation in u_{av} from 0.51 to 0.99 ft./sec.

It appears from the data available that the theories developed previously successfully explain the effects observed, at least qualitatively.

ABSORPTION ACCOMPANIED BY CHEMICAL REACTION IN PACKED TOWERS

A number of experiments have been made on the absorption of gases in packed towers under conditions involving chemical reaction between the solute and the solvent, including several of the industrially most important absorption procedures. While the results are very useful for design calculations, most of these experiments have failed to shed any light on the mechanism of the transfer process in the liquid.

One particularly interesting set of data has been reported by Vivian and Whitney[480] for the absorption of chlorine in water. As the chlorine dissolves, it reacts with the water according to the following chemical equations

$$Cl_{2\,gas} \rightleftarrows Cl_{2\,aq} \qquad (a)$$
$$Cl_{2\,aq} + H_2O \rightleftarrows HOCl + H^+ + Cl^- \qquad (b)$$

When reaction (b) reaches equilibrium, the dissolved chlorine is present in the water in three forms: unreacted molecular chlorine, Cl_2; hypochlorous acid, HOCl; and chloride ion, Cl^-. When physical equilibrium exists between the gas and liquid and when, in addition, the second, chemical reaction is at equilibrium, the following conditions apply according to the law of the mass action:

From reaction (*a*)

$$c_{Cl_2} = \frac{p}{H'} \tag{427}$$

From reaction (*b*)

$$\frac{(c_{HOCl})(c_{Cl^-})(c_{H^+})}{c_{Cl_2}} = K_e \tag{428}$$

If c represents the concentration of *total* dissolved chlorine and there is no excess of Cl^- or of H^+, then

$$c_{HOCl} = c_{Cl^-} = c_{H^+} = c - c_{Cl_2} = c - \frac{p}{H'} \tag{429}$$

Substituting in Eq. (428) and solving for c,

$$c = \frac{p}{H'} + \left(\frac{K_e p}{H'}\right)^{1/3} \tag{430}$$

This equation explains why the concentration of total dissolved chlorine is not proportional to the partial pressure of chlorine in the gas, as is

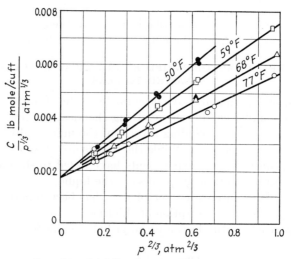

FIG. 159.   Solubility data for chlorine in water.

ordinarily true when no chemical reaction occurs and Henry's law applies in its usual sense. Whitney and Vivian[506] showed that straight lines could be obtained by plotting chlorine-solubility data as $c/p^{1/3}$ vs. $p^{2/3}$, as suggested by Eq. (430). A plot of this type is shown by Fig. 159. The values of the constants, which were determined from the slopes and intercepts of the lines, are shown in Table XXVIII and allow the concentration of any of the three forms of dissolved chlorine to be calculated. Reaction (*a*) is exothermic, while (*b*) is endothermic.

TABLE XXVIII. EQUILIBRIUM CONSTANTS FOR CHLORINE IN WATER[506]

Temperature, °F.	Henry's law coefficient, H', (atm.)(ft.^{3})/lb. mole	Equilibrium constant K_e, (lb. moles/ft.^{3})^2
50	141	7.10
59	171	8.55
68	213	10.7
77	256	12.8

Most of Vivian and Whitney's[480] absorption experiments were made with a 4-in.-diameter tower filled to a depth of 2 ft. with 1-in. ceramic Raschig rings, though a few data were taken with a 14-in.-diameter tower containing 8 ft. of the same packing. Figure 160 shows values of the absorption coefficient $K_L a$ plotted against the liquid mass velocity L. The coefficient is based on the logarithmic-mean difference between the values of c at the interface and in the bulk of the liquid, the value at the interface representing the concentration of *total* chlorine which would be in both chemical and physical equilibrium with the gas.

In a separate series of experiments Vivian and Whitney[480] also determined rates of desorption of oxygen from water, using the same apparatus. These data are also shown in Fig. 160. It is evident that the chlorine coefficients are abnormally low, even if allowance is made for the difference in the liquid diffusivities of chlorine and oxygen. Moreover, the effect of liquid rate on $K_L a$ is smaller than for the case of purely physical absorption. No effect of gas rate was observed, and there was no effect of the chlorine content of the gas. The effect of liquid temperature was essentially the same as that found by Sherwood and Holloway[418] for oxygen stripping. All the results correspond to conditions of purely physical absorption, except that the liquid rate had an abnormally small effect, and the magnitude of the liquid-film coefficients was surprisingly small.

The logical explanation of these results was given by Vivian and Whitney,[480] who pointed out that the rate of the physical reaction (*a*) at the interface is almost certain to be very large, though the chemical reaction (*b*) may be relatively slow. Thus, chlorine molecules may dissolve in the liquid and begin to diffuse into the liquid before reaction (*b*) has an opportunity to occur. If this should be true, the concentration of chlorine in the liquid at the interface would be that of dissolved, but unreacted chlorine, c_{Cl_2}, which is less than c, as shown by Eq. (429). If reaction (b) is so slow that the chlorine molecules penetrate a considerable distance into the liquid without reacting, then the driving force which is

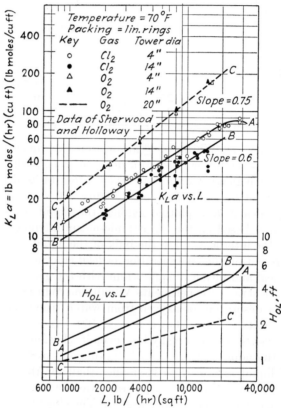

FIG. 160. Effect of liquor rate on normal K_La and H.T.U. for chlorine and oxygen in water. (*Data of Vivian and Whitney.*)

available to produce diffusion is Δc_{Cl_2} rather than Δc. Figure 161 shows a plot of gas and liquid compositions for one of the runs. At any value of the ordinate, the horizontal distance between the operating and equilibrium lines represents the liquid-film driving force. It is apparent that this driving force is smaller when the concentration is that of unreacted chlorine than when it is total chlorine. The mass-transfer coefficient based on the smaller driving force is larger and has been given the name "pseudo coefficient" by Vivian and Whitney.

Figure 162 shows the pseudo coefficients plotted against the liquid-flow rate. The effect of liquid rate is the same as before, but at high liquid rates the pseudo coefficients are seen to agree closely with the line predicted from the oxygen data. This behavior is perhaps not surprising. The time of exposure of the liquid stream on each packing piece in the tower is small at the high flow rates. If the time of exposure is less than the time required for reaction, the dissolved solute will be principally in the molecular form and the pseudo coefficient should be the correct one.

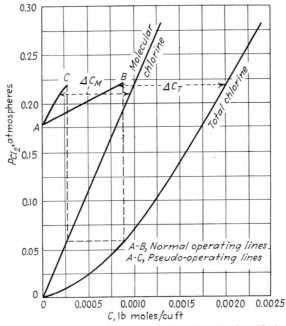

FIG. 161.   Pseudo operating diagram for determination of molecular-chlorine concentration differences.   (*From Vivian and Whitney.*)

If, on the other hand, the flow rate is low and the time of exposure long, then reaction (*b*) will occur near the interface and the ordinary coefficient is the proper one to use. The ordinary coefficient should agree with the oxygen data at low flow velocities, and the pseudo coefficient should agree at high velocities. Thus, the data of Vivian and Whitney[480] are in accord with the theory regarding the influence of simultaneous diffusion and slow first-order reaction in the liquid.

The absence of an effect of the chlorine content of the gas is also in agreement with these ideas. If the reaction takes place with the water, which is present throughout the film in large excess, Eqs. (420) and (421) for second-order reactions would not be expected to apply. Only when two reactants must diffuse toward each other for rapid reaction within the film should the gas composition influence $k_L a$.

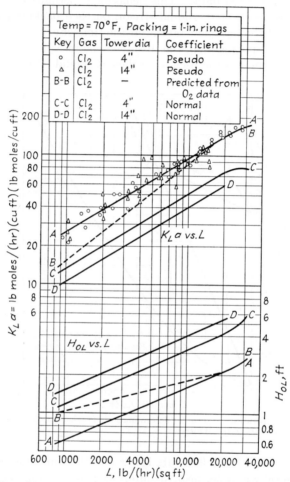

Fig. 162. Effect of liquor rate of pseudo $K_L a$ and pseudo H_{OL} for chlorine absorption in water. (*Data of Vivian and Whitney.*)

The concept of a pseudo coefficient of mass transfer was introduced previously in discussing the theory of the reversible first-order reaction in the film. The same type of transition from the pseudo coefficient to the ordinary one is expected from that theory, the ratio of the two coefficients being equal to $K + 1$, where K is the equilibrium constant for the reaction. A quantitative comparison of the chlorine data with the theory is not possible, however, inasmuch as the reverse reaction is of an order higher than the first. It may be that the absorption of Cl_2 in aqueous solutions of acids or metallic chlorides could be compared directly with the theory, owing to the large excess of hydrogen or chloride ions which would be present.

The absorption of sulfur dioxide in water has already been discussed in Chap. VIII as a case of physical absorption. Actually, however, this case is intermediate between purely physical absorption on the one hand and rapid chemical reaction on the other, just as for chlorine or ammonia

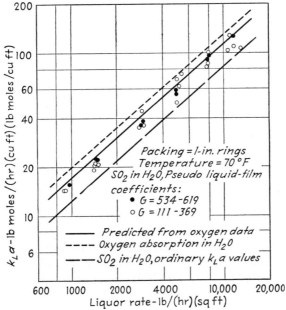

Fig. 163. Pseudo liquid-film coefficients at 70°F. for absorption of sulfur dioxide in water. (*Data of Vivian and Whitney.*)

or hydrogen sulfide dissolving in water. Whitney and Vivian[505] have been able to interpret their data for a packed absorber in essentially the same way as followed previously for chlorine.

Figure 163 shows ordinary liquid-film coefficients for SO_2, as well as pseudo coefficients based on concentrations of undissociated SO_2 as a function of L. The ordinary coefficients are lower than the values predicted from oxygen-desorption experiments, but the pseudo coefficients agree excellently over the whole range of liquid rates. It may be concluded, therefore, that SO_2 reacts slowly with water under these conditions, corresponding to a small value of $k_c\theta$ on Fig. 149.

A different approach to the problem of chemical reaction in the liquid phase in packed columns has been presented by Van Krevelen and Hoftijzer,[471] who have achieved some success in correlating data for several different systems with a single empirical equation. The basic concept of this development is that of diffusion of the solute into the liquid with simultaneous slow, irreversible, first-order chemical reaction. The results cannot be expected to apply, therefore, when the reaction is extremely rapid relative to the rate of diffusion and the rate of absorption is controlled by the rates of diffusion of each of two reactants.

Following the usual practice in Europe, Van Krevelen and Hoftijzer[471–473] chose to allow separately for the effects of the liquid rate on the wetted area of the packing and on the coefficients themselves. The following empirical equations express their results for the liquid-film resistance in the absence of chemical reaction

$$\frac{k_L'(\mu_L{}^2/g\rho_L{}^2)^{\frac{1}{3}}}{D_L} = 0.015 \left(\frac{L}{a\mu_L}\right)^{\frac{2}{3}} \left(\frac{\mu_L}{\rho_L D_L}\right)^{\frac{1}{3}} \tag{431}$$

$$\frac{a}{a_d} = 1 - e^{-0.40(L/\rho_L)} \tag{432}$$

When a reaction occurs, the value of k_L' is multiplied by the function $x/\tanh x$ with

$$x = \left(\frac{\mu_L{}^2}{g\rho_L{}^2}\right)^{\frac{1}{3}} \left(\frac{k_c}{D_L}\right)^{\frac{1}{2}}$$

as suggested by Eq. (431). Reaction-rate constants were employed as determined in separate kinetic experiments by Faurholt[137] for the liquid-phase combination of CO_2 with OH^- ions and with ammonia. The empirical constant in Eq. (431) was found to lie within the fivefold range from 0.009 to 0.045 for the absorption of CO_2 in aqueous NaOH, Na_2CO_3, and NH_4OH solutions.

That errors of 200 to 300 per cent are possible by this method may not be surprising in view of the approximations made. Equation (431) does not correlate the physical absorption data of Sherwood and Holloway[418] accurately, deviations as large as 50 per cent being found. The influence of packing size is much smaller than that indicated by the equation.

ABSORPTION OF CARBON DIOXIDE BY ALKALINE SOLUTIONS

The manufacture of liquid and solid carbon dioxide is an industry of considerable importance. Liquid carbon dioxide has long been used in manufactured beverages, and the solid form has come into prominence in recent years as a valuable refrigerant. Liquid carbon dioxide is shipped in heavy steel cylinders built to withstand the high vapor pressure of the product at ordinary temperatures. Solid carbon dioxide vaporizes at 1 atm. at $-110°F$. and is necessarily shipped in heavily insulated containers, trucks, or freight cars. Because both forms are expensive to handle and to ship, a considerable number of manufacturing plants have been constructed, the individual plants being only large enough to serve the localities within the relatively small economic shipping distance. In

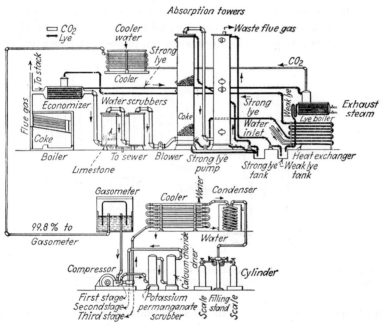

FIG. 164. Standard CO_2 absorption system. (*From G. C. Reich.*)

the large majority of these plants the source of CO_2 is flue gas obtained by burning coke under boilers. By careful control of the combustion process, employing thick fuel beds and regulating carefully the amount of secondary air, a gas containing 17 to 18 per cent CO_2 is obtained, from which CO_2 is recovered by absorption in a solution of carbonate and bicarbonate of either sodium or potassium, or in an aqueous solution of mono-, di-, or triethanolamine. The alkaline agent is converted first to the carbonate and then to the bicarbonate as more CO_2 is absorbed. The dissolved CO_2 may be liberated by heating. The gas so formed is dried, purified, and compressed to 55 to 75 atm. The liquefied product is either distributed as liquid in steel cylinders or cooled and expanded to form the solid. A flow sheet of the process using carbonate-bicarbonate solutions is shown diagrammatically in Fig. 164.[385] This method of manufacture may be divided into two parts: the production of pure dry CO_2 at 1 atm. pressure, and the manufacture of the liquid or solid product starting with the low-pressure pure gas. It is in the first part of the process that absorption plays such an important role.

Although most of the existing plants use flue gas as a source of CO_2, fermentation gases and lime-kiln gases may also be employed as raw materials. The gas obtained on burning limestone contains approximately 40 per cent CO_2, and the higher CO_2 concentration makes the absorption problem somewhat simpler and less expensive than when flue gas is used. Waste gases from fermentation processes frequently contain

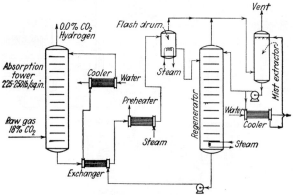

FIG. 165. Flow sheet of CO_2 absorption system using a solution of diaminoisopropanol as absorbent. (*From Standard Oil Development Co. and the Girdler Corporation.*)

still higher CO_2 contents. The solution employed as absorbent is most commonly a mixture of sodium carbonate and sodium bicarbonate, although in the past the potassium carbonates were sometimes employed. The lye concentrations are frequently expressed as pounds K_2CO_3 per cubic foot of solution, although sodium carbonate is actually being used, and "8 lb./ft.³" means a soda-lye solution of a strength chemically equivalent to that of a potash-lye solution containing 8 lb. K_2CO_3/ft.³

In the industrial manufacture of hydrogen, water gas containing principally CO_2 and hydrogen is treated to remove the CO_2. It frequently happens that the manufactured hydrogen is to be used under considerable pressure for hydrogenation or other purposes, so the CO_2 removal by absorption is carried out under pressure in order to reduce the size of the necessary absorption equipment and simplify the absorption problem. The pressure at which the absorption unit operates is determined by the relative costs of compression and absorption, since with increasing pressure the cost of compressing the unwanted CO_2 increases.

Figure 165 illustrates a typical installation for the removal of CO_2 from a gas obtained by the catalytic reaction of steam with methane, using a solution of monoethanolamine as absorbent. As shown in Fig. 165, the raw gas enters the bottom of the absorption tower, which operates at a pressure of 225 to 250 p.s.i. The scrubbing fluid enters the top of the tower, and the "foul" liquid from the base of the scrubber then passes through heat exchangers and steam preheaters to a disengaging drum where it is flashed at essentially atmospheric pressure, thereby releasing part of its absorbed CO_2. The liquid from the flash drum enters the top of the generator and is heated by steam coils in the bottom of the tower. The "fresh" fluid leaving the bottom of the tower is pumped through exchangers and coolers back to the top of the gas scrubber. The gas and steam leaving the flash drum and regenerator pass into a direct-contact cooler. This cooler is packed with spiral tile, and water is sprayed over the tile and cooled in external shell-and-tube-type coolers. The contact cooler serves the following two purposes: (1) steam leaving the system is condensed and returned to the system, thereby maintaining a constant solution concentration; (2) amine losses are reduced in that the CO_2 gas is continuously washed to remove small quantities of amine. A similar plant may be used for removal of hydrogen sulfide.

The following deals with the absorption of CO_2 by carbonate or amine solutions, as in the absorption processes outlined above. Although of less industrial importance, the absorption of CO_2 by sodium and potassium hydroxides will also be discussed, because of its bearing on the mechanism of the diffusional processes involved.

Solubility of CO_2 in Alkaline Solutions. Before dealing with the mechanism of the absorption of CO_2 in various solutions, it is desirable to summarize some of the principal data available on the equilibria involved. No attempt will be made to list all the data which are pertinent. Reference may be made to standard handbooks[363,409] or to the original sources. Alkaline solutions are chosen principally because of their very desirable equilibrium solubility characteristics, and it is well to keep these in mind in order to understand the advantage of chemical absorption over the simpler physical absorption in an inert solvent like water.

A suitable alkaline agent is one which is capable of reacting chemically with large quantities of CO_2 at the temperature of absorption, yet from which the dissolved gas can be expelled easily by heating moderately. Solutions of sodium carbonate satisfy this criterion, for the sodium bicarbonate which forms when CO_2 reacts with the carbonate ions is easily decomposed by heating. Figure 166 shows equilibrium partial pressures of CO_2 over a solution which is $1N$ with respect to sodium. The partial pressure increases rapidly with increased extent of the reaction but at 59°F. does not exceed 10 mm. Hg until the reaction is 50 per cent complete. Heating the solution to 212°F. with steam produces a tenfold increase in the CO_2 partial pressure. Data for this system may be represented by the equation

$$p_{CO_2} = \frac{137f^2N^{1.29}}{S(1 - f)(365 - t)} \tag{433}$$

where N = sodium normality
$\quad\quad f$ = fraction of total base present as bicarbonate
$\quad\quad t$ = temperature, °F.
$\quad\quad p_{CO_2}$ = equilibrium partial pressure of CO_2, mm. Hg
$\quad\quad S$ = solubility of pure CO_2 in water under a pressure of 1 atm., g. moles CO_2/liter[409]

The equation is based on the work of McCoy,[315] Sieverts and Fritzsche,[426] and Harte, Baker, and Purcell.[171] Sieverts and Fritzsche's data in the potassium carbonate-bicarbonate system may be approximated by Eq. (433) if the constants 137 and 365 be replaced by 45 and 302, respectively. Figure 166 may be employed if values of p_{CO_2} are read from the curve corresponding to $t + 63$ and the result multiplied by $^{45}\!/_{137}$.

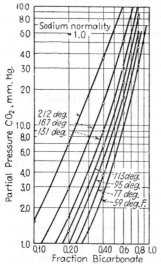

Equilibria for the water-soluble organic amines, which are being used extensively for CO_2 removal, have been studied by Mason and Dodge,[300] whose results are confirmed by Shneerson and Liebush.[424] Figure 167 shows typical data for monoethanolamine solutions. At a partial pressure of 100 mm. Hg the solubility of CO_2 in $2M$ monoethanolamine is approximately the same as in $2M$ diethanolamine and about twice as great as in triethanolamine. Bottoms has reported similar data for hydrogen sulfide in these solutions.

Fig. 166. Partial pressure of CO_2 over 1.0N sodium carbonate-bicarbonate solutions.

Absorption of CO_2 by Caustic Solutions. The absorption of CO_2 by solutions of KOH and NaOH has been studied by a number of investigators. In the majority of cases the rate of diffusion in the liquid phase or the rate of the chemical reactions occurring in the liquid phase very evidently determines the over-all rate of absorption. The problem of determining the true mechanism is difficult, because the principal factors which affect the liquid-film resistance have a similar effect on the rate of chemical reaction. Temperature, for example, has a large effect on diffusivities and viscosities of liquids, and the combined effect of these variables is quantitatively similar to the effect of temperature on rate of chemical reaction. The observed effects of temperature consequently

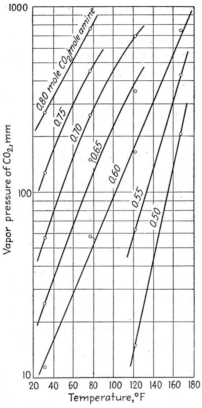

Fig. 167. Vapor pressure of CO_2 over $2N$ monoethanolamine solutions. (*Data of Mason and Dodge.*)

are of little value in distinguishing between processes controlled by diffusion and processes controlled by the rate of a chemical reaction. The determination of the mechanism is further complicated because the chemical kinetics and, in fact, the actual chemistry of the process are not well understood.

Payne and Dodge[355] list eight reactions which may be involved in the absorption process:

$$CO_{2\,gas} \rightleftarrows CO_{2\,dissolved} \tag{a}$$

$$CO_{2\,dissolved} + H_2O \rightleftarrows H_2CO_3 \tag{b}$$

$$H_2CO_3 \rightleftarrows H^+ + HCO_3^- \tag{c}$$

$$HCO_3^- \rightleftarrows H^+ + CO_3^{--} \tag{d}$$

$$H^+ + OH^- \rightleftarrows H_2O \tag{e}$$

$$CO_2 + OH^- \rightleftarrows HCO_3^- \tag{f}$$

$$HCO_3^- + OH^- \rightleftarrows CO_3^{--} + H_2O \tag{g}$$

$$CO_2 + 2OH^- \rightleftarrows CO_3^{--} + H_2O \tag{h}$$

The ionic reactions are believed to be very rapid, but the rates of the other reactions, which are not all independent, are not well known.

Various assumptions as to which of these reactions may be controlling lead to different pictures of the mechanism of the absorption process. Thus Hatta[175] assumes that the reactions are (a), (f), and (g) and that (g) is much more rapid than (f). Eucken and Grutzner[133] conclude that the over-all reaction

$$CO_2 + 2OH^- \rightleftarrows H_2O + CO_3^{--} \tag{h}$$

goes directly in the presence of free hydroxide and that the rate of reaction is very rapid. Whether or not the reaction occurs in one or two stages, if it is assumed along with Hatta[175] that the reaction occurs in a stagnant film at the interface, as pictured in Fig. 146, then it may be shown that the rate of absorption follows [Eq. (362)], with q representing one-half the concentration of OH^- in the main body of the liquid.

An experimental study of the absorption of carbon dioxide by sodium hydroxide solutions has been reported by Tepe and Dodge,[455] who used a 6-in.-diameter tower filled with 36 in. of 0.5-in. carbon Raschig rings. The over-all coefficient K_Ga was found to increase rapidly with increasing sodium hydroxide concentration up to a concentration of approximately $2N$ and to decrease with further increases in hydroxide concentration. The decrease was probably due to the greater viscosity and lower diffusivity in the liquid phase at the higher concentrations. K_Ga was also found to decrease linearly with increasing concentration of sodium carbonate, as shown by Fig. 168. Changes in the gas rate were found to have a negligible effect on K_Ga, indicating that the major resistance to absorption was in the liquid phase; yet the effect of liquid rate was found to correspond to $L^{0.28}$ rather than to the 0.6 or 0.7 power of L as is usually the case when absorption in the liquid occurs by diffusion alone. The value of K_Ga increased in proportion to the sixth power of the absolute liquid temperature. As noted from Fig. 168 and also from Table XXV, the rate of absorption of CO_2 in sodium hydroxide is greater than in any of the other common chemical absorbents.

When these results are considered in relation to the mechanism of the process in the liquid phase, it is apparent both from the large effect of liquid temperature and from the negligible effect of gas velocity that either the resistance to diffusion or the slowness of reaction in the liquid, or both, limit the absorption rate. As dissolved carbon dioxide and hydroxyl ions must come together in the liquid for reaction to occur, it is not surprising to find, in agreement with Eq. (421), that the concentra-

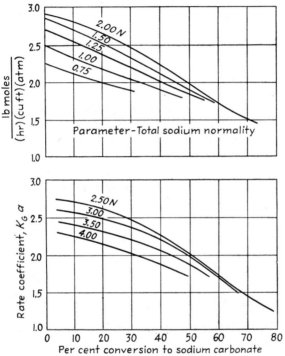

Fig. 168. Absorption of carbon dioxide in NaOH in a packed tower. Liquor rate = 1600 lb./(hr.)(ft.²); gas rate = 190 lb./(hr.)(ft.²); temperature = 78°F. (*Data of Tepe and Dodge.*)

tion of NaOH has a large effect on $K_G a$. It appears, however, that changes in the gas concentration have substantially no influence on $K_G a$, other variables being constant. This comparison is brought out by Table XXIX, which shows that, after a correction is applied to allow for the difference in the liquid rates in the two runs, the over-all coefficients are nearly equal, the difference in liquid temperature in the two runs being sufficient to account for the small difference in $K_G a$ which remains. This comparison shows, therefore, that it is not possible to assume that the process in the liquid phase is limited solely by the rate of diffusion of

TABLE XXIX. ABSORPTION OF CO_2 IN NaOH SOLUTION*

Run No.	% CO_2 in gas	Normality		Liquid temp., °F.	L	G	K_Ga
		NaOH	Na_2CO_3				
6	4.52 in	1.736 in	0.024 in	76 in	763	187	2.19
	0.42 out	0.931 out	0.830 out	91 out			
	2.47 av.	1.333 av.	0.427 av.	83.5 av.			
24	1.92 in	1.411 in	0.376 in	78 in	1537	193	2.51†
	0.65 out	1.296 out	0.491 out	77 out			
	1.28 av.	1.353 av.	0.433 av.	77.5 av.			

* Data of Tepe and Dodge.[455]

† This value of K_Ga = 2.06 lb. moles/(hr.)(ft.³)(atm.), when corrected to same liquid rate as in run 6 by assuming K_Ga proportional to $L^{1/3}$.

dissolved CO_2 and OH^- to a thin zone of rapid reaction. In this case, as brought out by Eq. (421), the over-all coefficient should depend as greatly on c_{Ai} (or p) as on q. It seems more reasonable to assume that the controlling step is a slow chemical reaction which occurs throughout the liquid film simultaneously with diffusion. If diffusion of NaOH occurs with relative ease compared to diffusion of CO_2 and its reaction, then Eq.

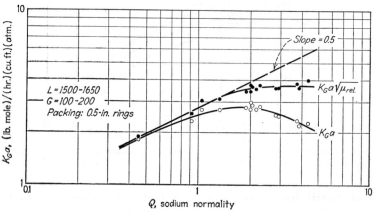

FIG. 169. Effect of sodium hydroxide concentration on rate of absorption of carbon dioxide. (*Data of Tepe and Dodge.*)

(388) should apply with k_c being taken as $k_{II}q$, the pseudo first-order velocity constant. For an irreversible reaction with $K = \infty$, the over-all coefficient should vary almost linearly with $q^{1/2}$, as shown by Eq. (399).

Figure 169 shows the effect of q on K_Ga for several of the runs reported by Tepe and Dodge under conditions of constant liquid rate and liquid temperature. The over-all gas-film absorption coefficient goes through a maximum as q varies. According to Eq. (399) a part of this variation should be due to the change in the diffusion coefficient of CO_2 in the liquid, which grows smaller as the viscosity increases. (According to the Stokes-Einstein equation D_L is inversely proportional to μ_L.)

Considering only the viscosity factor in Eq. (399), k_L' and also K_G should vary as $\mu^{1/2}$. The changing concentration of OH ions in the liquid will also influence k_L' owing to the use of the pseudo first-order reaction-rate constant k_c, which is proportional to the concentration of hydroxyl ions and approximately proportional to q. In addition, however, k_c may also depend to a slight extent on the liquid viscosity and also on the ionic strength of the solution if the rate-controlling reaction involves ions which are attracted by their ionic neighbors as well as by reacting CO_2 molecules, as explained by Moelwyn-Hughes.* If these kinetic effects are neglected, however, and if NaOH is assumed to be completely ionized, $K_G a$ should be proportional to $(q/\mu_L)^{1/2}$. The solid points on Fig. 169 have been corrected for the varying liquid viscosity by multiplying each ordinate by $\mu_L^{1/2}$. The line drawn through the data at the lower values of q has a slope of $\frac{1}{2}$, as required by the theory. The points representing high sodium normalities fall below the straight line, even after the viscosity correction has been applied. This would be explained by an influence of q on the wetted area of packing or by errors in the assumptions given above.

Equation (399) also explains why changes in the liquid rate have relatively little effect on $K_G a$ for CO_2 absorption in NaOH as compared with CO_2 in water. In the latter case, k_L varies with $u_s^{1/2}$, according to Eq. (397), and therefore approximately with $L^{1/3}$. When the irreversible reaction occurs, however, k_L is independent of the time of exposure of the liquid surface and is therefore independent of L. The observed proportionality between $K_G a$ and $L^{0.28}$ is probably due entirely to the effect of L on a.

Thus, it seems that the rate of absorption of CO_2 in NaOH solutions is limited by the velocity of a pseudo first-order reaction between dissolved CO_2 and OH^- in the liquid, the velocity of reaction being of the same order as the rate of diffusion.

Spector and Dodge[439] have reported similar data for the absorption of CO_2 in KOH solutions, showing that slightly larger coefficients are obtained for KOH than for NaOH. Van Krevelen and Hoftizjer[471] have also reported a few values of k_L for NaOH and KOH solutions, but unfortunately the original data were not tabulated, and it is difficult to determine what values of a were used. However, the conclusions regarding OH^- ion concentration are similar to those presented above.

* Moelwyn-Hughes, E. A., *Kinetics of Reactions in Solution*, pp. 93, 112, 2d ed., Oxford University Press, London, 1937.

Absorption of CO_2 in Alkaline Carbonate and Amine Solutions.
Comstock and Dodge,[95] Payne and Dodge,[356] Harte and Baker,[170] and
Furnas and Bellinger[148] have studied the absorption of CO_2 in Na_2CO_3 or
K_2CO_3 solutions in packed columns as large as 12 in. in diameter. The

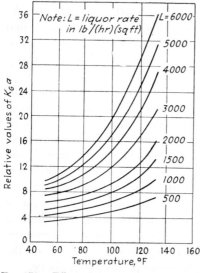

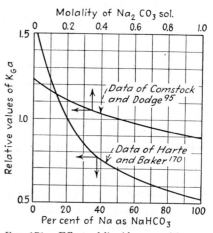

FIG. 170. Effect of temperature on over-all
mass-transfer coefficient for CO_2 absorption
in sodium carbonate–bicarbonate solutions
in packed towers.

FIG. 171. Effect of liquid composition on
over-all mass-transfer coefficient for CO_2
absorption in sodium carbonate–bicarbonate solutions in packed towers.

results are summarized for operation at 77°F., Na_2CO_3 molality equal
to 0.5, and 20 per cent of the sodium in the form of $NaHCO_3$, by the
equation[148]

$$K_Ga = C'L^{1-n}a_d^n \qquad (434)$$

in which C' and n are the constants listed in Table XXX. The effects of
temperature and of the concentrations of Na_2CO_3 and $NaHCO_3$ on K_Ga
are shown by Figs. 170 and 171. These data will not be reviewed in

TABLE XXX. CONSTANTS IN EQ. (434) FOR ABSORPTION OF CO_2 IN Na_2CO_3–$NaHCO_3$
SOLUTIONS*

Packing	C'	n	a_d, ft.²/ft.³
Raschig rings, ⅜-in..........	1.53×10^{-4}	0.56	148
1-in....................	0.81×10^{-4}	0.36	58
Berl saddles, 1-in............	1.00×10^{-4}	0.42	79

* From Furnas and Bellinger.[148]

detail, as the effects of different variables are similar to those previously discussed for NaOH solutions.

The industrial use of ethanolamine solutions for absorbing CO_2 has been discussed by Storrs and Reed[445] and by Reed and Wood.[384]   Typical values of $K_G a$ observed by Cryder and Maloney[100] using diethanolamine solutions in an 8-in.-diameter tower filled with ¾-in. Raschig rings are given by Figs. 172 and 173.   The coefficient was found to be substan-

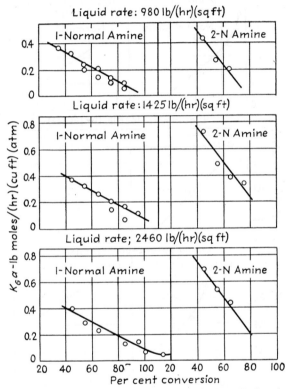

Fig. 172.   Mass-transfer coefficient for absorption of CO_2 by diethanolamine solutions. (*From Cryder and Maloney.*)

tially independent of G and to increase with increasing L in a manner typical of controlling liquid-phase resistance.   The coefficient varies with the concentration of the unreacted amine in the expected manner, increasing with increasing amine normality below about $3N$ but decreasing slightly with increasing amine concentration above this normality, owing to the increase in liquid viscosity.   Caution must be used in applying these data in design calculations because the coefficients are found to vary with the CO_2 content of the gas, $K_G a$ decreasing as the partial pressure of CO_2 becomes larger. This behavior is similar to that described above for chlorine absorption in ferrous chloride solution and is very likely associated with the second-order reaction between the dissolved acid gas and the alkaline amine.

When monoethanolamine is used in place of diethanolamine as the alkaline absorbent, the absorption coefficients are larger and the solubil-

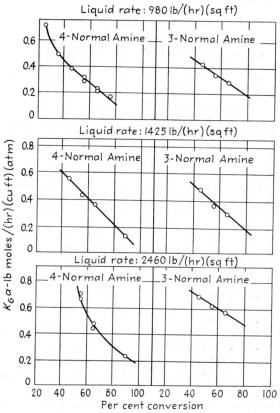

FIG. 173. Mass-transfer coefficient for absorption of CO_2 in diethanolamine solutions. (*From Cryder and Maloney.*)

ities of CO_2 in the two solutions are not greatly different. Cryder and Maloney[100] discussed the earlier data of Gregory and Scharmann,[165] pointing out that the coefficients for the mono-substituted amine are slightly greater. A more definite comparison may be made from the data of Shneerson and Liebush,[424] as shown by Table XXXI. Since these data were taken with a small laboratory column only 1-in. in diameter filled to a depth of 13.8 in. with 5- to 6-mm. glass rings, the absolute values of

TABLE XXXI. EFFECT OF TYPE OF AMINE ON THE OVER-ALL ABSORPTION
COEFFICIENT FOR PACKED COLUMN*

$L = 695$ lb./(hr.)(ft.^{2}); 3 to 5 per cent CO_2 in gas; 5 per cent of amine converted to carbonate; temperature of operation = 122°F.

Absorbent	K_Ga, lb. moles/(hr.)(ft.^{3})(atm.)
2M monoethanolamine	6.89
2M diethanolamine	2.83
3.5M triethanolamine	0.295

* Data of Shneerson and Liebush.[424]

K_Ga are probably too small, though the values for the different amines relative to each other are probably accurate.

Shneerson and Liebush[424] observed the same effect of the CO_2 partial pressure as had Cryder and Maloney. If the reaction between the carbon dioxide and the amine is very rapid and therefore takes place within a narrow zone as soon as the two molecules meet, it would be expected, in agreement with Eq. (421), that k_La would vary inversely with the gas partial pressure according to the equation

$$k_La = k_L'a \left(1 + \sqrt{\frac{D_B}{D_A}} \frac{q}{c_{Ai}}\right) \qquad (421a)$$

The upper part of Fig. 174 shows, however, that, while the ratio $k_La/k_L'a$ —after a suitable correction for the viscosity of the solutions—does increase with increasing values of q/c_{Ai}, the increase is less rapid than would be expected if the reaction were instantaneous. Furthermore, at the same ratio of amine concentration to CO_2 partial pressure, the more concentrated amine solutions give higher coefficients than do the less concentrated ones.

The two curves shown on the lower part of Fig. 174 bring out the fact that the rate of absorption of CO_2 (and, also, the rate of consumption of amine) is smaller at the lower gas compositions and, therefore, at the higher values of q/c_{Ai}. At higher values of q/c_{Ai}, therefore, the amine need not diffuse so rapidly toward the interface as at lower values of this ratio. The result is that the amine molecules tend to be distributed uniformly throughout the liquid layer when the absorption rate is low, and the rate of absorption is limited by the rate of reaction. Under these conditions the large excess of amine makes the reaction pseudo first order, the rate coefficient for which varies with the concentration of amine in the bulk of the liquid.

When the rate of absorption is limited by the rate of reaction and when the reaction is not reversible, Eq. (399) shows that $(k_La/k_L'a)(\mu_{rel}^{2/3})$ should increase in proportion to $k_c^{1/2}$. The lower dotted line on Fig. 174 shows that the ratio of absorption coefficients, corrected for viscosity, varies linearly with q, thus indicating that k_c is proportional to q^2, as in a third-order reaction. A similar conclusion was reached by Van Krevelen and Hoftijzer,[471] who suggest that the complete reaction takes place in two steps, the first being a dissociation of the amine and the second the combination of the fragments with CO_2.

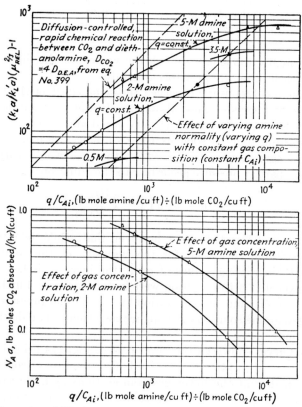

FIG. 174. Absorption of CO_2 in aqueous diethanolamine solution; $L = 695$ lb./(hr.)(ft.²). (*Data of Shneerson and Liebush.*)

ABSORPTION OF NITROGEN OXIDES

The absorption of nitrogen oxides to produce nitric acid, nitrites, or nitrates is an industrial problem of major importance. That it is also a technical problem of considerable complexity is witnessed by the enormous literature on the subject. It is significant, however, that most of the research on the mechanism of the process has been by chemists working primarily on the chemical aspects of the problem, relatively little attention having been paid to the importance of the diffusional resistance to interphase transfer.

Until about 1930 the standard process for the production of nitric acid was the reaction of sulfuric acid with sodium nitrate in a heated iron pot. The gases formed, consisting principally of HNO_2, NO_2, NO, and water vapor, pass to a condenser serving to collect the "drip acid," and so to a series of absorption towers in which the nitrogen oxides are absorbed to form 50 to 65 per cent nitric acid. Since the development of the various processes for the fixation of atmospheric nitrogen, however, nitric acid is more conveniently produced by the catalytic oxidation of ammonia, with subsequent absorption of the nitrogen oxides formed, which are present to the extent of 7 to 9 per cent in the gases to be treated. In the arc process for the direct oxidation of atmospheric nitrogen a dilute gas is produced containing only 1.2 to 1.8 per cent NO, which must be oxidized and the NO_2 absorbed. The absorption of this dilute gas requires such enormous equipment that the absorption towers represent over 40 per cent of the capital cost of the plant.[255] The absorption of nitrogen oxides is also of importance in the recovery of nitric acid from spent mixed acid, where gases containing up to 20 per cent nitrogen oxides are treated.

The oxides of importance are nitric oxide (NO), nitrogen dioxide (NO_2), the trioxide (N_2O_3), and the tetroxide (N_2O_4). Nitrous oxide (N_2O) is not ordinarily encountered in these processes. NO does not react with water and must be oxidized before absorption occurs. It combines with NO_2, however, forming N_2O_3, which reacts with water to form nitrous acid. NO_2 is stable at ordinary temperatures, being only 5 per cent dissociated into NO and oxygen at 430°F. It polymerizes readily to the tetroxide and at ordinary temperatures exists in the polymer form to an appreciable extent. At 77°F. and 1 atm., for example, a gas containing 10 per cent total NO_2 plus N_2O_4 will contain 6.75 per cent NO_2 and 3.25 per cent N_2O_4. This equilibrium is reached very rapidly, as is also that between NO_2, NO, and N_2O_3. For a 10 per cent gas the latter equilibrium at 77°F. corresponds to approximately 0.16 per cent N_2O_3, 4.9 percent NO, and 4.9 percent NO_2.

The principal reactions involved in the absorption process are probably the following:

$$2NO + O_2 \leftrightarrow 2NO_2 \qquad (a)$$
$$2NO_2 \leftrightarrow N_2O_4 \qquad (b)$$
$$2NO_2 \ (\text{or } N_2O_4) + H_2O \leftrightarrow HNO_3 + HNO_2 \qquad (c)$$
$$3HNO_2 \leftrightarrow HNO_3 + 2NO + H_2O \qquad (d)$$

The oxidation of NO is a trimolecular reaction with a negative temperature coefficient. It proceeds relatively slowly, the homogeneous reaction-rate constants having been obtained by Bodenstein.[36] There is no agreement as to whether NO_2 or N_2O_4, or both, react with water; Webb,[491] for example, believes that only N_2O_4 is absorbed, since the rate of absorption is very low at high temperatures corresponding to nearly complete dissociation to NO_2. The decomposition of the nitrous acid occurs rapidly, particularly if the solution is agitated. That reaction (d) does not hold up the nitric acid formation is evidenced by the fact that the acid product leaving the absorption towers contains only 0.2 to 0.3 per cent HNO_2. In addition to the above reactions, it is probable that N_2O_3 is absorbed and hydrolyzed directly to nitrous acid. A part of the NO liberated by the decomposition of nitrous acid may be oxidized in the liquid phase by oxygen diffusing in from the gas, although oxygen absorption is so slow that this is probably not important.

It should be evident from this brief summary of the chemistry of the process that there are three steps which may possibly control the rate of the over-all absorption. These are:

1. The oxidation of NO to NO_2 in the gas phase.

2. The physical diffusion of the reacting oxides from gas to liquid phase.

3. The chemical reaction in the liquid phase.

When the solvent is water or weak nitric acid, the oxidation of NO is the controlling reaction. Using a wetted-wall tower with water as the absorbent, Bolshakoff[41] found the rate of absorption to decrease with increasing gas rate when the gas feed consisted of a fresh mixture of NO and air containing 10 per cent NO. The decreased absorption is explained by the shorter time for oxidation in contact with water at the high gas rates. Taylor, Chilton, and Handforth[454] state that they were able to calculate the performance of commercial absorption units using formulas involving the rate constant for NO oxidation and the available equilibrium data for reactions (c) and (d). The only rate constants available in the literature are for the homogeneous gas-phase reaction, and it would appear that these could not be applied to the reaction taking place in an absorption tower, since Burdick[57] found water vapor, charcoal, and other surfaces to affect the reaction rate.

An oxidation chamber placed before the absorption towers to promote the oxidation of the NO is recommended by Webb. This recommendation is supported by the results of Bolshakoff, who obtained over ten times as much total absorption when the NO-air mixture was passed through an empty vessel before going to the wetted-wall tower. Webb does not, however, recommend alternate absorption and oxidation chambers, as proposed by Moscicki.[333] If the original gas fed to the absorption system is thoroughly oxidized, the only subsequent oxidation involved is that of the NO liberated by reaction (d). This will take place in the free space in the absorption equipment, and some of the reabsorption will probably occur as N_2O_3. This is not particularly desirable, since every 3 moles of N_2O_3 form directly only 2 moles of nitric acid with the liberation of 4 moles of NO, whereas 3 moles of N_2O_4 absorbed form directly 4 moles of nitric acid with the liberation of only 2 moles of NO to be reoxidized. The NO-NO_2-N_2O_3 equilibrium, however, allows only a small amount of N_2O_3 to form. The net result is probably a greater capacity if all the volume is used for absorption instead of using part for absorption and part for oxidation. Modern plants employ bubble-cap-plate absorbers operating under pressure, and the space between plates provides some time for oxidation.

Equilibria in the Reaction of NO_2 with H_2O. The strength of concentrated acid which can be produced is limited by the back pressure of NO_2 over the acid leaving the absorbers. The over-all reaction, obtained by adding reactions (c) and (d), is

$$3NO_2 + H_2O = 2HNO_3 + NO \tag{e}$$

The equilibrium constant for this reaction is

$$K = \frac{p_{NO} a_{HNO_3}^2}{p_{NO_2}^3 a_{H_2O}} \tag{435}$$

where a_{HNO_3} and a_{H_2O} represent the activities of HNO_3 and H_2O in the liquid. For convenience in application, this expression is usually separated into two parts, the first of which is a function of the equilibrium gas composition and the second of which depends only on the concentration of HNO_3 in the liquid.

$$K = K_1 K_2 = \frac{p_{NO}}{p_{NO_2}^3} \frac{a_{HNO_3}^2}{a_{H_2O}} \tag{436}$$

The product of K_1 and K_2 can be computed from standard-free-energy and vapor-pressure data, as shown by Wenner[498] and by Forsythe and Giauque.[141] Thus, it is possible to estimate values of $K_1 = p_{NO}/p_{NO_2}^3$ from standard data and to plot this ratio against the acid concentration. Figure 175 is such a plot. It also shows points based on the experimental data of Abel, Schmidt, and Stein,[1] Epshtein,[131] Denbigh and Prince,[107] and Chambers and Sherwood.[71] The ratio of NO to NO_2 in the gas at equilibrium with acid of a given strength is seen to decrease with increasing temperature, owing to the exothermic character of the reaction. Based on these equilibrium data, it may be shown that the maximum acid strength which is obtainable in atmospheric-pressure absorption at ordinary temperatures is about 68 weight per cent HNO_3.

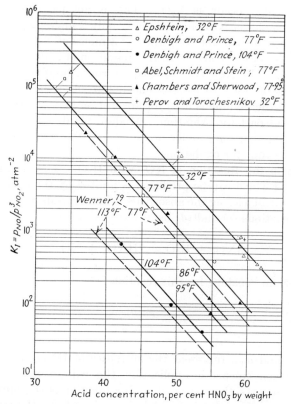

Fig. 175.   Equilibrium vapor pressures of NO_2 and NO over nitric acid.

Wenner[497] gives the following equation for the standard-free-energy change in the reaction:

$$2NO_2 \rightarrow N_2O_4 \tag{b}$$

$$\Delta F^0 = -13.693 + 42.21T, \qquad \text{cal./g. mole} \tag{437}$$

This corresponds to

$$\log_{10} K_3 = \frac{2993}{T} - 9.226, \qquad \text{atm.}^{-1} \tag{438}$$

Figure 176 shows the equilibrium proportions of NO_2 and N_2O_4 in gases at 86°F. and 1 atm. total pressure.

Illustration 42.   The gas entering the bottom plate of a nitric acid absorber contains 0.1 mole NO per mole mixture and 0.25 mole tetravalent nitrogen (either NO_2 or N_2O_4) per mole mixture.   The entering gas also contains 0.30 atm. partial pressure of oxygen, in addition to inert gas.   The total pressure is 1 atm.   The acid made by the absorption operation contains 50 per cent by weight of HNO_3, and the operation is isothermal at 86°F.

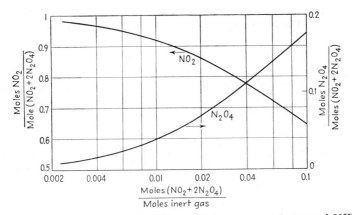

FIG. 176. Equilibrium between NO_2 and N_2O_4 in gases at 1 atm. and 86°F.

Estimate the composition of the gas entering the second plate and the strength of the acid leaving the second plate.

Solution. The following material balance results from the assumption that thermo-dynamic equilibrium is reached on the plate:

Component	Partial pressures, atm.	
	Entering plate	Leaving liquid surface
NO..............	0.1	$(p_{NO})_2 = K_1(p_{NO_2})_2^3$
$\left.\begin{matrix} NO_2 \\ N_2O_4 \end{matrix}\right\}$	0.25	$(p_{NO_2})_2$ $(p_{N_2O_4})_2 = K_3(p_{NO_2})_2^2$

Since three times the moles of NO evolved equals the moles of NO_2 absorbed,

$$3[K_1(p_{NO_2})_2^3 - 0.1] = 0.25 - [2K_3(p_{NO_2})_2^2 + p_{NO_2})_2]$$

From Fig. 175 at 77°F. and 50 per cent acid strength, $K_1 = 1100$ atm.$^{-2}$. From Eq. (438), $K_3 = 6.56$ atm.$^{-1}$. Letting $x = (p_{NO_2})_2$, the above equation reduces to

$$3300x^3 + 13.1x^2 + x - 0.55 = 0$$

Solution by trial and error, *e.g.*, by Horner's method, gives

$$x = 0.0520 \text{ atm.}$$

so that the composition of the gas leaving the plate is:

$$\text{NO: } (1100)(0.0520)^3 = 0.1546 \text{ atm.}$$
$$\text{NO}_2: \qquad\qquad\quad = 0.0520 \text{ atm.}$$
$$\text{N}_2\text{O}_4: (6.56)(0.0520)^2 = 0.0177 \text{ atm.}$$

The total equivalent partial pressure of combined nitrogen entering the plate (cal-culated as NO_2) is $0.1 + 0.25 = 0.35$ atm. The total equivalent partial pressure of nitrogen oxides in the gas leaving the liquid surface is $0.1546 + 0.0520 + (2)(0.0177)$ $= 0.2420$ atm.   The fraction of the initial oxides absorbed on the plate is, therefore,

$$f_1 = \frac{0.35 - 0.2420}{0.35} = 0.308$$

The strength of the acid leaving the next plate above the bottom plate is obtained from the following material balance around the bottom of the column and the ith plate.   A balance for the total liquid is

$$L_1'' = L_i'' + 54n_0f_{i-1}$$

where L_i'' represents the rate of total acid flow from the ith plate and n_0 is the number of moles of nitrogen oxides entering the absorber with the gas.   A similar balance for HNO_3 is

$$L_1''w_1 = L_i''w_i + 63n_0f_{i-1}$$

where w_i is the weight fraction of nitric acid in the liquid.   These equations result from the following over-all equation for the production of HNO_3:

$$\tfrac{1}{2}N_2O_5 + \tfrac{1}{2}H_2O \rightarrow HNO_3$$
$$54 \qquad\quad 9 \qquad\quad 63$$

The solution of w_i is

$$w_i = \frac{L_1''w_1 - 63n_0f_{i-1}}{L_1'' - 54n_0f_{i-1}}$$

Assuming in the present illustration that 5000 lb. of 50 per cent acid is made per hour and that 50 lb. moles/hr. of oxides enters the tower, the strength of acid leaving the second plate ($i = 2$) is found to be

$$w_2 = \frac{(5000)(0.5) - (63)(50)(0.308)}{5000 - (54)(50)(0.308)} = 0.366$$

or 36.6 per cent acid.

If the gas entering the first plate contains 0.3 atm. of oxygen and if the time of contact in the gas space between the liquid on the first plate and the bottom of the second plate is 4 sec., the amount of oxidation of NO to NO_2 may be calculated as follows: The rate of oxidation is given by

$$- \frac{dp_{NO}}{d\theta} = k''p_{NO}{}^2p_{O_2}$$

An approximate integration obtained by neglecting small terms gives

$$\frac{1}{(p_{NO})_3} = \frac{1}{(p_{NO})_2} + [2(p_{O_2})_2 - (p_{NO})_2]\frac{k''\theta}{2}$$

In the present illustration $k'' = 23.2$ (sec.$^{-1}$)(atm.$^{-2}$).[36]

$$\frac{1}{(p_{NO})_3} = \frac{1}{0.1546} + [(2)(0.3) - 0.1546]\frac{(23.2)(4)}{2}$$
$$= \frac{1}{0.0369}$$

The gas entering the second plate has the following composition:

$$NO: \qquad\qquad\qquad\qquad\qquad\qquad 0.0369 \text{ atm.}$$
$$NO_2 + N_2O_4: 0.0520 + (2)(0.0177) + 0.1546 - 0.0369 = 0.2051 \text{ atm.}$$
$$O_2: \qquad\qquad 0.3 - (\tfrac{1}{2})(0.1546 - 0.0369) = 0.2412 \text{ atm.}$$

The quantity of heat which must be removed from the liquid on a plate in order to maintain isothermal operation is obtained from a heat balance around the plate. If the acid temperature is to be held constant, only the heats of formation of the various components enter into the heat balance.

The number of theoretical trays required in a plate-type acid absorber may be calculated in this way from a succession of material and energy balances for each tray.

Effect of Temperature and Pressure on the Rate of Production.
Unlike most homogeneous reactions in the gas phase, the oxidation of NO proceeds more rapidly at low than at high temperatures. In so far as NO oxidation is controlling, it is desirable to have the absorption proceed at as low a temperature as may be practicable. Furthermore, the process of physical absorption is favored by low temperature because the solubility of NO_2 in nitric acid increases with decreasing temperature and the transfer across the liquid film is speeded up by the higher NO_2 concentration at the liquid-gas interface. The chemical reactions (c) and (d) in the liquid phase are retarded at low temperatures, but as these are relatively rapid anyway, the net result of low-temperature operation is beneficial. The equilibrium fixing the maximum strength of nitric acid is not appreciably affected by temperature.[58]

Modern plate-column absorbers are fitted with tubular coolers for the removal of the heat of reaction by cooling the acid on each plate. Although cooling in this way with available cooling water results in an appreciable increase in absorption capacity, Taylor, Chilton, and Handforth[454] state that the cost of additional cooling by artificial refrigeration is not ordinarily justified.

The important advantages of operating the absorber under increased pressure were recognized many years ago,[138,454,491] but high-pressure processes did not become commercially feasible until stainless-steel alloys capable of withstanding the corrosive action of hot acid became available. The development of the art of fabricating chrome-steel vessels has made possible the construction of large absorption towers of alloy steel capable of resisting both nitric acid and the desired high pressure.

At a given gas concentration the rate of oxidation of NO increases as the square of the total pressure, and the rate of physical absorption also increases rapidly with pressure. Furthermore, the chemical equilibrium is shifted favorably by increased pressure, making higher acid strengths possible. Taylor, Chilton, and Handforth[454] describe the operation of a pilot plant operating at 100 p.s.i. pressure, producing 5 tons of 60 per cent acid, and requiring an absorption system only one-twentieth the volume of an atmospheric-pressure plant producing the same amount of 50 per cent acid. Figure 177 shows the absorption system of a plant producing 25 tons of nitric acid at atmospheric pressure, requiring 10 towers each

Fig. 177.   Atmospheric-pressure absorption towers for nitric acid.   (*From Chilton and Taylor.*)

10 ft. in diameter and 50 ft. tall. The last two towers make sodium nitrite. Operating at 100 p.s.i. pressure, it is necessary to have only one tower $5\frac{1}{4}$ ft. in diameter and 40 ft. high, which will produce 25 tons of 60 per cent acid per day. Figure 178 shows several such units in a large nitric acid plant. In this case the nitric oxide is obtained by the oxidation of ammonia, this latter step also being carried out under pressure.

Mechanism of Absorption of Nitrogen Oxides. The kinetics of the absorption of oxides of nitrogen and their reaction with the liquid is complicated by the many different compounds of nitrogen and oxygen which occur. Nitrogen combines with oxygen in all its valence states from two to five. Not only NO_2 but also NO, N_2O_3, and N_2O_4 appear to be

Fig. 178. High-pressure chrome-iron towers for nitric acid. (*From Chilton and Taylor.*)

involved in the reactions with water or with an alkaline solution, and the anions formed contain nitrogen atoms in the pentavalent state as well as in the lower valences. Except for NO, which is relatively insoluble in and unreactive toward water and aqueous alkaline solutions, none of the oxides can be used in the completely pure state for experimental studies without the presence of at least small amounts of the others. Thus, NO_2

polymerizes rapidly to form small amounts of its dimer, N_2O_4 [reaction (b)]; NO is produced by the reaction of NO_2 with water [reaction (e)]; and NO and NO_2 combine in the gas to form small quantities of N_2O_3 according to the reaction

$$NO_2 + NO \rightarrow N_2O_3 \qquad\qquad (f)$$

In addition, there is evidence[70, 123] that NO_2 and H_2O may combine in the vapor state according to reaction (e), even though the free-energy change for the reaction is not so favorable when all the substances are gaseous as when the water and acid condense.[141]   It should be pointed out, however, that the evidence for the existence of the vapor-phase reaction is indirect. It consists mostly of reports that nitric acid mist is formed when NO_2 and H_2O vapor are brought together during absorption.   On the other hand, Kuzminikh and Udintzeva[258] attempted to measure the pressure change when NO_2 and H_2O were brought together at constant volume and constant temperature, but no significant fall in pressure was observed. Further direct kinetic experiments on the homogeneous gas reaction would be valuable.

When NO_2-N_2 mixtures are brought into contact with water or aqueous solutions, the rate of absorption is much smaller than would be expected if all the resistance to diffusion of NO_2 were in the gas film.   This is shown by the work of Chambers and Sherwood,[70] who used a 1.46-cm.-i.d., glass, wetted-wall column for measuring the rates of absorption of NO_2 in water as well as in nitric acid and in sodium hydroxide.   The results obtained seem at first sight to be anomalous.   The rate of absorption was nearly proportional to the gas velocity but was surprisingly small.   Moreover, the absorption rate varied considerably with the composition of the liquid, as shown by Fig. 179.   Furthermore, the dependence on liquid concentration was of an unusual type, the rate of absorption of the acid gas usually being considerably *smaller* in sodium hydroxide than in pure water.   If the reaction took place in the liquid phase according to the equation

$$2NO_2 + 2NaOH \rightarrow NaNO_2 + NaNO_3 + H_2O \qquad\qquad (g)$$

no nitric oxide should have appeared in the gas.   It was found, however, that the exit gas contained substantial quantities of this oxide and that the amount of nitrate ion produced in the liquid exceeded the amount of nitrite.   The temperature of the gas rose as it flowed through the absorber, though the liquid did not change its temperature.   An exothermic reaction appeared, therefore, to have taken place in the gas phase.

In order to explain these results, Chambers and Sherwood[70] postulated that the reaction between NO_2 and H_2O took place in the vapor, perhaps within the laminar film near the liquid surface. Once formed, the HNO_3 might condense into a fog, which would then be collected partially by the liquid layer. The presence of a mist in the main body of the gas was observed during several of the experiments.

The rate of production of HNO_3 by the gas-phase reaction would be expected to be greater, the larger the concentration of H_2O in the gas and, consequently, the larger the vapor pressure of water over the liquid layer. The partial pressure of water over the solutions decreases with increasing concentration in very much the same way as the absorption rate decreases

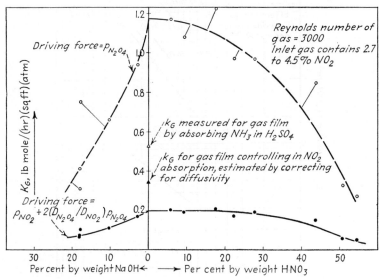

FIG. 179. Effect of solution concentration on rate of absorption of NO_2 from nitrogen. (*Data of Chambers and Sherwood.*)

with increasing concentration. The efficiency of collection of nitric acid mist by the liquid may be expected to increase with increasing gas velocity in the way observed. (The rate of collection of P_2O_5 smoke in a packed tower has been shown to increase approximately in proportion to the square of the gas rate.[26]) The assumed production of HNO_3 in the gas is also consistent with the presence of NO in the gas in contact with NaOH solutions, as well as the excess of nitrate over nitrite in the liquid.

Thus, the hypothesis of mist formation is consistent with the experimental observations, including the abnormally low absorption rates, for the rate of collection of heavy, relatively immobile mist particles may be expected to be more difficult than diffusion of NO_2 molecules through the gas film. When there is no opportunity for mist formation, as over concentrated caustic solutions, the low absorption coefficients observed must reflect the slowness of diffusion and reaction in the liquid.

This analysis of the mechanism of absorption of NO_2 is confirmed by the results of Eagleton, Langer, and T. H. Pigford,[123] who absorbed NO_2 from nitrogen in 46 per cent NaOH solution, using apparatus very similar to that of Chambers and Sherwood. The nitrogen gas was nearly dry as it came from the cylinder, and the partial pressure of water over the strong caustic was so low that the vapor-phase reaction was minimized

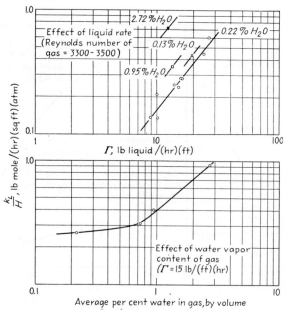

FIG. 180. Absorption of NO_2 in 46 per cent NaOH, using 0.46-in.-diameter wetted-wall column. (*Data of Eagleton, Langer, and Pigford.*)

and the resistance of the liquid phase emphasized. Figure 180 shows the effect of the liquid-flow rate on the liquid-film coefficient divided by the unknown Henry's law coefficient appropriate to the equilibrium between NO_2 in the gas and in the liquid. These values were obtained by subtracting the relatively small gas-film resistance from the measured over-all resistance. For a constant value of the average water content of the gas the liquid-film coefficient was found to vary nearly with the first power of the liquid rate. Liquid-film coefficients for pure physical absorption of gases in viscous liquids increase in proportion to the $\frac{1}{3}$ power of L [theoretically in proportion to the $-\frac{1}{2}$ power of the time of contact, according to Eq. (397)].

Figure 180 shows that the absorption coefficient varies with the water-vapor content of the gas. The effect is greatest when the water content is largest and may be negligible at the lowest concentrations. No visible acid mist was observed in the bulk of the gas except in one run. The original data show also that nearly equal-molal quantities of nitrite and nitrate were formed in the liquid for all the low-water-vapor runs, while there was an excess of nitrate in the liquid when mist formed.

Eagleton, Langer, and T. H. Pigford [123] also studied the absorption of nitrogen sesquioxide (N_2O_3) from nitrogen, using the same apparatus.

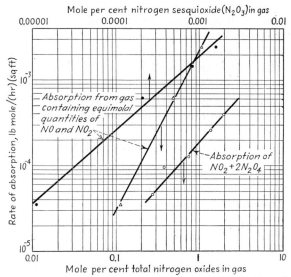

FIG. 181. Comparison of rates of absorption of NO_2 and N_2O_3—effect of concentration. (*Data of Eagleton, Langer, and Pigford.*) Wetted-wall tower; 46 per cent NaOH; Reynolds number of gas = 3300 to 3500; liquid-flow rate = 15 to 16 lb./(hr.)(ft.); temperature = 86°F.

Under these conditions the N_2O_3 actually dissociates into equal-molal quantities of NO and NO_2, and only very small concentrations of N_2O_3 remain. Figure 181 shows that, at the same percentage of total nitrogen oxides in the gas, N_2O_3 is absorbed as much as ten times faster than NO_2. Whereas the rate of absorption of NO_2 is proportional to its partial pressure in the gas, the rate of absorption of the equal-molal mixture of NO and NO_2 is proportional approximately to the square of the partial pressure of NO plus NO_2 in the gas. The small concentrations of N_2O_3 in equilibrium with NO and NO_2 may be estimated from the equilibrium constants reported by Verhoek and Daniels. [476] When the absorption rates are plotted against these concentrations, it is found that the rate is roughly proportional to the first power of the driving force, indicating that N_2O_3 is the oxide which reacts with the liquid. The reaction is probably

$$N_2O_3 + 2NaOH \rightarrow 2NaNO_2 + H_2O \qquad (h)$$

Liquid analyses showed that very little nitrate was present. It appears that, in spite of the very low concentrations of N_2O_3 in the gas, it is able to react rapidly with NaOH, owing to a greater solubility than NO_2, to a greater reaction-rate constant, or to both. Similar results were obtained by Astroshenko.[10]

On the basis of experiments in which NO_2 was absorbed in nitric acid in a small wetted-wall apparatus, Denbigh and Prince,[107] in agreement with Webb,[491] conclude that N_2O_4 is the form of the tetravalent oxide which is absorbed. Denbigh and Prince found that the absorption coefficient based on the partial pressure of N_2O_4 in the gas as a driving force was more nearly constant during each batch experiment than the coefficient based on the partial pressure of NO_2 or of total oxides. This indicated to them that the absorption rate is determined by the rate of the reaction (c') in the liquid.

$$N_2O_4 + H_2O \rightarrow HNO_3 + HNO_2 \qquad (c')$$

In concentrated acid solutions, or when NO exceeds its equilibrium partial pressure over the liquid, reaction (d) limits the rate of transfer and must be included in the kinetic equation, as shown by Denbigh and Prince.

$$3HNO_2 \rightarrow HNO_3 + 2NO + H_2O \qquad (d)$$

If the data of Chambers and Sherwood[71] are recalculated on the basis of N_2O_4 partial pressures as the driving force, the points at the top of Fig. 179 are obtained. These coefficients are larger than those for pure gas-film processes in the same apparatus. This seems rather unlikely. In strong NaOH solutions the rate of absorption is proportional to the NO_2 content of the gas and, therefore, to the square root of the N_2O_4 partial pressure. This indicates that NO_2 participates in the reaction with NaOH rather than N_2O_4.

Although Denbigh and Prince did not observe acid mist visually, they did not vary the gas velocity widely, and the changing acid composition in their experiments was a function of the changing gas composition, the acid strength increasing as the NO_2 content of the gas fell. It may be significant that they observed a decrease in the ordinary coefficient based on NO_2 partial pressures with increasing acid strength, an effect similar to that shown by Fig. 179.

If a mist actually forms in NO_2 absorption, it may be desirable to encourage its formation by introducing water vapor into the gas phase inside commercial absorbers. The acid mist would be collected subsequently by washing the gas with acid in separate pieces of equipment.

REMOVAL OF SULFUR DIOXIDE FROM FLUE GAS

The generally increasing interest in air conditioning and in the prevention of smoke nuisance in cities makes it appear probable that power plants located in thickly populated centers may in the future be required to remove sulfur dioxide as well as dust from their stack gases. The Battersea station of the London Power Company has an installation for SO_2 removal, made necessary by the requirements of the Port of London Authority. In this country the problem has received the attention of Chicago public utilities, which have financed a research problem carried out by Johnstone and coworkers at the University of Illinois.[242]

The SO_2 content of stack gases from the combustion of coal varies from 0.05 to 0.5 per cent, depending on the sulfur content of the fuel. The obvious procedure of scrubbing the gas with water is relatively expensive because of the low solubility of SO_2 and the necessity of using enormous quantities of water. Approximately 11 tons of water at 68°F. per ton of coal containing 1.0 per cent sulfur is the theoretical minimum for the recovery of 85 per cent of the SO_2 from a gas containing 0.3 per cent SO_2. Furthermore, the extremely low driving force available and the large liquid- and gas-flow rates make it necessary to employ an absorption apparatus having a large volume. The type of absorber used in any practical process for the treatment of stack gases must involve very low pressure drop, which adds to the difficulty of the problem.

In spite of these difficulties the London Power Company has installed a gas-washing plant using water as the principal solvent.[184] This plant consists of a series of spray chambers and towers partially filled with wood slats, the total scrubber volume being nearly 1,600,000 ft.[3]. It is designed to treat the gas from coal burned at the rate of 133 tons/hr., with SO_2 removal of approximately 90 per cent. The last of the banks of scrubbers is fed with a milk-of-lime solution, and no attempt is made to utilize the SO_2 in the resulting solutions. The washing system and related accessories added nearly $1 million to the plant investment, which cost corresponds to approximately 13 cents per ton of coal if the fixed charges are taken as 10 per cent per year. About 20 tons of water and 10 to 20 lb. of lime are used per ton of coal, representing an additional cost of 6 cents per ton of coal for pumping and for lime. The total cost of treating the gas is in the vicinity of 30 to 40 cents per ton of coal burned. This installation is very probably the largest gas-absorption unit in existence.

Johnstone's early work was directed primarily toward the discovery of additional agents which might serve to increase the solubility of SO_2 in water.   He found[223] that small amounts of ferric or manganese sulfates catalyzed the liquid-phase oxidation of the SO_2 absorbed and greatly increased the absorption capacity of the solution.   Treating a gas containing 0.325 per cent SO_2 in a single porous-plate absorber, he obtained recoveries of more than 95 per cent of the SO_2 with only 1 gal. water per 4000 ft.[3] gas.   The oxidation of the SO_2 absorbed produces sulfuric acid, which was obtained in concentrations as high as 40 per cent.   With the catalyst present in the liquid, the liquid-film resistance was reduced to such an extent that oxygen and not SO_2 absorption became controlling. Although the required absorption volume was still very large, this process appeared very promising until it was discovered that ordinary stack gases contain unknown inhibitors (probably phenol and other organic compounds) which stop the catalytic action of the added salts after the solution has been used but a few hours.   Liquid-phase oxidation of SO_2 by dissolved catalysts may prove to be of commercial importance in the recovery of SO_2 from waste gases where such inhibitors are not present.

Johnstone also discusses the possible use of other solutions which give promise of being economical.   With milk of lime there is no necessity of absorbing oxygen, and the rate of absorption is much higher.   Regeneration of the SO_2 is not feasible, however, and the calcium bisulfite formed is not valuable, so fresh lime must be supplied at the rate of about 140 lb./ton coal containing 3 per cent sulfur.   Buffered solutions of ammonium hydroxide appear more promising,[224] as SO_2 can be recovered by heating the solution produced, decomposing the ammonium sulfite formed.   Because the capacity of the alkaline solution to take up SO_2 is so large, the amount of solution to be circulated is not excessive.   The size of the required absorption unit is still large, although it is much smaller than when using water or for the oxidation process.   Johnstone[224] and Johnstone and Keyes[225] report data on the SO_2-NH_3-H_2O equilibria necessary in designing both absorber and stripper.   As no large installation has been made for the removal of SO_2 from flue gas by means of an ammonia solution as a solvent, it is not possible to compare the cost of the process with the costs at the Battersea station in London.   A pilot-plant study of an absorption process of this type has been described recently, however.[517]   By adjusting the pH of the ammonia solution, the liquid can be kept far enough on the alkaline side to minimize corrosion of steel equipment; yet the capacity of the solution for dissolving SO_2 can be kept large.

The Howden-I.C.I. process, developed in England[357] since the erection of the Battersea plant, is a noneffluent water system.   The gases are scrubbed with a solution of milk of lime or a slurry of powdered chalk and the pH carefully controlled to allow supersaturation with respect to calcium sulfate within the scrubber. From the scrubber the solution goes to a "delay tank," in which calcium sulfate precipitates and from which the solution is returned to the scrubber. By using the correct shape and material as packing and by careful control of the liquor system, precipitation on the packing surface is avoided.

In all processes for SO_2 removal which involve removal of the dissolved SO_2 from the absorbent by heating, excessive quantities of steam are required to remove the last traces of SO_2. Unless the solution is stripped thoroughly of its SO_2, however, there will be a small but finite equilibrium vapor pressure of SO_2 over the regenerated solution which is returned to the absorber, and this will limit the degree of removal of SO_2 from dilute stack gases. The use of a chemical process for regenerating the absorption liquid instead of a thermal process makes it possible to employ alkaline sodium sulfite-bisulfite solutions in the absorber. The equilibrium partial pressure of SO_2 over these solutions is so small[229] that essentially complete removal of SO_2 from stack gases containing less than 0.1 per cent SO_2 can be obtained. The partly converted sodium sulfite-bisulfite solution leaving the absorber may be regenerated by treating the solution with solid zinc oxide, the precipitated zinc sulfite being converted to the oxide by heating to a temperature of 570 to 660°F. A pilot-plant investigation of this process has been described by Johnstone and Singh.[232] The economic feasibility of the process depends on the market value of the large quantities of SO_2 which are produced.

SO_2 ABSORPTION FOR BISULFITE COOKING LIQUOR

Two absorption systems are commonly used for the production of the calcium bisulfite solution used in the manufacture of sulfite pulp. In the Barker milk-of-lime system, burner gas from the combustion of sulfur is passed into a combination packed and sieve-plate tower. The lower part of the tower is packed with a large-sized ceramic, manufactured packing material, and in the upper part are several perforated plates. Milk-of-lime solution is fed to the top plate, and the acid liquor is withdrawn from the bottom. Deep liquid seals are maintained on each plate, and the pressure drop through the tower is about 5 p.s.i. The strength of the liquor and the fraction of the total SO_2 present in the combined form are regulated by the amount and strength of limewater fed. The absorption is relatively rapid and the recovery good. Where dolomitic limestone is used, there is a greater sludge formation and the tendency to clog the sieve plates is greater. This clogging is avoided by the Paulson acid absorber, which employs a single large bubble cap on each plate. In these towers the liquor seals are 2 ft., and a tower 27 ft. high and 8 ft. in diameter is said to be ample for a 100-ton pulp mill. The Kimberly-Clark Chemipulp Acid System avoids the accumulation of solid deposits in a clever way by using two packed towers operated countercurrently in series. About once a week the rich-gas entry point is switched from one tower to the other. Thus, alkaline sludge which is deposited from the milk of lime at the alkaline end of the system is dissolved away during the next part of the cycle by reaction with the acid gas. Equilibrium data for the system $CaO-SO_2-H_2O$ are given by Beuschlein and Conrad.[32]

The other absorption system employs towers packed with broken limestone. Water is supplied at the top and runs down over the stone, the latter not only providing the surface of contact between gas and liquid but also supplying the source of calcium. Limestone is attacked by sulfurous acid and goes into solution as bisulfite with the liberation of CO_2. The stone is gradually dissolved and replaced by more stone introduced at the top of the tower. Accumulation of insoluble residue tends to clog the gas passage and necessitates occasional removal of the stone and refilling.

RECOVERY OF SO_2 FROM SMELTER GASES

The recovery of SO_2 from gases of intermediate concentrations (1 to 10 per cent) is relatively costly, not because of the difficulty of absorption by water, but because the resulting solutions are so dilute that the heat requirements for stripping the SO_2 are frequently excessive. A German process[495] uses a mixture of equal parts of xylidine and water as a solvent, with sodium carbonate to convert any xylidine sulfate to sodium sulfate, and heats the rich liquor to 175 to 212°F. in order to drive off the recovered SO_2 as a practically pure gas. The mixture of xylidine and water consists of two immiscible layers, but the xylidine sulfite formed is soluble in water, and the rich liquor going to the still is a single layer of xylidine sulfite dissolved in water. Toluidine may also be used.

Nomenclature for Chapter IX

a = area of interphase contact, ft.^{2}/ft.^{3} packed volume

a_d = specific surface area of dry packing, ft.^{2}/ft.^{3} packed volume

$a_0 = (k_c/D_A)^{1/2}$

$b = a_0 x_L/\tanh a_0 x_L$

B_F = thickness of flowing liquid layer, ft.

c, c_L = concentration of solute in the liquid, lb. moles/ft.^{3}

c_A = concentration of solute A, lb. moles/ft.^{3}

c_{Ai} = concentration of solute at the interface, lb. moles/ft.^{3}

c_e = solute concentration in the liquid corresponding to equilibrium with the partial pressure of solute in the main body of the gas, lb. moles/ft.^{3}

c_i = solute concentration in the liquid at the gas-liquid interface, lb. moles/ft.^{3}

c_0 = sum of initial values of c_A and c_B, lb. moles/ft.^{3}

D_v = diffusivity of the solute through the gas, ft.^{2}/hr.

D_A = liquid diffusivity for component A, ft^2/hr.

D_{AB} = liquid diffusivity for reaction product AB, ft^2/hr.

D_B = liquid-diffusion coefficient for component B, ft.^{2}/hr.

D_L = liquid-diffusion coefficient for solute, ft.^{2}/hr.

f = fraction of total base present as bicarbonate; also function in Eq. (388)

f_1 = fraction of entering nitrogen oxides absorbed on first plate of absorber

$F = N_A'/N_A$ = fraction of solute entering liquid phase which reaches the main body of the solution without reacting chemically

g = acceleration due to gravity = 4.17×10^8 ft./hr^2

G = superficial mass velocity of gas, lb./(hr.)(ft.^{2})

H = Henry's law constant = p_i/c_i

H' = Henry's law coefficient for the equilibrium between gaseous Cl_2 and dissolved but unreacted Cl_2, in water

k_c = reaction-rate constant for a first-order reaction in the liquid phase, hr.$^{-1}$

k'' = reaction-rate constant for the gas-phase oxidation of NO, atm.$^{-2}$ hr.$^{-1}$

k_{II} = reaction-rate constant for a second-order reaction in the liquid phase, ft.^{3}/(lb. mole)(hr.)

k_G = gas-film coefficient of mass transfer, lb. moles/(hr.)(ft.^{2})(atm.)

k_L = liquid-film coefficient of mass transfer, lb. moles/(hr.)(ft.^{2})(lb. mole/ft.^{3})

k_L' = liquid-film coefficient of mass transfer in the absence of chemical reaction, lb. moles/(hr.)(ft.^{2})(lb. mole/ft.^{3})

k_1'' = liquid-film coefficient of mass transfer, lb. moles/(hr.)(ft.^{2})(lb. mole reactant B/ft.^{3})

K = equilibrium constant for a reversible first-order chemical reaction in the liquid phase

$K_1 = p_{NO}/p_{NO_2}{}^3$ = equilibrium constant for the reaction of NO_2 with liquid H_2O, atm.$^{-2}$

K_3 = equilibrium constant for the reaction $2NO_2 \rightarrow N_2O_4$, atm.$^{-1}$

K_e = equilibrium constant for the liquid-phase reaction between dissolved chlorine and water; see Eq. (428)

K_G = over-all gas-film coefficient of mass transfer, lb. moles/(hr.) (ft.^{2})(atm.)

K_L = over-all liquid-film coefficient, lb. moles/(hr.)(ft.^{2})(lb. mole/ft.^{3})

L = superficial mass velocity of liquid, lb./(hr.)(ft.^{2})

L'' = rate of flow of acid in absorber, lb./hr.

m = concentration of reaction product AB in the liquid film, between the gas-liquid interface and the reaction zone lb. mole/ft.^{3} (see Fig. 146)

n = exponent in Eq. (434)

n_0 = rate of flow of nitrogen oxides into absorber, lb. atoms nitrogen/hr.

N = normality of base in Eq. (433)

N_A = diffusion rate of A, lb. moles/(hr.)(ft.^{2})

N_A' = diffusion rate of unreacted A at boundary between the main body of the liquid and the liquid film, moles/(unit time)(unit area)

N_{AB} = diffusion rate of the reaction product AB, moles/(unit time)(unit area)

N_B = diffusion rate of reactant B, lb. moles/(hr.)(ft.^{2})

p, p_A = partial pressure of solute in gas, atm.

p_{CO_2} = partial pressure of CO_2, mm. Hg

p_i = partial pressure of solute at liquid-gas interface, atm.

P = total pressure of system, atm.

q = in the case of absorption and chemical reaction, the concentration in the bulk of the solution of the substance reacting with the solute, lb. mole/ft.^{3}

R = gas-law constant, 0.08206 (liter)(atm.)/(g. mole)($^\circ$K.)

S = solubility of CO_2 in water, g. moles/liter at 1 atm. CO_2 pressure above the solution

t = temperature, $^\circ$F.

T = absolute temperature, $^\circ$K.

u_{av} = average velocity of flowing liquid film, ft./sec.

u_s = velocity of surface of flowing liquid film, ft./sec.

V = volume, ft.^{3}

w = weight fraction HNO_3 in solution

x_L = effective thickness of liquid film

x_L' = effective thickness of the liquid film from the gas-liquid interface to the reaction zone, ft.

x_L'' = effective thickness of the liquid film from the reaction zone to the main body of the liquid, ft.

Z = height of surface over which liquid film flows, ft.

α = constant related to the rate of penetration of the liquid film by the zone of rapid chemical reaction [see Eq. (408)]

ρ = density, lb./ft.^{3}

ρ_L = liquid density, lb./ft.^{3}

μ = viscosity

μ_G = viscosity of gas, lb./(hr.)(ft.)

μ_L = viscosity of liquid, lb./(hr.)(ft.)

μ_{rel} = viscosity of the liquid divided by the viscosity of pure water at the same temperature, lb./(hr.)(ft.)

Γ = rate of flow of the liquid layer, lb./(hr.)(ft. wetted perimeter)

θ = time, hr.

Problems

1. A packed absorber is to be designed to recover carbon dioxide from air for use in a dry-ice plant. Air containing 18 per cent CO_2 (by volume) enters the bottom of the tower at a rate of 100,000 ft.^{3}/hr. at standard conditions. The concentration in the exit gas is to be 1 per cent. The absorber operates at atmospheric pressure, and isothermal conditions will be assumed. The superficial mass velocity of the gas will be taken as 300 lb./(hr.)(ft.^{2}) at the entrance to the tower, and the inlet liquor rate is taken as 2500 lb./(hr.)(ft.^{2}). Calculate the tower height and volume for each of the following absorbing liquids:

Case I. Use 2N sodium carbonate solution at 131°F. The liquid entering the top of the tower will be assumed to be partially converted to the bicarbonate. The extent of conversion is given by

$$\frac{NaHCO_3}{2Na_2CO_3 + NaHCO_3} = 0.1 \text{ at top}$$

Case II. Use 2N diethanolamine solution at 122°F. Assume that the amine solution is initially 10 per cent converted to the CO_2 compound, *i.e.*, at the top of the tower the solution contains 0.05 mole CO_2 per mole of amine, $NH(C_2H_4OH)_2$.

Why is there an advantage of countercurrent operation in this case? Does the variation of K_Ga with conversion have an effect in this connection?

2. An absorption plant is to be designed to produce 250 tons of nitric acid per day (24 hr.), containing 65 per cent by weight of HNO_3 from nitrous gases produced by an ammonia-oxidation unit. The absorption system will recover 95 per cent of the nitrogen oxides from 2415 lb. moles/hr. of gases having the following composition by volume:

5.58% nitrogen oxides (calculated as NO_2)
6.02% oxygen
88.40% inert gases (calculated as N_2)

The nitrogen oxides contain both NO_2 and N_2O_4, but no NO.

The absorber is to be of the bubble-cap variety. The total pressure is 8 atm., and the pressure drop through the absorber is negligible. The temperature is held constant at 77°F. by the installation of cooling coils on the plates. The allowable vapor velocity corresponds to a mass velocity of 2000 lb./(hr.)(ft.²) at the base of the tower. The vertical distance from the liquid surface on a plate to the next plate above is 3 ft.

Weak acid (50 per cent HNO_3 by weight) is introduced into the absorber on an appropriate plate at a rate of 11,030 lb. acid (50 per cent HNO_3) per hr.

Calculate (a) the number of theoretical plates required, (b) the diameter of the column, (c) the quantity of heat to be removed at each plate.

Notes: 1. The gases leaving the liquid surface on a plate are assumed to be thermodynamically in equilibrium with the liquid leaving the same plate, according to the reaction

$$3NO_2 + H_2O = 2HNO_3 + NO$$

2. Negligible oxidation of NO to NO_2 occurs as the gases rise through the liquid on a plate. Between the surface of the liquid on a plate and the bottom of the next plate above, gas-phase oxidation occurs according to the reaction

$$2NO + O_2 = 2NO_2$$

Only the forward reaction need be considered. The rate constant in the equation

$$- \frac{dp_{NO}}{d\theta} = kp_{NO}{}^2 p_{O_2}$$

is 23.2(sec.$^{-1}$)(atm.$^{-2}$).

3. The polymerization reaction

$$2NO_2 = N_2O_4$$

proceeds so rapidly that NO_2 and N_2O_4 are always in equilibrium in the gas phase. The equilibrium constant is

$$K_3 = \frac{p_{N_2O_4}}{p_{NO_2}{}^2} = 8.0 \text{ atm.}^{-1} \text{ at } 77°F.$$

4. The heats of formation necessary for calculating the cooling capacity necessary on each plate are as follows:[497]

Substance	Heat of Formation, cal./g. mole
NO	21,526
NO_2	7,964
N_2O_4	2,235
H_2O	−68,315

Solution, HNO₃ in	Heat of Formation, cal./g. mole HNO₃
65% acid	−46,200
60% acid	−46,800
55% acid	−47,270
50% acid	−47,660
45% acid	−48,060
40% acid	−48,400
35% acid	−48,680
30% acid	−48,870
25% acid	−49,000
20% acid	−49,080
15% acid	−49,120
10% acid	−49,150
5% acid	−49,200
0% acid	−49,200

CHAPTER X

SOLVENT EXTRACTION

Separation of two or more components of a liquid solution is one of the commonest of chemical-engineering problems. The most usual procedures are evaporation, fractional crystallization, and distillation, in which separation is accomplished by taking advantage of the differing solubilities or volatilities of the components. Alternatively, it is often possible to accomplish the desired separation by bringing the liquid in contact with a second liquid which selectively removes one or more of the components of the solution so treated. Separation is accomplished because certain of the components are more readily soluble than others in the solvent employed. The solution and the solvent must not be completely miscible, since the purpose is to effect the desired separation by mechanical separation of the two liquid phases. The separation is accomplished without vaporization, though evaporation or distillation is usually required to recover the separated components from the two liquid product streams. Solvent extraction also refers to the treatment of a solid with a solvent, as in the extraction of oil from cottonseed. The present chapter, however, will be confined to solvent extraction processes in which a liquid solution is treated with a liquid solvent phase.

One of the common applications of extraction is in the separation of compounds differing as to chemical type but difficult to separate by distillation because their volatilities do not differ greatly. An example is the separation of aromatic and paraffin hydrocarbons in the solvent refining of lubricating oils. In other cases solvent extraction is employed because the components are heat-sensitive and tend to decompose at the ordinary temperatures of distillation or evaporation. Penicillin, streptomycin, and other biologicals produced in dilute solutions may be concentrated and purified by solvent extraction in order that the pure products may be recovered by fractional crystallization or precipitation.

In some cases extraction may prove economical in instances where distillation is also entirely practical. Thus Othmer and Trueger[353] claim heat savings for the solvent extraction of acetone and ethyl alcohol from dilute aqueous solutions, as compared with standard rectification practice for these separations. This claim is based on the fact that moderately concentrated extracts may be obtained by the use of proper solvents and that the heat requirement for distillation from these extracts may be less than for distillation of the original dilute aqueous solutions.

The solvent extraction process involves the four operations of (*a*) bringing solvent and solution into intimate contact, (*b*) separation of the two phases, (*c*) removal and recovery of solute from the extract phase, and (*d*) removal and recovery of solvent from each phase, usually by distillation. Contacting may be accomplished in any of the several types of equipment, such as baffle-plate mixers, mixers which employ impinging jets of the two liquid streams, agitated vessels containing the liquids, plate columns, packed towers, or centrifugal contactors. Separation may be accomplished by simple settling tanks or by means of centrifuges. The difficulty encountered in separating the phases is usually greatest when the phases are dispersed to a high degree in the contacting equipment. A large difference between the densities of the two phases tends to make separation easy, but the presence of emulsifying agents may cause more trouble in the separation process than a small density difference. After separation of the phases, the solvent is usually recovered by ordinary distillation of the solvent layer, termed the "extract," and of the treated solution, termed the "raffinate."

METHODS OF OPERATION

Single Contact. The simplest type of operation is the single contact, in which the solvent and solution are brought together for a single batch extraction. Solute is transferred from one phase to the other, and the

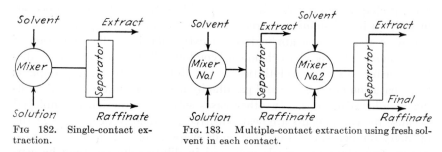

FIG 182. Single-contact extraction.

FIG. 183. Multiple-contact extraction using fresh solvent in each contact.

concentrations in the two phases approach equilibrium. The amount of solute extracted is determined by the amount of solvent employed, the equilibrium relations for the system (solution-solute-solvent) involved, and the extent to which it is possible to approach equilibrium.

The equipment employed for a single-contact extraction is shown diagrammatically in Fig. 182. As indicated above, the contacting equipment may be any one of a variety of types. In mixers of the jet or agitator types, the contact between phases may be so good that equilibrium is approached closely. The final extract and raffinate from such a single contact operation are essentially in equilibrium with each other, and the amount of solute which may be extracted with a given amount of solvent is definitely limited. Because the efficiency permitted by the equilibrium is usually low, this type of operation is seldom employed for large-scale work.

Multiple-contact Extraction, Using Fresh Solvent in Each Contact. Figure 183 shows an obvious improvement over the single-contact operation, the extraction being repeated on the raffinate from the first contact. The solute content of the raffinate may be reduced to any desired extent by increasing the number of contacts or stages. The concentrations of solute in the second and later separators are low, however, and this method of operation is uneconomical of solvent. Provided the distribution law (see below) holds, the maximum efficiency is obtained when the total solvent to be used is divided in equal parts,[433] the same quantity being employed in each stage. Thus if 1 volume of solution is to be extracted with 6 volumes of solvent, the best results are obtained by using 3 volumes of solvent in each mixer if the operation is two-stage, 2 volumes in each mixer if three-stage, or 1 volume in each mixer if six-stage.

Countercurrent Multiple-contact Extraction. If fresh solvent is used in each stage, the extract leaving the later stages is quite dilute and could be used in place of fresh solvent in treating the original solution. The

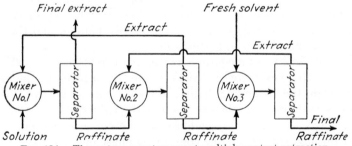

FIG. 184. Three-stage countercurrent multiple-contact extraction.

operation illustrated in Fig. 183, which is inefficient because it fails to utilize the solvent properties of the weaker extracts, may be greatly improved if solution and solvent are passed through the system in opposite directions. Figure 184 shows the type of operation employing this principle. The system illustrated involves three stages, although any number may be used. The solution to be treated enters the first mixer, as before, but all the fresh solvent enters the last mixer. The two streams pass in a countercurrent direction, the original solution being treated with extract from the second stage, etc., the final extract being removed from the first separator and the final raffinate from the last separator.   All the solvent passes through each stage, and the over-all efficiency, for a given amount of solvent and number of stages, is appreciably better than when part of the fresh solvent is used in each stage.

This type of operation, with from two to five stages, is commonly employed for commercial solvent extraction.   The operation may be either batch or continuous, as exemplified by systems of mixers and settlers, as used in batch operation, on the one hand or by the perforated-plate column on the other.   At first glance the latter would appear to be an example of continuous countercurrent flow but in reality should be classified as continuous multiple contact, since each plate acts as a combined mixer and settling chamber.

Continuous Countercurrent Extraction.   True countercurrent operation is approached in extraction equipment in which the two liquid phases pass continuously in opposite directions.   For example, a packed tower may be operated completely flooded with water moving slowly downward, while benzene dispersed as liquid drops rises continuously through the packing.   If the buoyancy of the benzene drops is such that their rate of rise through water is greater than the downward velocity of the water phase, then water and benzene will pass continuously in opposite directions through the equipment.   Unpacked "spray" towers are also employed, but the difficulty with both packed and spray equipment is that the drops of dispersed phase must be relatively large or the required counterflow of the two phases will not result.   This means that the surface for interphase transfer is necessarily limited, and the equipment is bulky in relation to performance.

Figure 185 illustrates a continuous countercurrent tower in which the heavy phase to be extracted is fed as the dispersed phase at the top and falls through the ascending lighter solvent phase.   In this case the raffinate is withdrawn at the bottom and the lighter extract at the top.   Alternatively, the lighter ascending phase may be dispersed, passing upward through the descending continuous phase of the heavier feed.

Use of Reflux.   In some applications of continuous or multiple-contact countercurrent extraction it is advantageous to use "reflux" in a manner analogous to the use of reflux in distillation.   Figure 186 is a typical flow diagram, showing the heavy feed phase supplied near the middle of the tower, with extract being withdrawn at the top and raffinate at the bottom.   The lower part is the exhausting section, corresponding to the operation illustrated in Fig. 185.   A mixer is shown, in which the solvent is saturated before entering the bottom of the tower.   This mixer is not essential, as the solvent phase would soon be saturated on entering the tower in any case.

The upper, or enriching, section of the tower is provided to recover components of the feed less soluble in the solvent than that desired in the extract.   Reflux is provided by removing solvent from the extract leaving the column so as to form a heavy extract phase saturated with solvent. Part of this is returned to the column; the remainder is withdrawn as extract product.   In this way the extract obtained is much richer than an extract of composition in equilibrium with the feed.   The quantitative advantages of this system are discussed in a later section.

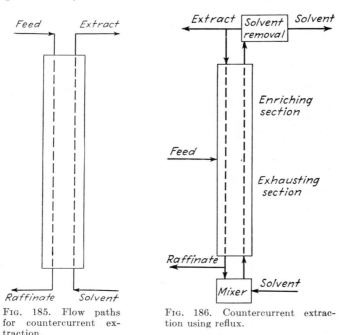

FIG. 185. Flow paths for countercurrent extraction.

FIG. 186. Countercurrent extraction using reflux.

It may be noted that the solvent extraction operation illustrated in Fig. 186 is quite analogous to the operation of a rectifying column for separation of two components by distillation.   The feed or heavy phase corresponds to the liquid phase in distillation, and the solvent corresponds to the vapor phase.   Solvent is supplied at the base of the column in place of heat, and solvent rather than heat is removed at the top in order to provide a reflux phase and product.   The correspondence of the two operations is made still more evident when it is remembered that solvent is usually recovered for reuse by distillation or evaporation, so that the use of solvent means the use of heat in a very real sense.

Separation of One Component from a Mixture.   The various flow diagrams which have been discussed are illustrations of means by which a single "cut" may be made, *i.e.*, a separation between two components in the feed, or between two groups of components. It is quite common, however, to employ solvent extraction to isolate a single component from a mixture of several in solution. This is done, for example, in the purification of streptomycin.[25,344]

The procedure is to "cut" between the desired component and the group either more or less soluble in the solvent and then to treat the extract or raffinate (whichever contains the desired product) so as to cut between the desired component and the other group of undesired materials. Figure 187 illustrates one way of doing this, for a case where the aqueous feed contains three components A, B, and C, and the solvent is completely immiscible with the aqueous solutions. The order of solubility in solvent is assumed to be C, B, A; and the bulk of these components appears in the extract from the first tower, the extract from the second tower, and in the raffinate, respectively.

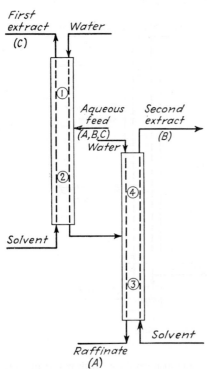

FIG. 187. Double "cascade" for isolation of a single solute B.

Quantitative understanding and design of extraction equipment requires the application of three basic tools: the necessary phase-equilibrium concepts and data; the appropriate material balances and the special stoichiometry of their application; and the diffusion-rate equations, with the special techniques useful in applying them to extraction. These will be discussed and illustrated in succeeding sections of this chapter.

EXTRACTION EQUIPMENT

From the foregoing descriptions of the several types of extraction processes, it is evident that equipment must be provided to serve three functions: bring the two phases into intimate contact so that rapid transfer of solute is possible; separate the two phases; and recover solvent and products from the two separated streams. Separate equipment may be provided for the contacting and separation, or both operations may be carried out in a single apparatus. The better the contacting, the more difficult the separation is apt to prove, and industrial equipment varies from the extreme of contacting by violent agitation, necessitating the use of centrifuges for separation, to countercurrent columns in which the contacting is relatively poor but the separation readily effected by gravity flow.

The principal types of extraction equipment are described briefly in the following sections. For more detailed descriptions of a wide variety of commercial extractors, reference should be made to the recent article by Morello and Poffenberger.[330] This excellent summary of commercial extraction equipment illustrates 23 types of diagrams and lists over 60 patent references. General performance data are given for some 47 extractors employed in a wide variety of commercial extraction processes.

Mixers. In countercurrent multiple-contact extraction each stage consists of a contactor followed by a separator. The contactors may consist of mixing vessels in which the two phases are brought together and agitated, either continuously or in intermittent batches. These mixers are of standard types, selected for their ability to mix and disperse two liquids. They are commonly cylindrical tanks fitted with mechanical stirrers of various designs or with air jets, if the liquids are relatively non-volatile. Long pipes with internal baffles may be used for continuous mixing, or the two liquids may simply be passed through a pump. High-speed mixers providing thorough dispersion and mixing may be assumed to accomplish the equivalent of one equilibrium contact or stage. Separation of the two phases is accomplished by centrifuges or by gravity settling, depending on the degree of dispersion of the drops of dispersed phase, the density difference, and the tendency to emulsify.

Spray Columns. Spray columns are used for continuous countercurrent extraction. The column consists of an empty vertical tube through which the two phases pass by gravity flow in opposite directions. If the dispersed phase is the lighter, it is fed at the bottom of the column through small holes in a distributor nozzle or plate. Drops of dispersed phase rise through the downward-flowing continuous phase and are collected and removed at the top. The continuous phase is fed at the top and removed at the bottom. If the heavier phase is to be dispersed, the distributor is placed at the top and the flow directions reversed. The natural interfacial level between phases is maintained at the proper height by an external siphon arm or other level control. As noted below, Blanding and Elgin[35] found the permissible throughput to be considerably greater if the feed and separating sections were larger than the column proper, with a flared or funnellike connection at the feed end. The limiting flow rates at which flooding occurs are greater in spray columns than in other countercurrent columns, and the required cross sections are smaller.   Drop size is important, and dispersed-phase distributors must be designed to produce uniform drops in the vicinity of $\frac{1}{8}$-in. diameter. In some systems studied, little tendency of the drops to coalesce was noted in several feet of vertical height, but this should be checked for each new system to be used in a spray column, especially where high columns are to be used without redistribution of the dispersed phase. In general, the phase to be supplied in the larger volume should be dispersed.

Packed Columns.   Following absorption practice, it is common to employ Raschig rings, Berl saddles, and other packing materials in vertical countercurrent extraction equipment.   Such packings have been used widely, although the height equivalent to an equilibrium stage or transfer unit is usually considerably greater than in gas absorption.

One of the two phases will preferentially wet the packing, and the flow conditions differ, depending on whether this phase is dispersed or continuous.   If the continuous phase wets the packing, the drops will pass through the packing like marbles on a pinboard, following a tortuous path.   If the dispersed phase wets the packing, it will pass through in the form of small rivulets, with no visual evidence that anything is moving. Transfer coefficients are less in the second case.

Some drop coalescence occurs in packed columns, but it is assumed that this stops after the drops have reached some equilibrium size.   It is not known, however, how important coalescence may be in reducing the effectiveness of very tall packed towers in which redistribution of the dispersed phase is not provided at several levels.

As in the case of spray towers, the distributor head should be located in an enlarged section of the tower in order to increase the allowable flow rates and reduce the cross section.   The packing support should be as open as possible, located preferably in an enlarged section at the lower end of the column.

Perforated Plates.   Bubble-cap columns fitted with V-notch or slotted caps give large drops and poor contacting and hence are not generally used.   Perforated or sieve plates, however, have proved useful.   These correspond to multiple spray-column sections with redistribution of the dispersed phase every few inches.   One reason for interest in such equipment was the possibility that contacting efficiency was greatest during and immediately after drop formation, and that the transfer rate would be increased by frequent redispersion of the dispersed phase.   The performance data reported have not indicated much improvement over spray columns with only one distributor, but the equipment works satisfactorily and provides insurance against the possibility of excessive coalescence. Simple perforated plates provide much better dispersion if the continuous phase preferentially wets the plates. As operated, the dispersed phase collects in pools above or below the plate, the head causing flow through the holes being provided by this column of liquid and the difference in density between the two phases. The continuous phase passes around this pool through a separate overflow pipe, as in a rectifying column.

Power-driven Extractors. Since gravity flow results in low velocities of one phase past another, the transfer coefficients are relatively low and the size of the equipment is large. In order to improve the contact between phases, mechanical power may be introduced into the equipment in order to increase the velocity of one phase relative to the second. The mixers previously described do this but require subsequent separation of the phases. The Podbielniak extractor and the Scheibel column employ mechanical power to improve the contacting but permit the separation of the liquid products without additional separators. These devices are described in a subsequent section (see pages 440 and 441). The Maycock extractor is a vertical tube with a rotating inner core.[306]

Wetted-wall Columns. Wetted-wall columns may be operated with two liquids in countercurrent flow and a stable cylindrical surface of contact between the two. The liquid preferentially wetting the wall forms the wall film, and the other fluid the core. The surface of contact per unit volume is small, and such equipment is not of industrial importance. It has proved of value in research studies, however, since the surface of contact is measurable, and the turbulence conditions in each stream are standard and reproducible.

PHASE EQUILIBRIA

In the case of two immiscible liquids, the equilibrium concentrations of a third component in each of the two phases are often related by the so-called "distribution law":

$$y = mx \tag{439}$$

where y = solute concentration, in one liquid (extract) phase
x = solute concentration, in the other (raffinate) phase
m = the "distribution coefficient"

Equilibrium data for such systems are usually reported[214] in terms of the distribution coefficients, which are analogous to Henry's law constants (see page 123). For many systems, however, m varies appreciably with concentration, and the relation (439) can hardly be called a "law." For example, if y represents the concentration of acetic acid in water as grams per liter, m at 77°F. is found to vary from 36 to 7 over the range of molalities of acetic acid in chloroform from 0.002 to 0.21.

In cases where the solute is associated in one or the other phase, forming double or triple molecules, the mass-action and equilibrium laws may be combined[208] to give the equilibrium relation. Thus, if the solute tends to form triple molecules in the extract phase, then by the mass-action law,

$$y_3 = k'y_1{}^3 \tag{440}$$

where y_3 = concentration of triple molecules
     y_1 = concentration of single molecules
     k' = mass-action constant
The total concentration y_T is given by

$$y_T = y_1 + 3y_3 = y_1 + 3k'y_1{}^3 \tag{441}$$

The distribution law may be assumed for the single molecules:

$$y_1 = mx$$

whence

$$y_T = mx + 3k'(mx)^3$$
$$= (m + 3k'm^3x^2)x \tag{442}$$

which is the new equilibrium expression. Because of the limited applicability of the distribution law, however, this treatment is seldom justified.

The distribution law does not apply when the two phases are miscible to any appreciable extent, although it is sometimes used over narrow ranges of concentrations. A more general relation is

$$\frac{y_A}{y_B} = \beta \frac{x_A}{x_B} \tag{443}$$

where y and x refer to compositions in extract and raffinate phases, respectively, and the subscripts refer to two components (solutes) A and B. This corresponds to

$$y = \frac{\beta x}{1 + (\beta - 1)x} \tag{444}$$

where y and x are compositions expressed on a solvent-free basis, *i.e.*, fraction A or B in a mixture of solutes A and B. Thus for the system n-heptane–aniline–methylcyclohexane at 77°F., Varteressian and Fenske[475] showed β to be nearly constant at 1.90 over a wide range of concentrations, where y_A and y_B are the weight fractions methylcyclohexane and n-heptane in the aniline layer, and x_A and x_B are the compositions of the same components in the hydrocarbon layer. These relations are identical

with the expressions of Raoult's law in terms of vapor and liquid compositions. For the system referred to, β is 1.90, whereas the relative volatility is 1.07, suggesting the probable advantage of extraction over distillation for the separation of the two hydrocarbons.

TRIANGULAR GRAPHS OF EQUILIBRIUM DATA

In many cases of practical importance the two phases are partially
miscible, and it is important to have solubility data as well as information
connecting the concentrations of an important component in the two
phases at equilibrium. The data are best expressed graphically, and it is
desirable to employ a graphical representation which can be used for
graphical stoichiometric calculations of extraction processes. Several
graphical forms may be employed, but the most usual is the triangular
diagram. Several types of equilibria will be illustrated by means of triangular diagrams.

1. *Component A is miscible in all proportions with B, likewise with C,
but B and C are but partially miscible.* This case is illustrated by Fig. 188.

Point A represents 100 per cent A, B represents 100 per cent B, and C 100 per cent C.
Any point H within the triangle represents a
mixture of the three components, in relative
amounts given by the perpendiculars HL,
HJ, and HK. The geometry of the figure
requires that these three percentages always
add to 100. BN represents the solubility of
C in B, and MC the solubility of B in C.
The region $NPFQM$ is the unstable, or two-
phase, region, mixtures such as O automatically splitting into two layers of compositions
P and Q. The "tie lines," of which PQ is one,

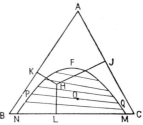

Fig. 188. Triangular diagram
for representing equilibrium
data on three-component system.

connect the points representing compositions of two phases in equilibrium.
The compositions of the two phases approach each other, as O is moved
vertically, and become equal (and so revert to one phase) at F, the
"plait point." For extraction calculations, it is necessary to have both
the solubility curve $NPFQM$ and the data on concentrations of phases in
equilibrium, as given by the tie lines.

Instead of a family of tie lines, a single conjugate line may be used to
represent the data on equilibrium between phases. A second triangle is
drawn having a base common to the first and the conjugate line located as
DRF in Fig. 189. Starting at any point P on the solubility curve, the
equilibrium concentration in the other phase is obtained by following a
line parallel to the side BD of the lower triangle until the conjugate line is

reached at T, and then turning back along a line parallel to the other side DC of the lower triangle until the desired point Q on the other branch of the solubility curve is located.   This procedure is indicated by the dotted lines PT and TQ of Fig. 189.

Another type of conjugate line, not requiring the lower second triangle, is represented by the curve FSN of Fig. 189.   To use this type of line, pass from a point Q on the right branch along a line QS parallel to the base BC to the point S on the conjugate line, and then up to the left parallel to AC, intersecting the left branch at the desired equilibrium point P.   Conjugate lines can be plotted if a few tie lines are known and are helpful for purposes of interpolation.   Correlation and extrapolation of tie-line data are discussed by

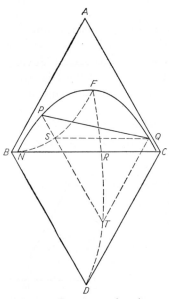

FIG. 189.   Two types of conjugate lines for representing equilibria between phases.

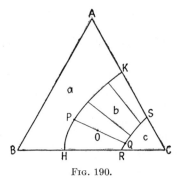

FIG. 190.

Bachman,[13] Brancker, Hunter, and Nash,[46] Othmer and Tobias,[352] and Bancroft and Hubard.[22]

2. *Component A is miscible in all proportions with B, but B and C, and A and C are but partially miscible.*   This case is illustrated by Fig. 190, in which regions a and c are single-phase and region b is two-phase.   A mixture of composition represented by point O will automatically split into two layers of compositions P and Q, as indicated by the tie line.   A variation of this type is one showing two unconnected two-phase regions similar to the single two-phase region of Fig. 188.

3. *Each component is only partially miscible with each of the other two.* Referring to Fig. 191, regions a are single-phase; regions b are two-phase; and c is the three-phase region.   Any point in region c represents a mixture which spontaneously splits into three phases of compositions E, F,

and G. Mixtures such as H, represented by points in region b, split into two layers of compositions J and K, as indicated by the appropriate tie line.

4. *One component is a solid.* Since the solubility of a liquid in a solid is negligible, the lines representing the phase boundaries pass directly to the apex of the triangle corresponding to the solid composition. In Fig. 190, for example, if C were a solid, the curve RS would disappear into the apex C, with the result shown in Fig. 192. Solutions of varying compositions along HK would all be in equilibrium with the solid C. Tie lines, such as PC, are obviously unnecessary.

Various other types are encountered, but that illustrated in Fig. 188 is much the commonest. Each of the diagrams illustrated is for a single temperature; the location of both solubility curve and tie lines varies with temperature.

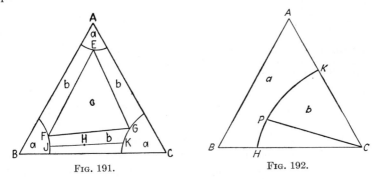

FIG. 191.   FIG. 192.

Smith[432] describes 11 systems which he calls "solutropes." In these rare cases the ratio of the solute concentrations in the two phases varies from less than unity to more than unity as the concentration varies. The slopes of tie lines on triangular phase diagrams for such systems are negative in one region and positive in another.

STOICHIOMETRIC CALCULATIONS

As pointed out above, different types of equipment are used to bring the two liquid phases in contact. In several of these, the intimacy of contact is excellent, and the phases, after separation, are very nearly in equilibrium. The calculation of the result of any specified system of operation with such equipment is, therefore, merely a matter of stoichiometry, with the aid of the equilibrium data. Because the equilibrium data are frequently difficult to express algebraically, the computations are apt to involve time-consuming trial and error, unless a graphical procedure is followed. Graphical methods have been developed for use with both ordinary and triangular graphs of the equilibrium data and are described below.

1. Phases Completely Immiscible—General Case of Batch Extraction.[208] In Fig. 193, curve OP represents the general type of equilibrium relation for this case. The ordinate y represents the solute concentration in the extract layer, and x the concentration in the raffinate layer, each expressed as pounds of solute per pound of solvent.

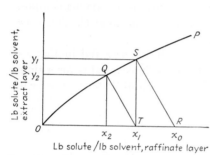

FIG. 193. Graphical construction for immiscible liquids; multiple contact using fresh solvent B in each stage.

Assume that an original solution of composition x_0 containing L lb. of pure solvent A, is to be treated with G lb. of pure solvent B *in a single equilibrium contact*. The resulting mixture separates into two layers of composition x_1 and y_1, in equilibrium. By a material balance,

$$Lx_0 = Lx_1 + Gy_1 \qquad (445)$$

or

$$\frac{y_1}{x_1 - x_0} = -\frac{L}{G} \qquad (446)$$

The composition of the original solution is represented by the point R; the compositions x_1 and y_1 are obtained from the equilibrium curve OP by the intersection at S of a line drawn through R with a slope $-L/G$, so that $y_1/(x_1 - x_0)$ will be equal to $-L/G$. Further extraction of the raffinate T with pure solvent in a second equilibrium contact will give raffinate and extract of compositions x_2 and y_2, found by the same method.

2. Phases Completely Immiscible—General Case of Countercurrent Multiple-contact Extraction. The material balance on the first stage (extract leaving, raffinate entering) is

$$Gy_2 + Lx_0 = Gy_1 + Lx_1 \qquad (447)$$

and for the nth stage,

$$Gy_{n+1} + Lx_{n-1} = Gy_n + Lx_n \qquad (448)$$

where the subscripts refer to the stage which the solution is leaving. By drawing a material balance around the first n stages, it follows that

$$Lx_0 + Gy_{n+1} = Lx_n + Gy_1$$
$$y_{n+1} = \frac{L}{G}(x_n - x_0) + y_1 \qquad (449)$$

The composition of the extract entering the nth stage is a linear function of the composition of the raffinate leaving the nth stage. The line representing this relation on a plot of y vs. x is the "operating line" and is based solely on the stoichiometry of the process.

Figure 194 represents the construction for a three-stage countercurrent extraction effecting the reduction of the raffinate concentration from x_0 to x_3; y_4 is 0, since a pure solvent is used. The line EF representing Eq. (449) is the operating line, drawn with a slope L/G.

If the initial and the desired final raffinate concentrations x_0 and x_n are specified, then the number of equilibrium stages required, using a given solvent ratio L/G, is obtained by stepping off the intervals GH, KL, MF, etc., after first placing the equilibrium curve and drawing the "operating line" EF through E with a slope L/G. The point E has the coordinates y_{n+1},x_n, where y_{n+1} is the solute concentration in the fresh solvent (zero in the diagram) and x_n is the final raffinate concentration.

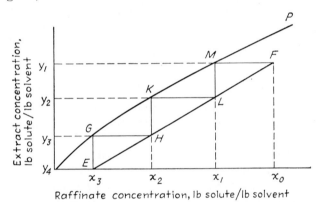

FIG. 194. Graphical construction for immiscible liquids; countercurrent multiple-contact extraction.

If the number of equilibrium stages is specified, then the calculation of the required solvent ratio for a specified x_n, or the calculation of the resulting concentration x_n, using a specified solvent ratio, is necessarily carried out by trial and error but is not time-consuming.

If it can be assumed that the two phases leaving each stage of the contacting equipment are essentially in equilibrium, then the number of equilibrium stages will be equal to the number of actual stages. If equilibrium cannot be assumed, because of inadequate contact of the phases, then a "stage efficiency" may be introduced. This is defined as the ratio of the calculated number of equilibrium stages to the number of actual stages or contacts required. Thus with an over-all efficiency of 50 per cent, the concentration x_0 would be reduced to x_3 in six stages, whereas Fig. 194 shows that only three equilibrium stages would be required. The stage efficiency depends on so many factors that the concept is employed only as an approximate basis for calculation when data on the system of interest are available.

3. Phases Completely Immiscible—Distribution Law Applicable. Batch Extractions. For the case of *a single equilibrium contact* the material balance is

$$Lx_0 = Lx_1 + Gy_1 = Lx_1 + Gmx_1 \tag{450}$$

whence

$$x_1 = \frac{L}{L + Gm} x_0 \tag{451}$$

If the same amount of fresh solvent is used in each of a series of n batch extractions, then

$$x_2 = \frac{L}{L + Gm} x_1 = \left(\frac{L}{L + Gm}\right)^2 x_0 \tag{452}$$

and

$$x_n = \left(\frac{L}{L + Gm}\right)^n x_0 \tag{453}$$

It can be shown that x_n will be a minimum for any given number of equilibrium stages and given total quantity of fresh solvent if equal quantities of solvent are used in each extraction, *i.e.*, if the total solvent is divided into n equal portions.

4. Phases Completely Immiscible—Distribution Law Applicable. Countercurrent Multiple-contact Extraction. The applicability of the distribution law means that both operating line *EF* and equilibrium curve *OP* of Fig. 194 are straight. The problem of relating the total extraction to the number of steps or stages, the slope of the equilibrium curve, and the position of the operating line, is the same problem in geometry as was solved by Kremser (see page 146) for gas absorption. This important relation is

$$\frac{x_0 - x_n}{x_0 - (y_{n+1}/m)} = \frac{(mG/L)^{n+1} - (mG/L)}{(mG/L)^{n+1} - 1} \tag{454}$$

From Eq. (449) it is evident that the slope of the operating line *EF* is L/G; the ratio mG/L, which will be represented by the single symbol R, is the ratio of the slope m of the equilibrium curve to the slope of the operating line. The left-hand side of Eq. (454) is the ratio of the change in composition of the raffinate to the change which would be accomplished were it to come to equilibrium with the solvent fed, *i.e.*, the left-hand side is the fractional approach to equilibrium.

If solute is being extracted from the solvent (to which the composition y and the flow rate G refer), as in the enriching section, then the relative positions of the operating and equilibrium lines of Fig. 194 are reversed, and the Kremser equation becomes

$$\frac{y_0 - y_n}{y_0 - mx_{n+1}} = \frac{(L/mG)^{n+1} - (L/mG)}{(L/mG)^{n+1} - 1} \tag{455}$$

or

$$P = \frac{R^{n+1} - R}{R^{n+1} - 1} \tag{456}$$

It is important to note the direction of diffusion in assigning appropriate values to P and R in using Eq. (456). If solute is passing *into the solvent*

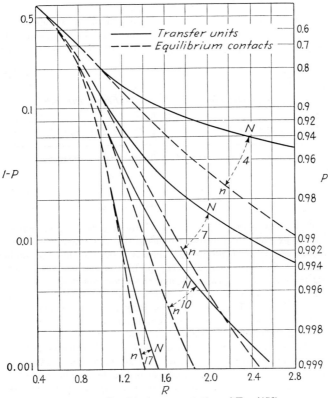

Fig. 195. Graphical representation of Eq. (456).

(y,G), then Eq. (454) applies and R is mG/L; if solute is passing *out of the solvent* (y,G) into the raffinate (x,L), then Eq. (455) applies and R is L/mG.

The nature of this relation is shown by the dotted curves of Fig. 195, where the left-hand side of Eq. (454) or (455) is represented by the symbol P. When R is less than 0.5, R and P are essentially equal for any practical number of contacts or stages. When R is unity, P is equal to $n/(n + 1)$. The graph is extended to very high values of P so as to be useful in the estimation of the extraction of very valuable materials, where very high recoveries are necessary. In most commercial extraction equipment, R for the main constituent will be between 0.5 and 2.0, usually between 1.1 and 2.0.

The problem of the transient or unsteady-state conditions following a sudden change in feed composition is treated by Lapidus and Amundson[264] for the case of countercurrent multiple-stage operations with systems for which the distribution law holds.

Illustration 43. An aqueous solution contains a small amount of a valuable solute A together with an impurity B present to the extent of 25 per cent of the amount of A. It is desired to employ a countercurrent multiple-contact extraction process

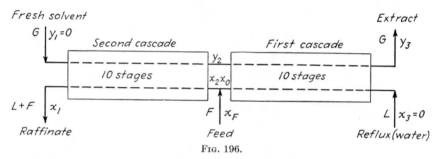

Fig. 196.

to recover 90 per cent of the solute A in a relatively pure state after removal of the solvent from the extract. It is arbitrarily decided that no more than 4 per cent of B should be recovered in the same process, since it is desired that the product contain not much more than 1 per cent B. The problem is to select a suitable solvent. Assume that the distribution law holds, and the m for each solute can be obtained in the laboratory by simple single-contact extractions and analyses of the resulting layers of extract and raffinate. What solvent selectivity, expressed as m_A/m_B, is necessary to accomplish the purpose if a double system of multiple-contact units is employed, with reflux, using 10 equilibrium contacts in each?

Solution. The proposed process is illustrated by the flow diagram of Fig. 196. On each side of the feed there is a "cascade" of 10 equilibrium stages, arranged for countercurrent flow of extract and raffinate, as in Fig. 186. The symbols indicate the flow rate as pounds per hour and the composition as pounds of solute per pound of solvent in each stream. Fresh water is supplied as reflux to the first cascade.

The procedure will be to derive a general relation for the recovery of solutes A and B in terms of the distribution coefficients m_A and m_B, and the flow rates of solvent and water. The resulting relations will then be plotted and the required ratio m_A/m_B obtained from the resulting curves.

By a material balance on the first cascade,

$$Lx_0 = G(y_2 - y_3) \tag{457}$$

and

$$\frac{L}{G}\frac{x_0}{y_2} = \frac{y_2 - y_3}{y_2 - 0} = \frac{R_1^{n+1} - R_1}{R_1^{n+1} - 1} = P_1 \tag{458}$$

where R_1 is L/mG.

By a material balance on the second cascade,

$$(F + L)(x_2 - x_1) = Gy_2 \tag{459}$$

and

$$\frac{G}{F+L}\frac{y_2}{x_2} = \frac{x_2 - x_1}{x_2 - 0} = \frac{R_2^{n+1} - R_2}{R_2^{n+1} - 1} = P_2 \tag{460}$$

where R_2 is $Gm/(L + F)$.

By a material balance around the feed point,

$$x_2(L + F) = x_F F + x_0 L \tag{461}$$

whence

$$\frac{x_2}{x_F} = \frac{(F/L) + (x_0/x_F)}{1 + (F/L)} \tag{462}$$

Combining Eqs. (458), (460), and (461),

$$\frac{x_0}{x_F} = \frac{FP_1P_2}{L(1 - P_1P_2)} \tag{463}$$

and from Eq. (461)

$$\frac{x_1}{x_F} = \frac{x_2}{x_F}(1 - P_2) \tag{464}$$

Let the fraction of solute A (or B) in the feed which is recovered in the extract be Q. Then the fraction lost in the raffinate is given by

$$1 - Q = \frac{x_1(L + F)}{x_F F} \tag{465}$$

Substituting Eqs. (462) to (464) in Eq. (465),

$$Q = \frac{P_2 - P_1P_2}{1 - P_1P_2} \tag{466}$$

Since R_1 and R_2 are related by

$$R_2 = \frac{Gm}{L+F} = \frac{L}{R_1(L+F)} = \frac{1}{R_1[1 + (F/L)]} \tag{467}$$

it is possible to express Q as a function of R_1 and F/L; this has been done graphically for an n of 10 in each cascade, as shown in Fig. 197. These curves may be used for either component A or B.

Various sets of operating conditions may be employed to obtain the specified recovery. For example, if R_1 is chosen as 0.3, then F/L must be 2.19 to obtain 90 per cent recovery of A. At this value of F/L the recovery of B is 4 per cent if R_1 for B is chosen as about 1.15. In this case

$$\frac{m_A}{m_B} = \frac{L}{m_B G}\frac{m_A G}{L} = \frac{R_{1B}}{R_{1A}} = \frac{1.15}{0.3} = 3.8$$

This procedure is repeated to obtain the curve of Fig. 198, which shows that 90 per cent recovery of A and 4 per cent recovery of B are obtained at an F/L of 0.4 with a ratio of distribution coefficients m_A/m_B of 2.0.

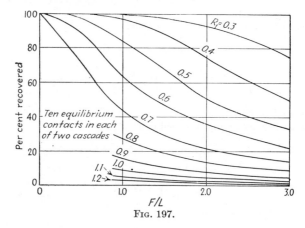

Fig. 197.

In the laboratory search for a suitable solvent, therefore, it is necessary to find a solvent with a selectivity m_A/m_B of 2.0 or greater.

Illustration 44. Extend the derivations given in the solution to Illustration 43 to cover the separation of one component of a mixture by the use of a four-cascade extraction system such as that illustrated in Fig. 187. Assume the distribution law to hold for the "key component" B and for the two components A and C nearest B from the point of view of solubility in the solvent employed.

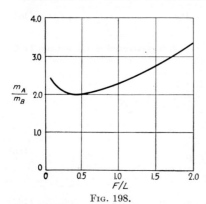

Fig. 198.

Assume m for each component is the same in all four cascades, and that $m_A = 0.5$, $m_B = 2.0$, and $m_C = 8.0$. A recovery of 98 per cent of A is required, and the equipment to be employed is the equivalent of seven equilibrium contacts in each of the four cascades. What purity of the solvent-free product B may be expected?

Solution. The flow diagram of the process is shown in Fig. 187; the cascades will be referred to by number as indicated on that diagram. The cascades will be referred to by numerical subscripts; inlet and outlet compositions will be referred to by primes and double primes. Then

$$P_1 = \frac{y_1' - y_1''}{y_1''}; \qquad R_1 = \frac{L_1}{mG_1} \tag{468}$$

$$P_2 = \frac{x_2' - x_2''}{x_2'}; \qquad R_2 = \frac{mG_1}{L_1 + F} \tag{469}$$

where L_1 is the water fed to 1, G_1 is the solvent fed to 2, and F is the feed rate   Note that x_1' and y_2' are zero, and $y_2'' = y_1'$.

Then by definition

$$f_1 = \frac{y_1''G_1}{x_F F} = \text{fraction leaving in first extract} \tag{470}$$

From Eq. (468),

$$y_1'' = y_1'(1 - P_1) = y_2''(1 - P_1) \tag{471}$$

By a material balance on the second cascade,

$$(L_1 + F)(x_2' - x_2'') = G_1 y_2'' \tag{472}$$

From Eq. (469),

$$x_2' - x_2'' = x_2' P_2 \tag{473}$$

By a material balance around the feed point,

$$x_2'(L_1 + F) = x_1'' L_1 + x_F F$$

or

$$\frac{x_2'}{x_F} = \frac{x_1'' L_1}{L_1 + F} + \frac{F}{L_1 + F} \tag{474}$$

By a material balance on the first cascade,

$$x_1'' L_1 = G_1(y_1' - y_1'') = G_1 P_1 y_1' = \frac{G_1 P_1 y_1''}{1 - P_1} = \frac{f_1 x_F F P_1}{1 - P_1} \tag{475}$$

Substituting Eqs. (471) to (475) successively in Eq. (470),

$$\begin{aligned}
f_1 &= \frac{y_2''(1 - P_1)G_1}{x_F F} = \frac{(1 - P_1)(L_1 + F)(x_2' - x_2'')}{x_F F G_1} \\
&= \frac{(1 - P_1)(L_1 + F)x_2' P_2}{x_F F} = \frac{(1 - P_1)(L_1 + F)P_2}{F}\left[\frac{x_1'' L_1}{(L_1 + F)x_F} + \frac{F}{L_1 + F} \right] \\
&= \frac{(1 - P_1)P_2}{F}\left(\frac{x_1'' L_1}{x_F} + F \right) = (1 - P_1)P_2\left(\frac{x_1'' L_1}{F x_F} + 1 \right) \\
&= (1 - P_1)P_2\left(\frac{f_1 P_1}{1 - P_1} + 1 \right)
\end{aligned}$$

Whence,

$$f_1 = \frac{P_2(1 - P_1)}{1 - P_1 P_2} \tag{476}$$

and

$$f_2 = 1 - f_1 = \frac{1 - P_2}{1 - P_1 P_2} \tag{477}$$

For the second cascade, it follows by inspection that

$$f_3 = f_2 \frac{1 - P_3}{1 - P_3 P_4} = \frac{(1 - P_2)(1 - P_3)}{(1 - P_1 P_2)(1 - P_3 P_4)} \tag{478}$$

and

$$f_4 = f_2 \frac{P_3(1 - P_4)}{1 - P_3 P_4} = \frac{P_3(1 - P_2)(1 - P_4)}{(1 - P_1 P_2)(1 - P_3 P_4)} \tag{479}$$

It may be seen that $f_1 + f_3 + f_4 = 1$, as called for by an over-all material balance.

Equations (454) and (455) or Fig. 195 may be employed to obtain P_3 and P_4, where

$$P_3 = \frac{x_3' - x_3''}{x_3'}; \qquad R_3 = \frac{mG_2}{L_1 + L_2 + F} \tag{480}$$

$$P_4 = \frac{y_4' - y_4''}{y_4'}; \qquad R_4 = \frac{L_2}{mG_2} \tag{481}$$

where L_2 and G_2 are the water and solvent rates to the second pair of cascades.

In applying these relations to the numerical problem, it may be seen that there are various solutions, depending on the values chosen for R_1, R_2, R_3, and R_4. R_1 and R_2 must be chosen so that most of component B leaves the bottom of the second cascade, while most of component C leaves in the first extract. R_3 and R_4 must be chosen so as to separate B and A. All values of R should be in the range less than 2.0 for the key component.

As an example, suppose $R_1 = R_3 = 1.8$ and $R_2 = R_4 = 0.328$ for the key component B. Then using Fig. 195 for seven equilibrium contacts, $P_1 = P_3 = 0.992$, and $P_2 = P_4 = 0.328$. Substituting these values in Eqs. (476), (478), and (479), $f_1 = 0.004$, $f_3 = 0.012$, and $f_4 = 0.984$. That is, 98.4 per cent of the B in the feed is recovered in the second extract.

For component A, m is one-fourth as great, whence, from Eqs. (468), (469), (480), and (481), $R_1 = 3.6$, $R_2 = 0.164$, $R_3 = 0.9$, and $R_4 = 0.656$. Substituting these values, $f_1 = 0$, $f_3 = 0.962$, and $f_4 = 0.038$. Similarly, for component C, $f_1 = 0.917$, $f_3 = 0$, and $f_4 = 0.083$.

The second extract will contain 98.4 per cent of the B in the feed, 3.8 per cent of the A in the feed, and 8.3 per cent of the C. The extract containing the recovered B could doubtless be made to contain somewhat less of A and C by choosing more appropriate values of R_1, R_2, R_3, and R_4.

Substituting the assumed values of R_1, R_2, R_3, and R_4 in the definitions given by Eqs. (468), (469), (480), and (481), there are obtained the values $L_1 = 1.44$, $L_2 = 3.52$, $G_1 = 0.4$, and $G_2 = 5.36$, on the basis of $F = 1$. This check is necessary, since certain assumed values of the four R's would indicate the desired recovery of B but would lead to negative values of one or more of the water- or solvent-flow rates.

The indicated separation is good, but the solvent rate G_2 is quite large. Admittedly, a better choice of values for the four R's might give similar recovery and separation with lower solvent requirement.

In many cases the equilibrium relation is sensitive to various additives, and m can be changed appreciably by changing the pH, by the salt effect of appropriate additives, or by other means. This deliberate variation in m may change the ratios of the m's for the several solutes, making the separation either easier or more difficult. Even though separation is not affected, modification of m makes it possible to employ a more suitable value of R without requiring excessive solvent rates. In a case such as the example outlined above, it might be possible to reduce the required solvent rate G_2 by changing the pH in the second cascade.

5. Solvent Partially Miscible with the Solution to Be Treated. In this general case the equilibrium is best represented by a triangular diagram. The stoichiometric computations are conveniently carried out by graphical construction on such a diagram, as has been explained by Hunter and Nash,[207] Evans,[134] and by Varteressian and Fenske.[475]

Before this procedure is described, it is important to point out certain properties of triangular diagrams. Figure 199 shows a diagram similar to Fig. 188, with the solubility curve and the tie lines. It is not difficult to prove that, if a mixture of A, B, and C, represented by the point P, is mixed with a solution of composition R, the composition of the resulting mixture will be represented by a point Q lying on a straight line connecting P with R. Furthermore, the position of Q will be such that the distances PQ and QR are in the ratio of the amounts of R and P mixed, $i.e.$,

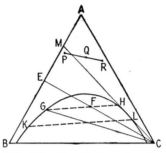

$$\frac{PQ}{QR} = \frac{\text{amount of } R}{\text{amount of } P} \qquad (482)$$

FIG. 199. Graphical construction for stiochiometric computations.

If the point Q should fall within the two-phase region on the diagram, then the resulting mixture will split into two phases having the compositions indicated by the points at the ends of the tie line through Q. The amount of each resulting phase will be in inverse proportion to the distance of Q from the end of the tie line.

Figure 199 shows the construction for a two-stage multiple-contact extraction using fresh solvent in each stage. The material to be treated has a composition represented by the point E and is brought in contact with solvent C. The resulting mixture F, lying within the two-phase region, will separate into two layers of compositions G and H, as determined by the tie line through F. The raffinate G is treated with further solvent, and the final raffinate K obtained. The compositions of the two extracts are given by points H and L. The amounts of each material may be determined from the known amounts of original solution and of solvent used and by a calculation of the amounts of the phases separated, using the rule represented by Eq. (482).

Figure 200 represents the construction for a two-stage countercurrent multiple-contact system, employing the solvent C to treat the original solution E. The procedure is by trial and error and may be started in various ways. Assume, for example, that the final extract is to have a composition H. Then for the extraction process as a whole,

$$E + C = H + K = F$$

where the letters represent both amount and composition of the several mixtures. Point F lies on EC, and its position is determined by the relative amounts of solution E and solvent C used. The final raffinate K is determined as the intersection of HF with the solubility curve. The intermediate raffinate and extract have compositions G and L, as yet undetermined. By material balances on the separate stages it follows that

$$E + L = G + H \quad \text{and} \quad G + C = K + L$$

whence

$$K - C = G - L = E - H$$

Application of the rule of Eq. (482) shows that the straight lines HE, LG, and CK will intersect in a common point O. Point O represents a mixture having a negative solvent content and hence is of geometric significance only.

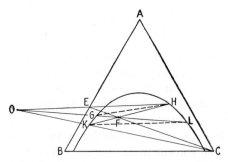

FIG. 200. Construction for two-stage countercurrent multiple-contact extraction.

Since the location of H has been assumed, K may be located by extending HF. Point O is then located as the intersection of CK and HE. Point G is located at the other end of the tie line through H, and L is obtained by extending OG. Points L and K should then be found to lie on a common tie line; if not, point H was incorrectly assumed, and the procedure must be repeated with another assumed composition of the final extract. With three or more stages the construction is the same but employs a correspondingly greater number of tie lines and construction lines through O.

Referring again to Fig. 199, the material obtained by removing the solvent from the extract has a composition represented by the intersection on AB of a straight line from the apex C through the point representing the composition of the extract. With systems of the type illustrated in Fig. 199, the maximum concentration of A in the distilled extract will be represented by M, where CM is tangent to the solubility curve.

The final raffinate K, after two extractions, may be compared with the original solution E. It is evident that the separation effected, and the completeness of the removal of A from the raffinate, will depend to a large extent on the position of the tie lines. Had the tie lines sloped more steeply up to the right, the separation would have been easier, in that K would have been lower. Conversely, if the tie lines had sloped down to the right, K would have fallen on the solubility curve nearer to the line EC. In the latter case, C would be a poor solvent for the separation of A and B, but B would be an excellent solvent for the separation of A and C.

6. Graphical Design Calculations for Extraction with Reflux—General Case with Equilibrium Contacts. The application of reflux to extraction has been described in a previous section and is illustrated by the typical flow diagram shown as Fig. 186. Considering both enriching and exhausting sections to be equivalent to a number of equilibrium contacts, it is evident that the graphical construction using the triangular diagram, as described in the preceding section, may be extended to provide a basis of design of the double tower or double cascade. This procedure is well described by Varteressian and Fenske[475] and by Elgin and Wynkoop.[129] Alternatively, it is convenient to employ a graphical method based on the Ponchon diagram, as suggested by Thiele[457] and by Randall and Longtin;[383] this method is developed and clearly presented by Maloney and Schubert.[295] Still a third graphical method employs a rectangular-coordinate equilibrium curve similar to the McCabe-Thiele diagram used in distillation. This last is awkward, because the operating lines are curved and difficult to locate. For the present purpose it is sufficient to describe one of the three; the method based on the Ponchon diagram will be chosen because it seems to be the most easily understood. Other graphical methods are described by Bull and Coli.[56]

Assume the feed to consist of a mixture of solutes A and B, saturated with solvent. Let A be the constituent for which the solvent exhibits a preferential solubility. Referring to Fig. 186, let S be the pounds of solvent withdrawn at the top, P be the extract product leaving the top, and O_R be the reflux (saturated with solvent). Considering the nth equilibrium stage in the enriching section, let L_{n+1} be the raffinate stream entering from the stage above, and G_n be the extract stream leaving the nth stage. Because it is an equilibrium stage or contact, the streams L_n and G_n are in equilibrium. Let the symbols P, O_R, L, and G be defined as weight per unit time on a solvent-free basis, $i.e.$, weight of A plus B. Now let S_E and S_R represent pounds of solvent per pound of A plus B in extract and raffinate streams, respectively.

Using these symbols, a solvent balance is written around the upper part of the column, above the nth stage. The solvent in the rising extract stream is $G_n S_{E,n}$; that in the descending raffinate stream is

$L_{n+1}S_{R,n+1}$. The solvent in the product is $PS_{R,P}$ and in the reflux is $O_R S_{R,P}$. The solvent balance is

$$G_n S_{E,n} - L_{n+1}S_{R,n+1} = S + PS_{R,P} \tag{483}$$

But the solvent removed from the separator is also obtained by considering that the extract going to the separator has its solvent content reduced from $S_{E,P}$ to $S_{R,P}$, whence

$$G_n S_{E,n} - L_{n+1}S_{R,n+1} = (P + O_R)(S_{E,P} - S_{R,P}) + PS_{R,P} \tag{484}$$

or

$$\frac{G_n S_{E,n} - L_{n+1}S_{R,n+1}}{P} = \left(\frac{O_R}{P} + 1\right)(S_{E,P} - S_{R,P}) + S_{R,P} \tag{485}$$

in which the ratio O_R/P is the reflux ratio.

Equation (485) is developed in order that the graphical method may be explained. The graph employed is one of solvent ratios vs. phase composition (on a solvent-free basis), as shown in the upper section of Fig. 201. Phase solubility data are plotted on this single graph as two lines of S_E vs. y, and S_R vs. x. A common abscissa is used for x and y, the weight fraction A on a solvent-free basis in raffinate and extract layers, respectively [for example, $y = A/(A + B)$]. The upper curve represents S_E vs. y for the system illustrated. The raffinate layer in this case contains so little solvent that S_R is only about 0.1, and the curve of S_R vs. x essentially coincides with the base line.

The two curves of S_E and S_R vs. y and x represent solubility data; equilibrium data are represented by the solid tie lines such as JL. The abscissas at L and J represent the compositions of extract and raffinate layers in equilibrium.

The lower graph on Fig. 201 is not essential to the graphical computation, but the equilibrium curve RST is plotted as y vs. x as a convenient reference for locating tie lines on the upper graph. The difference $y - x$ at equilibrium (the distance JK) is given as the horizontal distance between RST and the 45 deg. line RVT.

Proceeding to the illustration of the graphical procedure, assume that it is desired to separate a 50 per cent mixture of A and B into a raffinate and extract product containing 10 and 90 per cent A, all on a solvent-free basis. Let it be desired to determine the number of equilibrium stages for a reflux ratio of 5.

Referring to the upper diagram, the feed, extract, and raffinate compositions are given by points F, K, and G, respectively. The extract layer leaving the top stage of the column is represented by point L. The difference $S_{E,P} - S_{R,P}$ appearing in Eq. (485) is the vertical distance LK, and the right-hand side of the equation is represented by point M, where LM is five times LK (reflux ratio 5).

The extract layer leaving the top stage is given by point L, and the raffinate layer passing to the stage below, in equilibrium, is found at J by

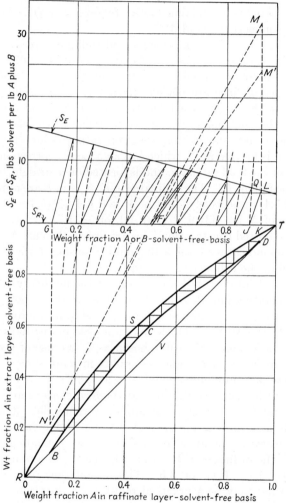

Fig. 201. Ponchon graphical representation of countercurrent extraction with reflux. (*After Maloney and Schubert.*)

following the solid tie line LJ. The extract layer entering the top stage is related to the raffinate J by Eq. (485) and by the fact that it is saturated with solvent. It must be represented by some point Q on the extract saturation curve, such that Eq. (485) holds. If the letters designating points are taken as representing both amount and composition per unit of extract product, then Eq. (485) becomes

$$Q - J = M \qquad (486)$$

and by the straight-line mixing law it follows that Q is located on a straight line connecting J and M.

For any stage, therefore, the extract and raffinate streams leaving are located at the ends of tie lines; the extract entering and the raffinate leaving are located on straight lines through point M. Starting at L, these two types of lines are placed alternately as the solid and dotted sections, giving the saw-toothed construction shown, and the number of stages above the feed point is found to be seven in the case illustrated.

It may be readily shown that the "operating point" for conditions below the feed is located at N, which has an abscissa corresponding to the composition of the final raffinate, and is located on a straight line through M and the feed point F. The ordinates of F, K, and L are approximately 0.1, 0.1, and 5.4, respectively; that of M is $0.1 + (6)(5.4 - 0.1)$, or 31.9. The ordinate of N is $-[31.9 - (2)(0.1)]$, or -31.7. To the left of the feed point the dotted construction lines are drawn through N. The completed diagram indicates a total of 13 equilibrium stages, 7 in the enriching section and 6 in the exhausting section.

As a matter of interest, but not as part of the necessary construction, the curved operating line BCD has been added to the lower graph. The steps representing equilibrium stages are also shown, in order to indicate the analogy to the McCabe-Thiele diagram used in distillation.

The reflux ratio was arbitrarily chosen as 5; the use of greater reflux would result in fewer stages, and less reflux in more stages. As in distillation, there is a minimum reflux ratio at which the operating line or operating point indicates equilibrium at the feed concentration and leads to an infinite number of stages. At minimum reflux the dotted construction segment and the tie line coincide at the feed point, and the corresponding operating point is located at M' by extending the tie line through F. The ordinate at M' is 24, whence the minimum reflux ratio is $(24 - 5.4)/(5.4 - 0.1)$, or 3.5. This calculation provides a useful guide as to what may be a practical reflux ratio to employ. Similarly, total reflux places the operating point at an infinite ordinate, and the dotted construction lines are all vertical. This gives a limiting minimum number of equilibrium stages for the required separation.

The illustration used is for a ternary system of the type shown in Fig. 190 and is essentially identical with the example used by Varteressian and Fenske, by Elgin and Wynkoop, and by Maloney and Schubert.[295] In practice it is found that the type of system illustrated by Figs. 188 and 189 is much more common than that used in these illustrations, and it is unfortunate that the graphical methods described are difficult to use for these common applications.

Figure 202, for example, illustrates the system water–acetone–methyl isobutyl ketone, with saturation curve $CAPD$ and conjugate line COP. Let it be desired to recover acetone from a 20 per cent aqueous solution (point F) by extraction with methyl isobutyl ketone. Since the extract phase A in equilibrium with the feed corresponds very nearly to the maximum possible acetone concentration (solvent-free, indicated by point B) of any extract layer, it follows that no enriching section is required, and reflux is not beneficial. The problem is to design an exhausting column, fed at the top. If the graphical construction of Fig. 200 is attempted, it is found that the operating point is far

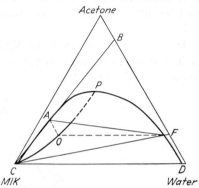

Fig. 202.   System acetone–methyl isobutyl ketone–water.

outside the triangle and that the precision is very poor in drawing the construction lines. If the Ponchon method is attempted, the curve of S_E vs. y covers an extremely narrow range of values of y, and the procedure is very difficult. Perhaps the best method in this case is to construct the type of diagram illustrated by the lower half of Fig. 201, locating the curved operating line by trial-and-error calculation, based on a material balance around the bottom of the column. No method obviating these difficulties appears to have been developed.

SOLVENT EXTRACTION OF HYDROCARBON MIXTURES

In the solvent refining of lubricating oils, the object is to separate in the extract a high proportion of the undesirable "naphthenic" compounds, leaving a raffinate containing an increased proportion of the "paraffinic" compounds. The improvement of the raffinate is measured by the change of any one of several criteria, such as the viscosity index[*]

---

[*] The viscosity index is an empirical measure of the temperature coefficient of viscosity. It is defined arbitrarily in terms of the viscosities at 100 and 210°F. in such a way that a standard, good, Pennsylvania-base lubricating oil has a V.I. of 100, and a standard, poor oil has a V.I. of 0 (see Dean and Davis;[104] also Davis, Lapeyrouse, and Dean[103]).

(V.I.) or viscosity gravity coefficient* (V.G.C.).   Oils having a high V.I. have a low temperature coefficient of viscosity, a property desirable in automotive lubricating oils.   The V.G.C. is reduced by proper solvent refining, the better oils having low values of this criterion.

The problem is no longer that of the relatively simple ternary system, but involves a complex system of solvent and a large number of different and unknown hydrocarbons.   A method of attack proposed by Hunter and Nash[208] appears to have considerable promise and will be described briefly.

It is first assumed that the V.G.C. of a mixture of two oils will be a weighted mean of the two values of the V.G.C. for the two oils.   This assumption does not appear to have been proved directly but is borne out

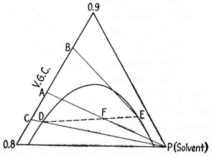

FIG. 203.   Ternary diagram for representation of complex hydrocarbon-solvent equilibria.

by the comparison of experimental and calculated results for various cases of solvent treating.   A ternary diagram is constructed, the three apexes representing, respectively, the solvent, an oil with a low V.G.C. (say, 0.80), and an oil with a high V.G.C. (say, 0.90).   Such a diagram is represented in Fig. 203.   Laboratory extractions then serve to determine the solubility curves and the tie lines, as in the case of a normal ternary system.   For example, suppose 1 volume of an oil having a V.G.C. of A is shaken with an equal volume of solvent.   The mixture will be represented by point F, located on a straight line AP midway between A and P.   A raffinate and extract are obtained, and the solvent content of each is determined.   Also, the V.G.C. of each solvent-free layer is measured. Point E representing the composition of the extract is then located on a straight line connecting P with B, the V.G.C. of the solvent-free extract, at a position determined by the measured solvent-oil ratio in the extract.

* The viscosity gravity constant is a constant in an empirical relation between the specific gravity and the viscosity.   Paraffinic oils exhibit a low specific gravity and a low V.G.C., and the naphthenic oils a high specific gravity and a high V.G.C. for any given viscosity (Hill and Coats[186]).

Similarly, point D is located from the V.G.C. of the solvent-free raffinate C, and the solvent-oil ratio CD/DP of the raffinate. Thus one tie line and two points on the solubility curve are determined. Similar tests serve to locate other tie lines and other points on the solubility curve, and the result is a diagram similar to Fig. 203. Using this diagram, the stoichiometric computations are entirely similar to those described for actual ternary systems.

Although Hunter and Nash used two values of the V.G.C. as the basis for applying the triangular equilibrium diagram, other authors have used such properties as V.I., aniline point, and specific gravity. As indicated above, it is necessary that the property chosen be one which varies linearly with the composition of a mixture of solvent and raffinate.

Solvents Employed in Commercial Processes. Apparently the first commercial petroleum-refining process based on solvent extraction was the Edeleanu process, in which liquid sulfur dioxide or a mixture of liquid SO_2 with benzene is the solvent. This process has been used widely in Europe, as well as in this country. It has been described in many articles and is the subject of a recent book.[106]

Important developments in this field in the United States include the furfural process (The Texas Co.) employing furfural at 200 to 220°F. as the solvent; the Chlorex process (Standard Oil Co. of Indiana) using β,β-dichloroethyl ether at room temperature as solvent; the nitrobenzene process (Atlantic Refining Co.) using nitrobenzene at about 50°F.; the phenol process (M. W. Kellogg Co., Imperial Oil Co.) using phenol at 100 to 180°F.; the crotonaldehyde process (Foster Wheeler Co.); and the Duo-Sol process (Max B. Miller Co., Socony-Vacuum Oil Co.), in which propane and a mixture of phenol and cresylic acid are the solvents. Kalichevsky[234] lists the principal refineries employing solvent refining, indicating the process and the nominal charging capacity. This shows a total installed capacity of the order of 70,000 bbl./day, as of about 1938.

For detailed information on the several processes see Kalichevsky,[234] and Dunstan, "The Science of Petroleum."[122] The latter reference includes several authoritative articles by users of the different processes.

Although hydrogen sulfide is removed from sour natural gas and other gas mixtures by absorption in ethanolamines (Girdler Corp.)[444] and other absorbents, it may also be removed from mixtures with hydrocarbons in the liquid phase. One such process (Shell Development Co.) uses an aqueous solution of tripotassium phosphate as solvent.[518] Potassium acid phosphate and hydrosulfide are formed, the reaction being reversed and hydrogen sulfide evolved when the extract is heated to about 235°F. A simple countercurrent extractor packed with 1-in. rings is used. Figure

204 is a general view of a Unisol plant for sulfur removal from gasoline by extraction with liquid methanol.

A review of the solubility relations between liquid hydrocarbons and other liquids, together with a bibliography of phase-equilibrium data, is given by Francis.[143]

Fig. 204. Unisol extraction plant for removal of sulfur compounds from gasoline using methanol as solvent. (*C. F. Braun and Co.*)

RATE EQUATIONS

Application of the Two-film Theory. The basis of the rate equations developed in Chap. V is the principle that rate of interphase transfer is proportional to a potential or driving force expressed as a difference in concentrations of the substance diffusing. Diffusion from one liquid phase to a second liquid immiscible with the first is analogous to gas absorption in that the solute must cross two fluid films in diffusing from the main body of one liquid phase to the main body of the second. It is assumed that the resistances of the two liquid films are additive and that the concentrations at the contact interface correspond to equilibrium between the two phases.

The basic equation expresses the rate of diffusion through the two films in series:

$$N_A \, dA = k_R \frac{\rho_R}{M_A} (x - x_i) \, dA = k_E \frac{\rho_E}{M_A} (y_i - y) \, dA \qquad (487)$$

Here N_A is the rate of transfer as pound mole per hour per unit of phase-contact area, A is the area of contact between phases, k_R and k_E are the film coefficients for raffinate and extract layers, and y and x represent the solute concentrations: x in main raffinate stream, x_i in raffinate at phase boundary, y_i in the extract at phase boundary, and y in the main extract layer. The interface concentrations x_i and y_i are assumed to be in equilibrium, as given by tie lines on the phase-equilibrium diagram. The true nature of the potential which governs rate of diffusion is not known, and it is common for the potential to be expressed in a variety of units, such as mole fraction, pound mole per cubic foot, weight friction, etc. These variations are permissible, though it must be remembered that the transfer coefficients will have different units and different numerical values depending on the units of driving force used.

Following the analogy to gas absorption, the over-all transfer coefficient is defined in terms of concentrations in the main streams:

$$N_A \, dA = K_R \frac{\rho_R}{M_A} (x - x_e) \, dA = K_E \frac{\rho_E}{M_A} (y_e - y) \, dA \qquad (488)$$

Solute concentrations in the two phases are based on different solvents and cannot be subtracted to obtain the over-all potential or driving force. (At equilibrium, for example, there is no transfer; yet the concentrations x and y are not the same.) The driving force is taken to be the difference between the actual bulk concentration and the concentration corresponding to equilibrium with the main body of the other phase. Thus x is the main raffinate concentration, and x_e is the raffinate concentration in equilibrium with the bulk extract y. Similarly, y_e is the extract composition in equilibrium with the bulk raffinate concentration x.

In cases where the distribution law holds and where the equilibrium between the two phases can be expressed by

$$y = mx \qquad (489)$$

$x - x_e$ is proportional to $y_e - y$, and the relation between over-all and film coefficients is given by

$$\frac{1}{K_E} = \frac{1}{k_E} + \frac{m\rho_E}{k_R \rho_R} \qquad (490)$$

and

$$\frac{1}{K_R} = \frac{1}{k_R} + \frac{\rho_R}{mk_E \rho_E} \qquad (491)$$

The film transfer coefficients k_E and k_R are presumably independent of solute composition. As indicated by Eqs. (490) and (491), however, the over-all coefficients K_E and K_R will vary with solute concentration unless the distribution law holds and m is constant.

In many common types of extraction equipment, including mixers, spray towers, and packed towers, the area of interfacial contact between the phases is not known, and it is convenient to associate the unknown contact area per cubic foot of equipment with the transfer coefficient, giving the products k_Ea, k_Ra, K_Ea, and K_Ra. Thus Eq. (488) becomes

$$N_A a \, dV = K_R a \, \frac{\rho_R}{M_A} \, (x - x_e) \, dV = K_E a \, \frac{\rho_E}{M_A} \, (y_e - y) \, dV \qquad (492)$$

which expresses the rate of diffusion of solute from raffinate to extract in a differential volume of equipment. Equations (490) and (491) obviously apply to coefficients on a volume basis.

As in absorption, the relative diffusional resistances of the two films, represented by the terms on the right-hand side of Eq. (490) or (491), vary widely with the relative solubility of diffusing solute in the two phases. Thus when m is large (solute much more soluble in extract than in raffinate layer), it is evident that the extract film resistance is small, and K_Ra and k_Ra will be approximately equal in magnitude. Conversely, if m is very small (solute more soluble in raffinate), K_Ea and k_Ea approach equality. In these cases one or the other film is said to be controlling, and the over-all coefficients are applicable whether or not the distribution law holds. In such cases it is desirable to express experimental data in terms of concentrations in the phase which controls.

In most cases the transfer of total material between phases is not great, and it is a fair approximation to assume the total flow rates L and G to be constant through the equipment. In this case the material balance for a continuous countercurrent tower becomes

$$SL \, dx = SG \, dy = M_A N_A a \, dV \qquad (493)$$

and the tower height is given by

$$Z = \frac{V}{S} = \int_{x_1}^{x_2} \frac{L \, dx}{K_R a \rho_R (x - x_e)} = \int_{y_1}^{y_2} \frac{G \, dy}{K_E a \rho_E (y_e - y)} \qquad (494)$$

Here Z and S represent the tower height and cross section, respectively.

Equation (494) is employed for the estimation of the height of tower required in order to obtain specified concentration changes in continuous countercurrent extraction. In using this equation, it is convenient to prepare a graph showing both equilibrium and operating lines as y vs. x, as illustrated in a previous section of the chapter. This graph is used to obtain the driving forces $x - x_e$ or $y_e - y$, and the height Z is obtained by a graphical integration as the area under a graph of $1/(x - x_e)$ or $1/(y_e - y)$ vs. x or y, between appropriate limits.   A logarithmic-mean driving force may be used in case the equilibrium curve is straight over the range in which it is employed.

Transfer Units in Extraction.   Using the concept of transfer units, as described in Chap. V, for gas absorption, it is possible to apply similar relations to extraction.   Thus

$$N_{T,OR} = \int_{x_1}^{x_2} \frac{dx}{x - x_E} \tag{495}$$

and

$$N_{T,OE} = \int_{y_1}^{y_2} \frac{dy}{y_E - y} \tag{496}$$

where $N_{T,OR}$ is the number of over-all transfer units based on concentrations in the raffinate phase, and $N_{T,OE}$ is the similar quantity based on concentrations in the extract phase.   These are measures of the separation to be accomplished.

Since the height of a transfer unit (H.T.U.) is simply the tower height divided by the number of transfer units, it follows from Eq. (494) that

$$(\text{H.T.U.})_{OR} = \frac{Z}{N_{T,OR}} = \frac{L}{\rho_R K_R a} \tag{497}$$

and

$$(\text{H.T.U.})_{OE} = \frac{G}{\rho_E K_E a} \tag{498}$$

Similarly, from the additivity of resistances expressed by Eqs. (490) and (491), it follows that

$$(\text{H.T.U.})_{OR} = (\text{H.T.U.})_R + \frac{L}{mG} (\text{H.T.U.})_E \tag{499}$$

and

$$(\text{H.T.U.})_{OE} = (\text{H.T.U.})_E + \frac{mG}{L} (\text{H.T.U.})_R \tag{500}$$

where the single subscripts refer to single-film resistances.

It should be pointed out that the above presentation of rate equations, film resistances, and transfer units is greatly simplified, as compared with the theory as frequently presented in the literature.   The more complicated treatments allow for changing flow rates through the tower, the effect on diffusion of the varying concentration of nondiffusing solvent in the films, counterdiffusion of solvent from extract to raffinate, etc.   In the present state of development of the art, however, these complications seem hardly justified. Even the basic theory of additivity of resistances has not been demonstrated experimentally for diffusion between two liquid streams, and over-all coefficients and H.T.U.'s are known only approximately for a few systems. Until more basic work is done on the physics of the process, only the simpler relations here presented seem justified.

Number of Transfer Units—Distribution Law Applicable. In the general case, the required tower height should be obtained by a graphical integration, as described above. Alternatively, the number of over-all transfer units may be determined by graphical integration of Eq. (495) or (496). In cases where the distribution law holds, the calculation may be made algebraically, giving the equations

$$N_{T,OR} = \frac{1}{1 - R} \ln \left[(1 - R) \frac{x_2 - (y_1/m)}{x_1 - (y_1/m)} + R \right] \qquad (501)$$

where diffusion is from raffinate to extract, and

$$N_{T,OR} = \frac{1}{R - 1} \ln \left[\frac{R - 1}{R} \frac{y_1 - mx_2}{y_2 - mx_2} + \frac{1}{R} \right] \qquad (502)$$

where diffusion is from extract to raffinate. Here R represents the ratio L/mG. $N_{T,OE}$ is obtained by multiplying $N_{T,OR}$ by R for each case.

These relations simplify considerably when one of the streams fed contains none of the solute to be extracted. For example, $N_{T,OE}$ *for the case of diffusion from solvent* (G) *to raffinate* (L) is given by

$$N_{T,OE} = \frac{R}{R - 1} \ln \frac{R - P}{R(1 - P)} \qquad (503)$$

where P is the fraction extracted, $(y_1 - y_2)/y_1$. This can be arranged to give

$$P = \frac{R - Re^p}{1 - Re^p} \qquad (504)$$

where

$$p = \frac{N(R - 1)}{R}$$

The relation between $N_{T,OE}$ and P for this case has been plotted as P vs. R on Fig. 195 for several values of $N_{T,OE}$. It is evident that the number of transfer units approximates the number of equilibrium contacts over a wide range.

Equations (501) to (504) describe the same phenomena previously discussed in the case of countercurrent gas absorption by a liquid in systems where Henry's law applies, and the relations for extraction and gas absorption would appear identical except for a dilemma involving nomenclature. In the interest of clarity the preceding discussion has assumed that solute is being extracted from a raffinate (often an aqueous) phase into an extract (solvent) phase, and the rate equations have been written accordingly. L and x have referred to raffinate phase and G and y to extract phase. m has been defined by the relation $y = mx$.

In the usual case of gas absorption the raffinate is the gas phase, the liquid absorbent is the extract phase. Thus for gas absorption N_{OG} is the same as $N_{T,OE}$ as given above, providing R is taken as L/mG, where $y = mx$. If $N_{T,OE}$ is obtained by multiplying the right-hand side of Eq. (502) by R, the result is identical with Colburn's equation for N_{OG} as given by Perry.[361] Thus Fig. 28 in Perry or Fig. 40 may be used to obtain $N_{T,OE}$.

PERFORMANCE DATA ON CONTINUOUS COUNTERCURRENT EXTRACTION EQUIPMENT

Numerous publications in recent years have described experimental investigations of solvent extraction with typical systems in packed, perforated-plate, spray, and wetted-wall columns and in other types of extraction equipment. These data have not been correlated, however, and the available experimental results are useful as a basis for only a very rough estimate in the design of new equipment. The principal reason for this unsatisfactory situation is that transfer coefficients in extraction equipment depend on such a large number of variables.

As in the case of gas absorption, the individual film resistances depend on diffusivities and turbulence conditions in the two streams. In the case of extraction, however, the surface of contact between the phases (a ft.^{2}/ft.^{3}) depends on many more characteristics of the system and of the equipment. In an unpacked spray column, for example, the surface depends on the drop size and number of drops per unit volume. Drop size is determined by the feed-nozzle port size, the rate of feed to each port, the densities and viscosities of the two phases, and the interfacial tension between the phases. Too-large drops become flat rather than spherical. Number of drops per unit volume depends on the feed rate per unit of column cross section and on the rate of rise or fall of the drops passing through the continuous phase. Rate of rise depends on flow rate of the continuous phase, drop size, and the densities and viscosities of the two liquid phases. The total surface of contact between the phases is related to the holdup, and several investigators report data on holdup in different kinds of equipment.

According to the two-film theory, the relative importance of the two additive resistances depends on the solubility coefficient m as well as on the nature of the two films. It would be expected, therefore, that $K_A a$ would depend on the solubility and on the choice of phase to be dispersed. The limited data available indicate that these factors are less important than those which affect a, and it is a general rule that the phase fed in the larger volumetric rate should be dispersed. A possible exception to this rule is noted in the case of packed columns where one phase wets the packing but the other does not; in such cases the phase which wets the packing should probably be made the continuous phase. The reason is that, if the phase wetting the packing is made the dispersed phase, it passes over the packing in tiny rivulets, in which case the contact surface between phases is relatively small as compared to the case of the same flow as discrete droplets. Whether or not $K_A a$ depends on the direction of diffusion has not been established; comparable tests are difficult to make since the physical properties of the system change with the presence of the solute in one or the other phase.

In the light of these many complications it is remarkable that the data compare as well as they do. Typical data are presented below for packed, spray, and perforated-plate columns, with brief descriptions of the operating conditions. Table XXXII summarizes a selected list of investigations and indicates the nature of the data which have been published. It should be noted that the numerical value of $K_A a$ depends on the phase chosen as the basis for expressing the driving force in concentrations. In most cases $K_A a$ is expressed in terms of concentrations in the aqueous phase, although exceptions will be noted in the case of certain data on spray columns and columns packed with small saddles. No attempt has been made to collect all the published data; only representative data from the more important investigations of recent years are presented.

Spray Columns. Figure 205 summarizes a number of representative studies of small columns operated without packing. In each case the aqueous phase was continuous, the organic solvent being dispersed as drops at the bottom of the column. $K_A a$ is plotted vs. dispersed-phase flow rate, since it appears to be the most important variable. Continuous-phase flow rate has only a minor effect on $K_A a$. As indicated by the table under the figure, the data cover a very wide range of solubilities, but the values of $K_A a$ do not fall in the same order as the values of m. Since the over-all H.T.U. is the ratio of the flow rate to $K_A a$ ($K_A a$ expressed in terms of concentrations in the same phase whose flow rate is used), it follows by inspection that the over-all values of H.T.U. vary from about 1.5 to 10 ft., except in a few cases for curves A, B, and C, for which the values are considerably greater.

TABLE XXXII. SUMMARY OF REPRESENTATIVE INVESTIGATIONS OF COUNTERCURRENT EXTRACTION

Authors	System	Column diameter, in.	Packing	Misc. data	Ref.
Allerton, Strom, and Treybal	Toluene–benzoic acid–water; Kerosene–benzoic acid–water	3.6	Perforated plates, ½-in. carbon rings	Holdup, flooding	4
Appel and Elgin	Toluene–benzoic acid–water	2	None–spray; ½-in. saddles	Single drops	5
Blanding and Elgin	Solvent naphtha–water; MIK–water	2.4	None–spray; ½-in. saddles, rings, spheres	Flooding (only)	35
Brinsmade and Bliss	MIK–acetic acid–water	0.85	None–wetted wall		47
Colburn and Welsh	Isobutyl alcohol–water	3.7	½-in. rings		92
Comings and Briggs	Benzene–water, with aniline, benzoic acid, and acetic acid as solutes	0.47, 0.63, and 0.85 1.89 5.88 7.45	None–wetted wall; ½-in., 1-in. saddles; ½-in., ¾-in., 1-in. rings		93
Elgin and Browning	Isopropyl ether–acetic acid–water	2	None–spray		127
Fallah, Hunter, and Nash	Kerosene–phenol–water		None–wetted wall		136
Johnson and Bliss	MIK–acetic acid–water; MIK–propionic acid–water; MIK–benzoic acid–water; Benzene–acetic acid–water	1.8	None–spray	Holdup	222

TABLE XXXII. SUMMARY OF REPRESENTATIVE INVESTIGATIONS OF COUNTERCURRENT EXTRACTION. (*Continued*)

Authors	System	Column diameter, in.	Packing	Misc. data	Ref.
Pyle, Colburn, and Duffey	Ethyl ether–acetic acid–water	$8\frac{5}{8}$	Perforated plates	Flooding	380
Phillips and Thacker	MIK–acetic acid–water	3	None—spray; $\frac{3}{8}$-in. rings		364
Knight	Toluene–furfural–water	4	$\frac{1}{2}$-in. saddles		252
Meissner, Stokes, Hunter, and Morrow	MEK–water–CaCl₂ brine	3.6	None—spray; $\frac{1}{2}$-in. rings; $\frac{1}{2}$-in. saddles		318
Moulton and Walkey	MEK–water	3.75	Perforated plates		334
Row, Koffolt, and Withrow	Toluene–benzoic acid–water	8.75	Spray (empty); $\frac{1}{2}$-in. rings and saddles; perforated plates; bubble caps; wire-cloth packing	Holdup, flooding	394
Sherwood, Evans, and Longcor	Benzene–acetic acid–water MIK–acetic acid–water	3.5	Spray (empty); $\frac{1}{2}$-in. and 1-in. rings; $\frac{1}{2}$-in. saddles	Single drops	416
Treybal and Dumoulin	Toluene–benzoic acid–water	3.6	Perforated plates		464
Treybal and Work	Benzene–acetic acid–water	1	None—wetted wall		465

NOTE: MEK–methyl ethyl ketone; MIK–methy isobutyl ketone.

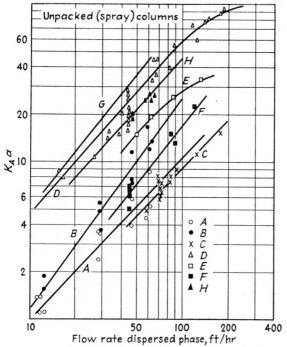

FIG. 205. Extraction in unpacked spray columns.

Curve	Solute	Solvents	Phase dispersed	Flow rate, Continuous phase, ft./hr.	Approximate m	Phase on which $K_A a$ based	Ref.
A	Benzoic acid	Toluene-water	Toluene	11–53	10	Water	394
B	Benzoic acid	Toluene-water	Toluene	100–180	10	Water	394
C	Acetic acid	Isopropyl ether–water	Ether	37–223	2.2	Water	127
D	Acetic acid	MIK-water	MIK	45	0.5	MIK	222
E	Propionic acid	MIK-water	MIK	45	2	MIK	222
F	Acetic acid	Benzene-water	Benzene	45	0.03	Benzene	222
G	Benzoic acid	Toluene-water	Toluene	44–133	10–11	Water	5
H	Water	MEK-brine	MEK	16–36	.....	MEK	318

Row, Koffolt, and Withrow's data[394] cover a wide range of flow rates with a solvent distributor having $\frac{1}{16}$-, $\frac{3}{32}$-, and $\frac{1}{8}$-in. holes. Best results were with $\frac{1}{16}$-in. holes, represented by the two lines on Fig. 205. Line *B* is for a higher range of flow rates of the continuous phase, as indicated by the table.

Row, Koffolt, and Withrow obtained an excellent correlation of their data by plotting $(H.T.U.)_{ow}$ vs. $(L_c/L_D)(dc_c/dc_D)$, where L_c and L_D are the flow rates of the continuous and disperse phases, and dc_c/dc_D is the slope of the equilibrium curve in the operating range. This method of plotting is based on the additivity of resistances expressed in terms of H.T.U.'s, with certain assumptions regarding the constancy of $(H.T.U.)_w$, etc. The resulting graph shows points on straight lines passing nearly through the origin. L_c appears in numerator of both ordinate and abscissa and nearly cancels out. The result is approximately the same as concluding $K_A a$ to be proportional to L_D, with a minor effect of L_c.

Elgin and Browning[127] employed a single spray nozzle to introduce the dispersed phase and obtained data for transfer of acetic acid in both directions with both phases dispersed. The data shown are for the single case of transfer from isopropyl ether to water with the ether dispersed; better transfer coefficients were obtained in the other cases. The spread of points from line C is not large in view of the wide range of values of L_c.

Johnson and Bliss[222] describe a careful study of spray extraction and point out a number of practical considerations relating to such equipment. They included a study of distributor design and port size, finding these important in relation to both transfer rate and flooding. For their system a port diameter of 0.1 in. gave the maximum flow rates consistent with drop uniformity. These authors studied four solute-solvent combinations, and they propose a basis for estimating $K_A a$ for a new solute-solvent pair in a case where data are available on another system.

Appel and Elgin[5] report data obtained using three methods of introducing the dispersed phase; the line shown on Fig. 205 represents their data using a grade H Filtros porous glass disk giving drops of toluene about 0.2 in. diameter. Higher values of $K_W a$ were obtained with a second Filtros disk giving 0.06- to 0.12-in. drops, and considerably lower coefficients were obtained when a single commercial spray nozzle was employed.

Sherwood, Evans, and Longcor[416] obtained values of $K_A a$ of 7.7 to 10 (based on concentrations in the solvent phase) at an L_D of 30 and L_c from 10 to 60 for the extraction of acetic acid from water by benzene with benzene dispersed, and values from 16 to 46 when methyl isobutyl ketone was used in place of benzene, with $L_D = 40$ and L_c varied from 40 to 90.

Hayworth and Treybal[180] report an interesting study of the mechanics of drop formation in a two-phase system, the variables being nozzle hole size, feed rate, interfacial tension, and velocity of continuous phase. The results are well correlated by means of a theory developed on the basis of an analysis of the forces acting on the drop at the instant of release from the nozzle.

Packed Columns. Representative data on ½-in. rings and Berl saddles are shown in Figs. 206 and 207. Sources of other data on packing are indicated in Table XXXII. For such materials the effect of distributor design is evidently less than in spray columns, since the degree of dispersion of the dispersed phase tends to be determined primarily by the packing, except perhaps in short columns.

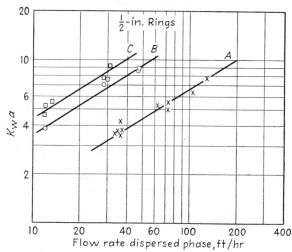

FIG. 206. Extraction in columns packed with ½-in. rings.

Curve	Solute	Solvents	Phase dispersed	Flow rate, continuous phase, ft./hr.	Approximate m	Ref.
A	Benzoic acid	Kerosene-water	Kerosene	25–100	2.5	4
B	Benzoic acid	Toluene-water	Toluene	12–15	10–11	394
C	Benzoic acid	Toluene-water	Toluene	21–86	10–11	394

Curves B and C of Fig. 206 show the results of Row, Koffolt, and Withrow[394] for ½-in. rings over two different ranges of values of L_c. Curve A represents the results of Allerton, Strom, and Treybal,[4] who used kerosene as the dispersed phase. The lower values are probably due more to the fact that the kerosene wet the packing, passing up through the tower in the form of rivulets and not as drops, than to the difference in the distribution coefficient. Additional data on ½-in. rings are given by Sherwood, Evans, and Longcor, who found a large effect of L_c. Their data for water–acetic acid–benzene, expressed as $K_A a$ in terms of concentrations in the benzene phase, fall about on curve C of Fig. 206 but

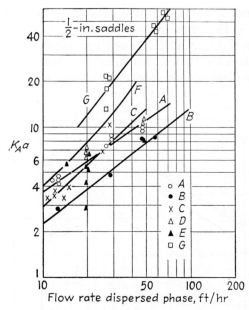

Fig. 207.   Extraction in columns packed with ½-in. saddles.

Curve	Solute	Solvents	Phase dispersed	Flow rate, continuous phase, ft./hr.	Approximate m	Phase on which $K_A a$ based	Ref.
A	Benzoic acid	Toluene-water	Toluene	20–102	10–11	Water	394
B	Benzoic acid	Toluene-water	Toluene	11–14	10–11	Water	394
C	Furfural	Water-toluene	Toluene	20–63	2.4	Water	252
D	Benzoic acid	Benzene-water	Water	58.6	7	Water	93
E	Benzoic acid	Benzene–aqueous-alkaline	Aqueous	58.6	.....	Benzene	93
F	Benzoic acid	Toluene-water	Toluene	44–66	10–11	Toluene	5
G	Water	MEK-brine	MEK	16–34	>0.1	MEK	318

spatter badly because of the large effect of L_c. Their data on water–acetic acid–MIK show much higher values of the transfer coefficient (three to five times as large) when $K_A a$ is based on concentrations in the MIK phase.

Figure 207 summarizes the data from several sources for ½-in. Berl saddles with systems covering a wide range of values of relative solubilities. Row, Koffolt, and Withrow's data are represented by two lines for different ranges of L_c. Except for curve G the spread of the data is not large in view of the variety of systems used and the range of relative solubilities. Meissner, Stokes, Hunter, and Morrow[318] studied the interesting case of dehydration of a solvent by extraction of water into a calcium chloride brine. Sherwood, Evans, and Longcor's data are not shown because of their large effect of L_c. For water–acetic acid–benzene they obtained values of $K_A a$ (concentrations in benzene phase) of 10 to 14 at $L_D = 30$. For water–acetic acid–MIK their values of $K_A a$ (concentrations in MIK phase) ranged from 20 to 88 at $L_D = 40$ as L_c increased from 10 to 70 ft./hr.

The effect of the addition of wetting agents in a packed column has been explored by Chu, Taylor, and Levy,[78] using a laboratory column packed with $\frac{1}{4}$-in. rings. Benzoic acid was extracted from water by benzene, with water as the dispersed phase. A small addition of surface-active agent increased the transfer coefficient, but further addition caused a decrease. It is concluded that the decrease in interfacial tension is beneficial, but that too much additive leads to an appreciable added diffusional resistance, due to the blocking action of the molecules of additive concentrated at the interface.

Effect of Tower Height for Spray and Packed Columns. Most of the data in the literature (except those on commercial extractors collected by Morello and Poffenberger[330]) were obtained with short laboratory columns, and the effect of tower height is not indicated. Sherwood, Evans, and Longcor studied extraction from single drops of solvent rising in water and report that some 40 per cent approach to equilibrium was obtained at the distributor nozzle, as the drops were formed. Licht and Conway,[283] however, found only some 5 to 17 per cent extraction during drop formation and release for the extraction of acetic acid from single drops of water using isopropyl ether, methyl isobutyl ketone, and ethyl acetate as the continuous phase. They report 6 to 13 per cent extraction at the other end of the column, where the water drop crossed the interface into the aqueous phase. Geankoplis and Hixson[156] report data on the effect of column length for short sections of a spray tower of 1.45 in. i.d. used to extract ferric chloride from an acid aqueous phase with isopropyl ether as the dispersed phase. They found $(H.T.U.)_{OW}$ to increase with column length, especially at low ether rates. Comings and Briggs noted an apparent effect of column length, and caution against the extrapolation of laboratory data for the design of tall columns. Nandi and Viswanathan[338] operated a small spray column with the system nitrobenzene–acetic acid–water. They found $(H.T.U.)_{OE}$ to decrease from 3.0 to 0.5, with the solvent dispersed. The corresponding reduction in $(H.T.U.)_{OE}$ was from 2.5 to 1.5 ft. with the aqueous phase dispersed.

These authors concluded that some 45 per cent of the extraction in a 3-ft. column occurs in the first 6 in.

Phillips and Thacker[364] studied the effect of column height by operating 3-in.-i.d. spray and packed columns at heights varying from 5 to 30 ft. The system employed was methyl isobutyl ketone–acetic acid–water, with the ketone dispersed. The packing consisted of ⅜-in. rings. Their data are summarized by Figs. 208 and 209, in which $(H.T.U.)_{ow}$ is

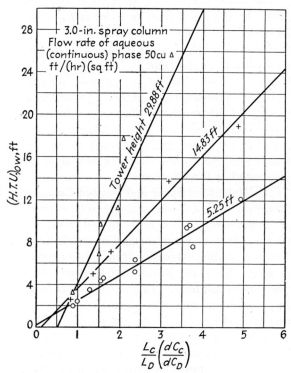

Fig. 208.   Effect of column height on extraction in 3-in. spray column.

plotted in the manner suggested by Row, Koffolt, and Withrow. Since L_c was held constant and since dC_c/dC_D varied but slightly, this amounts to plotting $1/K_wa$ vs. $1/L_D$. It is evident that $(H.T.U.)_{ow}$ varied widely for both packed and spray towers, although the effect is small at large ketone rates (small values of the abscissa). At low ketone rates, $(H.T.U.)_{ow}$ varies nearly with tower height, indicating that nearly as much extraction occurs in 5 ft. as in 30 ft. These results bear out the suspected danger of extrapolating laboratory data on short columns and suggest the importance of redistributing the dispersed phase every few feet in tall commercial columns.

Perforated Plates. Figure 210 shows the results of three investigators of perforated-plate columns. The spread of the data is not large, perhaps because most of the results were for the single system benzoic acid–toluene–water.

In the operation of these columns, the light phase collects under the plate, forming an inverted head causing flow through the perforations. Depending on the design, high solvent rates may cause this accumulation

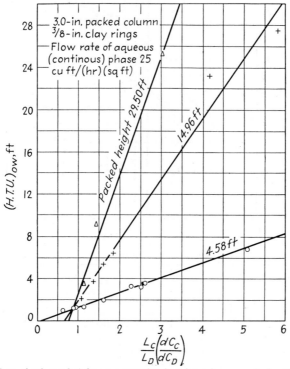

FIG. 209. Effect of column height on extraction in 3-in. column packed with ⅜-in. rings.

of solvent to occupy too large a fraction of the space between plates or may cause the solvent to stream through the holes into the continuous phase without drop formation. Plate spacing is of some importance in ensuring proper column functioning. The importance of the rapid extraction during drop formation is suggested by the data of Treybal and Dumoulin, who obtained much higher values of $K_A a$ with 3-in. than with 6- or 9-in. plate spacings.

Row, Koffolt, and Withrow also obtained data on bubble-cap columns similar to perforated columns, in the sense that the caps were pierced with a large number of small holes and were not of the V-notch or slotted type commonly used in distillation. Their values of $(H.T.U.)_{ow}$ for this design were similar to their results for perforated plates.

Moulton and Walkey,[334] using a perforated-plate column, provide one of the few sets of data on extraction in a case where one solvent is partially

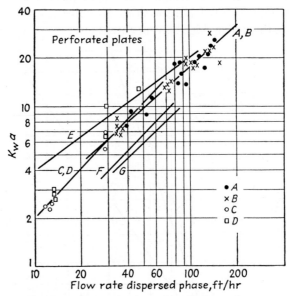

FIG. 210. Extraction in perforated-plate columns.

Curve	Solute	Solvents	Phase dispersed	Flow rate, continuous phase, ft./hr.	Approximate m	Plate spacing, in.	Hole diameter, in.	Ref.
A	Benzoic acid	Toluene-water	Toluene	36–77	10	4.75	3/16	4
B	Benzoic acid	Kerosene-water	Kerosene	25–136	2.5	4.75	3/16	4
C	Benzoic acid	Toluene-water	Toluene	11–37	10	6	1/8	394
D	Benzoic acid	Toluene-water	Toluene	11–37	10	6	3/32	394
E	Benzoic acid	Toluene-water	Toluene	16–33	10	3	3/16	464
F	Benzoic acid	Toluene-water	Toluene	23–40	10	6	3/16	464
G	Benzoic acid	Toluene-water	Toluene	23–39	10	9	3/16	464

miscible in the second. Their data cover the extraction of methyl ethyl ketone from gasoline by water using plate spacings of 3 and 6 in. and $\frac{1}{8}$-in. plate perforations. The dispersed phase was the gasoline. These authors report their data in the form of plate efficiencies, defined as the ratio of observed equilibrium stages to actual plates. The results show efficiencies varying from 3.6 to 8.6 per cent, for values of L_D from 2.3 to 16.4 and L_c from 14 to 69.

Pyle, Colburn, and Duffey[380] employed a perforated-plate column for the extraction of acetic acid from water by ethyl ether, reporting their results in terms of plate efficiencies. Five sets of interchangeable plates were used in order to study the effects of hole size, hole area as a fraction of plate area, and plate spacing. Plate efficiencies of 30 per cent were obtained with 1.77 and 3.34 per cent free area, and 32 to 33 per cent with

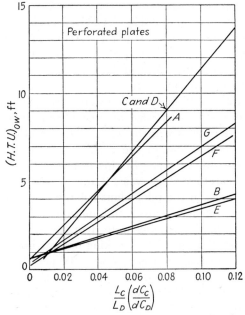

FIG. 211. Replot of data on perforated-plate columns. (For key see Fig. 210.)

5 per cent free area, all with 0.11-in. holes. They recommend ether depths of 0.25 to 1.0 in. below such plates at ether rates of 200 to 600 gal./(hr.)(ft.²). The effect of hole size was small for the range of holes sized from 0.0635 to 0.201 in. Increase in plate spacing resulted in an increase in plate efficiency from 30 per cent at 5-in. spacing to 48 to 58 per cent at 20-in. spacing.

Figure 211 represents the data on perforated plates (for key, see legend of Fig. 210) plotted, as suggested by Row, Koffolt, and Withrow, as $(H.T.U.)_{ow}$ vs. $(L_c/L_D)(dC_c/dC_D)$, with straight lines representing the points for each series of tests. The values of $(H.T.U.)_{ow}$ of several feet again suggest the low equivalent plate efficiency of such equipment.

Scheibel Column. The continuous extraction column proposed by Scheibel consists of alternate empty and packed sections, with a central vertical shaft fitted with agitator blades in each empty section. The agitated empty sections provide the contact between phases; the packed sections are primarily entrainment separators to permit partial coalescence and vertical flow of the dispersed phase.

The only data available on equipment of this type are those reported by Scheibel for a 1-in. laboratory column[401] and for a 12-in. pilot-plant column,[402] in both of which wire cloth was used in the packed sections. The laboratory column was used for the extraction of *o*- and *p*-chloronitrobenzenes from solution in Skellysolve C (dispersed) by methanol, for which Scheibel reports 0.4 to 1.1 equilibrium stages for each actual stage consisting of one mixing section and one packed section. The height of the mixing section was varied from $\frac{3}{8}$ to 1 in., and the height of the packed section from $\frac{1}{2}$ to 2 in. The total height required per equilibrium stage varied from 2.2 to 3.9 in. for this system. Stage efficiency increased somewhat as the shaft speed was increased from 1000 to 1400 r.p.m. Similar results were obtained in the extraction of acetic acid from water by methyl ethyl ketone and in the extraction of ethyl and isopropyl alcohols from water by xylene. In this last case the minimum height equivalent to a theoretical stage was 4.2 in.

The systems studied in the pilot-plant column were *o*-xylene–acetone–water, *o*-xylene–acetic acid–water, and methyl isobutyl ketone–acetic acid–water. The mixing sections were 3 in. high, and the separating sections were 9 and 13.5 in. high. Taking one mixing and one packing section as a stage, the stage efficiencies were 100 per cent or better at the optimum agitator speeds of 300 to 500 r.p.m. In other words, equilibrium stages were obtained with heights of less than 1 ft. Flooding rates varied with the systems employed, but combined flow rates of 350 to 600 gal./(hr.)(ft.²) were obtained before the column flooded.

These results indicate excellent possibilities for the reduction of tower heights by the use of such columns.

Podbielniak Extractor. This is a commercial design of "package" extraction equipment, consisting of a long metal sheet coiled in a spiral and caused to rotate at high speed within a fixed casing. The two liquid streams are fed in countercurrent flow through the spiral passage, the heavier liquid being held as a moving film on the outer wall of the passage by the large centrifugal force. Relatively high velocities of one liquid over the other are maintained without physical mixing of the phases. In some designs the spiral sheet is perforated in places, allowing the heavier liquid to spray through the lighter liquid in the next outer passage.

These devices are widely used in the pharmaceutical industry, being favored because of their versatility. They are used in the recovery of penicillin from fermentation broth, where a series of such extractors recovers 80 per cent or more of the penicillin present in concentrations of 0.04 per cent or less in the broth. Each unit provides something of the order of four to seven equilibrium contacts, handling several hundred gallons per hour of each stream. They have the advantage of very low holdup in relation to throughput, which means that decomposition of product is minimized in the treatment of materials which are unstable under extraction conditions.

LIMITING LIQUID RATES IN CONTINUOUS COUNTERCURRENT COLUMNS

Transfer coefficients have been expressed as functions of the rates of flow of the two phases, where these rates are expressed on the basis of a unit cross-sectional area. The selection of a value of the transfer coefficient permits the estimation of the required height of the column. For practical design purposes it is equally important to have information regarding the allowable flow rates of the two phases, since these determine the minimum column cross section.

As the dispersed-phase rate increases at constant flow rate of the continuous phase, it is observed that the holdup increases and the drops of dispersed phase are crowded more closely together. The net cross section available for flow of the continuous phase is decreased, and the velocity of the drops relative to adjacent continuous phase increases. The increased drag on the drops is eventually sufficient to carry them in the direction of flow of the continuous phase. When this point is reached, the dispersed phase will not enter the column proper and is discharged along with the effluent continuous phase. When this happens, the column is said to "flood." The change from normal operation to flooding conditions occurs quite suddenly, with only a small increase in dispersed-phase flow rate. The same thing happens if the rate of flow of continuous phase is increased at a constant or moderate flow rate of dispersed phase. It follows that the column will flood at any value of either flow rate if the other flow rate is sufficiently great. The flooding point evidently depends on both flow rates.

Transfer coefficients increase with both flow rates and are greatest as the flooding point is approached. It is desirable, therefore, to operate near the flooding point, but not to exceed it. In order to avoid flooding, it is customary to operate well below the limiting rates and with a column cross section appreciably larger than the minimum actually required.

There are relatively few data available on flooding of extraction columns. Blanding and Elgin[35] studied the systems solvent naphtha–water and methyl isobutyl ketone–water in a 2.4-in.-i.d. column operated

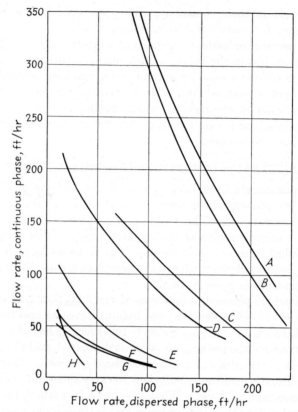

FIG. 212.   Data on flooding in countercurrent extraction columns; organic phase dispersed in water.

Curve	Ref.	Type of column	Dispersed phase
A	35	Spray—approximately ⅛-in. drops	Naphtha
B	35	Spray—approximately ⅛-in. drops	MIK
C	4	Perforated plates	Toluene-kerosene
D	35	Packed—½-in. saddles	MIK
E	35	Packed—½-in. rings	Naphtha
		Packed—½-in. saddles	MIK
F	394	Packed—½-in. saddles	Toluene
G	394	Packed—½-in. rings	Toluene
H	394	Perforated plates	Toluene

without packing (spray) and packed with ½-in. balls, rings, and saddles.

Their results for the spray column are shown as curves A and B of Fig. 212, and it is evident that the flooding rates are high compared with the other data shown. Three nozzles were used to feed the dispersed phase; the data shown were obtained with the distributor nozzle which gave drops about ⅛-in. in diameter. Little difference in flooding rates is noted for the two systems, although the interfacial tension was much greater for naphtha–water than for ketone–water.

Blanding and Elgin report that the design of the feed and discharge ends of the column had a marked influence on flooding rates, and they employed a column flared at the dispersed-phase feed end in order that the continuous-phase velocity would be low in the region where the drops left the distributor. The column was likewise enlarged at the other end and the continuous phase fed in radially over a weir. The authors report that this design as much as doubles the permissible throughput. Their data must be used with caution, therefore, in the design of columns not incorporating the end enlargements.

Figure 212 also shows the data of Blanding and Elgin on ½-in. saddles and rings (curves D and E). Here again the enlarged ends were used, and the flow rates may be as much as twice those permissible in columns where feed and separation occur in sections of the same diameter as the packed section. Blanding and Elgin observed no drop coalescence in the spray tower, even up to flooding, but report marked coalescence in the packed column at half the flooding velocities. This may explain the fact that slopes of $K_A a$ vs. L_D are steeper for spray than for packed towers (Figs. 205 and 206).

Curves F, G, and H represent the data of Row, Koffolt, and Withrow for ½-in. saddles and rings and for a perforated-plate column. Curve C was obtained by Allerton, Strom, and Treybal with perforated plates having ³⁄₁₆-in. holes spaced to occupy 13.6 per cent of the plate area. Pyle, Colburn, and Duffey[380] report data on the capacity of perforated plates of different designs, correlating their results in terms of an orifice coefficient applicable to the calculation of solvent head under a plate as a function of solvent rate, hole size, and number of holes.

More recently, Ballard and Piret[21] report data on flooding of a 3.75-in.-i.d. column packed with ½-in. porcelain rings, using water as the continuous phase and a wide variety of organic liquids as the dispersed phase. They describe a "transition point" in column operation, at which drop size starts to increase markedly and flooding may occur with increase in either flow rate. Flow rates at the transition point are somewhat lower than at certain flooding. Employing dimensionless groups of the probable variables, Ballard and Piret obtained an excellent correlation of their data in the form of the line shown in Fig. 213. Here ϕ is defined by

$$\phi = \frac{u_c \rho_c^{0.83} \mu_c^{0.1} a^{0.65}}{g^{0.55} \Delta\rho^{0.93} F} \left(\frac{\sigma_{WS}}{\sigma_{WA} + \sigma_{SA}}\right)^{0.4} \tag{505}$$

where u_c is the velocity of the continuous phase, (ft./hr.), ρ_c the density of the continuous phase (lb./ft.³), μ_c the viscosity of the continuous phase [lb./(hr.)(ft.)], a the surface of the packing (ft.²/ft.³), g the acceleration due to gravity (ft./hr.²), $\Delta\rho$ the difference in density between the two phases (lb./ft.³), F the fraction voids in the packing, σ_{WA} and σ_{SA} are the surface tension (against air) for continuous and dispersed phases, respectively, and σ_{WS} is the interfacial tension between the two phases.

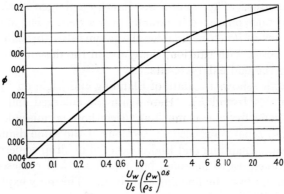

FIG. 213. Ballard and Piret correlation of flooding in packed extraction columns.

Although Blanding and Elgin's flooding data lie above the curve shown in Fig. 213 (indicating allowable velocities at least twice as large), this correlation is probably the most useful available at the present time for packed columns and systems in which the dispersed phase does not wet the packing. Not only are Ballard and Piret's data well correlated, but it is shown that the results may be extrapolated to give good checks with data on flooding of packed gas-absorption towers. For this application the surface-tension term in parentheses becomes unity, and the correlation becomes quite similar to that recommended by Sherwood, Shipley, and Holloway[422] for gas-liquid systems.

Nomenclature for Chapter X

a = surface of contact between phases, ft.²/ft.³
A = surface of contact between phases, ft.²
c = solute concentration, lb. moles/ft.³
f = fraction solute in stream leaving cascade

F = feed rate, lb./(hr.)(ft.^{2}); also fraction voids in packing

g = acceleration due to gravity, ft./hr.^{2}

G = flow rate of extract or solvent phase, lb./(hr.)(ft.^{2})

(H.T.U.)$_O$ = height of over-all transfer unit, ft.

k = mass-transfer coefficient, lb. moles/(hr.)(ft.^{2})(lb. mole/ft.^{3})

k' = mass-action constant

K = over-all mass-transfer coefficient, lb. moles/(hr.)(ft.^{2})(lb. mole/ft.^{3})

L = flow rate of raffinate or aqueous phase, lb./(hr.)(ft.^{2})

m = distribution coefficient = y/x at equilibrium

n = number of stages

N_A = rate of transfer of solute A between phases, lb. moles/(hr.)(sq. ft.)

N_{OG} = number of over-all transfer units for gas-liquid transfer, based on concentrations in gas phase

$N_{T,O}$ = number of over-all transfer units

O_R = weight reflux per unit time, on solvent-free basis

$p = N(R - 1)/R$

P = fractional approach to equilibrium with inlet stream in counter-current apparatus; also weight of extract product per unit time on solvent-free basis, lb./hr.

Q = fraction solute in feed recovered in extract

$R = L/mG$ (or mG/L)

S = column cross section, ft.^{2}

S_E = lb. solvent/lb. total solute in extract stream

S_R = lb. solvent/lb. total solute in raffinate

u_c = velocity of continuous phase, ft./hr.

V = active volume of extractor, ft.^{3}

x = solute concentration in aqueous or raffinate phase, lb./lb.

y = solute concentration in solvent or extract phase, lb./lb.

Z = tower height, ft.

β = selectivity coefficient, defined by Eq. (443)

μ_c = viscosity of continuous phase, lb./(hr.)(ft.)

ρ = density of liquid phase, lb./ft.^{3}

$\Delta\rho$ = difference in density between phases, lb./ft.^{3}

σ = interfacial tension; σ_{WA} for continuous phase–air; σ_{SA} for dispersed phase–air; σ_{WS} between two liquid phases

ϕ = defined by Eq. (505)

Subscripts

0 = entering first stage

$1, 2, \ldots, n$ = leaving stage 1, 2, $\ldots$, n; also refers to section 1, 2, $\ldots$ of a cascade or series of cascades

A, B, C = solutes A,B,C

c = continuous phase

D = dispersed phase

e = at equilibrium

E = extract, or solvent, phase

F = feed

i = conditions at interface

R = raffinate, or aqueous, phase

W = aqueous phase

Single prime refers to inlet, double prime to outlet, of cascade.

Problems

1. A solution of 40 per cent acetic acid in water is to be extracted with isopropyl ether in a single batch extraction at room temperature. Determine the per cent recovery of acetic acid in the extract, if the amount of solvent is (*a*) equal in weight to the solution to be extracted, and (*b*) one-half the weight of the solution.

Solubility data (weight per cent):

c_W	99.3	90.0	80.0	70.0	60.0	50.0	40.0
c_E	0	9.0	18.6	27.8	36.3	42.7	46.8

c_W		30.0	27.0	20.0	15.0	10.0	5.0
c_E		48.5	48.3	45.5	39.8	31.0	17.0

Equilibrium data (weight per cent acetic acid):

Water	9.0	18.4	23.0	27.7	36.0	42.7	46.8	48.0	48.4	48.3
Ether	3.0	6.8	9.7	12.7	20.0	27.6	36.4	41.3	46.0	48.3

The solubility of water in isopropyl ether is negligible.

2. The following two procedures are to be considered for the batch extraction at 63°F. of an aqueous solution containing 75 weight per cent acetaldehyde: (*a*) one stage, using an amount of toluene equal in weight to the solution; (*b*) the same total amount of toluene: one-half used in a first stage, and one-half in a second stage for the treatment of the first raffinate. Assuming equilibrium to be attained in each stage, calculate the per cent aldehyde recovered as extract and the pounds of solvent used per pound of aldehyde recovered for each method proposed.

Solubility data at 63°F. (weight per cent):

c_T	0.05	1.0	2.0	4.9	10.8	16.7	24.7	42.0	99.96
c_A	0	49.0	55.8	63.6	69.1	70.9	68.2	55.2	0
c_W	99.95	50.0	42.2	31.5	20.1	12.4	7.1	2.8	0.04

Equilibrium data (weight per cent acetaldehyde):

Water	9.0	17.0	22.2	27.8	30.3	48.7	62.2
Toluene	4.3	9.0	13.8	18.0	19.8	35.3	54.7

3. An aqueous solution containing 6.25 lb. benzoic acid per ft.[3] is to be extracted with carbon tetrachloride. What is the minimum ratio of CCl_4 to feed for the extraction of 90 per cent of the benzoic acid in a continuous countercurrent process?

Benzoic acid exists as single molecules in water but is believed to be associated as double molecules in CCl_4. Equilibrium at the operating temperature is given by

$$c_W = 25.6 \sqrt{c_c}$$

where c_W = lb. benzoic acid/ft.³ in water phase
c_c = lb. benzoic acid/ft.³ in CCl_4 phase

The two phases are essentially immiscible, and volume changes due to benzoic acid content may be neglected.

4. An aqueous solution of benzoic acid containing 0.013 lb./gal. is to be extracted with benzene to recover benzoic acid. What is the theoretical minimum ratio of solvent to solution to obtain 50 per cent recovery using continuous countercurrent extraction?

Equilibrium data at operating temperature, expressed as pounds of benzoic acid per gallon of solvent and aqueous phases:

c_B...........	0.00152	0.0204	0.051	0.152	0.204
c_W...........	0.00087	0.0038	0.0059	0.011	0.013

5. Ten gallons of aqueous solution containing 0.013 lb. benzoic acid per gal. are to be extracted in one or more batch extractions. Calculate the per cent recovery obtainable with 5, 10, or 20 gal. benzene, (*a*) using the entire quantity of solvent in a single batch extraction in each case; (*b*) using half the solvent in a first extraction and half to treat the first raffinate in a second extraction; (*c*) using three extractions, with one-third of the total solvent in each stage; (*d*) using two extractions, using 7 gal. solvent in the first stage, and 3 in the second; (*e*) using two extractions, using 3 gal. solvent in the first stage and 7 in the second.

Assume that equilibrium is reached in each extraction stage. Equilibrium data are given in the preceding problem.

6. Referring to the preceding problem, assume a total of 10 gal. benzene is to be used in two single extractions. How much solvent should be used in each stage to obtain the maximum recovery of benzoic acid?

7. Referring again to Prob. 5, what recovery is possible if continuous countercurrent extraction is employed with solvent-solution ratios of 0.5 and 1.0 in two, three, or four equilibrium stages?

8. It is desired to reduce the methyl mercaptan concentration in a cracked-naphtha fraction from 0.0031 to 0.0003 lb./gal. by scrubbing with a 12°Bé. caustic at 70°F. If the caustic recirculation rate is 0.0060 gal. per gal. naphtha, calculate the number of equilibrium stages required, (*a*) dividing the total of 0.0060 gal. caustic into equal parts for use in each contact; (*b*) using countercurrent multiple-contact extraction.

Equilibrium concentrations of methyl mercaptan between caustic solutions and naphtha may be calculated from the equilibrium constant for the following reaction:

$$NaOH + CH_3SH = CH_3SNa + H_2O$$

At 70°F.,

$$K = \frac{[H_2O][CH_3SNa]}{[NaOH][CH_3SH]} = 58.8$$

where the bracketed terms represent molal concentrations of the various reactants in naphtha.

Additional data:

Density of naphtha............................. 4.89 lb./gal.
Average molecular weight of naphtha............. 56.0
Vapor pressure of pure mercaptan................ 25.5 p.s.i.a.
Vapor pressure water over caustic............... 0.363 p.s.i.a.
Concentration of NaOH......................... 0.736 lb./gal. sulfur-free caustic

Assume naphtha and caustic to be completely immiscible. Assume the molal ratio of mercaptan to water present in solutions is equal to the ratio of their partial pressures over the solutions, and assume that mercaptan dissolved in naphtha follows Raoult's law.

9. An aqueous solution of oxalic acid containing 0.50 lb. acid per gal. is extracted with ether, using continuous countercurrent extraction in a packed column. The ether rate is 13.6 gal. per gal. solution, and the acid concentration in the aqueous phase is to be reduced to 0.05 lb./gal. How many equilibrium contacts will be required?

The two phases may be assumed to be immiscible. Equilibrium data at the operating temperature are given below, where c_W and c_E are acid concentrations as pound moles per gallon in aqueous and solvent phases, respectively:

$c_E \times 10^5$.........	1.92	8.33	16.7	25.0	33.4	50.0
c_W/c_E.............	19	17	14.9	13.8	13.1	12.1

10. Ether is to be used to extract triethylamine (TEA) from an aqueous solution of 40 weight per cent TEA and 60 weight per cent water. The ether will be removed from the extract by distillation.

a. What is the maximum possible weight per cent TEA of the resulting solution, after removal of the ether?

b. What weight of ether is required per pound of initial solution if one equilibrium stage is employed, and the composition obtained in part *a* is desired?

c. What per cent recovery of TEA is obtained in part *b*?

Solubility data at operating temperature (in per cent):

TEA.....	2.0	5.0	10.0	15.0	20.0	30.0	40.0
Ether....	10.5	9.0	8.0	8.1	9.9	15.0	23.0

TEA.....	45.0	47.0	47.8	45.0	40.0	30.0	20.0
Ether....	28.3	32.0	37.5	47.5	54.7	65.6	76.6

Equilibrium data (weight per cent TEA):

In water layer.	2.0	4.0	6.0	8.0	10.0	12.0	14.0	15.5
In ether layer.	10.7	20.4	29.2	36.2	41.8	45.1	46.9	47.0

11. A solution of triethylamine in water, containing 15 weight per cent TEA, is extracted with ether in a countercurrent multiple-contact apparatus. The ether used amounts to 28.8 lb. per lb. original TEA solution.

a. How many equilibrium stages are required to obtain a final raffinate containing 1.0 per cent TEA?

b. What is the corresponding per cent recovery of TEA in the extract?

Equilibrium data are given in the preceding problem.

12. A mixture of triethylamine and ether containing 50 per cent by weight of each component is saturated with water and fed into the bottom of a packed extraction column. The solvent is water, which is fed into the top of the column after first being saturated with the raffinate leaving the top of the column. The remainder of the raffinate not returned as reflux with the water is withdrawn as raffinate product. It is desired to reduce the triethylamine in the raffinate product to 5 per cent by weight (on a water-free basis). The reflux ratio is defined as the ratio of raffinate returned in the water phase to the raffinate withdrawn as raffinate product. A reflux ratio of twice the theoretical minimum is to be used. Determine the number of equilibrium contacts required, using a sharp pencil for graphical constructions, and large-scale plots.

13. Evans (thesis in chemical engineering, M.I.T., 1938) reports data on extraction of acetic acid from water by benzene in a laboratory column packed with $\frac{1}{2}$-in. Berl saddles to a depth of 4.65 ft. In a typical run the following concentrations (pound moles of acetic acid per cubic foot of liquid) were obtained: acid in, 0.0617; acid out, 0.0567; benzene in, 0.000018; benzene out, 0.00189. The acid rate was 10 ft.^{3} per hr. per ft.^{2} tower cross section. What was the (H.T.U.)$_O$ based on concentrations in the benzene phase?

In the narrow range of acid concentrations encountered, the concentration of acetic acid in the acid layer may be taken as twenty-nine times the concentration of acetic acid in the benzene layer (concentrations as pound moles per cubic foot). The two phases may be assumed to be completely immiscible.

APPENDIX

DETERMINATION OF OPTIMUM DIMENSIONS AND OPERATING CONDITIONS FOR ABSORBERS*

An abbreviated treatment of the calculation of the economic optimum gas velocity and column diameter was given in Chap. VI. A more complete treatment, including other elements of the general economic problem, will now be presented. The costs to be included are as follows:

a. Initial cost of packing and shell, including cost of installation

b. Cost of power during operation

c. Value of the solute which is lost in the exit gases owing to incomplete recovery in the absorber

d. Cost of recovering the solute in substantially pure form by distillation from the rich solvent

1. Letting c_1 represent the *annual* cost of the absorber per cubic foot of packed space, the annual fixed charges are $c_1 S Z$.

2. The cost of power is found as follows: Multiply the volumetric gas rate (GS/ρ_G) by the pressure drop across the absorber $(\Delta p Z)$, by the number of hours of operation per year (θ), and by the unit power cost (c_2') in units of dollars per foot-pound, we obtain $c_2'\theta \, \Delta p Z S G/\rho_G$.

3. If the value of the solute at its concentration in the rich liquor leaving the absorber is c_4 dollars per pound mole of solute, the value of the lost solute is $c_4\theta G_M S y_2$.

4. The cost of the stripping operation, which is carried out in separate equipment outside the absorber, is more difficult to evaluate in an exact way. This cost results from fixed charges and operating costs, which must be adjusted to their optimum values by considering the principles of distillation which are involved. No attempt will be made here to study these competing factors in detail; it will be assumed instead that the total cost of the distillation or stripping operation is proportional to the amount of vapor (usually steam) supplied to the bottom of the stripper, and the amount of vapor required will be computed by multiplying the minimum amount of vapor by a factor which is chosen on the basis of experience with distillation design problems. Let L_{MS} represent the molal liquid reflux rate to the stripper and D the molal rate of nearly pure solute produced in the stripping operation. If we assume that the concentrated liquid leaving the absorber is heated to its boiling point before it is introduced into the stripper, the molal vapor rate at the bottom of the stripper is the same as that leaving the top tray of the stripper, $L_{MS} + D$. Assuming that the optimum reflux ratio L/D is r times the minimum value, the required vapor rate is $[r(L_{MS}/D)_{\min} + 1] \, G_M S(y_1 - y_2)$, and the annual cost of the stripping operation is $c_5\theta[r(L_{MS}/D)_{\min} + 1] \, G_M S(y_1 - y_2)$ where c_5 represents the cost of steam per pound mole.

The minimum reflux ratio $(L_{MS}/D)_{\min}$ is found after determining the slope of the operating line in Fig. 214 which passes through the point $(1,1)$ and which intersects

---

* The developments in this section follow closely results obtained by Colburn.[83]

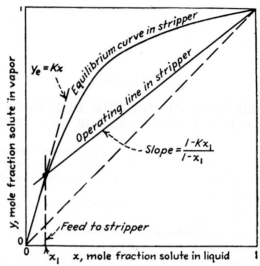

FIG. 214.   Graphical calculation of minimum reflux ratio in stripping column.

the equilibrium line $y_e = kx$ at $x = x_1$, the mole fraction of solute in the absorber effluent.   This slope is given by

$$\left(\frac{L_{MS}}{G_{MS}}\right)_{\min} = \frac{1 - kx_1}{1 - x_1} \tag{506}$$

from which

$$\left(\frac{L_{MS}}{D}\right)_{\min} = \frac{1 - kx_1}{(k - 1)x_1} \tag{507}$$

By a material balance on the absorber,

$$x_1 = \frac{G_M}{L_M}(y_1 - y_2) \tag{508}$$

assuming complete removal of solute from the solvent in the stripper.   The cost of recovering the solute from the solvent is therefore

$$c_5\theta G_M S(y_1 - y_2)\left[r\,\frac{1 - (kG_M/L_M)(y_1 - y_2)}{(k - 1)(G_M/L_M)(y_1 - y_2)} + 1\right]$$

The total annual cost of treating 1 lb./hr. of the gas fed to the absorber is obtained by adding the costs computed in paragraphs 1 to 4 and dividing the sum by GS, or by $M_G G_M S$, where M_G is the average molecular weight of the gas.   Thus, we obtain

$$\frac{\text{T.A.C.}}{GS} = \frac{c_1 Z}{G} + \frac{c_2'\theta\,\Delta pZ}{\rho_G} + \frac{c_4\theta y_2}{M_G} + \frac{c_5\theta(y_1 - y_2)}{M_G}\left[r\,\frac{1 - (kG_M/L_M)(y_1 - y_2)}{(k - 1)(G_M/L_M)(y_1 - y_2)} + 1\right] \tag{509}$$

The optimum operating conditions are found by partially differentiating the right side of Eq. (509) with respect to G, y_2, and $m_2 G_M/L_M$ and setting each of the partial derivatives equal to zero.

Since G does not occur by itself in the last two terms, only the first two terms contribute to the partial derivative with respect to G. Furthermore, Z is a factor in each of the first two terms, and its value does not influence the optimum value of G. The choice of the optimum gas velocity was discussed in Chap. VII. The value of G given there may be used here in the more general economic balance.

$$G_{\text{opt}} = \left(\frac{c_1 \rho_G{}^2}{2c_2'b'\theta} \right)^{\frac{1}{3}} \tag{510}$$

where the pressure drop per unit of packed height is taken equal to $b'G^2/\rho_G$.

Substituting this optimum value of G into Eq. (509), we find that the first two terms may be written as

$$\frac{\text{T.A.C.}}{GS} = \left(\frac{c_1}{G_{\text{opt}}} + \frac{c_2'\theta b'G_{\text{opt}}{}^2}{\rho^2} \right) Z$$

$$= \frac{c_1}{G_{\text{opt}}} \left(1 + \frac{1}{2} \right) Z = \frac{c_1'Z}{G_{\text{opt}}} \tag{511}$$

where $c_1' = 1.5c_1$, the annual cost of power and fixed charges per cubic foot of packed space.

In order to find the optimum degree of recovery of the solute, we must differentiate Eq. (509) with respect to y_2. Since the required value of Z is greater, the smaller the value of y_2, the variation of the first two terms must be considered in making this balance. The last term also contains y_2, but if we assume that the recovery is to be nearly complete, y_2 will be much smaller than y_1, with the result that its influence on the last term will be negligibly small. With this assumption,

$$\frac{\partial(\text{T.A.C.}/GS)}{\partial y_2} = \frac{c_1'}{G} \frac{\partial Z}{\partial y_2} + \frac{c_4\theta}{M_G} \tag{512}$$

Since

$$Z = H_{OG}N_{OG} = H_{OG} \frac{\ln \left[\left(1 - \frac{mG_M}{L_M} \right) \frac{y_1 - mx_2}{y_2 - mx_2} + \frac{mG_M}{L_M} \right]}{1 - (mG_M/L_M)} \tag{513}$$

$$\frac{\partial Z}{\partial y_2} = H_{OG} \frac{- \left(1 - \frac{mG_M}{L_M} \right) \frac{y_1 - mx_2}{(y_2 - mx_2)^2}}{\left(1 - \frac{mG_M}{L_M} \right) \left[\left(1 - \frac{mG_M}{L_M} \right) \frac{y_1 - mx_2}{y_2 - mx_2} + \frac{mG_M}{L_M} \right]} \tag{514}$$

Assuming $y_1 >> y_2$, this reduces approximately to

$$\frac{\partial Z}{\partial y_2} = - \frac{H_{OG}}{[1 - (mG_M/L_M)](y_2 - mx_2)} \tag{515}$$

Introducing this into Eq. (512) and setting the right side equal to zero, we obtain

$$(y_2 - mx_2)_{\text{opt}} = \frac{c_1'H_{OG}}{[1 - (mG_M/L_M)]c_4\theta G_M} \tag{516}$$

To find the optimum liquid-gas ratio, *i.e.*, the optimum amount of solvent, we differentiate Eq. (509) partially with respect to mG_M/L_M.

$$\frac{\partial(\text{T.A.C.}/GS)}{\partial(mG_M/L_M)} = \frac{c_1'}{G} \frac{\partial Z}{\partial(mG_M/L_M)} - \frac{c_5\theta rm}{(k-1)(mG_M/L_M)^2} \tag{517}$$

Differentiating Eq. (513) with respect to mG_M/L_M,

$$\frac{\partial Z}{\partial(mG_M/L_M)} = H_{OG} \left\{ \frac{-\dfrac{y_1 - mx_2}{y_2 - mx_2} + 1}{\left(1 - \dfrac{mG_M}{L_M}\right)\left[\left(1 - \dfrac{mG_M}{L_M}\right)\dfrac{y_1 - mx_2}{y_2 - mx_2} + \dfrac{mG_M}{L_M}\right]} \right.$$
$$\left. + \frac{\ln\left[\left(1 - \dfrac{mG_M}{L_M}\right)\dfrac{y_1 - mx_2}{y_2 - mx_2} + \dfrac{mG_M}{L_M}\right]}{\left(1 - \dfrac{mG_M}{L_M}\right)^2} \right\} \quad (518)$$

Assuming $y_1 \gg y_2$ as before,

$$\frac{\partial Z}{\partial(mG_M/L_M)} = H_{OG} \left\{ \frac{\ln\left[\left(1 - \dfrac{mG_M}{L_M}\right)\dfrac{y_1 - mx_2}{y_2 - mx_2}\right] - 1}{[1 - (mG_M/L_M)]^2} \right\} \quad (519)$$

Introducing this into Eq. (517), the optimum liquid-to-gas ratio is found to be given by

$$\left(\frac{L_M}{mG_M} - 1\right)^2 = \frac{c_1'H_{OG}(k-1)}{c_5\theta rm} \left\{ \ln\left[\left(1 - \frac{mG_M}{L_M}\right)\frac{y_1 - mx_2}{y_2 - mx_2}\right] - 1 \right\} \quad (520)$$

Equation (520) is easily solved by trial and error for mG_M/L_M.

The differentiations leading to Eq. (520) were made by assuming that H_{OG} is independent of the liquid rate. This is not quite correct, as may be seen from the data presented in Chap. VIII. If an empirical equation for the relationship is available, the influence of L on H_{OG} may be allowed for in the derivation. The extension to this more involved case was given by Colburn (see Perry,[359] page 708) and will not be repeated here.

Illustration 45. Estimate the optimum value of mG_M/L_M for an absorber used to recover acetone vapor from air by water absorption followed by stripping with open steam. The temperature rise of the scrubbing liquid in the absorber will be neglected.

The following conditions are assumed: $c_1' = \$4.35$ per cubic foot per year; $c_5 = \$0.0108$ per pound mole, *i.e.*, 30 cents per 1000 lb. steam times 2, the assumed ratio of total annual distillation cost to the total annual steam cost; $r = 1.25$; $G_M = 25.4$ lb. moles/(hr.)(ft.²); $\theta = 8400$ hr./year operation; $m = 2.7$; $k = 23$; $y_1/y_2 = 435$; $x_2 = 0$.

Solution. Equation (520) is solved by trial and error, assuming $mG_M/L_M = 0.7$ as a first approximation. Thus,

$$\left(\frac{L_M}{mG_M} - 1\right)^2 = \frac{(4.35)(2.5)(23-1)[\ln{(0.3)(435)} - 1]}{(0.0108)(8400)(1.25)(25.4)(2.7)} = 0.119$$

$$\frac{mG_M}{L_M} = \frac{1}{1 + \sqrt{0.119}} = 0.74$$

A second trial, assuming $mG_M/L_M = 0.74$ on the right side, gives $mG_M/L_M = 0.75$.

A more complete solution, allowing for the influence of L_M on H_{OG}, is found by multiplying the logarithm inside the bracket by $1 + n\left[(L_M/mG_M) - 1\right]$, where H_{OG} is taken proportional to $(G/L)^n$. When this factor is used in this illustrative example, with $n = 0.5$, the result is changed only slightly. It is found that $mG_M/L_M = 0.72$.

REFERENCES

1. ABEL, E., H. SCHMIDT, and M. STEIN, Z. Elektrochem., **36**, 692 (1930).
2. ACKERMAN, G., Forschungsheft, No. 382, 1–16 (1937).
3. ADAMS, F. W., Trans. Am. Inst. Chem. Engrs., **28**, 162 (1932).
4. ALLERTON, J., B. O. STROM, and R. E. TREYBAL, Trans. Am. Inst. Chem. Engrs., **39**, 173 (1943).
5. APPEL, F. J., and J. C. ELGIN, Ind. Eng. Chem., **29**, 451 (1937).
6. ARNOLD, J. H., J. Am. Chem. Soc., **52**, 3937 (1930).
7. ARNOLD, J. H., Ind. Eng. Chem., **22**, 1091 (1930).
8. ARNOLD, J. H., Physics, **4**, 255, 334 (1933).
9. ARNOULD, J., Chimie & industrie, **21**, 478 (1930).
10. ASTROSHENKO, V. S., J. Applied Chem. (U.S.S.R.), **12**, 167–80 (1939).
11. ATKINS, G. T., and W. B. FRANKLIN, Refiner Natural Gasoline Mfr., **15**, No. 1, 30 (1936).
12. AWBERRY, J. H., and E. GRIFFITHS, Proc. Phys. Soc. (London), **44**, Pt. 2, 132 (1932).
13. BACHMAN, I., Ind. Eng. Chem., Anal. Ed., **12**, 38 (1940).
14. BADGER, W. L., and W. L. McCABE, "Elements of Chemical Engineering," 1st ed., McGraw-Hill Book Company, Inc., New York, 1931.
15. BAIN, W. A., and O. A. HOUGEN, Trans. Am. Inst. Chem. Engrs., **40**, 29, 389, 393 (1944).
16. BAKER, T. C., Ind. Eng. Chem., **27**, 977 (1935).
17. BAKER, T., T. H. CHILTON, and H. C. VERNON, Trans. Am. Inst. Chem. Engrs., **31**, 296 (1935).
18. BAKER, T., and J. S. STOCKHARDT, Ind. Eng. Chem., **22**, 376 (1930).
19. BAKHMETEFF, B. A., "The Mechanics of Turbulent Flow," Princeton University Press, Princeton, N.J., 1936.
20. BAKHMETEFF, B. A., and N. V. FEODOROFF, J. Applied Mechanics, **4**, A97 (1937); **5**, A86 (1938).
21. BALLARD, J. H., and E. L. PIRET, Ind. Eng. Chem., **42**, 1088 (1950).
22. BANCROFT, W. D., and S. C. HUBARD, J. Am. Chem. Soc., **64**, 347 (1942).
23. BANERJI, S. K., and H. M. WADIA, Mem. Indian Meteor. Dept., **25**, Pt. 9, 291 (1932).
24. BARNET, W. I., and K. A. KOBE, Ind. Eng. Chem., **33**, 436 (1941).
25. BARTELS, C. R., and G. KLEIMAN, Chem. Eng. Progress, **45**, 589 (1949).
26. BASKERVILLE, W. H., Trans. Am. Inst. Chem. Engrs., **37**, 79 (1941).
27. BEARLE, W. G., G. A. McVICAR, and J. B. FERGUSON, J. Phys. Chem., **34**, 1310 (1930).
28. BEDINGFIELD, C. H., JR., and T. B. DREW, Ind. Eng. Chem., **42**, 1164 (1950).
29. BENEDICT, M., Chem. Eng. Progress, **43**, 41 (1947).
30. BENEDICT, M., in Encyclopedia of Chemical Technology, R. E. Kirk and D. F. Othmer (eds.), The Interscience Encyclopedia, New York, 1950.
30a. BENEDICT, M., G. B. WEBB, and L. C. RUBIN, J. Chem. Phys., **8**, 334–345 (1940); **10**, 747–758 (1942); Chem. Eng. Progress, **47**, 419–422 (1951).

30b. BENEDICT, M., G. B. WEBB, L. C. RUBIN, and L. FRIEND, Paper presented at Pittsburgh meeting of American Institute of Chemical Engineers, December, 1947.

31. BERTETTI, J. W., *Trans. Am. Inst. Chem. Engrs.*, **38**, 1023 (1942).

32. BEUSCHLEIN, W. L., and R. H. CONRAD, *Paper Trade J.*, **99**, 75, (Sept. 20, 1934).

33. BIGELOW, F. H., *Am. Monthly Weather Rev.*, (1907), (1908), (1910).

34. BLAKE, F. C., *Trans. Am. Inst. Chem. Engrs.*, **14**, 415 (1922).

35. BLANDING, F. H., and J. C. ELGIN, *Trans. Am. Inst. Chem. Engrs.*, **38**, 305 (1942).

36. BODENSTEIN, M., *Helv. Chim. Acta*, **18**, 743 (1935).

37. BOELTER, L. M. K., *Trans. Am. Inst. Chem. Engrs.*, **39**, 557 (1943).

38. BOELTER, L. M. K., H. S. GORDON, and J. R. GRIFFIN, *Ind. Eng. Chem.*, **38**, 596 (1946).

39. BOELTER, L. M. K., and S. HORI, *Trans. Am. Soc. Heat. Vent. Engrs.*, **49**, 309 (1943).

40. BOELTER, L. M. K., R. C. MARTINELLI, and F. JOHASSEN, *Trans. Am. Soc. Mech. Engrs.*, **63**, 447 (1941).

41. BOLSHAKOFF, P. E., S.M. thesis in chemical engineering, M.I.T., 1934.

42. BONNET, W. H., Ph.D. thesis in chemical engineering, Univ. of Delaware, 1949.

43. BORDEN, H. M., and W. SQUIRES, JR., reported by Sherwood and Holloway, *Trans. Am. Inst. Chem. Engrs.*, **36**, 21 (1940).

44. BOSWORTH, R. C. L., *Australian Chem. Inst. J. & Proc.*, **13**, 53 (1946).

45. BRAMLEY, A., and A. K. BREWER, *Science*, **90**, 165 (1939).

46. BRANCKER, A. V., T. G. HUNTER, and A. W. NASH, *Ind. Eng. Chem., Anal. Ed.*, **12**, 35 (1940).

47. BRINSMADE, D. S., and H. BLISS, *Trans. Am. Inst. Chem. Engrs.*, **39**, 679 (1943).

48. BROWN, G. G., "Unit Operations," p. 584, John Wiley & Sons, Inc., New York, 1950.

49. BROWN, G. G., D. L. KATZ, G. G. OBERELL, and R. C. ALDEN, "Natural Gasoline and the Volatile Hydrocarbons," Natural Gasoline Association of America, Tulsa, 1948.

50. BROWN, G. G., and M. SOUDERS, *Oil Gas J.*, **31**, No. 5, 34 (1932). Compare also Brown and Souders, "The Science of Petroleum," Vol. II, p. 1557, Oxford University Press., New York, 1938; *Refiner*, **11**, 376 (1932).

51. BROWN, G. G., and M. SOUDERS, *Oil Gas J.*, **32** (45), 114 (1934).

52. BROWN, G. G., and M. SOUDERS, "Separation of Petroleum Hydrocarbons by Distillation," in "The Science of Petroleum," Vol. II, Sec. 25, Oxford University Press., New York, 1938.

53. BROWNELL, L. E., and D. M. KATZ, *Chem. Eng. Progress*, **43**, 537–548 (1947).

54. BRUNJES, A. S., and M. J. P. BOGART, *Ind. Eng. Chem.*, **35**, 255 (1943).

55. BRUNNER, E., *Z. physik. Chem.*, **47**, 67ff. (1904).

56. BULL, F. W., and G. J. COLI, *Bull. Virginia Polytech. Inst.* 72, November, 1949.

57. BURDICK, C. L., *J. Am. Chem. Soc.*, **44**, 244 (1922).

58. BURDICK, C. L., and E. W. FREED, *J. Am. Chem. Soc.*, **43**, 518 (1921).

59. BURKE, S. P., and W. B. PLUMMER, *Ind. Eng. Chem.*, **20**, 1196 (1928).

60. BURNSIDE, H. E. W., Sc.D. thesis in chemical engineering, M.I.T., 1938.

61. BUTCHER, C. H., *Ind. Chemist*, **4**, 446 (1928); **5**, 455 (1928); **8**, 131 (1932).

62. CANTELO, R. C., C. W. SIMONS, E. M. GILES, and F. A. BRILL, *Ind. Eng. Chem.*, **19**, 989 (1927).

63. CAREY, J. S., "Distillation," Sec. 9 *in* J. H. Perry, "Chemical Engineers' Handbook," 3d ed., pp. 597–598, McGraw-Hill Book Company, Inc., New York, 1950.
64. CARLSON, H. C., *Ind. Eng. Chem.*, **38**, 14–15, 33–34 (1946).
65. CARLSON, H. C., and A. P. COLBURN, *Ind. Eng. Chem.*, **34**, 581 (1942).
66. CARMAN, P. C., *Trans. Inst. Chem. Engrs. (London)*, **15**, 150–166 (1937); *J. Soc. Chem. Ind. (London)*, **57**, 225 (1938); **58**, 1 (1939).
67. CARPENTER, L. G., *Colo. Agr. Expt. Sta. Ann. Rept.*, **4**, 29 (1941).
68. CARRIER, W. H., *Trans. Am. Soc. Mech. Engrs.*, **33**, 1005 (1911).
69. CARRIER, W. H., and C. O. MACKEY, *Trans. Am. Soc. Mech. Engrs.*, **59**, 33 (1937).
70. CHAMBERS, F. S., and T. K. SHERWOOD, *Ind. Eng. Chem.*, **29**, 1415 (1937); *Trans. Am. Inst. Chem. Engrs.*, **33**, 579 (1937).
71. CHAMBERS, F. S., and T. K. SHERWOOD, *J. Am. Chem. Soc.*, **59**, 316 (1937).
72. CHAPMAN, W., *Trans. Roy. Soc. (London)*, **A217**, 165 (1917).
73. CHAPMAN, S., and T. G. COWLING, "Mathematical Theory of Non-Uniform Gases," Cambridge University Press, New York, 1939.
74. CHILTON, T. H., private communication, 1949
75. CHILTON, T. H., and A. P. COLBURN, *Ind. Eng. Chem.*, **26**, 1183 (1934).
76. CHILTON, T. H., and A. P. COLBURN, *Ind. Eng. Chem.*, **27**, 255 (1935).
77. CHILTON, T. H., and A. P. COLBURN, *Trans. Am. Inst. Chem. Engrs.*, **26**, 178 (1931).
78. CHU, J. C., C. C. TAYLOR, and D. J. LEVY, *Ind. Eng. Chem.*, **42**, 1157 (1950).
79. CHURCH, P. E., and C. A. GOSLINE, JR., paper presented at May, 1946, meeting of American Geophysical Union.
80. CLUSIUS, K., and G. DICKEL, *Naturwissenschaften*, **26**, 546(L) (1938).
81. CLUSIUS, K., and G. DICKEL, *Z. physik. Chem.*, **B44**, 397 (1939).
82. COGAN, J. C., and J. P. COGAN, thesis in chemical engineering, M.I.T., 1932.
83. COLBURN, A. P., collected papers on the teaching of chemical engineering, American Society for Engineering Education. Summer School for Teaching of Chemical Engineering, Pennsylvania State College, 1936.
84. COLBURN, A. P., *Ind. Eng. Chem.*, **22**, 967 (1930).
85. COLBURN, A. P., *Ind. Eng. Chem.*, **28**, 526 (1936).
86. COLBURN, A. P., *Ind. Eng. Chem.*, **33**, 459 (1941).
87. COLBURN, A. P., *Trans. Am. Inst. Chem. Engrs.*, **29**, 174 (1933).
88. COLBURN, A. P., *Trans. Am. Inst. Chem. Engrs.*, **35**, 211 (1939).
89. COLBURN, A. P., and T. B. DREW, *Trans. Am. Inst. Chem. Engrs.*, **33**, 197 (1937).
90. COLBURN, A. P., and A. G. EDISON, *Ind. Eng. Chem.*, **33**, 457 (1941).
91. COLBURN, A. P., and O. A. HOUGEN, *Ind. Eng. Chem.*, **26**, 1178 (1934).
92. COLBURN, A. P., and D. G. WELSH, *Trans. Am. Chem. Engrs.*, **38**, 179 (1942).
93. COMINGS, E. W., and S. W. BRIGGS, *Trans. Am. Inst. Chem. Engrs.*, **38**, 143 (1942).
94. COMINGS, E. W., J. T. CLAPP, and J. F. TAYLOR, *Ind. Eng. Chem.*, **40**, 1076 (1948).
95. COMSTOCK, C. W., and B. F. DODGE, *Ind. Eng. Chem.*, **29**, 520 (1937).
96. COOPER, C. M., U.S. patent 2,398,345 (1945).
97. COOPER, C. M., R. CHRISTL, and L. C. PEERY, *Trans. Am. Inst. Chem. Engrs.*, **37**, 979 (1941).
98. COOPER, C. M., G. A. FERNSTROM, and S. A. MILLER, *Ind. Eng. Chem.*, **36**, 504–509 (1944).
99. COPE, J. Q., W. K. LEWIS, and H. C. WEBER, *Ind. Eng. Chem.*, **23**, 887 (1931).

100. CRYDER, D. S., and J. O. MALONEY, Trans. Am. Inst. Chem. Engrs., **37**, 827 (1941).

100a. DANCKWERTS, P. V., Trans. Faraday Soc., **46**, 300 (1950).

101. DAVIES, J. A., Ind. Eng. Chem., **39**, 774 (1947).

102. DAVIS, G. H. B., M. LAPEYROUSE, and E. W. DEAN, Oil Gas J., 92 (Mar. 31, 1932).

103. DAVIS, H. S., and G. S. CRANDALL, J. Am. Chem. Soc., **52**, 3757, 3769 (1930).

104. DEAN, E. W., and G. H. B. DAVIS, Chem. & Met. Eng., **36**, 618 (1929).

105. DEED, D. W., P. W. SCHUTZ, and T. B. DREW, Ind. Eng. Chem., **39**, 766 (1947).

106. DEFIZE, J. C. L., "On the Edeleanu Process," D. B. Centen, Amsterdam, 1938.

107. DENBIGH, K. G., and A. J. PRINCE, J. Chem. Soc., **59**, 791 (1947).

108. DEVINS, B. P., thesis in chemical engineering, M.I.T., 1948.

109. DODGE, B. F., Ind. Eng. Chem., **24**, 1353 (1932).

110. DODGE, B. F., "Thermodynamics for Chemical Engineers," p. 97, McGraw-Hill Book Company, Inc., New York, 1944.

111. DODGE, B. F., and O. E. DWYER, Ind. Eng. Chem., **33**, 485 (1941).

112. DOHERTY, T. B., and F. C. JOHNSON, reported by Sherwood and Holloway, Trans. Am. Inst. Chem. Engrs., **36**, 21 (1940).

113. DREW, T. B., Trans. Am. Inst. Chem. Engrs., **26**, 26 (1931).

114. DREW, T. B., Trans. Am. Inst. Chem. Engrs., **35**, 681 (1939).

115. DRICKAMER, H. G., and J. R. BRADFORD, Trans. Am. Inst. Chem. Engrs., **39**, 319 (1943).

116. DROPKIN, D., Cornell Univ. Eng. Expt. Sta. Bull. 23, July, 1936; 26, October, 1939.

117. DRYDEN, H. S., Ind. Eng. Chem., **31**, 416 (1939)

118. DRYDEN, H. S., Quart. Applied Math, **1**, 7 (1943).

119. DUKLER, A. E., private communication, 1950.

120. DUKLER, A. E., thesis in chemical engineering, Univ. of Delaware, 1949.

121. DUNCAN, D. W., J. H. Koffolt, and J. R. WITHROW, Trans. Am. Inst. Chem. Engrs., **38**, 259 (1942).

122. DUNSTAN, A. E. (ed.), "The Science of Petroleum," Vol. 3, pp. 1818–1929, Oxford University Press, New York, 1938.

123. EAGLETON, L. C., R. M. LANGER, and T. H. PIGFORD, S.M. thesis, M.I.T., 1948.

124. EDMISTER, W. C., Chem. Eng. Progress, **44**, 615 (1948).

125. EDMISTER, W. C., Ind. Eng. Chem., **35**, 837 (1943).

126. EINSTEIN, A., Ann. Physik, **17**, 549 (1905).

127. ELGIN, J. C., and F. M. BROWNING, Trans. Am. Inst. Chem. Engrs., **31**, 439 (1935).

128. ELGIN, J. C., and F. B. WEISS, Ind. Eng. Chem., **31**, 435 (1939).

129. ELGIN, J. C., and R. WYNKOOP, "Solvent Extraction" in J. H. Perry, "Chemical Engineers' Handbook," 3d ed., McGraw-Hill Book Company, Inc., New York, 1950.

130. ENSKOG, D., Physik. Z., **12**, 56, 533 (1911).

131. EPSHTEIN, D. A., J. Gen. Chem. (U.S.S.R.), **9**, 792 (1939).

132. ERGUN, S., and A. A. ORNING, Ind. Eng. Chem., **41**, 1179 (1949).

133. EUCKEN, A., and H. B. GRÜTZNER, Z. physik. Chem., **125**, 385 (1927).

134. EVANS, T. W., Ind. Eng. Chem., **26**, 439 (1934).

135. FAIRLIE, A. M., Chem. & Met. Eng., **39**, 76 (1932).

136. FALLAH, J., T. G. HUNTER, and A. W. NASH, J. Soc. Chem. Ind. (London), **54**, 49T (1935).

137. FAURHOLT, C., *J. chim. phys.*, **21**, 400 (1923); **22**, 1 (1925).
138. FAUSER, G., *Chem. & Met. Eng.*, **35**, 474 (1928).
139. FELLINGER, L., Sc.D. thesis in chemical engineering. M.I.T., 1941.
140. FITZGERALD, D., *Trans. Am. Soc. Chem. Engrs.*, **15**, 581 (1886).
141. FORSYTHE, W. R., and W. F. GIAUQUE, *J. Am. Chem. Soc.*, **64**, 48 (1942).
142. FOUST, H. C., D. E. MACK, and J. H. RUSHTON, *Ind. Eng. Chem.*, **36**, 517–522 (1944).
143. FRANCIS, A. W., *in* A. Farkas (ed.), "Physical Chemistry of Hydrocarbons," Chap. 7, Academic Press, Inc., New York, 1950.
144. FRIEDMAN, S. J., and C. O. MILLER, *Ind. Eng. Chem.*, **33**, 885 (1941).
145. FROESSLING, N., *Gerlands Beitr. Geophys.*, **32**, 170 (1938).
146. FRÖLICH, P. K., E. F. TAUCH, J. J. HOGAN, and A. A. PEER, *Ind. Eng. Chem.*, **23**, 548 (1934).
147. FURNAS, C. C., *U.S. Bur. Mines Bull.* 307, 1929.
148. FURNAS, C. C., and F. BELLINGER, *Trans. Am. Inst. Chem. Engrs.*, **34**, 251 (1938).
149. FURNAS, C. C., and M. L. TAYLOR, *Trans. Am. Inst. Chem. Engrs.*, **36**, 135 (1939).
150. FURRY, W. H., and R. C. JONES, *Phys. Rev.*, **57**, 561A (1940).
151. FURRY, W. H., and R. C. JONES, *Phys. Rev.*, **69**, 459 (1946).
152. FURRY, W. H., R. C. JONES, and L. ONSAGER, *Phys. Rev.*, **57**, 1083 (1939).
153. GAFFNEY, B. J., and T. B. DREW, *Ind. Eng. Chem.*, **42**, 1120 (1950).
154. GAMSON, B. W., G. THODOS, and O. A. HOUGEN, *Trans. Am. Inst. Chem. Engrs.*, **39**, 1 (1943).
155. GAMSON, B. W., and K. M. WATSON, *Natl. Petroleum News*, Tech. Sec., **36**, R665, R623 (August–September, 1944).
156. GEANKOPLIS, C. J., and A. N. HIXSON, *Ind. Eng. Chem.*, **42**, 1144 (1950).
157. GEDDES, R. L., *Trans. Am. Inst. Chem. Engrs.*, **42**, 79 (1946).
158. GERSTER, J. A., A. P. COLBURN, W. E. BONNET, T. CARMODY, *Chem. Eng. Progress*, **45**, 716 (1949).
159. GILLILAND, E. R., *Ind. Eng. Chem.*, **26**, 681 (1934).
160. GILLILAND, E. R., private communication, February, 1932.
161. GILLILAND, E. R., and T. K. SHERWOOD, *Ind. Eng. Chem.*, **26**, 516 (1934).
162. GOLDSTEIN, S. (ed.), "Modern Developments in Fluid Dynamics," Oxford University Press, New York, 1938.
163. GOOD, A. J., M. H. HUTCHINSON, and W. C. ROUSSEAU, *Ind. Eng. Chem.*, **34**, 1445 (1942).
164. GREENEWALT, C. H., *Ind. Eng. Chem.*, **18**, 1291 (1926).
165. GREGORY, L. B., and W. G. SCHARMANN, *Ind. Eng. Chem.*, **29**, 514 (1937).
166. GRIMLEY, S. S., *Trans. Inst. Chem. Engrs. (London)*, **23**, 228 (1945).
167. GROSVENOR, W. M., *Trans. Am. Inst. Chem. Engrs.*, **1**, 184 (1908).
168. GUYER, A., and B. TOBLER, *Chem. Fabrik*, **1934**, 145. See also A. Guyer, B. Tobler, and R. H. Farmer, *ibid.*, 265; **1936**, 5.
169. HAPPEL, J., *Ind. Eng. Chem.*, **41**, 1161 (1949).
170. HARTE, C. R., and E. M. BAKER, *Ind. Eng. Chem.*, **21**, 1128 (1933).
171. HARTE, C. R., E. M. BAKER, and H. H. PURCELL, *Ind. Eng. Chem.*, **25**, 528 (1933).
172. HARTLEY, G. S., *Trans. Faraday Soc.*, **27**, 10 (1931).
173. HASLAM, R. T., R. L. HERSHEY, and R. H. KEAN, *Ind. Eng. Chem.*, **16**, 1224 (1924).
174. HASLAM, R. T., W. P. RYAN, and H. C. WEBER, *Trans. Am. Inst. Chem. Engrs.*, **15**, 177 (1923).

175. HATTA, S., *Techol. Repts. Tôhoku Imp. Univ.*, **8**, 1 (1928–1929).
176. HATTA, S., *Techol. Repts., Tôhoku Imp. Univ.*, **10**, 119 (1932).
177. HATTA, S., and M. KATORI, *J. Soc. Chem. Ind. Japan*, **37**, 280B (1934).
178. HATTA, S., T. UEDA, and A. BABA, *J. Soc. Chem. Ind. Japan*, **37**, 383 (1934).
179. HAUSEN, E., *Z. ges. Kälte-Ind.*, **32**, 93, 114 (1928); *Forsch. Gebiete Ingenieurw.*, **7**, 177 (1936).
180. HAYWORTH, C. B., and R. E. TREYBAL, *Ind. Eng. Chem.*, **42**, 1174 (1950).
181. HENLEY, E. C., S.B. thesis in chemical engineering, Univ. of Delaware, 1949.
182. HERTZ, G., *Z. Physik*, **79**, 108 (1932).
183. HESS, I. H., S.M. thesis in chemical engineering, Univ. of Delaware, 1950.
184. HEWSON, G. H., S. L. PEARCE, A. POLLITT, and R. L. REES, *J. Soc. Chem. Ind. (London)*, **52**, 593 (1933).
185. HIGBIE, R., *Trans. Am. Inst. Chem. Engrs.*, **31**, 365 (1935).
186. HILL, J. B., and H. B. COATS, *Ind. Eng. Chem.*, **20**, 641 (1928).
187. HILPERT, R., *Forschungsheft*, No. 355, 21 (July–August, 1932).
188. HIMUS, G. W., *Trans. Inst. Chem. Engrs. (London)*, **7**, 166 (1929).
189. HINCHLEY, J. W., and G. W. HIMUS, *Trans. Inst. Chem. Engrs. (London)*, **2**, 57 (1924).
190. HINE, T. B., *Phys. Rev.*, **24**, 79 (1924).
191. HIRSCH, M., "Die Trockentechnik," Springer, Berlin, 1927.
192. HIRSCHFELDER, J. O., R. B. BIRD, and E. L. SPOTZ, *Chem. Revs.*, **44**, 205 (1949); *J. Chem. Phys.*, **16**, 968 (1948); *Trans. Am. Soc. Mech. Engrs.*, **71**, 921 (1949). See also C. F. Curtiss, and J. O. HIRSCHFELDER, *J. Chem. Phys.*, **17**, 550 (1949).
193. HITCHCOCK, L. B., Sc.D. thesis in chemical engineering, M.I.T., 1933. See also *Ind. Eng. Chem.*, **26**, 1158 (1934); *ibid.*, **27**, 461 (1935); *Trans. Am. Inst. Chem. Engrs.*, **36**, 347 (1935).
194. HIXSON, A. W., and C. E. SCOTT, *Ind. Eng. Chem.*, **27**, 307 (1935).
195. HOBSON, M., and G. THODOS, *Chem. Eng. Progress*, **45**, 519 (1949).
196. HODGSON, J. R., S.M. thesis in chemical engineering, M.I.T., 1949.
197. HOFFMAN, E., *Forsch. Gebeite Ingenieurw.*, **11**, 159 (1940).
198. HOFMANN, H. E., *Ind. Eng. Chem.*, **24**, 135 (1932).
199. HOLBROOK, G. E., and E. M. BAKER, *Ind. Eng. Chem.*, **26**, 1063 (1934).
200. HOLLINGS, H., and L. SILVER, *Trans. Inst. Chem. Engrs. (London)*, **12**, 49 (1934).
201. HOLMES, R. C., private communication, 1947. Compare J. H. Perry, "Chemical Engineers' Handbook," 3d ed., p. 686, McGraw-Hill Book Company, Inc., New York, 1950.
202. HORTON, G., and W. B. FRANKLIN, *Ind. Eng. Chem.*, **32**, 1384 (1940).
203. HOTTEL, H. C., personal communication, 1949.
204. HOUGEN, O. A., and K. M. WATSON, "Chemical Process Principles," Part II, p. 666, John Wiley & Sons, Inc., New York, 1947.
205. HOUGHTON, H. G., *Physics*, **2**, 467 (1932); **4**, 419 (1933).
206. HOUGHTON, H. G., and W. H. RADFORD, *Papers Phys. Oceanog. Meteorol., Mass. Inst. Technol. and Woods Hole Oceano. Inst.*, **6**, No. 3 (October, 1938).
207. HUNTER, T. G., and A. W. NASH, *J. Soc. Chem. Ind. (London)*, **53**, 95T (1934).
208. HUNTER, T. G., and A. W. NASH, *World Petroleum Congr.*, **2**, 340 (1933).
209. HURT, D. M., *Ind. Eng. Chem.*, **35**, 522 (1943).
210. HURTER, F., *J. Soc. Chem. Ind. (London)*, **12**, 227 (1893).
211. INGERSOLL, L. R., O. J. ZOBEL, and A. C. INGERSOLL, "Heat Conduction," pp. 190*ff.*, McGraw-Hill Book Company, Inc., New York, 1949.

212. International Critical Tables, Vol. 3, McGraw-Hill Book Company, Inc., New York, 1928.
213. International Critical Tables, Vol. 3, p. 248, McGraw-Hill Book Company, Inc., New York, 1928.
214. International Critical Tables, Vol. 3, p. 418; McGraw-Hill Book Company, Inc., New York, 1928.
215. JACKSON, M. L., and N. H. CEAGELSKE, *Ind. Eng. Chem.*, **42**, 1188 (1950).
216. JACKSON, R. M., and T. K. SHERWOOD, *Trans. Am. Inst. Chem. Engrs.*, **37**, 959 (1941).
217. JAKOB, M., and W. DOW, *Trans. Am. Soc. Mech. Engrs.*, **68**, 123 (1946).
218. JEANS, J. H., "The Dynamical Theory of Gases," 3d ed., Chap. XIII, p. 307, Cambridge University Press, New York, 1921.
219. JENNESS, L. C., and J. G. L. CAULFIELD, *Paper Trade J.*, **109**, (26), 37 (1939).
220. JENNY, F. J., thesis in chemical engineering, M.I.T., 1936.
221. JESSER, B. W., and J. C. ELGIN, *Trans. Am. Inst. Chem. Engrs.*, **39**, 277 (1942).
222. JOHNSON, H. F., JR., and H. BLISS, *Trans. Am. Inst. Chem. Engrs.*, **42**, 331 (1946).
223. JOHNSTONE, H. F., *Combustion*, **5**, No. 2, 19 (1933).
224. JOHNSTONE, H. F., *Ind. Eng. Chem.*, **27**, 587 (1935).
225. JOHNSTONE, H. F., and D. B. KEYES, *Ind. Eng. Chem.*, **27**, 659 (1935).
226. JOHNSTONE, H. F., and R. V. KLEINSCHMIDT, *Trans. Am. Inst. Chem. Engrs.*, **34**, 181 (1938).
227. JOHNSTONE, H. F., and R. L. PIGFORD, *Trans. Am. Inst. Chem. Engrs.*, **37**, 25 (1941).
228. JOHNSTONE, H. F., R. L. PIGFORD, and J. H. CHAPIN, *Trans. Am. Inst. Chem. Engrs.*, **37**, 95 (1941).
229. JOHNSTONE, H. F., H. J. READ, and H. W. BLANKMEYER, *Ind. Eng. Chem.* **30**, 101 (1938).
230. JOHNSTONE, H. F., and H. E. SILCOX, *Ind. Eng. Chem.*, **39**, 808 (1947).
231. JOHNSTONE, H. F., and A. D. SINGH, *Ind. Eng. Chem.*, **29**, 286 (1937).
232. JOHNSTONE, H. F., and A. D. SINGH, *Ind. Eng. Chem.*, **32**, 1037–1049 (1940).
233. JOHNSTONE, H. F., and G. C. WILLIAMS, *Ind. Eng. Chem.*, **31**, 993 (1939).
234. KALICHEVSKY, V. A., "Modern Methods of Refining Lubricating Oils," Reinhold Publishing Corporation, New York, 1938.
235. KALINSKE, A. A., and C. L. PIEN, *Ind. Eng. Chem.*, **36**, 220 (1944).
236. KALINSKE, A. A., and J. M. ROBERTSON, *Eng. News-Record*, 53, (Apr. 10, 1941).
237. KALINSKE, A. A., and E. R. VAN DRIEST, Proceedings Fifth International Congress of Applied Mechanics, 1938.
238. KAMEI, S., S. MIZUNI, and S. SHIOMI, *J. Soc. Chem. Ind. Japan*, **38**, 460B (1935).
239. KATZ, D. L., and K. H. HACHMUTH, *Ind. Eng. Chem.*, **29**, 1072 (1937).
240. KAY, W. C., private communication, April, 1934.
241. KEMP, H. S., and C. PYLE, *Chem. Eng. Progress*, **45**, 435 (1949).
242. KEYES, D. B., *J. Soc. Chem. Ind. (London)*, **53**, 692 (1934).
243. KIRKBRIDE, C. G., *Ind. Eng. Chem.*, **26**, 425 (1934).
244. KIRKBRIDE, C. G., *Petroleum Refiner*, **23**, 321 (1944).
245. KIRKBRIDE, C. G., and J. W. BERTETTI, *Ind. Eng. Chem.*, **35**, 1242 (1943).
246. KIRSCHBAUM, E., *Forsch. Gebeite Ingenieurw.*, **5**, 245 (1934); *Z. Ver. deut. Ing.*, **80** (1), 633 (1936).

247. KIRSCHBAUM, E., Z. Ver deut. Ing., **75**, 1212 (1931).

248. KIRSCHBAUM, E., and K. KEINZLE, Chem. Fabrik, **14**, 191 (1941).

249. KLEINSCHMIDT, R. V., Chem. & Met. Eng., **46**, 487 (1939).

250. KLEINSCHMIDT, R. V., and A. W. ANTHONY, Trans. Am. Soc. Mech. Engrs., **63**, 349 (1941). See also F. F. Pease, U.S. patent 1,992,762 (1935); A. W. Anthony, U.S. patent 1,986,913 (1935).

251. KLIBANOUR, T. M., V. V. POMERANTSEV, and D. A. FRANK-KAMENETSKY, J. Tech. Phys. (U.S.S.R.), **12**, 14–30 (1942).

252. KNIGHT, O. S., Trans. Am. Inst. Chem. Engrs., **39**, 439 (1943).

253. KOWALKE, O. L., O. A. HOUGEN, and K. M. WATSON, Bull. Univ. Wis., Eng. Expt. Sta. Ser., No. 68, 1925.

254. KOZENY, J., Sitzber. Akad. Wiss. Wien, **136** (IIa), 271 (1927).

255. KRASE, N. W., in H. A. Curtis (ed.), "Fixed Nitrogen," Reinhold Publishing Corporation, New York, 1932.

256. KREBS, R. W., thesis, Univ. of Illinois, 1938.

257. KREMSER, A., Natl. Petroleum News, **22**, No. 21, 42, (May 21, 1930).

258. KUZMINYKH, I. N., and V. S. UDINTSEVA, Khimstroǐ, **6**, 523–526 (1934).

259. LANDOLT-BORNSTEIN, "Physikalische-Chemische Tabellen," Eg. IIIa, Springer-Verlag, Berlin (1923).

260. LANGMUIR, I., J. Am. Chem. Soc., **37**, 426 (1915).

261. LANGMUIR, I., J. Am. Chem. Soc., **38**, 2221–2295 (1916).

262. LANGMUIR, I., Phys. Rev., **12** (2), 368 (1918).

263. LANGMUIR, I., and V. J. SCHAEFER, J. Franklin Inst., **235**, 119 (1943).

264. LAPIDUS, L., and N. R. AMUNDSON, Ind. Eng. Chem., **42**, 1071 (1950).

265. LATZKO, H., Z. angew. Math. Mech., **1**, 288 (1921); trans. in Natl. Advisory Comm. Aeronaut. Tech. Mem. 1068, 1944.

266. LENARD, P., Meteor. Z., **21**, 249 (1904); Ann. Physik, **65** (IV), 629 (1921).

267. LEVA, M., Chem. Eng. Progress, **43**, 549 (1947).

268. LEVA, M., and M. GRUMMER, Chem. Eng. Progress, **43**, 633 (1947).

269. LEVA, M., M. GRUMMER, M. WEINTRAUB, and M. POELCHIK, Chem. Eng. Progress, **44**, 511 (1948).

270. LEWIS, G. N., and M. RANDALL, "Thermodynamics," p. 190, McGraw-Hill Book Company, Inc., New York, 1923.

271. LEWIS, W. K., Ind. Eng. Chem., **28**, 257 (1936).

272. LEWIS, W. K., Mech. Eng., **55**, 567 (1933).

273. LEWIS, W. K., Trans. Am. Inst. Chem. Engrs., **20**, 1 (1927).

274. LEWIS, W. K., Trans. Am. Soc. Mech. Engrs., **44**, 329 (1922).

275. LEWIS, W. K., and K. C. CHANG, Trans. Am. Inst. Chem. Engrs., **21**, 127 (1928).

276. LEWIS, W. K., and W. C. KAY, Oil Gas J., **32**, 40, 114 (Mar. 29, 1934).

277. LEWIS, W. K., and C. S. KEEVIL, Ind. Eng. Chem., **20**, 1058 (1928).

278. LEWIS, W. K., and C. D. LUKE, Trans. Am. Soc. Mech. Engrs., **54**, 55 (1932).

279. LEWIS, W. K., and L. SQUIRES, Ind. Eng. Chem., **29**, 109 (1937).

280. LEWIS, W. K., L. SQUIRES, and C. E. SANDERS, Ind. Eng. Chem., **27**, 1395 (1935).

281. LEWIS, W. K., and W. G. WHITMAN, Ind. Eng. Chem., **16**, 1215 (1924).

282. LEWIS, W. K., JR., Ind. Eng. Chem., **28**, 399 (1936).

283. LICHT, W., JR., and J. B. CONWAY, Ind. Eng. Chem., **42**, 1151 (1950).

284. LINTON, W. H., JR., and T. K. SHERWOOD, Chem. Eng. Progress, **46**, 258 (1950).

285. LIZNAR, J., Meteor. Z., **31**, 339 (1914).

286. LOBO, W. E., L. FRIEND, F. HASHMALL, and F. ZENZ, Trans. Am. Inst. Chem. Engrs., **41**, 693 (1945).

287. LOHRISCH, W., *Mitt. Forsch.*, **322**, 46 (1929).
288. LONDON, A. L., H. B. NOTTAGE, and L. M. K. BOELTER, *Ind. Eng. Chem.*, **33**, 467 (1941).
289. LUKE, C. D., Sc.D. thesis in chemical engineering, M.I.T., 1934.
290. LURIE, M., and M. MICHAILOFF, *Ind. Eng. Chem.*, **28**, 345 (1936).
291. MACH, E., *Dechema Monograph*, **6**, 38 (1933); *Z. Ver. deut. Ing. Forsch.* **375**, 1935.
292. MAIER, C. G., *U.S. Bur. Mines Bull.* 431, 1940.
293. MAISEL, D. S., and T. K. SHERWOOD, *Chem. Eng. Progress*, **46**, 131, 172 (1950).
294. MAJIMA, M., and S. TOGINO, *Bull. Inst. Phys. Chem. Research* (Tokyo), **9**, 339 (1930); from *Physik. Ber.*, **12**, 2540 (1931).
295. MALONEY, J. O., and A. E. SCHUBERT, *Trans. Am. Inst. Chem. Engrs.*, **36**, 741 (1940).
296. MARK, J. G., data quoted by Sherwood, *Trans. Am. Inst. Chem. Engrs.*, **28**, 107 (1932).
297. MARKHAM, A. E., and K. A. KOBE, *Chem. Revs.*, **28**, 519 (1941).
298. MARSHALL, W. R., and R. L. PIGFORD, "Application of Differential Equations to Chemical Engineering Problems," Univ. of Delaware, 1947.
299. MARTINELLI, R. C., *Trans. Am. Soc. Mech. Engrs.*, **69**, 947 (1947).
300. MASON, J. W., and B. F. DODGE, *Trans. Am. Inst. Chem. Engrs.*, **32**, 27 (1936).
301. Mattioli, G. D., *Forsch. Gebeite Ingenieurw.*, **11**, 149 (1940).
302. MAXWELL, J. C., "Diffusion," Encyclopaedia Britannica, 9th ed., 1877.
303. MAXWELL, J. C., "Scientific Papers," Vol. 2, p. 57, Cambridge University Press, New York, 1890.
304. MAXWELL, J. C., "Scientific Papers," Vol. 2, p. 343, Cambridge University Press, New York, 1890.
305. MAXWELL, J. C., "Scientific Papers," Vol. 2, p. 625, Cambridge University Press, New York, 1890. Reprinted from Encyclopaedia Britannica, article on "Diffusion," 9th ed., 1877.
306. MAYCOCK, R. L., U.S. patent 2,474,007 (1949).
307. MAYO, F., T. G. HUNTER, and A. W. NASH, *J. Soc. Chem. Ind. (London)*, **44**, 375T (Nov. 15, 1935).
308. MCADAMS, W. H., "Heat Transmission," 2d ed., p. 259, McGraw-Hill Book Company, Inc., New York, 1942.
309. MCADAMS, W. H., "Heat Transmission," 2d ed., p. 62 for h_r, p. 221 for h, McGraw-Hill Book Company, Inc., New York, 1942.
310. MCADAMS, W. H., "Heat Transmission," 2d ed., p. 206, McGraw-Hill Book Company, Inc., New York, 1942.
311. MCADAMS, W. H., "Heat Transmission," 2d ed., p. 221, Fig. 111, McGraw-Hill Book Company, Inc., New York, 1942.
312. MCADAMS, W. H., "Heat Transmission," 2d ed., p. 231, McGraw-Hill Book Company, Inc., New York, 1942.
313. MCADAMS, W. H., "Heat Transmission," 2d ed., p. 236, Fig. 122, McGraw-Hill Book Company, Inc., New York, 1942.
314. MCADAMS, W. H., J. B. POHLENZ, and R. C. ST. JOHN, *Chem. Eng. Progress*, **45**, 241 (1949).
315. MCCOY, H. N., *Am. Chem. J.*, **29**, 437 (1903).
316. MCELGIN, J., and D. C. WILEY, *Trans. Am. Soc. Heat. Vent. Engrs.*, **46**, 139 (1940).
317. MEHTA, J. J., and R. H. PAREKH, S.M. thesis in chemical engineering, M.I.T., 1939.

318. MEISSNER, H. P., C. A. STOKES, C. M. HUNTER, and G. M. MORROW, *Ind. Eng. Chem.*, **36**, 917 (1944).
319. MERKEL, F., *Forschungsarb.*, **275**, (1925).
320. MEYER, O. E., "Kinetic Theory of Gases" (transl. from the 2d rev. ed.), Longmans, Roberts and Green, London, 1899.
321. MICHAELS, A. S., thesis in chemical engineering, M.I.T., 1946.
322. MICKLEY, H. S., *Chem. Eng. Progress*, **45**, 739 (1949).
323. MILLAR, F. G., *Can. Meteor. Mem.*, **1**, No. 2 (1937).
324. MILLER, E. G., S.B. thesis in chemical engineering, Univ. of Delaware, 1948.
325. "Modern Developments in Fluid Mechanics," S. Goldstein (ed.), Oxford University Press, New York, 1938.
326. MOLSTAD, M. C., R. G. ABBEY, A. R. THOMPSON, and J. F. McKINNEY, *Trans. Am. Inst. Chem. Engrs.*, **38**, 387 (1942).
327. MOLSTAD, M. C., P. FAREVAAG, and J. A. FARRELL, *Ind. Eng. Chem.*, **30**, 1131 (1938).
328. MOLSTAD, M. C., J. F. McKINNEY, and R. G. ABBEY, *Trans. Am. Inst. Chem. Engrs.*, **39**, 605 (1943).
329. MOLSTAD, M. C., and L. F. PARSLEY, JR., *Chem. Eng. Progress*, **46**, 20 (1950).
330. MORELLO, V. S., and N. POFFENBERGER, *Ind. Eng. Chem.*, **42**, 1021 (1950).
331. MORRELL, C. E., W. J. PALTZ, J. W. PACKIE, W. C. ASBURY, and C. L. BROWN, *Trans. Am. Inst. Chem. Engrs.*, **42**, 473 (1946).
332. MORTON, D. S., *J. Phys. Chem.*, **33**, 384 (1929).
333. MOSCICKI, I., *Chimie & industrie*, **2**, 1303 (1919).
334. MOULTON, R. W., and J. E. WALKEY, *Trans. Am. Inst. Chem. Engrs.*, **40**, 695 (1944).
335. MULLALY, J. M., and H. JACQUES, *Phil. Mag.*, **48**, 1105 (1924).
336. MURPHREE, E. V., *Ind. Eng. Chem.*, **17**, 747 (1925).
337. MURPHREE, E. V., *Ind. Eng. Chem.*, **24**, 726 (1932).
338. NANDI, S. K., and T. R. VISWANATHAN, *Current Sci. (India)*, **15**, 162 (June, 1946).
339. NEUMANN, F., as described by F. Weber, "Differential Gleichungen," Reimann, Braunschweig, 1910.
340. NEWMAN, A. B., *Trans. Am. Inst. Chem. Engrs.*, **27**, 310 (1931).
341. NIEDERMAN, H. H., E. D. HOWE, J. P. LONGWELL, R. A. SEBAN, AND L. M. K. BOELTER, *Heating Piping Air Conditioning*, **13**, 591–597 (1941).
342. NIKURADSE, J., *Forschungsheft*, No. 356 (1932); No. 361 (1933).
342a. O'BRIEN, L. J., and L. F. STUTZMAN, *Ind. Eng. Chem.*, **42**, 1181 (1950).
343. O'CONNELL, H. E., *Trans. Am. Inst. Chem. Engrs.*, **42**, 741 (1946).
344. O'KEEFE, A. E., M. A. DOLLIVER, and E. T. STILLER, *J. Am. Chem. Soc.*, **71**, 2452 (1949).
345. OLDERSHAW, C. F., L. SEMENSON, T. BROWN, and F. RADCLIFF, *Chem. Eng. Progress*, **43**, 371 (1947).
346. OMAN, A. O., and K. M. WATSON, *Natl. Petroleum News*, **36**, R795 (1944).
347. OTHMER, D. F., and R. F. BENENATI, *Ind. Eng. Chem.*, **37**, 299 (1945).
348. OTHMER, D. F., R. C. KOLLMAN, and R. E. WHITE, *Ind. Eng. Chem.*, **36**, 963 (1944).
349. OTHMER, D. F., and F. R. MORELEY, *Ind. Eng. Chem.*, **38**, 751 (1946).
350. OTHMER, D. F., and E. G. SCHEIBEL, *Trans. Am. Inst. Chem. Engrs.*, **37**, 211 (1941).
351. OTHMER, D. F., and E. G. SCHEIBEL, *Trans. Am. Inst. Chem. Engrs.*, **38**, 339 (1942).

352. OTHMER, D. F., and P. E. TOBIAS, *Ind. Eng. Chem.*, **34**, 693 (1942).
353. OTHMER, D. F., and E. TRUEGER, *Trans. Am. Inst. Chem. Engrs.*, **37**, 597 (1941).
354. PASQUILL, F., *Proc. Roy. Soc. (London)*, **182A**, 75 (1943).
355. PAYNE, J. W., and B. F. DODGE, *Ind. Eng. Chem.*, **24**, 630 (1932).
356. PAYNE, J. W., and B. F. DODGE, *Ind. Eng. Chem.*, **26**, 856 (1934).
357. PEARSON, J. L., G. NONHEBEL, and P. H. N. ULANDER, *J. Inst. Fuel*, **8**, 119 (1935).
358. PEAVY, C. C., and E. M. BAKER, *Ind. Eng. Chem.*, **29**, 1056 (1937).
359. PERRY, J. H., "Chemical Engineers' Handbook," 3d ed., McGraw-Hill Book Company, Inc., New York, 1950.
360. PERRY, J. H., "Chemical Engineers' Handbook," 3d ed., p. 539, McGraw-Hill Book Company, Inc., New York, 1950.
361. PERRY, J. H., "Chemical Engineers' Handbook," 3d ed., p. 554, McGraw-Hill Book Company, Inc., New York, 1950.
362. PERRY, J. H., "Chemical Engineers' Handbook," 3d ed., Sec. 8, McGraw-Hill Book Company, Inc., New York, 1950.
363. PERRY, J. H. "Chemical Engineers' Handbook," 3d ed., Sec. 10, McGraw-Hill Book Company, Inc., New York, 1950.
364. PHILLIPS, O., and D. R. THACKER, S.M. thesis in chemical engineering, M.I.T., 1950.
365. "Physical and Thermodynamic Properties of Hydrocarbons," American Petroleum Institute, Project No. 44, U.S. National Bureau of Standards, Washington, D.C., 1947.
366. PIGFORD, R. L., in J. H. Perry (ed.), "Chemical Engineers' Handbook," 3d ed., McGraw-Hill Book Company, Inc., New York, 1950.
367. PIGFORD R. L., thesis in chemical engineering, Univ. of Illinois, 1941.
368. PIGFORD, R. L., unpublished data, 1947.
369. PIGFORD, R. L., and C. PYLE, *Ind. Eng. Chem.*, **43**, 1649–1662 (1951).
370. PIPES, L. A., "Applied Mathematics for Engineers and Physicists," McGraw-Hill Book Company, Inc., New York, 1946.
371. POHLHAUSEN, K., *Z. angew. Math. Mech.*, **10**, 252 (1921).
372. POWELL, A. R., *Ind. Eng. Chem.*, **31**, 789 (1939).
373. POWELL, R. W., *Phil. Mag.* **29**, (7), 274 (1940).
374. POWELL, R. W., *Proc. Brit. Assoc. Refrig.*, **36**, 61 (1939–1940).
375. POWELL, R. W., *Trans. Faraday Soc.*, **39**, 311 (1943).
376. POWELL, R. W., *Trans. Inst. Chem. Engrs. (London)*, **18**, 36 (1940).
377. POWELL, R. W., and E. GRIFFITHS, *Trans. Inst. Chem. Engrs. (London)*, **13**, 175 (1935).
378. POZIN, M. E., *J. Applied Chem. (U.S.S.R.)*, **20**, 345–352, 353–359, 963–975, (1947). See also M. E. POZIN and M. A. Smirnova, *ibid.*, 754–761; and H. C. Carlson, *Ind. Eng. Chem.*, **41**, 12–15 (1949).
379. PRANDTL, L., *Z. Physik*, **11**, 1072 (1910); **29**, 487 (1928).
380. PYLE, C., A. P. COLBURN, and H. R. DUFFEY, *Ind. Eng. Chem.*, **42**, 1036 (1950).
381. PYOTT, W. T., C. A. JACKSON, and R. L. HUNTINGTON, *Ind. Eng. Chem.*, **27**, 821 (1935).
382. RAGATZ, E. G., "Straight-Line Chart Determination of Absorber Extraction Efficiency," Clark Bros. Co., Olean, N.Y., 1948.
383. RANDALL, M. A., and B. LONGTIN, *Ind. Eng. Chem.*, **30**, 1063, 1188, 1311 (1938).
383a. RANZ, W. E., and W. R. MARSHALL, JR., paper presented at the Columbus, Ohio, meeting of the American Institute of Chemical Engineers, Dec. 5, 1950.

384. REED, R. M., and W. R. WOOD, *Trans. Am. Inst. Chem. Engrs.*, **37**, 363 (1941).
385. REICH, G. T., *Chem. & Met. Eng.*, **38**, 136–141 (1931).
386. REICHARDT, H., *Z. angew. Math. Mech.*, **20**, 297 (1940).
387. REYNOLDS, B. M., and F. W. SAUNDERS, thesis in chemical engineering, M.I.T. 1920. Quoted in Ref. 489.
388. REYNOLDS O., *Proc. Manchester Lit. Phil. Soc.*, **8** (1874). Reprinted in "Scientific Papers of Osborne Reynolds," Vol. II, Cambridge University Press, New York, 1901.
389. RHODES, F. H., *Ind. Eng. Chem.*, **26**, 1333 (1934); **27**, 272 (1935).
390. RICHARDS, R. L., S.B. thesis in chemical engineering, Univ. of Delaware, 1950.
391. RICHARDSON, L. F., and D. PROCTOR, *Mem. Roy. Meteor. Soc.*, **1**, 1 (1926).
392. ROBINSON, C. S., *Mech. Eng.*, **45**, 99 (1923).
393. ROLAND, C. H., D. E. SMITH, and H. H. KAVALER, *Oil Gas J.*, **39**, No. 46, 128, 130 (1940).
394. ROW, S. B., J. H. KOFFOLT, and J. R. WITHROW, *Trans. Am. Inst. Chem. Engrs.*, **37**, 559 (1941).
395. ROWHER, C., *U.S. Dept. Agr. Tech. Bull.* 271, 1931.
396. SAGE, B. H., H. S. BACKUS, and W. N. LACEY, *Ind. Eng. Chem.*, **27**, 686 (1935).
397. SAGE, B. H., J. A. DAVIES, J. E. SHERBORNE, and W. N. LACEY, *Ind. Eng. Chem.*, **28**, 1328 (1936).
398. SAGE, B. H., H. M. LAVENDER, and W. N. LACEY, *Ind. Eng. Chem.*, **32**, 743 (1940).
399. SANDSTROM, C. O., *Chem. & Met. Eng.*, **39**, 270 (1932).
400. SARCHET, B. R., *Trans. Am. Inst. Chem. Engrs.*, **38**, 283 (1942).
401. SCHEIBEL, E. G., *Chem. Eng. Progress*, **44**, 681, 771 (1948).
402. SCHEIBEL, E. G., and A. E. KARR, *Ind. Eng. Chem.*, **42**, 1048 (1950).
403. SCHEIBEL, E. G., and D. F. OTHMER, *Trans. Am. Inst. Chem. Engrs.*, **40**, 611 (1944).
404. SCHOENBORN, E. M., and W. J. DOUGHERTY, *Trans. Am. Inst. Chem. Engrs.*, **40**, 51, 402 (1944).
405. SCHUBAUER, G. B., *Natl. Advisory Comm. Aeronaut. Tech. Rept.* 524, 1935.
406. SCHULMAN, H. L., and M. C. MOLSTAD, *Ind. Eng. Chem.*, **42**, 1058 (1950).
407. SEEBOLD, J. A., and E. R. GILLILAND, *Ind. Eng. Chem.*, **33**, 1143 (1941).
408. SEIDELL, A., "Solubility of Non-Electrolytes," D. Van Nostrand Company, Inc., New York, 1941.
409. SEIDELL, A., "Solubilities of Inorganic and Metal Organic Compounds," 3d ed., D. Van Nostrand Company, Inc., New York, 1940.
410. SELHEIMER, C. W., M. SOUDERS, R. L. SMITH, G. G. BROWN, *Ind. Eng. Chem.*, **24**, 515 (1932).
411. SHARPLEY, B. F., and L. M. K. BOELTER, *Ind. Eng. Chem.*, **30**, 1125 (1938).
412. SHEPHERD, C. B., C. HADLOCK, and R. C. BREWER, *Ind. Eng. Chem.*, **30**, 388 (1938).
413. SHERWOOD, T. K., *J. Meteor.*, **6**, 416 (1949).
414. SHERWOOD, T. K., *Trans. Am. Inst. Chem. Engrs.*, **36**, 177 (1940).
415. SHERWOOD, T. K., *Trans. Am. Inst. Chem. Engrs.*, 817 (1940).
416. SHERWOOD, T. K., J. E. EVANS, and J. V. A. LONGCOR, *Ind. Eng., Chem.*, **31**, 1144 (1939).
417. SHERWOOD, T. K., and F. A. L. HOLLOWAY, *Trans. Am. Inst. Chem. Engrs.*, **36**, 21 (1940).

418. SHERWOOD, T. K., and F. A. L. HOLLOWAY, *Trans. Am. Inst. Chem. Engrs.*, **36,** 39, (1940).

419. SHERWOOD, T. K., and F. J. JENNY, *Ind. Eng. Chem.*, **27,** 265 (1935).

420. SHERWOOD, T. K., and C. E. REED, "Applied Mathematics in Chemical Engineering," McGraw-Hill Book Company, Inc., New York, 1939.

421. SHERWOOD, T. K., and C. E. REED, "Applied Mathematics in Chemical Engineering," p. 224, McGraw-Hill Book Company, Inc., New York, 1939.

422. SHERWOOD, T. K., G. H. SHIPLEY, and F. A. L. HOLLOWAY, *Ind. Eng. Chem.*, **30,** 765 (1938).

423. SHERWOOD, T. K., and B. B. WOERTZ, *Ind. Eng. Chem.*, **31,** 1034 (1939).

424. SHNEERSON, A. L., and A. G. LIEBUSH, *J. Applied Chem. (U.S.S.R.)*, **21,** 869–879 (1946).

425. SHRADER, E. F., *Phys. Rev.*, **69,** 439 (1946).

426. SIEVERTS, A., and A. FRIZSCHE, *Z. anorg. u. allgem. Chem.*, **133,** 1 (1924).

427. SIMMONS, C. W., and H. B. OSBORNE, *Ind. Eng. Chem.*, **26,** 529 (1934).

428. SIMON, R., *Phys. Rev.*, **69,** 596 (1946).

429. SIMPSON, W. M., and T. K. SHERWOOD, *Refrig. Eng.* **52,** 535 (1946).

430. SLEIGHT, R. B., *J. Agr. Research*, **10,** No. 5 (July 30, 1917).

431. SMITH, A. S., *Ind. Eng. Chem.*, **26,** 1167 (1934).

432. SMITH, A. S., *Ind. Eng. Chem.*, **42,** 1206 (1950).

433. SMITH, E. L., *J. Soc. Chem. Ind. (London)*, **47,** 159T (1928).

434. SMYTH, H. C., "Atomic Energy for Military Purposes," Princeton University Press, Princeton, N. J., 1945.

435. SOUDERS, M., and G. G. BROWN, *Ind. Eng. Chem.*, **24,** 519 (1932).

436. SOUDERS, M., and G. G. BROWN, *Ind. Eng. Chem.*, **26,** 98 (1934).

437. SOUDERS, M., C. W. SELHEIMER, and G. G. BROWN, *Ind. Eng. Chem.*, **24,** 517 (1932).

438. SPALDING, J. D., S.B. thesis in chemical engineering, M.I.T., 1946.

439. SPECTOR, N. A., and B. F. DODGE, *Trans. Am. Inst. Chem. Engrs.*, **42,** 827 (1946).

440. STANTON, T. E., and J. R. PANNELL, *Trans. Roy. Soc. (London)*, **A214,** 199–224 (1914).

441. STEFAN, *Sitzber. Akad. Wiss. Wien*, **63,** (2), 63 (1871).

442. STEFAN, *Sitzber. Akad. Wiss. Wien*, **65,** (2), 323 (1872).

443. STEPHENS, E. J., and G. A. MORRIS, *Chem. Eng. Progress*, **47,** 232–242 (1951).

444. STORRS, B., *Ind. Eng. Chem., News Ed.*, **17,** 627 (1939).

445. STORRS, B., and R. M. REED, *Trans. Am. Soc. Mech. Engrs.*, **64,** 299 (1942).

445a. SUROWIEC, A. J., and C. C. FURNAS, *Trans. Am. Inst. Chem. Engrs.*, **38,** 53 (1942).

446. SUTHERLAND, W., *Phil. Mag.*, **38,** 1 (1894).

447. SUTTON, O. G., *Proc. Roy. Soc. (London)*, **135,** 143 (1932).

448. SUTTON, O. G., *Quart. J. Roy. Meteor. Soc.*, **73,** 257 (1947).

449. SUTTON, O. G., *Quart. J. Roy. Meteor. Soc.*, **73,** 426 (1947).

450. TAECKER, R. G., and O. A. HOUGEN, *Chem. Eng. Progress*, **45,** 188 (1949).

451. TAKAHASI, S., *J. Meteor. Soc. (Japan)*, **13,** 302 (1935); *Geophys. Mag. (Japan)*, **10,** 321 (1936).

452. TAYLOR, G. I., *Brit. Advisory Comm. Aeronaut., Repts. and Mem.*, **272,** 423 (1916).

453. TAYLOR, G. I., *Proc. London Math. Soc.*, **20,** 196 (1921).

454. TAYLOR, G. B., T. H. CHILTON, and S. L. HANDFORTH, *Ind. Eng. Chem.*, **23,** 860 (1931).

455. TEPE, J. B., and B. F. DODGE, *Trans. Am. Inst. Chem. Engrs.*, **39**, 255 (1943).
456. THIESENHUSEN, H., *Gesundh. Ing.*, **53**, 113 (1930).
457. THIELE, E. W., *Ind. Eng. Chem.*, **27**, 392 (1935).
458. TILLER, F. M., and R. S. TOUR, *Trans. Am. Inst. Chem. Engrs.*, **40**, 317 (1944).
459. TILLSON, P., S.M. thesis, M.I.T., 1939.
460. TOPLEY, B., and R. WHYTLAW-GRAY, *Phil. Mag.*, **4**, 873 (1927).
461. TOUR, R. S., and F. LERMAN, *Trans. Am. Inst. Chem. Engrs.*, **35**, 709, 719 (1939); **40**, 79 (1944).
462. TOWLE, W. L., and T. K. SHERWOOD, *Ind. Eng. Chem.*, **31**, 457 (1939).
463. TOWLE, W. L., T. K. SHERWOOD, and L. A. SEDER, *Ind. Eng. Chem.*, **31**, 462 (1939).
464. TREYBAL, R. E., and F. E. DUMOULIN, *Ind. Eng. Chem.*, **34**, 709 (1942).
465. TREYBAL, R. E., and L. T. WORK, *Trans. Am. Inst. Chem. Engrs.*, **36**, 203 (1942).
466. TURKHAN, E. YA, *J. Applied Chem. (U.S.S.R.)*, **21**, 927 (1948).
467. UCHIDA, S., and S. FUJITA, *J. Soc. Chem. Ind. Japan*, Suppl. Binding, **40**, 238B (1937); **41**, 275B (1938).
468. UCHIDA, SHUN-ICHI, and SHIGERU MAEDA, *J. Soc. Chem. Ind. Japan*, Suppl. Binding, **38**, 625 (1935).
469. VAN DRIEST, E. R., *J. Applied Mech.*, **13**, A-231 (1946).
470. VAN KREVELEN, D. W., and P. J. HOFTIJZER, *Chem. Eng. Progress*, **46**, 29 (1950).
471. VAN KREVELEN, D. W., and P. J. HOFTIJZER, *Chem. Eng. Progress*, **44**, 529–536 (1948).
472. VAN KREVELEN, D. W., and P. J. HOFTIJZER, *Rec. trav. chim.*, **66**, 49 (1947).
473. VAN KREVELEN, D. W., P. J. HOFTIJZER, and C. J. VAN HOOREN, *Rec. trav. chim.* **66**, 513 (1947).
474. VAN MIEGHEM, J., *Bull. classe sci., Acad. roy. Belg.*, **27**, 85 (1941).
475. VARTERESSIAN, K. A., and M. R. FENSKE, *Ind. Eng. Chem.*, **29**, 270 (1937).
476. VERHOEK, F. H., and F. DANIELS, *J. Am. Chem. Soc.*, **53**, 1250 (1931).
477. VINK, D. J., A. M. AMES, R. A. DAVID, and D. L. KATZ, *Oil Gas J.*, **39**, No. 28, 34 (1940).
478. VINT, A. W., S.M. thesis in chemical engineering, M.I.T., 1932.
479. VIVIAN, J. E., Sc.D. thesis in chemical engineering, M.I.T., 1945.
480. VIVIAN, J. E., and R. P. WHITNEY, *Chem. Eng. Progress*, **43**, 691 (1947); **44**, 54 (1948).
481. VON KÁRMÁN, TH., *J. Roy. Aeronaut. Soc.*, **41**, 1109 (1937).
482. VON KÁRMÁN, TH., *Trans. Am. Soc. Mech. Engrs.*, **61**, 705 (1939).
483. VYAZOVOV, V. V., *J. Tech. Phys. (U.S.S.R.)*, **10**, 1519–1532 (1940).
484. VYRUBOW, D. N., *J. Tech. Phys. (U.S.S.R.)*, **9**, 1923 (1939).
485. WADE, S. H., *Trans. Inst. Chem. Engrs. (London)*, **20**, 1 (1942).
486. WALKER, W. H., W. K. LEWIS, and W. H. MCADAMS, "Principles of Chemical Engineering," 1st ed., McGraw-Hill Book Company, Inc., New York, 1923.
487. WALKER, W. H., W. K. LEWIS, and W. H. MCADAMS, "Principles of Chemical Engineering," 2d ed., McGraw-Hill Book Company, Inc., New York, 1927.
488. WALL, F. T., *J. Phys. Chem.*, **50**, 235 (1946).
489. WALTER, J. F., and T. K. SHERWOOD, *Ind. Eng. Chem.*, **33**, 493 (1941).
490. WATSON, K. M., and R. L. SMITH, *Natl. Petroleum News*, **28**, No. 27, 29–30, 32, 34–36 (July, 1936).
491. WEBB, H. W., "Absorption of Nitrous Gases," Edward Arnold & Co., London, 1923.
492. WEBBER, C. E., *Am. Inst. Mining Met. Engrs. Tech. Pub.* 1252, 1940.

493. WEBER, H. C., "Chemical Engineering Thermodynamics," pp. 108, 194, John Wiley & Sons, Inc., New York, 1939.
494. WEBER, H. C., and K. NILSSON, *Ind. Eng. Chem.*, **18**, 1070 (1926).
495. WEIDMANN, H., and G. ROESNER, *Ind. Eng. Chem., News Ed.*, **14**, 105 (1936).
496. WEISMAN, J., and C. F. BONILLA, *Ind. Eng. Chem.*, **42**, 1099 (1950).
497. WENNER, R. R., "Thermochemical Calculations," McGraw-Hill Book Company, Inc., New York, 1941.
498. WENNER, R. R., "Thermochemical Calculations," pp. 215–221, 277–290, McGraw-Hill Book Company, Inc., New York, 1941.
499. WHITE, A. M., *Trans. Am. Inst. Chem. Engrs.*, **31**, 390 (1935).
500. WHITE, G. E., *Trans. Am. Inst. Chem. Engrs.*, **36**, 359 (1940).
501. WHITE, R. E., and D. F. OTHMER, *Trans. Am. Inst. Chem. Engrs.*, **38**, 1067 (1942).
502. WHITMAN, W. G., *Chem. & Met. Eng.*, **29**, No. 4 (July 23, 1923).
503. WHITMAN, W. G., and G. H. B. DAVIS, *Ind. Eng. Chem.*, **18**, 264 (1926).
504. WHITMAN, W. G., L. LONG, and H. W. WANG, *Ind. Eng. Chem.*, **18**, 363 (1926).
505. WHITNEY, R. P., and J. E. VIVIAN, *Chem. Eng. Progress*, **45**, 323 (1949).
506. WHITNEY, R. P., and J. E. VIVIAN, *Ind. Eng. Chem.*, **33**, 741 (1941).
507. WHYTLAW-Gray, R., and H. S. PATTERSON, "Smoke," Edward Arnold & Co., London, 1932.
508. WIEGAND, J. H., *Trans. Am. Inst. Chem. Engrs.*, **35**, 679 (1939).
509. WILHELM, R. H., and M. KWAUK, *Chem. Eng. Progress*, **44**, 201 (1948).
510. WILKE, C. R., *Chem. Eng. Progress*, **45**, 218 (1949).
511. WILKE, C. R., and O. A. HOUGEN, *Trans. Am. Inst. Chem. Engrs.*, **41**, 445 (1945).
512. WILLIAMS, G. C., Sc.D. thesis in chemical engineering, M.I.T., 1942.
513. WILLIAMS, G. C., R. B. AKELL, and C. P. TALBOTT, *Chem. Eng. Progress*, **43**, 585 (1947).
514. WILSON, H. A., *Proc. Cambridge Phil. Soc.*, **12**, 406 (1904).
515. WINDING, C. C., and A. J. CHENEY, JR., *Ind. Eng. Chem.*, **40**, 1087 (1948).
516. WINKELMAN, *Ann. Physik*, **22**, 1, 154 (1884); **23**, 203 (1884); **26**, 105 (1885); **33**, 445 (1888); **36**, 93 (1889).
517. WOOLLAM, J. P. V., and A. JACKSON, *Trans. Inst. Chem. Engrs.* (*London*), **23**, 43 (1945).
518. ZAHNSTECHER, L. W., *Heat Eng.*, **25**, 61 (1950).

292. Weber, H. C., "Thermodynamic Measurements: Thermodynamics," pp. 106-104, John Wiley & Sons, Inc., New York, 1939.

293. Weining, S. C., and K. Stinson, Ind. Eng. Chem., 18, 1010 (1926).

294. Weinrich, H., and C. Boryasky, Ind. Eng. Chem., Anal. Ed., 14, 105 (1930).

295. Wenzke, J., and C. E. Bonilla, Ind. Eng. Chem., 42, 1069 (1950).

296. Wenzel, L. A., "Thermochemical Calculations," McGraw-Hill Book Company, Inc., New York, 1941.

297. Wenner, R. R., "Thermochemical Calculations," pp. 215-221, 217-220, McGraw-Hill Book Company, Inc., New York, 1941.

298. White, A. H., Trans. Am. Inst. Chem. Engrs., 21, 400 (1928).

299. White, T. F., Trans. Am. Inst. Chem. Engrs., 35, 355 (1940).

300. White, R. R., and D. F. Othmer, Trans. Am. Inst. Chem. Engrs., 38, 1067 (1942).

301. Whitman, W. G., Chem. & Met. Eng., 29, no. 4, 146-48, 1923.

302. Winkelmann, W. G., and C. H. Hayes, Ind. Eng. Chem., 18, 201 (1926).

303. Winkelmann, R. G., J. Levin, and H. W. Wilson, Ind. Eng. Chem., 18, 384 (1926).

304. Winslow, R. R., and L. F. Vivian, Chem. Eng. Progress, 46, 357 (1950).

305. Infrared, R. B., and L. F. Vivian, Am. Anal. Chem., 23, 711 (1951).

306. Worthington, H., and H. C. Harrison, "Steam," Edward Arnold & Co., London, 1943.

307. Winston, J. H., Trans. Am. Inst. Chem. Engrs., 35, 670 (1939).

308. Winslow, T. H., and M. Benedict, Chem. Eng. Progress, 44, 207 (1948).

309. Wood, C. E., Chem. Eng. Progress, 45, 218 (1949).

310. Winter, C. H., and O. A. Hougen, Trans. Am. Inst. Chem. Engrs., 41, 510 (1945).

311. Wisniak, C. C., Sc.D. thesis in chemical engineering, M.I.T., 1943.

312. Williams, C. C., H. B. Abendt, and C. F. Talbott, Chem. Eng. Progress, 43, 629 (1947).

313. White, H. A., Proc. Cambridge Phil. Soc., 15, 100 (1901).

314. Wismann, U. C., and A. T. Chester, Ind. Ind. Eng. Chem., 40, 1057 (1948).

315. Wickenden, Inst. Spirit. 33, 1, 151 (1951); 33, 205 (1951); 56, 162 (1951); 33, 314 (1955); 36, 15 (1956).

316. Woolley, J. A. A., and A. Jackson, Trans. Inst. Chem. Engrs. (London), 33, 43 (1955).

317. Zauderer, F. A., Heat Eng., 25, 61 (1956).

INDEX